Human Biology

7e

Cecie Starr | Beverly McMillan

CENGAGE
Learning™

Australia • Brazil • Japan • Korea • Mexico • Singapore • Spain • United Kingdom • United States

CENGAGE
Learning™

Human Biology: 7e

Cecie Starr | Beverly McMillan

Executive Editors:
Michele Baird
Maureen Staudt
Michael Stranz

Project Development Manager:
Linda deStefano

Senior Marketing Coordinators:
Sara Mercurio
Lindsay Shapiro

Production/Manufacturing Manager:
Donna M. Brown

PreMedia Services Supervisor:
Rebecca A. Walker

Rights & Permissions Specialist:
Kalina Hintz

Cover Image:
Getty Images*

© 2008, 2005 Cengage Learning

For product information and technology assistance, contact us at
Cengage Learning Customer & Sales Support, 1-800-354-9706

For permission to use material from this text or product, submit all requests online at **cengage.com/permissions**
Further permissions questions can be emailed to
permissionrequest@cengage.com

ISBN-13: 978-0-495-45252-2

ISBN-10: 0-495-45252-1

Cengage Learning
5191 Natorp Boulevard
Mason, Ohio 45040
USA

Cengage Learning is a leading provider of customized learning solutions with office locations around the globe, including Singapore, the United Kingdom, Australia, Mexico, Brazil, and Japan. Locate your local office at:
international.cengage.com/region

Cengage Learning products are represented in Canada by Nelson Education, Ltd.

For your lifelong learning solutions, visit **custom.cengage.com**

Visit our corporate website at **cengage.com**

Printed in the United States of America

CONTENTS IN BRIEF

What Kind of World Do We Live In?

Glance at a newspaper or click on your Web browser and you may wonder what kind of world you're living in. Headlines mingle news about various wars or political wrangles with tips for managing your love life or choosing food supplements. On any given day you'll read about how infectious diseases such as "bird flu" pose global threats, or about the devastation caused by a natural catastrophe such as an earthquake. Often there are stories about human activities that have major impacts on nature. We hear more and more about global warming, polar ice caps and glaciers melting, and other regions experiencing record storms, droughts, and heat waves. During the Persian Gulf War, pollution from intentional fires set in oil fields seriously damaged some of the Earth's most spectacular coral reefs,

and we still don't know today if they will ever recover.

But while coping with an environmental disaster or predicting the course of a flu epidemic are challenging, we humans have an ace in the hole. We learned a long time ago that it is possible to study nature, including ourselves, in a systematic way that may help us understand the natural world and our place in it. We can observe carefully, come up with ideas, and find ways to test them. With time we can learn a great deal about factors that affect our health, environmental concerns, and a host of other issues. That's what this book is for—to help give you a fuller understanding of how your body works and where we humans fit in the world around us.

Each chapter in this book will give you a chance to express your opinion on an issue that is challenging us today. When you cast your vote on this book's website you will be able to see how others feel about current concerns related to the environment, health, and ethical dilemmas.

 How Would You Vote? Middle Eastern seas support spectacular coral reef ecosystems. Should the United States provide funding to help preserve the reefs? Cast your vote online at www.thomsonedu.com/biology/starr/humanbio.

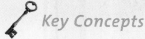

Key Concepts

THE NATURE OF LIFE
All living things share some basic features, including the genetic material DNA and the ability to take in and use energy and materials. A cell is the smallest unit that can be alive.

LIFE'S DIVERSITY
We humans are one of many millions of kinds of living things. Nature is organized from simple to complex, starting with nonliving atoms. Whole organisms are part of this continuum. The entire living world, the biosphere, is the most encompassing level of life's organization.

STUDYING LIFE
Biology is a way of thinking critically about the natural world. Biologists make systematic observations, hypotheses, and predictions. They often test their predictions by way of experiments in nature and in the laboratory. Critical thinking provides all of us with a means to evaluate information objectively.

Links to Earlier Concepts

This book follows nature's levels of organization, from atoms to the biosphere. This first chapter provides a broad view of where we humans fit in the world of life. Later chapters will introduce you to the chemical foundations of life and how our body cells are built and operate. This background paves the way for a survey of how the body's tissues, organs, and organ systems function. You will also learn about genes, the principles that guide inheritance, and basic concepts of evolution and ecology.

You will discover that each chapter in this book builds upon previous ones. Keychain icons mark cross-references to earlier sections where you can review related topics.

1.1 The Characteristics of Life

Picture a group of hikers, carefully making their way up slippery stairs next to a waterfall. Without thinking about it, you know that the hikers are alive and the stairs are not. But could you explain why?

Living and nonliving things share some common features. For instance, both are made up of atoms, which are the smallest units of nature's fundamental substances. On the other hand, wherever we look in the living world we find that all living things share some characteristics that nonliving ones don't have. These basic features of life are:

1. **Living things take in energy and materials.** Like other animals, and many other kinds of organisms, we humans take in energy and materials by consuming food (Figure 1.1). Our bodies use the energy and materials to build and operate their parts in ways that keep us alive.

2. **Living things sense and respond to changes in their environment.** For example, a tulip's petals close up when night falls, and you might put on a sweater or turn up the heat on a chilly afternoon.

3. **Living things reproduce and grow.** Organisms can make more of their own kind, based on instructions in DNA, the genetic material. Only living things have DNA. Guided by the instructions in their DNA, most organisms develop through a series of life stages. For us humans, the basic life stages are infancy, childhood, adolescence, and adulthood.

4. **Living things consist of one or more cells.** A **cell** is an organized unit that can live and reproduce by itself, using energy, the required raw materials, and instructions in DNA. Cells are the smallest units that can be alive. The energy to power cell activities comes from another special chemical found only in living things, ATP.

5. **Living things maintain homeostasis.** The term **homeostasis** (hoe-me-oh-STAY-sis) means "staying the same." Homeostasis is a state in which the physical and chemical conditions of the environment *inside* the body

are being maintained within life-supporting limits. This internal environment consists of the fluid, including blood, that surrounds our cells. For now, the key point to keep in mind is that maintaining homeostasis is crucial for the survival of every living cell in the body. Later chapters will provide a more complete picture of how body systems help in this task.

> *Living organisms share characteristics that nonliving objects do not have.*
>
> *All living things take in and use energy and materials, and they sense and can respond to changes in their environment.*
>
> *Living things can reproduce and grow, based on instructions in DNA. The cell is the smallest unit that can be alive.*
>
> *Organisms maintain the internal state called homeostasis.*

Figure 1.1 A child taking in energy by eating food. His body will extract energy and raw materials from the food and use them for processes that are required to keep each of the child's cells, and the whole child, alive.

1.2 Our Place in the Natural World

Human beings arose as a distinct group of animals during an evolutionary journey that began billions of years ago.

Figure 1.3 Bonobos (*left*) are our closest primate relatives. Like us, they walk upright and use tools. Only humans have a capacity for sophisticated language and technology.

HUMANS HAVE EVOLVED OVER TIME

In biology, **evolution** means change in the body plan and functioning of organisms through the generations. It is a process that began billions of years ago on the Earth and continues today. In the course of evolution, major groups of life forms have emerged.

Figure 1.2 provides a snapshot of how we fit into the natural world. Humans, apes, and some other closely related animals are primates (PRY-mates). Primates are mammals, and mammals make up one group of "animals with backbones," the vertebrates (VER-tuh-braytes). Of course, we share our planet with millions of other animal species, as well as with plants, fungi, countless bacteria, and other life forms. Biologists classify living things according to their characteristics, which in turn reflect their evolutionary heritage. Notice that Figure 1.2 shows three domains of life. Animals, plants, fungi, and microscopic organisms called protists are assigned to kingdoms in a domain called Eukarya. The other two domains are reserved for bacteria and some other single-celled life forms. Some biologists prefer different schemes. For example, for many years all living things were simply organized into five kingdoms—animals, plants, fungi, protists, and bacteria. The key point is that despite the basic features all life forms share, evolution has produced a living world of incredible diversity.

HUMANS ARE RELATED TO ALL OTHER ORGANISMS—AND HUMANS ALSO HAVE SOME DISTINCTIVE FEATURES

Because of evolution, humans are related to every other life form and we share characteristics with many of them. For instance, we and all other mammals have body hair, a feature that no other vertebrate has. We share the most characteristics with apes, our closest primate relatives (Figure 1.3). But humans also have some distinctive features that evolved as traits of our primate ancestors were modified. For example, we have great manual dexterity due to the arrangement of muscles and bones in our hands and the wiring of our nervous system to operate them. Even more astonishing is the human brain. Relative to overall body mass it is the largest brain of any animal, and it gives us the capacity for sophisticated language and analysis, for developing advanced technology, and for a remarkably wide variety of social behaviors.

Figure 1.2 *Animated!*
Classifying life. Humans are one of more than a million species in the Animal Kingdom, which is part of the domain Eukarya. Plants, fungi, and some other life forms make up other kingdoms in Eukarya. The domains Bacteria and Archaea contain vast numbers of single-celled organisms.

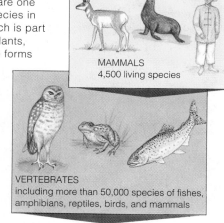

MAMMALS
4,500 living species

VERTEBRATES
including more than 50,000 species of fishes, amphibians, reptiles, birds, and mammals

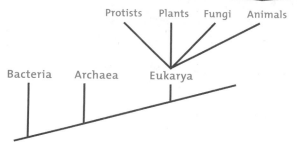

Protists   Plants   Fungi   Animals

Bacteria   Archaea   Eukarya

Like all life forms, human beings arose through evolution—change in the details of the body plan and functions of organisms through the generations.

Features that set humans apart from other complex animals include sophisticated verbal and analytical skills and exceptionally complex social behaviors.

1.3 Life's Organization

The world of life is organized from the simple to the complex. The illustration below gives you an overview of how these levels connect.

LIFE IS ORGANIZED ON MANY LEVELS

When you look closely at the living world, it doesn't take long to realize that nature is organized on many different levels (Figure 1.4). At the most basic level are atoms. Next come molecules, which are combinations of atoms. Atoms and molecules are the nonliving materials from which cells are built. In a multicellular organism such as a human, cells are organized into tissues—muscle, the epithelium of your skin, and so forth. Different kinds of tissues make up organs, and coordinated systems of organs make up whole complex organisms.

We can study the living world on any of its levels. Many courses in human biology focus on organ systems, and a good deal of this textbook explores their structure and how they function.

Nature's organization doesn't end with individuals. Each organism is part of a population, such as the Earth's whole human population. When we cast the net a little farther, populations of different organisms interact in communities, the populations of all species occupying the same area. Communities in turn interact in ecosystems. The most inclusive level of organization is the **biosphere**. This term refers to all parts of Earth's waters, crust, and atmosphere in which organisms live.

ORGANISMS ARE CONNECTED THROUGH THE FLOW OF ENERGY AND CYCLING OF MATERIALS

Organisms must take in energy and materials to keep their life processes going. Where do these essentials come from? Energy flows into the biosphere from the sun. This solar energy is captured by "self-feeding" life forms such as plants, which use a sunlight-powered process called photosynthesis to make fuel for building tissues, such as a corn kernel. Raw materials such as carbon that are needed to build the corn come from air, soil, and water. Thus self-feeding organisms are the living world's basic food producers. Animals, including humans, are the consumers: When we eat plant parts, or feed on animals that have done so, we take in materials and energy to fuel our body functions. You tap directly into stored energy when you eat corn on the cob, and you tap into it indirectly when you eat the meat of a chicken that fed on corn. Organisms such as bacteria and fungi obtain energy and materials when they decompose tissues, breaking down biological molecules to substances that

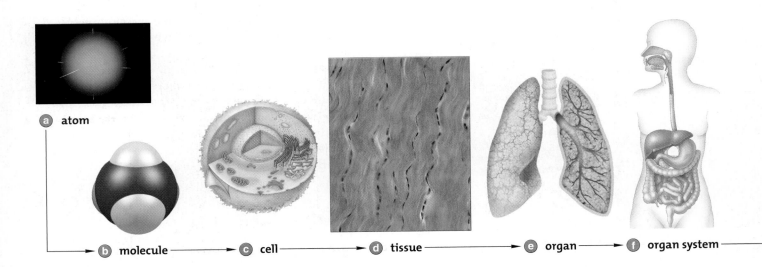

a atom

b molecule ——→ **c** cell ——→ **d** tissue ——→ **e** organ ——→ **f** organ system ——

Figure 1.4 *Animated!* An overview of the levels of organization in nature.

can be recycled back to producers. By way of this one-way flow of energy through organisms, and the cycling of materials among them, every part of the living world is linked to every other part. Figure 1.5 summarizes these relationships, which we'll return to in Chapter 25.

Because of the interconnections among organisms, it makes sense to think of ecosystems as webs of life. With this perspective, we can see that the effects of events in one part of the web will eventually ripple through the whole, and may even affect the entire biosphere. For example, we see evidence of large-scale impacts of human activities in phenomena such as global warming, the loss of biodiversity in many parts of the world, acid rain, and a host of other problems.

Nature is organized on several levels, starting with nonliving materials and culminating with the whole living world, the biosphere.

Life's organization is sustained by a flow of energy from the sun and the cycling of raw materials among organisms.

As a result of the interconnections between living things, ecosystems are webs of life. What happens in one part of the web ripples through the whole.

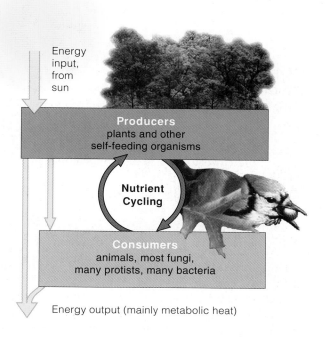

Energy input, from sun

Producers
plants and other self-feeding organisms

Nutrient Cycling

Consumers
animals, most fungi, many protists, many bacteria

Energy output (mainly metabolic heat)

Figure 1.5 *Animated!* The flow of energy and the cycling of materials in the biosphere.

g multicellular organism → **h** population → **i** community → **j** ecosystem → **k** the biosphere

1.4 Science Is a Way of Learning about the Natural World

How do researchers go about discovering how anything in nature works? Said another way, what exactly do we mean when we talk about "science"?

SCIENCE IS AN APPROACH TO GATHERING KNOWLEDGE

The word "science" can conjure up images of white-coated researchers, test tubes, and sophisticated laboratories. In fact, however, the basic ingredients in "doing science" are simple curiosity and a healthy skepticism. Science blends these ingredients, and the result is a systematic way of gathering knowledge about the natural world. This information-gathering system is sometimes called the **scientific method**, but there is no rigid script for it (Figure 1.6). The following practices are common in scientific research. It's likely that some of them are commonsense things you yourself do.

1. **Observe some aspect of the natural world, then ask a question about it or identify a problem to explore**. For example, in the late 1990s, a fat substitute called Olestra® was approved for use in foods. Concocted from vegetable oil and sugar, Olestra is indigestible and has been touted as a dieter's dream. When potato chips made with Olestra came on the market, however, some consumers reported intestinal ailments, including gas, diarrhea, and cramps. Curious researchers at Johns Hopkins University began to wonder: Was Olestra causing the problems?

2. **Develop a hypothesis**. A hypothesis is a tentative explanation for an observation or how some natural process works. In the case of a scientific hypothesis, there must be some objective way of testing it, such as through experiments. The Johns Hopkins scientists hypothesized that Olestra can indeed cause cramps and they had an idea for an experiment to test this explanation.

3. **Make a prediction**. As a first step in testing their hypothesis, the scientists made a prediction: People who eat food containing Olestra are more likely to have intestinal side effects than people who do not. As in this example, a prediction states what you should observe about the question or problem if the hypothesis is valid.

4. **Test the prediction**. To see if their prediction was accurate, the researchers invited almost 1,100 people aged 13 to 38 to watch a movie in a Chicago theater. They were divided into two roughly equal groups and given unmarked bags of potato chips. One group received chips made with Olestra while the other group received regular chips. When the scientists later interviewed the participants, they found that about 15.8 percent of those

Figure 1.6 In the laboratory or in the field, scientists can pursue their research in different ways. One researcher may emphasize observing and describing phenomena. Another may focus on using experiments to test hypotheses.

in the Olestra group complained of intestinal problems—but so did 17.6 percent in the "regular" group. As a result, this experiment provided no evidence that eating Olestra-laced potato chips causes intestinal ills, at least after a one-time use. The experiment wasn't a "failure," however. A properly designed test is supposed to reveal flaws. If the findings don't support the prediction, then some factor that influenced the test may have been overlooked, or the hypothesis may simply have been wrong.

5. **Repeat the tests or develop new ones**—the more the better. Hypotheses that are supported by the results of repeated testing are more likely to be correct.

6. **Analyze and report the test results and conclusions**. Scientists typically publish their findings in scientific journals, with a detailed description of their methods so that other researchers can try the same test and see if they obtain the same result.

EXPERIMENTS ARE MAJOR SCIENTIFIC TOOLS

Experimenting is a time-honored way to test a prediction that flows from a hypothesis. An **experiment** is a test carried out under controlled conditions that a researcher can manipulate. Figure 1.7 shows the typical steps followed, using the Olestra study as an example.

To get meaningful test results, experimenters use safeguards. They begin by reviewing information that may bear on their project. The makers of Olestra had conducted tests on human subjects before their product was approved, and the Johns Hopkins study considered these reports. Then the researchers designed a **controlled experiment**, one that would test only a single prediction of a hypothesis at a time. In this case, it was the prediction that people who consume Olestra have a greater chance of developing intestinal side effects.

Almost any aspect of the natural world is the result of interacting variables. As the term suggests, a **variable** is a factor that can change with time or in different circumstances. Researchers design experiments to test one variable at a time. They also set up a **control group** to which one or more experimental groups can be compared. The control group was identical to the experimental one except for the variable being studied—chips containing Olestra. Identifying possible variables, and eliminating unwanted ones, is extremely important if an experiment is to produce reliable results. For instance, if some people in the Olestra study had had a prior history of unrelated intestinal difficulties, they could have skewed the study results. Likewise, if any of the participants included people who were already eating foods made with Olestra, it would have been impossible for the experimenters to determine if any reported side effects were due not to the single bag of chips but to long-term use.

Scientists usually can't observe all the individuals in a group they want to study. In studies of a food additive such as Olestra it certainly would be difficult to include every possible consumer. If the sample is too small, however, differences among research subjects might distort the findings. To avoid this problem, researchers use a sample group that is large enough to be representative of the whole. That is why the Olestra study included such a large number of participants.

SCIENCE IS AN ONGOING ENTERPRISE

Did the Johns Hopkins study give Olestra a green light as a trouble-free food additive? No. One reason is that "doing science" requires a researcher to draw logical conclusions about any findings. That is, the conclusion cannot be at odds with the evidence used to support it. Based on the results of their Olestra experiment, the Johns Hopkins scientists could not conclude that the promising "fake fat" did cause intestinal problems. On the other hand, their limited, one-time experiment also could not give Olestra a clean bill of health. In fact, in

Hypothesis
Olestra® causes intestinal cramps.

↓

Prediction
People who eat potato chips made with Olestra will be more likely to get intestinal cramps than those who eat potato chips made without Olestra.

↓

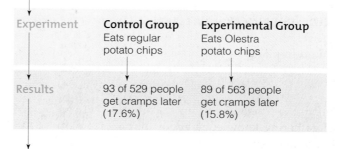

Experiment	Control Group Eats regular potato chips	Experimental Group Eats Olestra potato chips
Results	93 of 529 people get cramps later (17.6%)	89 of 563 people get cramps later (15.8%)

↓

Conclusion
Percentages are about equal. People who eat potato chips made with Olestra are just as likely to get intestinal cramps as those who eat potato chips made without Olestra. These results do not support the hypothesis.

Figure 1.7 A typical sequence of steps followed in a scientific experiment.

the years since Olestra was first developed, the United States Food and Drug Administration (FDA) has received more than 20,000 consumer complaints alleging problems, and Olestra has been reformulated to reduce certain side effects. Today a variety of processed foods sold in the United States are made with Olestra, but the jury may still be out on its potential effects in some people, and some advocates say that more research is needed. For this reason regulators in Canada and Britain still have not approved it for use in human food.

Not all scientists perform experiments. In some cases careful observations, often made over a period of years, are the basis for predictions about natural events.

A scientific approach to studying nature is based on asking questions, formulating hypotheses, making predictions, devising tests, and then objectively reporting the results.

Controlled experiments are one way to test scientific ideas. This kind of experiment explores a single variable and uses a control group as a standard to which experimental results can be compared.

1.5 Science in Action: Cancer, Broccoli, and Mighty Mice

Scientific advances that benefit human health often come about when researchers ask creative questions and then perform experiments to get at the answers. In this section we look at a real-life example of the scientific method in action, step by step.

Scientists in the United States and Japan cooperated on the research, exploring this question: Does a substance found in plants of the cabbage family, such as broccoli, somehow boost the body's defenses against cancer? And if so, how? The teams worked with mice, which are easy to maintain in the laboratory. Mice also are mammals, so their cells function much like human cells, increasing the likelihood that experimental findings will be relevant to human beings.

We already know that some plants contain chemicals that can be useful against human cancers. The yew tree, for example, was the original source of the drug taxol, which combats ovarian and uterine tumors. Broccoli and its cabbage family relatives such as cauliflower have long been thought to contain substances that help protect against the changes in cells that can lead to cancer (Figure 1.8). One of those substances is a compound called sulforaphane, so that is where the research teams started.

The researchers' overall hypothesis was that a diet rich in sulforaphane would help protect against cancer. To test that idea carefully, however, would require a series of experiments. In their first study, following good scientific methodology, they established a control group of mice that would eat a normal diet while a test group would be fed food that contained large amounts of sulforaphane. If nothing about the test group changed with this diet, the experiments might have ended there. But while no changes were detected in the control group (the expected outcome), the test animals' cells began making abnormally large quantities of a protein that short-circuits the development of cancer. And when both groups of mice were then exposed to a *carcinogen*—a substance that can cause cancer—the test mice developed fewer cancers than the controls did.

Armed with evidence that sulforaphane boosts the body's natural cancer defenses, the teams asked another question: What would happen if mice that couldn't make the natural cancer-inhibiting protein were exposed to carcinogens? Their hypothesis was that such abnormal mice, which have a genetic mutation that prevents their cells from making the protein, would be especially prone to develop tumors. For their experimental tests the teams again used two groups of mice, a test group and a control. After thirty weeks, the stomachs of the mutant mice were full of tumors—a whopping fourteen,

Figure 1.8 Experiments with mice have supported a hypothesis that vegetables in the cabbage family contain substances that are protective against cancer when they work in concert with natural defenses in body cells.

on average. The normal mice also developed tumors, but fewer of them—an average of ten—and their tumors did not grow as large as those of the test group.

Now the researchers repeated the experiment, but altered a variable so they could test a new hypothesis: that sulforaphane provides protection against cancer even when body cells lack natural defenses. This time there were two test groups, normal and mutant mice that would both receive the treatments, and control groups of each type that would be exposed to the carcinogen but not the drug treatment. (The drug was one that is chemically similar to sulforaphane.) After another thirty-week trial, the results were thought-provoking. The normal mice had developed only half as many tumors as before, so the sulforaphane-like drug seemed to help them fend off cancer. But all the mutant mice developed just as many tumors as before. Based on these results, the scientists had to conclude that a diet rich in sulforaphane is not by itself an effective anticancer strategy. The body's cells must also be able to mount their own defenses. This finding also reinforces how important it is to try to avoid carcinogens that may be in our environment. This is a topic you will read more about in Chapter 23.

Every day, scientists develop hypotheses and make predictions that are testable, often through a process of experimentation.

STUDYING LIFE

1.6 Science in Perspective

Several decades ago our world began to be dominated by science, and biology has been a big part of that change. Day by day, knowing more about the nature and limits of science becomes crucial for "biology consumers."

Antibiotics. Insights into genetic disease, cancer, and global problems such as the thinning ozone layer and water pollution (Figure 1.9). Advances like these—not to mention technologies such as genetic engineering and the Internet—have changed our lives. So what is the overall role of science in human affairs? We know that the practice of science can yield powerful ideas, like the theory of evolution, that explain key aspects of life. At the same time, we also know that science is only one part of human experience.

A SCIENTIFIC THEORY EXPLAINS A LARGE NUMBER OF OBSERVATIONS

You've probably said, "I've got a theory about that!" Whatever "that" is, you are really saying that you have an untested idea about something. In science, a **theory** is exactly the opposite: It is an explanation of a broad range of related natural events and observations that is based on repeated, careful testing of hypotheses.

A hypothesis usually becomes accepted as a theory only after years of testing by many scientists. Then, if the hypothesis has not been disproved, scientists may feel confident about using it to explain more data or observations. The theory of evolution by natural selection—a topic we will look at in Chapter 24—is a prime example of a "theory" that is supported by tens of thousands of scientific observations.

Science demands critical thinking, so a theory can be modified, and even rejected, if results of new scientific tests call it into question. It's the same with other scientific ideas. Today, for instance, sophisticated technologies are giving us a new perspective on subjects such as how our immune system operates to defend the body against disease threats. Some "facts" in this textbook one day will likely be revised as we learn more about various processes. This willingness to reconsider ideas as new information comes to light is a major strength of science.

SCIENCE HAS LIMITS

Science requires an objective mind-set, and this means that scientists can only do certain kinds of studies. No experiment can explain the "meaning of life," for example, or why each of us dies at a certain moment. Those kinds of questions have subjective answers, shaped by our experiences and beliefs. Every culture and society has its own standards of morality and esthetics,

Figure 1.9 Science in our service: (**a**) Microbiologist Rita Colwell working to improve drinking water in Bangladesh. (**b**) Ozone thinning above Antarctica in 1996.

and there are hundreds or thousands of different sets of religious beliefs. All guide their members in deciding what is important and good and what is not. By contrast, the external world, rather than internal conviction, is the only testing ground for scientific views.

Because science does not involve value judgments, it sometimes has been or can be used in controversial pursuits. The discovery of atomic power in the early twentieth century, and its continuing use today, is one example; some people also are worried about issues such as the use of animals in scientific research and the consequences of genetic modification of food plants. The debate over the genetic modification of human beings grows stronger by the day. Meanwhile, whole ecosystems are being altered by technologies that allow millions of a forest's trees to be cut in a single year, and hundreds of millions of fishes to be taken from the sea. These are matters we can't leave to the scientific community alone to guide the wise use of scientific knowledge. That responsibility also belongs to us.

A scientific theory is a testable explanation about the cause or causes of a broad range of related natural phenomena. It remains open to tests, revision, and even rejection if new evidence comes to light.

Science has limits. Scientific beliefs can only be tested in nature, and responsibility for the wise use of scientific information must be shared by all.

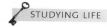

STUDYING LIFE

1.7 Critical Thinking in Science and Life

Having a solid set of critical thinking skills will help you make the most of your study of human biology. As you'll now see, those skills can also help everyone make well-reasoned decisions about health issues, environmental controversies, and other concerns.

Have you ever tried a new or "improved" product and been disappointed when it didn't work as expected? Everyone learns, sometimes the hard way, how useful it can be to cast a skeptical eye on advertising claims or get an unbiased evaluation of, say, a used car you are considering buying. This sort of objective evaluation of information is **critical thinking**.

Scientists use critical thinking in their work, and when they review findings reported by others. One reason this approach is so important is that even when a scientist tries to be objective, there is always a chance that pride or bias will creep in. Critical thinking is a smart practice in everyday life, too, because many decisions we face involve scientific information. Will an herbal food supplement really boost your immune system? Is it safe to eat irradiated food? The critical thinking skills listed in Figure 1.10 aren't complicated, and they can be helpful tools for assessing a wide range of issues.

CONSIDER THE SOURCE

An easy way to begin evaluating a piece of information is to look carefully at where it is coming from and how it is presented. Two simple strategies for sifting the factual wheat from the unreliable or biased chaff are the following:

LET CREDIBLE SCIENTIFIC EVIDENCE, NOT OPINIONS OR HEARSAY, DO THE CONVINCING For instance, if you are concerned about reports that heavy use of a cell phone might cause brain cancer, material published on the website of the American Cancer Society is much more likely to be reliable than something cousin Fred heard a friend say at work. The friend's information may be correct, but neither you nor your cousin can know for sure without investigating further.

QUESTION CREDENTIALS AND MOTIVES For example, if an advertisement is printed in the format of a news story, or a product is touted on TV by someone being paid to sing its praises, your critical thinking antennae should go up. Is the promoter merely trying to sell a product with the help of "scientific" window dressing? Can any facts presented be checked out? Responsible

A Critical Thinking Checklist

✓ **Do** gather information or evidence from reliable sources.

✓ **Don't** rely on hearsay.

✓ **Do** look for facts that can be checked independently and for signs of obvious bias (such as paid testimonials).

✓ **Don't** confuse *cause* with *correlation*.

✓ **Do** separate *facts* from *opinions*.

Figure 1.10 A critical thinking checklist.

scientists try to be cautious and accurate in discussing their findings and are willing to supply the evidence to back up their statements.

EVALUATE THE CONTENT

Even if information seems authoritative and unbiased, critical thinking is shaped by two other considerations. One is awareness of the difference between the *cause* of something and factors that are only *related* to an event or phenomenon. Suppose, for example, that a television program presents statistics correlating shark attacks on surfers in Florida with the cycles of tides during the summer months. Does this information, which in fact is gathered by scientists, mean that the cycles *cause* shark attacks? No, even though the two may indeed be *related* because sharks may come closer to shore under certain tide conditions. But pinning down the cause of shark attacks will require a great deal more understanding of shark behavior and other factors.

It also is important to keep in mind the difference between facts and opinions or speculation. A **fact** is a piece of information that can be verified, such as the price of a loaf of bread. An *opinion*—whether the bread tastes good—can't be verified because it involves a subjective judgment. Likewise, a marketer's prediction that many consumers will favor a new brand of bread is speculation, at least until there are statistics to back up the hype.

Thinking critically allows us to make decisions based on objective information. It is important to evaluate both the source and the content of information and to understand the difference between facts and opinions and between cause and correlation.

1.8 Are Herbal Supplements Safe?

Each year Americans spend more than $4 billion on herbal food supplements to ward off ailments ranging from the common cold and forgetfulness to depression, stress, and high cholesterol. Some of the biggest and most controversial sellers have been products containing ephedrine (Figure 1.11), derived from the plant ephedra. The FDA banned ephedra products in 2004 after 155 people died from strokes or heart attack while using the substance as a weight-loss "metabolism booster." Ephedra marketers sued, denying any link between their product and the deaths, and in 2005 the federal ban was overturned. More studies are under way.

Controversy has swirled around several other herbal supplements as well. In 2000 a study of echinacea's effectiveness in warding off colds found "no significant effect on either the occurrence of infection or the severity of illness." In 2002 research on St. John's wort, an herb touted for soothing depression, no biological effect was detected either.

With so much at stake, it's not surprising that the debate over herbal supplements is fierce. As the battle goes on, alert consumers are likely to be the ultimate winners. Recognizing that millions of people are buying and using herbal supplements, the National Institutes of Health has stepped up its support for scientifically rigorous testing of various herbal products. The American Medical Association recommends that anyone using herbal supplements check with a physician about possible harmful side effects. Consumers can also get reliable updates from the National Institutes of Health website at www.nih.gov.

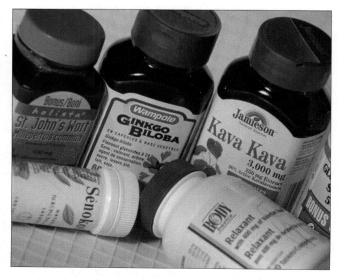

Figure 1.11 Herbal food supplements are a $4-billion-plus industry in the United States.

Summary

Section 1.1 Humans have the following characteristics found in all forms of life (Table 1.1):

a. They take in and use energy and materials from the environment.

b. They sense and respond to specific changes in the environment.

c. They can grow, develop, and reproduce, based on instructions contained in their DNA.

d. They are composed of cells. A cell is the smallest unit that can show the characteristics of life.

e. In homeostasis, internal physical and chemical conditions are maintained within limits that support the ongoing functioning of an organism's cells.

Section 1.2 Earth's life forms all have come about through a process of evolution. The evolutionary heritage of each type of organism is reflected in how biologists classify it. Moving from the most general category to the most specific, humans are classified as animals, vertebrates, mammals, and, finally, primates.

The defining features of humans include a large and well-developed brain that correlates with great manual dexterity and sophisticated skills for language and mental analysis. Humans also possess an advanced capacity for technological innovation and the ability to engage in a complex set of social behaviors.

Section 1.3 The living world is highly organized. Atoms, molecules, cells, tissues, organs, and organ systems make up whole, complex organisms. Each organism is a member of a population, populations live together in communities, and communities form ecosystems. The biosphere is the most inclusive level of biological organization. The organization of life is sustained by a continual flow of energy and cycling of raw materials.

Thomson NOW! *Explore levels of biological organization.*

Table 1.1 Summary of Life's Characteristics
1. Living things take in and use energy and materials.
2. Living things sense and respond to changes in their surroundings.
3. Living things reproduce and grow based on information in DNA.
4. Living things consist of one or more cells.
5. Living things maintain the internal steady state called homeostasis.

Section 1.4 Science is an approach to gathering knowledge. There are many versions of the scientific method. The following elements are important in all of them (Table 1.2):

a. Hypothesis: a possible explanation of a specific phenomenon in nature. A hypothesis is scientific only if it can be tested in ways that might disprove it.

b. Prediction: a claim about what an observer can expect to see in nature if a theory or hypothesis is correct.

c. Test: an effort to gather actual observations that support or contradict the predicted findings.

d. Conclusion: a statement about whether a hypothesis should be accepted, rejected, or modified, based on tests of the predictions it generated.

Predictions that flow from hypotheses can be tested by repeated observations or by experiments in nature or in the laboratory.

Experiments are tests that allow researchers to control and adjust the conditions under which they make observations.

Researchers design experiments to test one variable at a time. A variable is an aspect of an object or event that may differ over time and between subjects. Experimenters directly manipulate the variable they are studying in order to test their prediction.

A controlled experiment will have a control group that provides a baseline against which one or more experimental groups are compared. Ideally, it is the same as each experimental group except in the one variable being investigated.

A reputable scientist must draw logical conclusions about any findings. That is, conclusions cannot be at odds with the evidence used to support them.

Section 1.6 Systematic observations, hypotheses, predictions, and tests are the foundation of scientific theories. A theory is a thoroughly tested explanation of a broad range of related phenomena.

Table 1.2	Scientific Method Review
Hypothesis	Possible explanation of a natural event or observation
Prediction	Proposal or claim of what testing will show if a hypothesis is correct
Experimental test	Controlled procedure to gather observations that can be compared to prediction
Control group	Standard to compare test group against
Variable	Aspect of an object or event that may differ with time or between subjects
Conclusion	Statement that evaluates a hypothesis based on test results

Section 1.7 Critical thinking allows us to evaluate information objectively. Critical thinking skills include scrutinizing information sources for bias, seeking reliable opinions, and separating the causes of events from factors that may only be associated with them.

Review Questions

1. For this and all other chapters, make a list of the boldface terms in the text. Write a definition next to each, and then check it against the one in the text.

2. As a human, you are a living organism. List all the characteristics of life that you exhibit.

3. Why is the concept of homeostasis meaningful in the study of human biology?

4. What is meant by biological evolution?

5. Study Figure 1.4. Then, on your own, summarize what is meant by biological organization.

6. Explain what we mean by "the one-way flow of energy and the cycling of materials" through the biosphere.

7. Why does it make sense to think of ecosystems as webs of life?

8. Define and distinguish between:
   a. a hypothesis and a scientific theory
   b. an observational test and an experimental test
   c. an experimental group and a control group

Self-Quiz
Answers in Appendix V

1. Instructions in _____ govern how organisms are built and function.

2. A _____ is the smallest unit that can live and reproduce by itself using energy, raw materials, and DNA instructions.

3. _____ is a state in which an organism's internal environment is being maintained within a tolerable range.

4. Humans are _____ (animals with backbones); like other primates, they also are _____.

5. Starting with cells, nature is organized on at least _____ levels.

6. A scientific approach to explaining some aspect of the natural world includes all of the following except _____.

   a. a hypothesis   c. faith-based views
   b. testing   d. systematic observations

7. A controlled experiment should have all the features listed below except _____.

   a. a control group   c. a variable
   b. a test subject   d. several testable predictions

8. A related set of hypotheses that collectively explain some aspect of the natural world makes up a scientific _____.

   a. prediction   d. authority
   b. test   e. observation
   c. theory

9. The diagram below depicts the concept of _____.
   a. evolution
   b. reproduction
   c. levels of organization
   d. energy transfers in the living world

Critical Thinking

1. The following diagram shows ways that the same materials—here, a set of tiles—can be put together in different ways. How does this example relate to the role of DNA as the universal genetic material in organisms?

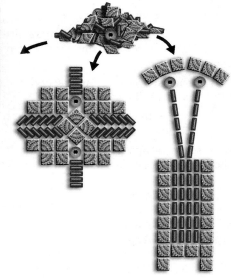

2. Court witnesses are asked "to tell the truth, the whole truth, and nothing but the truth." Research shows, however, that eyewitness accounts of crimes often are unreliable because even the most conscientious witnesses misremember details of what they observed. Can you think of other factors that might affect the "truth" a court witness presents?

3. Design a test (or series of tests) to support or refute this hypothesis: A diet that is high in salt is associated with hypertension (high blood pressure), but hypertension is more common in people with a family history of the condition.

4. In popular magazine articles on health-related topics, the authors often recommend a specific diet or dietary supplement. What kinds of evidence should the articles describe so you can decide whether you should accept their recommendations?

5. A scientific theory about some aspect of nature rests upon inductive reasoning. The assumption is that, because an outcome of some event has been observed to happen quite regularly, it will happen again. We can't know this for certain because there is no way to account for all possible variables that may affect the outcome. To illustrate this point, Garvin McCain and Erwin Segal offer a parable:

> Once there was a highly intelligent turkey. It lived in a pen attended by a kind, thoughtful master, and had nothing to do but reflect on the world's wonders and regularities. Morning always began with the sky getting light, followed by the clop, clop, clop of its master's friendly footsteps, then by the appearance of delicious food. Other things varied—sometimes the morning was warm and sometimes cold—but food always followed footsteps. The sequence of events was so predictable it became the basis of the turkey's theory about the goodness of the world. One morning, after more than 100 confirmations of the goodness theory, the turkey listened for the clop, clop, clop, heard it, and had its head chopped off.

Scientists understand that all thoroughly tested theories about nature have a high probability of being correct. They realize, however, that any theory is subject to being modified if contradictory evidence becomes available. The absence of absolute certainty has led some people to conclude that "facts are irrelevant—facts change." If that is so, should we just stop doing scientific research? Why or why not?

6. Some years ago Dr. Randolph Byrd and his colleagues started a study of 393 patients admitted to the San Francisco General Hospital Coronary Care Unit. In the experiment, born-again Christian volunteers were asked to pray daily for a patient's rapid recovery and for prevention of complications and death.

None of the patients knew if he or she was being prayed for. None of the volunteers or patients knew each other. Byrd categorized how each patient fared as "good," "intermediate," or "bad." He concluded that patients who had been prayed for fared a little better than those who had not. His was the first experiment that had documented statistically significant results that seemed to support the prediction that prayer might have beneficial effects for seriously ill patients.

His published results engendered a storm of criticism, mostly from scientists who cited bias in the experimental design. For instance, Byrd had categorized the patients after the experiment was over, instead of as they were undergoing treatment, so he already knew which ones had improved, stayed about the same, or gotten worse. Think about how experimenters' bias might play a role in how they interpret data. Why do you suppose the experiment generated a heated response from many in the scientific community? Can you think of at least one other variable that might have affected the outcome of each patient's illness?

Explore on Your Own

As you read in Section 1.4, having a sample of test subjects or observations that is too small can skew the results of experiments. This phenomenon is called *sampling error*. To demonstrate this for yourself, all you need is a partner, a blindfold, and a jar containing beans of different colors—jelly beans will do just fine (Figure 1.12). Have your partner stay outside the room while you combine 120 beans of one color with 280 beans of the other color in a bowl. This will give you a ratio of 30 to 70 percent. With the bowl hidden, blindfold your partner; then ask him or her to pick one bean from the mix. Hide the bowl again and instruct your friend to remove the blindfold and tell you what color beans are in the bowl, based on this limited sample. The logical answer is that all the beans are the color of the one selected.

Next repeat the trial, but this time ask your partner to select 50 beans from the bowl. Does this larger sample more closely approximate the actual ratio of beans in the bowl? You can do several more trials if you have time. Do your results support the idea that a larger sample size more closely reflects the actual color ratio of beans?

a Natalie, blindfolded, randomly plucks a jelly bean from a jar of 120 green and 280 black jelly beans, a ratio of 30 to 70 percent.

b The jar is hidden before she removes her blindfold. She observes a single green jelly bean in her hand and assumes the jar holds only green jelly beans.

c Still blindfolded, Natalie randomly picks 50 jelly beans from the jar and ends up with 10 green and 40 black ones.

d The larger sample leads her to assume one-fifth of the jar's jelly beans are green and four-fifths are black (a ratio of 20 to 80). Her larger sample more closely approximates the jar's green-to-black ratio. The more times Natalie repeats the sampling, the greater the chance she will come close to knowing the actual ratio.

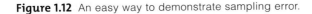

Figure 1.12 An easy way to demonstrate sampling error.

It's Elemental

Like everything else on Earth, your body consists of chemicals, some of them solids, others liquid, still others gases. Each of these chemicals consists of one or more elements. An **element** is a fundamental form of matter. No ordinary process can break it down to other substances. There are ninety-two natural elements on Earth, and researchers have created other, artificial ones.

Organisms consist mostly of just four elements: oxygen, carbon, hydrogen, and nitrogen. The human body also contains some calcium, phosphorus, potassium, sulfur, sodium, and chlorine, plus trace elements. A **trace element** is one that represents less than 0.01 percent of body weight. Trace elements are vital; for example, your

red blood cells can't carry oxygen without the trace element iron.

Atoms of elements can combine into molecules—the first step in biological organization. Molecules in turn can combine to form larger structures, as described shortly. The body's chemical makeup is finely tuned. For example, many trace elements found in our tissues—such as arsenic, selenium, and fluorine—are toxic in amounts larger than normal. Fluoride, which is added to many toothpastes and drinking water supplies, is a form of fluorine. Although it helps prevent tooth decay, too much of it can damage teeth and bones, cause birth defects, or even death.

As you will read often in this book, the body's ability to manage changes that disturb its chemistry is vital to maintaining the stable internal state of homeostasis.

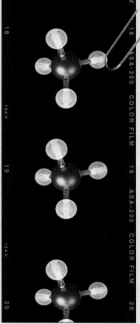

Human Body	
Oxygen	65%
Carbon	18
Hydrogen	10
Nitrogen	3
Calcium	2
Phosphorus	1.1
Potassium	0.35
Sulfur	0.25
Sodium	0.15
Chlorine	0.15
Magnesium	0.05
Iron	0.004

Earth's Crust	
Oxygen	46.6%
Silicon	27.7
Aluminum	8.1
Iron	5.0
Calcium	3.6
Sodium	2.8
Potassium	2.1
Magnesium	1.5

 How Would You Vote? Many communities add fluoride to drinking water supplies. Do you want it in yours? Cast your vote online at www.thomsonedu.com/biology/starr/humanbio.

Key Concepts

ATOMS BOND
Bonds between atoms form molecules. Both the number of an atom's electrons and how they are arranged determine whether it can bond with another atom.

WATER AND BODY FLUIDS
Life depends on key properties of water. Substances that are dissolved in the water of body fluids have important effects on body functions.

BIOLOGICAL MOLECULES
Cells build complex carbohydrates and lipids, proteins, and nucleic acids from simple subunits that contain the element carbon. All of these large molecules have a backbone of carbon atoms. Groups of atoms bonded to the backbone help determine a molecule's properties.

Links to Earlier Concepts

Atoms are the nonliving raw materials from which living cells and organisms are built. The processes that harness atoms and assemble them into the many different parts of cells all are guided by the DNA we inherit from our parents—and that was inherited by all the generations that came before us. In addition to being constructed according to a DNA blueprint, each of our living cells is surrounded by watery fluid. That is why this chapter gives you some background about the properties of water, which are essential to the body's ability to maintain homeostasis in body fluids (1.1–1.3).

2.1 Atoms, the Starting Point

LINK TO SECTION 1.3

A million atoms could fit on the period at the end of this sentence. The parts of atoms determine how the molecules of life are put together.

ATOMS ARE COMPOSED OF SMALLER PARTICLES

An **atom** is the smallest unit that retains the properties of a given element. In spite of their tiny size, all atoms are composed of more than a hundred kinds of subatomic particles. The ones we are concerned with in this book are **protons**, **electrons**, and **neutrons**, illustrated in Figure 2.1.

All atoms have one or more protons, which carry a positive charge, marked by a plus sign (p^+). Except for hydrogen, atoms also have one or more neutrons, which have no charge. Neutrons and protons make up the atom's core, the atomic nucleus. Electrons move around the nucleus, occupying most of the atom's volume. They have a negative charge, which we write as e^-. An atom usually has an equal number of electrons and protons.

Each element is assigned its own "atomic number," which is the number of protons in its atoms. As Table 2.1 indicates, the atomic number for the hydrogen atom, which has one proton, is 1. For the carbon atom, which has six protons, the atomic number is 6.

Each element also has a "mass number"—the sum of the protons and neutrons in the nucleus of its atoms. For a carbon atom, with six protons and six neutrons, this number is 12.

Knowing atomic numbers and mass numbers allows a chemist to gauge whether and how substances will interact. This kind of information also helps us predict how substances will behave in cells, in the body, and in the environment.

ISOTOPES ARE VARYING FORMS OF ATOMS

All atoms of a given element have the same number of protons and electrons, but they may *not* have the same number of neutrons. When an atom of an element has more or fewer neutrons than the most common number, it is called an **isotope** (EYE-so-tope). For instance, while a "standard" carbon atom will have six protons and six neutrons, the isotope called carbon 14 has six protons and *eight* neutrons. These two forms of carbon atoms also can be written as ^{12}C and ^{14}C. The prefix *iso-* means

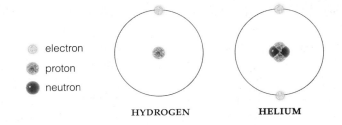

electron
proton
neutron

HYDROGEN   HELIUM

Figure 2.1 *Animated!* A simple model of atoms of hydrogen and helium. These sketches are simplified; at the scale used here, the nuclei of these atoms would be invisible specks.

same, and all isotopes of an element interact with other atoms in the same way. Most elements have at least two isotopes. Cells can use any isotope of an element for their metabolic activities, because the isotopes behave the same as the standard form of the atom in chemical reactions.

Have you heard of radioactive isotopes? A French scientist discovered them in 1896, after he had set a chunk of rock on top of an unexposed photographic plate in a desk drawer. The rock contained some isotopes of uranium, which emit energy. This unexpected chemical behavior is what we today call radioactivity. A few days after the Frenchman's plate was exposed to the uranium emissions, he was astonished to see that a faint image of the rock appeared on it.

The nucleus of a **radioisotope** is unstable and stabilizes itself by emitting energy and particles (other than protons, electrons, and neutrons). This process, called radioactive decay, takes place spontaneously and it transforms a radioisotope into an atom of a different element at a known rate. For instance, over a predictable time span, carbon 14 becomes nitrogen 14. Scientists can use radioactive decay rates to determine the age of very old substances. This chapter's *Science Comes to Life* describes some ways radioisotopes are used in medicine.

Table 2.1	Atomic Number and Mass Number of Elements Common in Living Things		
Element	Symbol	Atomic Number	Most Common Mass Number
Hydrogen	H	1	1
Carbon	C	6	12
Nitrogen	N	7	14
Oxygen	O	8	16
Sodium	Na	11	23
Magnesium	Mg	12	24
Phosphorus	P	15	31
Sulfur	S	16	32
Chlorine	Cl	17	35
Potassium	K	19	39
Calcium	Ca	20	40
Iron	Fe	26	56
Iodine	I	53	127

An atom is the smallest unit of matter that has the properties of a particular element. Atoms have one or more positively charged protons, negatively charged electrons, and (except for hydrogen) neutrons.

Most elements have two or more isotopes—atoms that differ in the number of neutrons.

2.2 Medical Uses for Radioisotopes

To someone who is ill, radioisotopes can be of keen interest. For example, they can allow a physician to diagnose disease with exquisite precision—and without requiring the patient to undergo exploratory surgery. Radioisotopes also are part of the treatment of certain cancers. Regardless of the use, radioisotopes always are handled with great care. For safety's sake, clinicians use only radioisotopes with extremely short half-lives. **Half-life** is the time it takes for half of a quantity of a radioisotope to decay into a different, more stable isotope.

TRACKING TRACERS   Various devices can detect radioisotope emissions. Thus, radioisotopes can be employed in tracers. A **tracer** is a substance with a radioisotope attached to it, rather like a shipping label, that a physician can administer to a patient. The tracking device then follows the tracer's movement through a pathway or pinpoints its destination.

SAVING LIVES   In nuclear medicine, radioisotopes are used under carefully controlled conditions to diagnose and treat diseases. Serious illnesses involving the thyroid are a case in point. The thyroid is the only gland in the human body that takes up iodine. After a tiny amount of a radioactive isotope of iodine, iodine 123, is injected into a patient's bloodstream, the thyroid can be scanned, producing the kinds of images you see in Figure 2.2.

Treatments for some cancers rely on radiation from radioisotopes to destroy or impair the activity of cells that are not functioning properly. For instance, such

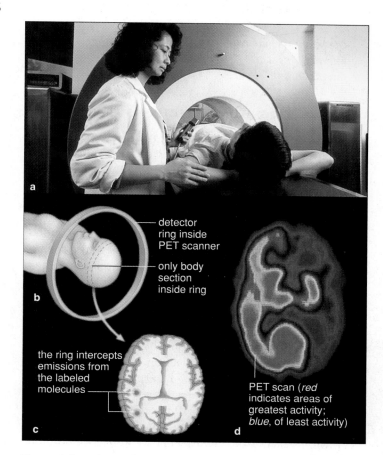

detector ring inside PET scanner

only body section inside ring

the ring intercepts emissions from the labeled molecules

PET scan (*red* indicates areas of greatest activity; *blue*, of least activity)

Figure 2.3 *Animated!*   (**a**) Patient being moved into a PET scanner. Inside (**b**), a ring of detectors intercepts the radioactive emissions from labeled molecules that were injected into the patient. Computers color-code the number of emissions from each location in the scanned body region. (**c**) Brain scan of a child who has a neurological disorder. (**d**) Different colors in a brain scan signify differences in metabolic activity. The right half of this brain shows little activity. By comparison, cells of the left half absorbed and used the labeled molecule at expected rates.

normal thyroid

enlarged

cancerous

Figure 2.2 Scans of the thyroid gland from three patients who have ingested radioactive iodine, which is taken up by the thyroid.

radiation therapy can be used to target a small, localized cancer—one that has not spread—and bombard it with radium 226 or cobalt 60.

Patients with irregular heartbeats use artificial pacemakers powered by energy emitted from plutonium 238. (This dangerous radioisotope is sealed in a case to block damaging emissions.) Used with positron-emission tomography (PET), radioisotopes provide information about abnormalities in the metabolic functions of specific tissues. The radioisotopes are attached to the sugar glucose or to some other biological molecule, then injected into a patient, who is moved into a PET scanner (Figure 2.3*a,b*). When cells in a target tissue absorb glucose, emissions from the radioisotope can be used to produce a vivid image of changes in metabolic activity. PET has been extremely useful for studying human brain activity (Figure 2.3*d*).

2.3 What Is a Chemical Bond?

Life requires chemical reactions, and in each one, atoms interact. This section explains what makes those essential interactions possible.

INTERACTING ATOMS: ELECTRONS RULE!

There are three ways atoms can interact: A given atom may share one or more of its electrons, it can accept extra ones, or it can donate electrons to another atom. *Which* of these events takes place depends on how many electrons an atom has and how they are arranged.

If you have ever played with magnets you know that like charges (++ or −−) repel each other and unlike charges (+−) attract. Electrons carry a negative charge, so they are attracted to the positive charge of protons. On the other hand, electrons repel each other. In an atom, electrons respond to these pushes and pulls by moving around the atomic nucleus in "shells." A shell is not a flat, circular track around the nucleus; it has three dimensions, like the space inside a balloon, and the electron or electrons inside it travel in "orbitals." Figure 2.4 shows one way of visualizing these three-dimensional spaces.

You can think of an orbital as a room in an apartment building—the atom—that allows exactly two renters per room. Hence no more than two electrons can occupy an orbital. Because atoms of different elements differ in how many electrons they have, they also differ in how many of their "rooms" are filled.

Hydrogen is the simplest atom. It has one electron in a single shell (Figure 2.5a). In atoms of elements other than hydrogen, the first shell holds two electrons. Any additional electrons are in shells farther from the nucleus.

The shells around an atom's nucleus are equivalent to energy levels. The shell closest to the nucleus is the lowest energy level. Each shell farther out from the nucleus is at a progressively higher energy level. Because the atoms of different elements have different numbers of electrons, they also have different numbers of shells that electrons can occupy. A shell can have up to eight electrons, but not more. This means that larger atoms, which have more electrons than smaller ones do, also have more shells. The known elements, listed in Appendix II, include some that have many shells to hold all their electrons.

CHEMICAL BONDS JOIN ATOMS

A union between the electron structures of atoms is a **chemical bond**. We can think of bonds as the glue that joins atoms into molecules. How does this "glue" come about? An atom is most stable when its outer shell is filled. Atoms that have too few electrons to fill their outer shell tend to form chemical bonds with other atoms in order to do so. Atoms of oxygen, carbon, hydrogen, and nitrogen—the four most abundant elements in the human body—are like this. As shown in Figure 2.5, hydrogen and helium atoms have a single shell. It is full when it contains two electrons. Other kinds of atoms that have unfilled outer shells take part in chemical bonds that fill their outer shell with eight electrons. Check for electron vacancies in an atom's outer shell and you have a clue as to whether the atom will bond with others. When its outer shell has one or more vacant "slots," an atom may give up electrons, gain them, or share them.

In Figure 2.5 you can count the electron vacancies in the outer shell of each of the atoms pictured. Atoms like helium, which have no vacancies, are said to be *inert*. They usually don't take part in chemical reactions.

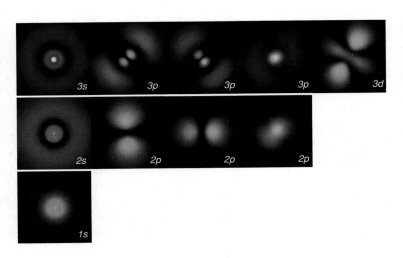

third energy level (second floor)

3s   3p   3p   3p   3d

second energy level (first floor)

2s   2p   2p   2p

first energy level (closest to the basement)

1s

...and so on if there are more electrons in the third level. There also may be more energy levels in large atoms.

Figure 2.4 *Animated!* One way to visualize the three-dimensional arrangements of an atom's electrons. A hydrogen atom, which has only one electron, has just a single orbital. The small letters s, p, and d indicate different paths that electrons travel in each energy level.

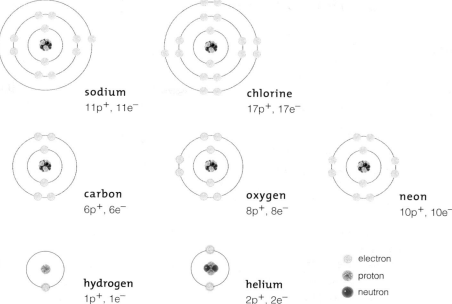

ⓒ The **third shell** shows the third energy level, a combined set of nine orbitals that have room for 18 electrons in total. Sodium has one electron in the third shell, and chlorine has seven. Both have vacancies, so both form chemical bonds.

sodium
11p⁺, 11e⁻

chlorine
17p⁺, 17e⁻

ⓑ The **second shell** shows the second energy level. It has four orbitals with room for up to eight electrons. Carbon has six electrons, two in the first shell and four in the second shell, so it has four vacancies. Oxygen has two. Both atoms form chemical bonds. Neon, with no vacancies, does not.

carbon
6p⁺, 6e⁻

oxygen
8p⁺, 8e⁻

neon
10p⁺, 10e⁻

ⓐ The **first shell** shows the first energy level, a single orbital with room for two electrons. Hydrogen has one electron in this orbital. Hydrogen gives up its electron easily. A helium atom has two electrons in this orbital. Having no vacancies, helium does not usually form chemical bonds.

hydrogen
1p⁺, 1e⁻

helium
2p⁺, 2e⁻

electron
proton
neutron

Figure 2.5 *Animated!* Shell model. Using this model it is easy to see the vacancies in each atom's outer orbitals. Each circle represents all of the orbitals on one energy level. The larger the circle, the higher the energy level.

ATOMS CAN COMBINE INTO MOLECULES

When chemical bonding joins atoms, the new structure is a **molecule**. Many molecules contain atoms of only one element. Molecular nitrogen (N_2), with its two nitrogen atoms, is an example. Figure 2.6 explains how to read the notation used in representing chemical reactions that occur between atoms and molecules.

Many other kinds of molecules are **compounds**. That is, they consist of two or more elements in proportions that never vary. For example, water is a compound. Every water molecule has one oxygen atom bonded with two hydrogen atoms. No matter where water molecules are—in rain clouds or in a lake or in your bathtub—they *always* have twice as many hydrogen as oxygen atoms.

In a **mixture**, two or more kinds of molecules simply mingle. The proportions don't necessarily vary, although they may. For example, the sugar sucrose is a compound of carbon, hydrogen, and oxygen. If you swirl together molecules of sucrose and water, you'll get a mixture—sugar-sweetened water. If you increase the amount of sucrose in the mixture relative to water, you will still have a mixture—just an extremely sweet one, such as syrup.

We use symbols for elements when writing *formulas*, which identify the composition of compounds. For example, water has the formula H_2O. Symbols and formulas are used in *chemical equations*, which are representations of reactions among atoms and molecules.

In written chemical reactions, an arrow means "yields." Substances entering a reaction (reactants) are to the left of the arrow. Reaction products are to the right. For example, the reaction between hydrogen and oxygen that yields water is summarized this way:

$$2H_2 \ + \ O_2 \ \longrightarrow \ 2H_2O$$

4 hydrogens 2 oxygens   4 hydrogens, 2 oxygens

Note that there are as many atoms of each element to the right of the arrow as there are to the left. Although atoms are combined in different forms, none is consumed or destroyed in the process. The total mass of all products of any chemical reaction equals the total mass of all its reactants. All equations used to represent chemical reactions, including reactions in cells, must be balanced this way.

Figure 2.6 *Animated!* Chemical bookkeeping.

Electrons move in orbitals, volumes of space around an atom's nucleus. In a simple model, orbitals are arranged as a series of shells. The successive shells correspond to increasing levels of energy.

An orbital can contain only one or two electrons. Atoms with unfilled orbitals in their outermost shell tend to interact with other atoms; those with no vacancies do not.

In molecules of an element, all of the atoms are the same kind. In molecules of a compound, atoms of two or more elements are bonded together, in proportions that stay the same. In a mixture, the proportions can vary.

2.4 Important Bonds in Biological Molecules

The atoms in biological molecules are held together by a few kinds of bonds. Mainly, these are the bonds known as ionic, covalent, and hydrogen bonds, as summarized in Table 2.2.

AN IONIC BOND JOINS ATOMS THAT HAVE OPPOSITE CHARGES

Overall, an atom carries no charge because it has just as many electrons as protons. That balance can change if an atom has a vacancy—an unfilled orbital—in its outer shell. For example, a chlorine atom has one vacancy and therefore can gain one electron. A sodium atom, on the other hand, has a single electron in its outer shell, and that electron can be knocked out or pulled away. When an atom gains or loses an electron, the balance between its protons and its electrons shifts, so the atom becomes *ionized*; it has a positive or negative charge. An atom that has a charge is called an **ion**.

It's common for neighboring atoms to accept or donate electrons among one another. When one atom loses an electron and one gains, both become ionized. Depending on conditions inside the cell, the ions may separate, or they may stay together as a result of the mutual attraction of their opposite charges. An association of two ions that have opposing charges is called an **ionic bond**. Figure 2.7

shows how sodium ions (Na^+) and chloride ions (Cl^-) interact through ionic bonds, forming NaCl, or table salt.

ELECTRONS ARE SHARED IN A COVALENT BOND

In a **covalent bond**, atoms *share* two electrons. The bond forms when two atoms each have a lone electron in their outer shell and each atom's attractive force "pulls" on the other's unpaired electron. The tug is not strong enough to pull an electron away completely, so the two electrons occupy a shared orbital. Covalent bonds are stable and much stronger than ionic bonds.

In structural formulas, a single line between two atoms means they share a single covalent bond. Molecular hydrogen, a molecule that consists of two hydrogen atoms, has this kind of bond and can be written as H—H. In a *double* covalent bond, two atoms share two electron pairs, as in an oxygen molecule (O=O). In a *triple* covalent bond, two atoms share three pairs of electrons. A nitrogen molecule (N≡N) is this way. All three examples are gases. When you breathe, you inhale H_2, O_2, and N_2 molecules.

In a *nonpolar* covalent bond, the two atoms pull equally on electrons and so share them equally. The term "nonpolar" means there is no difference in charge at the two ends ("poles") of the bond. Molecular hydrogen is a

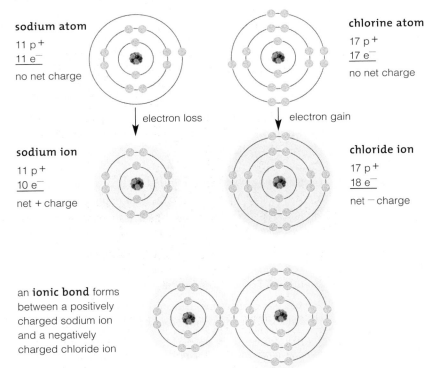

sodium atom
11 p$^+$
11 e$^-$
no net charge

chlorine atom
17 p$^+$
17 e$^-$
no net charge

electron loss

electron gain

sodium ion
11 p$^+$
10 e$^-$
net + charge

chloride ion
17 p$^+$
18 e$^-$
net − charge

an **ionic bond** forms between a positively charged sodium ion and a negatively charged chloride ion

(a) Ionic bonds. A sodium atom loses the one electron in its outer shell, becoming a positively charged sodium ion (Na^+). A chlorine atom gains an electron in its outer shell, becoming a negatively charged chloride ion (Cl^-). The two ions form an ionic bond: They stay together by the mutual attraction of opposite charges. A crystal of table salt, or NaCl, is a cube-shaped lattice of ionically bonded sodium and chloride ions.

Figure 2.7 *Animated!* Important bonds in biological molecules.

simple example. Its two hydrogen atoms, each with one proton, attract the shared electrons equally.

In a *polar* covalent bond, two atoms do not share electrons equally. Why not? The atoms are of different elements, and one has more protons than the other. The one with the most protons pulls more, so its end of the bond ends up with a slight negative charge. We say it is "electronegative." The atom at the other end of the bond ends up with a slight positive charge. For instance, a water molecule (H—O—H) has two polar covalent bonds. The oxygen atom carries a slight negative charge, and each of the two hydrogen atoms has a slight positive charge.

A HYDROGEN BOND IS A WEAK BOND BETWEEN POLAR MOLECULES

A **hydrogen bond** is a weak attraction that has formed between a covalently bound hydrogen atom and an electronegative atom in a different molecule or in another part of the same molecule. The dotted lines in Figure 2.7c depict this link.

Hydrogen bonds are weak, so they form and break easily. Even so, they are essential in biological molecules. For example, the genetic material DNA is built of two parallel strands of chemical units, and the strands are

Table 2.2	Major Chemical Bonds in Biological Molecules
Bond	Characteristics
Ionic	Joined atoms have opposite charges.
Covalent	Strong; joined atoms share electrons. In a *polar* covalent bond one end is positive, the other negative.
Hydrogen	Weak; joins a hydrogen (H^+) atom in one polar molecule with an electronegative atom in another polar molecule.

held together by hydrogen bonds. In Section 2.6 you will read how hydrogen bonds between water molecules contribute to water's life-sustaining properties.

An ion forms when an atom gains or loses electrons, and so acquires a positive or negative charge. In an ionic bond, ions of opposite charge attract each other and stay together.

In a covalent bond, atoms share electrons. If the electrons are shared equally, the bond is nonpolar. If the sharing is not equal, the bond is polar—slightly positive at one end, slightly negative at the other.

In a hydrogen bond, a covalently bound hydrogen atom attracts a small, negatively charged atom in a different molecule or in another part of the same molecule.

molecular hydrogen (H—H)

Two hydrogen atoms, each with one proton, share two electrons in a single covalent bond that is nonpolar.

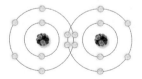

molecular oxygen (O=O)

Two oxygen atoms, each with eight protons, share four electrons in a double covalent bond, also nonpolar.

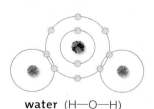

water (H—O—H)

Two hydrogen atoms each share an electron with oxygen. The resulting two covalent bonds form a water molecule. These bonds are polar. The oxygen exerts a greater pull on the shared electrons, so it bears a slight negative charge. Each of the hydrogens has a slight positive charge.

b Covalent bonds. Two atoms with unpaired electrons in their outer shell become more stable by sharing electrons. Two electrons are shared in each covalent bond. When the electrons are shared equally, the covalent bond is nonpolar. If one atom exerts more pull on the shared electrons, the covalent bond is polar.

hydrogen bond

water molecule   ammonia molecule

Two molecules interacting in one hydrogen (H) bond.

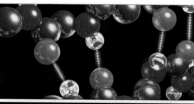

H bonds helping to hold part of two large molecules together.

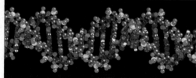

Many H bonds hold DNA's two strands together. Individually, each H bond is weak, but collectively they stabilize DNA's large structure.

c Hydrogen bonds. Such bonds can form when a hydrogen atom is already covalently bonded in a molecule. The hydrogen's slight positive charge weakly attracts an atom with a slight negative charge that is already covalently bonded to something else. As shown above, this can happen between one of the hydrogen atoms of a water molecule and the nitrogen atom of an ammonia molecule.

2.5 Antioxidants

The process in which an atom or molecule loses one or more electrons to another atom or molecule is called *oxidation*. It's what causes a match to burn and an iron nail to rust, and it is part of all kinds of important metabolic events in body cells. Unfortunately, the countless oxidations that go on in our cells also release highly unstable molecules called **free radicals**. Each one is a molecule (such as O_2^-) that includes an oxygen atom lacking a full complement of electrons in its outer shell. To fill the empty slot, a free radical can easily "steal" an electron from another, stable molecule. This theft disrupts both the structure and functioning of the affected molecule.

In large numbers, free radicals pose a serious threat to essential molecules, including a cell's DNA. Cigarette smoke and the ultraviolet radiation in sunlight produce additional free radicals in the body.

An **antioxidant** is a substance that can give up an electron to a free radical before the rogue does damage to DNA or some other vital cell component. The body makes some antioxidants, including the hormone melatonin (Chapter 15), that neutralize free radicals by giving up electrons to them. This home-grown chemical army isn't enough to balance the ongoing production of free radicals, however. This is why many nutritionists recommend adding antioxidants to the diet by eating lots of the foods that contain them, using supplements only in moderation.

Ascorbic acid—vitamin C—is an antioxidant, as is vitamin E. So are some carotenoids, such as alpha carotene, which are pigments in orange and leafy green vegetables, among other foods (Figure 2.8). Antioxidant-rich foods typically also are low in fat and high in fiber.

Figure 2.8 Antioxidants occur in many plant-derived foods, especially orange and green vegetables and fruits.

2.6 Life Depends on Water

Life on our planet probably began in water, and for all life forms it is indispensable. Our blood is more than 90 percent water, and water helps maintain the shape and internal structure of our cells. Many chemical reactions required for life processes require water, or occur only after other substances have dissolved in it. Three unusual properties of water suit it for its key roles in the body, starting with the fact that water is liquid at body temperature.

HYDROGEN BONDING MAKES WATER LIQUID

Any time water is warmer than about 32°F or cooler than about 212°F, it is a liquid. Therefore it is a liquid at body temperature; our watery blood flows and our cells have the fluid they need to maintain their structural integrity and to function properly. What keeps water liquid? You may recall that while a water molecule has no net charge, it does carry charges that are distributed unevenly. The water molecule's oxygen end is a bit negative and its hydrogen end is a bit positive (Figure 2.9a). This uneven charge distribution makes water molecules polar, able to attract other water molecules and form hydrogen bonds with them. Collectively, the bonds are so strong that they hold the water molecules close together (Figure 2.9b and 2.9c). This effect of hydrogen bonds is why water is always in a liquid state unless its temperature falls to freezing or rises to the boiling point.

Water attracts and hydrogen-bonds with other polar substances, such as sugars. Because polar molecules are

slight negative charge
on the oxygen atom

(−)

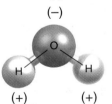

Overall, the molecule carries no net charge

(+)   (+)

a   slight positive charge
on each hydrogen atom

Figure 2.9 *Animated!* Water, a substance essential for life.
(**a**) Polarity of a water molecule.

(**b**) Hydrogen bonds between molecules in liquid water (dashed lines).

(**c**) Water's cohesion. When a pebble strikes liquid water, the blow forces molecules away from the surface. The individual water molecules don't scatter every which way, however, because hydrogen bonds pull inward on those at the surface. As a result, the molecules tend to stay together in droplets.

attracted to water, they are said to be **hydrophilic**, or "water-loving." Water repels nonpolar substances, such as oils. Hence nonpolar molecules are **hydrophobic**, or "water-dreading." We will return to these concepts when we examine cell structure in Chapter 3.

WATER CAN ABSORB AND HOLD HEAT

Water's hydrogen bonds give it a high *heat capacity*—they enable water to absorb a great deal of heat energy before it warms significantly or evaporates. This is because it takes a large amount of heat to break the many hydrogen bonds that are present in water. Water's ability to absorb significant heat before becoming hot is the reason it was used to cool hot automobile engines in the days before alcohol-based coolants became available. In a similar way, water helps stabilize the temperature inside cells, which are mostly water. The chemical reactions in cells constantly produce heat, yet cells must stay fairly cool because their proteins can only function properly within narrow temperature limits.

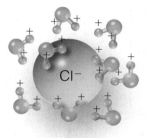

Figure 2.10 *Animated!* Clusters of water molecules around ions. The clusters are called "spheres of hydration."

When enough heat energy is present, hydrogen bonds between water molecules break apart and do not re-form. Then liquid water evaporates—molecules at its surface begin to escape into the air. When a large number of water molecules evaporate, heat energy is lost. This is why sweating helps cool you off on a hot, dry day. Your sweat is 99 percent water. When it evaporates from the millions of sweat glands in your skin, heat leaves with it.

WATER IS A BIOLOGICAL SOLVENT

Water also is a superb *solvent*, which means that ions and polar molecules easily dissolve in it. In chemical terms a dissolved substance is called a **solute**. When a substance dissolves, water molecules cluster around its individual molecules or ions and form "spheres of hydration." This is what happens to solutes in blood and other body fluids. Most chemical reactions in the body occur in water-based solutions.

Figure 2.10 shows what happens when you pour some table salt (NaCl) into a cup of water. After a while, the salt crystals separate into Na^+ and Cl^-. Each Na^+ attracts the negative end of some of the water molecules while each Cl^- attracts the positive end of others.

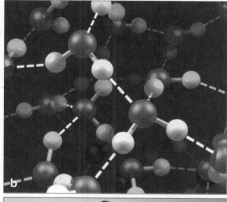

A water molecule is polar. This polarity allows water molecules to hydrogen-bond with one another and with other polar (hydrophilic) substances. Water molecules tend to repel nonpolar (hydrophobic) substances.

Among other effects, the hydrogen bonds in water help it stabilize temperature in body fluids and allow it to dissolve many substances.

2.7 Acids, Bases, and Buffers: Body Fluids in Flux

Ions dissolved in the fluids inside and outside cells influence cell structure and functioning. Especially important are hydrogen ions, which affect many body functions.

THE pH SCALE INDICATES THE CONCENTRATION OF HYDROGEN IONS

The water in the human body contains various ions. Some of the most important are **hydrogen ions**, which have far-reaching effects because they are chemically active and there are so many of them. At any instant, some water molecules are breaking apart into H^+ and **hydroxide ions** (OH^-). These ions are the basis for the **pH scale** (Figure 2.11), which measures the concentration (relative amount) of H^+ in water, blood, and other fluids. Pure water (not rainwater or tap water) always has just as many H^+ as OH^- ions. This state is neutrality, or pH 7, on the pH scale (Figure 2.11).

Starting at neutrality, each change by one unit of the pH scale corresponds to a tenfold increase or decrease in the concentration of H^+. One way to get a personal sense of range is to taste a bit of baking soda (pH 9), and then follow it with water (7), and then lemon juice (2.3).

ACIDS GIVE UP H+ AND BASES ACCEPT H+

You've probably heard of "acids" and "bases," but what are they, chemically? An **acid** is a substance that donates protons (H^+) to other solutes or to water molecules when it dissolves in water. A **base** accepts H^+ when it dissolves in water. When either an acid or a base dissolves, OH^- then forms in the solution as well. *Acidic* solutions, such as lemon juice and the gastric fluid in your stomach, release more H^+ than OH^-; their pH is below 7. *Basic* solutions, such as seawater, baking soda, and egg white, release more OH^- than H^+. Basic solutions are also called *alkaline* fluids; they have a pH above 7.

The fluid inside most human cells is about 7 on the pH scale. Body cells also are surrounded by fluids, and the pH values of most of those fluids are slightly higher, ranging between 7.3 and 7.5. The pH of the fluid portion of blood is in the same range.

To a chemist most acids are either weak or strong. Weak ones, such as carbonic acid (H_2CO_3), don't readily donate H^+. Depending on the pH, they just as easily accept H^+ after giving it up, so they alternate between acting as an acid and acting as a base. On the other hand, strong acids totally give up H^+ when they dissociate in water. Hydrochloric acid (HCl), nitric acid (HNO_3), and sulfuric acid (H_2SO_4) are examples.

High concentrations of strong acids or strong bases can be important in the body. For instance, when you eat, cells in your stomach are stimulated to secrete HCl, which separates into H^+ and Cl^- in water. The H^+ ions make your stomach fluid more acidic, and the increased acidity switches on enzymes that can digest (chemically break down) food particles. The acid also helps kill harmful bacteria. However, eating a meal that contains too much of certain kinds of foods can lead to "acid stomach." Antacids such as milk of magnesia are strong bases. In your stomach, milk of magnesia releases magnesium ions and OH^-, which combines with excess H^+ in your stomach fluid. This chemical reaction raises the fluid's pH, and your acid stomach goes away.

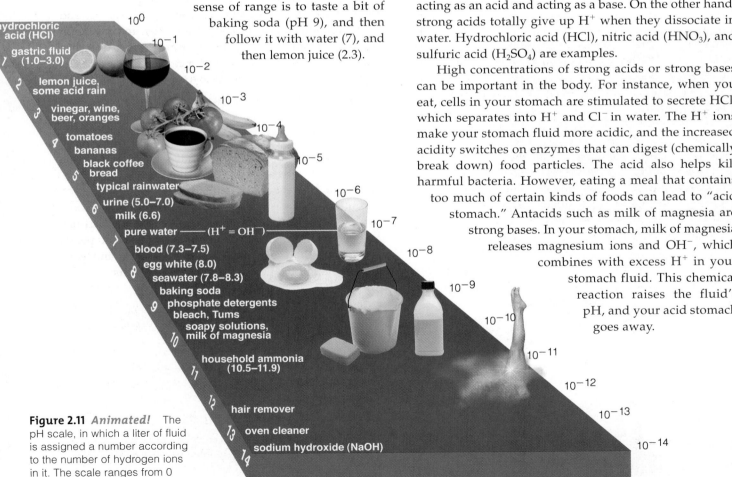

hydrochloric acid (HCl) — 10^0
gastric fluid (1.0–3.0) — 10^{-1}
lemon juice, some acid rain — 10^{-2}
vinegar, wine, beer, oranges — 10^{-3}
tomatoes bananas black coffee bread — 10^{-4}
typical rainwater — 10^{-5}
urine (5.0–7.0) milk (6.6) — 10^{-6}
pure water — ($H^+ = OH^-$) — 10^{-7}
blood (7.3–7.5) — 10^{-8}
egg white (8.0) seawater (7.8–8.3) baking soda — 10^{-9}
phosphate detergents bleach, Tums soapy solutions, milk of magnesia — 10^{-10}
household ammonia (10.5–11.9) — 10^{-11}
— 10^{-12}
hair remover — 10^{-13}
oven cleaner sodium hydroxide (NaOH) — 10^{-14}

Figure 2.11 *Animated!* The pH scale, in which a liter of fluid is assigned a number according to the number of hydrogen ions in it. The scale ranges from 0 (most acidic) to 14 (most basic).

High concentrations of strong acids or bases also can have a harmful effect on the world around us. Read the labels on bottles of ammonia, drain cleaner, and other common household products and you'll learn that many of them can cause severe chemical burns. So can sulfuric acid in car batteries. Smoke from fossil fuels, exhaust from motor vehicles, and nitrogen fertilizers release strong acids, which alter the pH of rain (Figure 2.12). The resulting acid rain is an ongoing environmental problem considered in more detail in Chapter 25.

Figure 2.12 Sulfur dioxide emissions from a coal-burning power plant. Camera lens filters revealed the otherwise invisible emissions. Sulfur dioxide and other airborne pollutants dissolve in water vapor to form acidic solutions. They are a major component of acid rain.

BUFFERS PROTECT AGAINST SHIFTS IN pH

Chemical reactions in cells are sensitive to even slight shifts in pH, because H^+ and OH^- can combine with many different molecules and change their functions. Normally, control mechanisms minimize undesirable shifts in pH, as they do when HCl enters the stomach in response to a meal. Many of the controls involve buffer systems.

A **buffer system** is a partnership between a weak acid and a base, which work together to counter slight shifts in pH. The system forms when the acid dissolves in water. Remember, when a strong base enters a fluid, the OH^- level rises. But a weak acid neutralizes part of the added OH^- by combining with it. By this interaction, the weak acid's partner forms. If a strong acid floods in later, the base will accept H^+ and become its partner in the system.

A key point to remember is that the action of a buffer system can't make new hydrogen ions or eliminate those that already are present. It can only bind or release them.

Several buffer systems operate in the blood and in tissue fluids—the internal environment of the body. For example, reactions in the lungs and kidneys help control the acid–base balance of this environment at levels suitable for life (Sections 9.5 and 10.8). For now, consider what happens when the blood level of H^+ falls and the blood is not as acidic as it should be. At times like this, carbonic acid that is dissolved in blood releases H^+ and becomes the partner base, bicarbonate:

$$H_2CO_3 \longrightarrow HCO_3^- + H^+$$

carbonic acid   bicarbonate

When the blood becomes more acidic, more H^+ is bound to the base, thus forming the partner acid:

$$HCO_3^- + H^+ \longrightarrow H_2CO_3$$

bicarbonate   carbonic acid

Uncontrolled shifts in the pH of body fluids can be disastrous. If blood's pH (7.3–7.5) declines to even 7, a person will fall into a *coma*, a state of unconsciousness. An increase to 7.8 can lead to *tetany*, a potentially fatal condition in which the body's skeletal muscles contract uncontrollably. In *acidosis*, carbon dioxide builds up in the blood, too much carbonic acid forms, and blood pH plummets. The condition called *alkalosis* is an abnormal increase in blood pH. Left untreated, both acidosis and alkalosis can be lethal.

A SALT RELEASES OTHER KINDS OF IONS

Salts are compounds that release ions *other than* H^+ and OH^- in solutions. Salts and water often form when a strong acid and a strong base interact. Depending on a solution's pH value, salts can form and dissolve easily. Consider how sodium chloride forms, then dissolves:

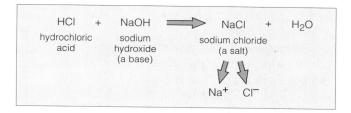

Many salts dissolve into ions that have key functions in cells. For example, the activity of nerve cells depends on ions of sodium, potassium, and calcium, and your muscles contract with the help of calcium ions.

Hydrogen ions (H^+) and other ions dissolved in the fluids inside and outside cells affect cell structure and function.

Acidic substances release H^+, and basic (alkaline) substances accept them. Certain acid–base interactions, such as in buffer systems, help maintain the pH value of a fluid—that is, its H^+ concentration.

A buffer system counters slight shifts in pH by releasing hydrogen ions when their concentration is too low or by combining with them when the concentration is too high.

Salts release ions other than H^+ and OH^-.

2.8 Molecules of Life

LINK TO
SECTION
2.4

Carbohydrates, lipids, proteins, and nucleic acids—the four classes of biological molecules—all are built on atoms of the element carbon.

BIOLOGICAL MOLECULES CONTAIN CARBON

Each of the molecules of life is an **organic compound**: it contains the element carbon and at least one hydrogen atom. Chemists once thought organic substances were those obtained from animals and vegetables, as opposed to "inorganic" ones from minerals. Today, however, there is evidence that organic compounds were present on Earth before organisms were.

CARBON'S KEY FEATURE IS VERSATILE BONDING

Our bodies are mostly oxygen, hydrogen, and carbon. Their oxygen and hydrogen are mainly in the form of water. Remove that, and carbon makes up more than half of what's left.

Carbon's importance to life starts with its versatile bonding behavior. As the sketch below shows, *each carbon atom can share pairs of electrons with as many as four other atoms.* The covalent bonds are fairly stable, because the carbon atoms share pairs of electrons equally. Such bonds link carbon atoms together in chains.

These form a backbone to which hydrogen, oxygen, and other elements can attach.

single covalent bond

carbon atom

The angles of the covalent bonds help produce the three-dimensional shapes of organic compounds. A chain of carbon atoms, bonded covalently one after another, forms a backbone from which other atoms can project:

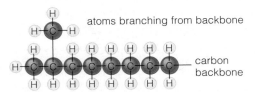

atoms branching from backbone

carbon backbone

Often, the backbone coils back on itself in a ring, as in the following diagrams:

or

carbon rings

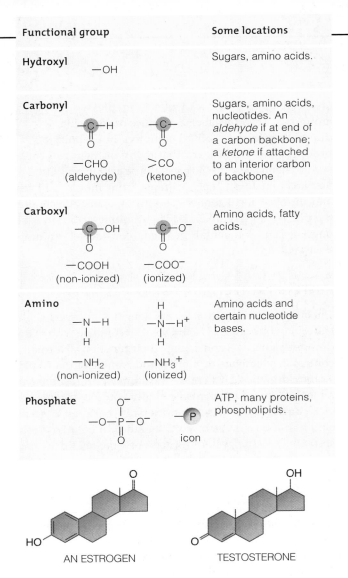

Functional group		Some locations
Hydroxyl —OH		Sugars, amino acids.
Carbonyl —CHO (aldehyde)	>CO (ketone)	Sugars, amino acids, nucleotides. An *aldehyde* if at end of a carbon backbone; a *ketone* if attached to an interior carbon of backbone
Carboxyl —COOH (non-ionized)	—COO⁻ (ionized)	Amino acids, fatty acids.
Amino —NH₂ (non-ionized)	—NH₃⁺ (ionized)	Amino acids and certain nucleotide bases.
Phosphate	icon	ATP, many proteins, phospholipids.

AN ESTROGEN   TESTOSTERONE

Figure 2.13 *Animated!*   Examples of functional groups. The sex hormones estrogen and testosterone (bottom) differ chemically because their hydroxyl groups attach to different carbons.

FUNCTIONAL GROUPS AFFECT THE CHEMICAL BEHAVIOR OF ORGANIC COMPOUNDS

A carbon backbone with only hydrogen atoms attached to it is a hydrocarbon, which is a very stable structure. Besides hydrogen atoms, biological molecules also have **functional groups**, which are particular atoms or clusters of atoms that are covalently bonded to carbon and can influence the chemical behavior of organic compounds.

Figure 2.13 shows a few functional groups. Sugars and other organic compounds classified as alcohols have one or more hydroxyl groups (—OH). Water forms hydrogen bonds with hydroxyl groups, which is why sugars can dissolve in water. The backbone of a protein forms by reactions between amino groups and carboxyl groups. As you will see shortly, the backbone is the start

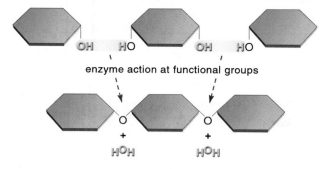

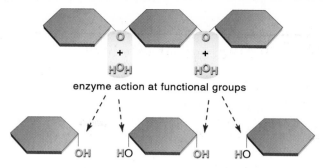

a Two condensation reactions. Enzymes remove an —OH group and an H atom from two molecules, which covalently bond as a larger molecule. Two water molecules form.

b Hydrolysis, a water-requiring cleavage reaction. Enzyme action splits a molecule into three parts, then attaches an H atom and an —OH group derived from a water molecule to each exposed site.

Figure 2.14 *Animated!* (*above*) Examples of metabolic reactions that build, rearrange, and break apart most biological molecules. (*right*) Hydrolysis reactions in the digestive system break starch molecules (polymers) in corn kernels into smaller chemical units (sugar monomers).

of bonding patterns that produce the protein's three-dimensional structure. Amino groups also can combine with hydrogen ions and act as buffers against decreases in pH. The functional groups of sex hormones shown in Figure 2.13 help account for differences between males and females.

CELLS HAVE CHEMICAL TOOLS TO ASSEMBLE AND BREAK APART BIOLOGICAL MOLECULES

How do cells put together the organic compounds they need for their structure and functioning? The details can fill whole books, but here you only need to focus on a few basic concepts. First, whatever happens in a cell requires energy. This rule holds regardless of whether a cell is building, rearranging, or even breaking apart large organic compounds needed for its operations. Chemical reactions in cells also require a class of proteins called **enzymes**, which make metabolic reactions take place faster than they would on their own. Different enzymes facilitate different kinds of reactions. Two reactions that go on constantly in cells are those called condensation and hydrolysis.

CONDENSATION REACTIONS   As a cell builds or changes organic compounds, a common step is the **condensation reaction**. Often in this kind of reaction, enzymes remove a hydroxyl group from one molecule and an H atom from another, then speed the formation of a covalent bond between the two molecules (Figure 2.14*a*). The discarded hydrogen and oxygen atoms may combine to form a molecule of water (H_2O). Because this kind of reaction often forms water as a by-product, condensation is sometimes called *dehydration* ("un-watering") *synthesis*. Cells can use series of condensation reactions to assemble

polymers. *Poly-* means many, and a **polymer** is a large molecule built of three to millions of subunits. The individual subunits, called **monomers**, may be the same or different.

HYDROLYSIS REACTIONS   **Hydrolysis** is like condensation in reverse (Figure 2.14*b*). In a first step, enzymes that act on particular functional groups split molecules into two or more parts; then they attach an —OH group and a hydrogen atom from a molecule of water to the exposed sites. With hydrolysis, cells can break apart large polymers into smaller units when these are required for building blocks or energy.

Carbohydrates, lipids, proteins, and nucleic acids are the main biological molecules. All are organic compounds.

Organic compounds have carbon backbones. The backbone allows bonding arrangements that help give organic compounds their three-dimensional shapes.

Functional groups are covalently bonded to the carbon backbone of organic compounds. The groups increase the structural and functional diversity of organic compounds.

Enzymes speed the chemical reactions cells use to build, rearrange, and break down organic compounds. These reactions include the combining or splitting of molecules, as in condensation and hydrolysis reactions.

2.9 Carbohydrates: Plentiful and Varied

Carbohydrates are the most abundant biological molecules. Cells use them in building cell parts, or package them for energy in forms that can be stored or transported elsewhere in the body.

Most **carbohydrates** consist of carbon, hydrogen, and oxygen atoms in a 1:2:1 ratio. Because of differences in their structure, chemists separate carbohydrates into three major classes, **monosaccharides**, **oligosaccharides**, and **polysaccharides**.

SIMPLE SUGARS—THE SIMPLEST CARBOHYDRATES

"Saccharide" comes from a Greek word meaning sugar. A *mono*saccharide, meaning "one monomer of sugar," is the simplest carbohydrate. It has at least two —OH groups joined to the carbon backbone plus an aldehyde or a ketone group. Monosaccharides usually taste sweet and dissolve easily in water. The most common ones have a backbone of five or six carbons; for example, there are five carbon atoms in deoxyribose, the sugar in DNA. Glucose, the main energy source for body cells, has six carbons, twelve hydrogens, and six oxygens. (Notice how it meets the 1:2:1 ratio noted above.) Glucose is a building block for larger carbohydrates (Figure 2.15*a*). It also is the parent molecule (precursor) for many compounds, such as vitamin C, which are derived from sugar monomers.

OLIGOSACCHARIDES ARE SHORT CHAINS OF SUGAR UNITS

Unlike the simple sugars, an *oligo*saccharide is a short chain of two or more sugar monomers that are united by dehydration synthesis. (*Oligo-* means a few.) The type known as *di*saccharides consists of just two sugar units. Lactose, sucrose, and maltose are examples. Lactose (a glucose and a galactose unit) is a milk sugar. Sucrose, the most plentiful sugar in nature, consists of one glucose and one fructose unit (Figure 2.15*c*). You consume sucrose when you eat fruit, among other plant foods. Table sugar is sucrose crystallized from sugar cane and sugar beets.

Proteins and other large molecules often have oligosaccharides attached as side chains to their carbon backbone. Some chains have key roles in activities of cell membranes, as you will read in Chapter 3. Others are important in the body's defenses against disease.

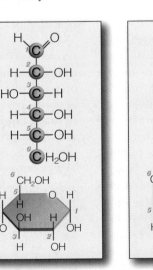

a Structure of glucose

b Structure of fructose

c Formation of a sucrose molecule from two simple sugars

glucose

fructose

sucrose

+ **H₂O**

Figure 2.15 Straight-chain and ring forms of (**a**) glucose and (**b**) fructose. For reference purposes, the carbon atoms of simple sugars are commonly numbered in sequence, starting at the end closest to the molecule's aldehyde or ketone group. (**c**) Condensation of two monosaccharides (glucose and fructose) into a disaccharide (sucrose).

BIOLOGICAL MOLECULES

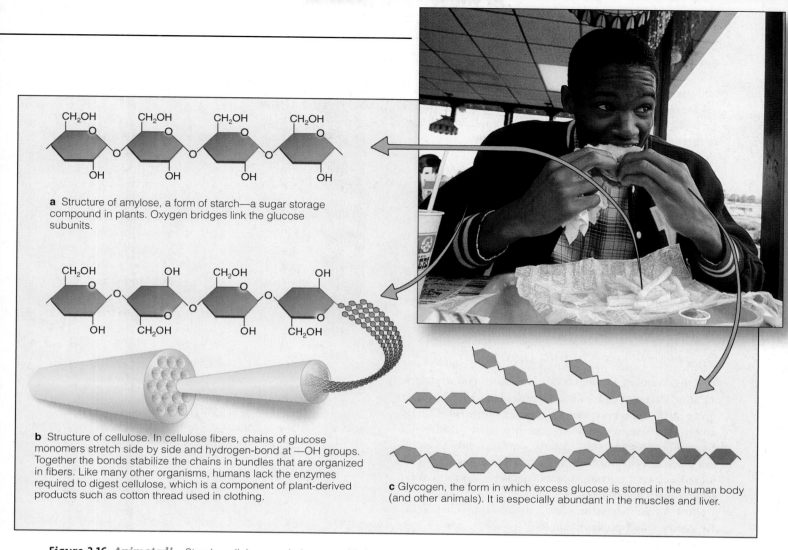

a Structure of amylose, a form of starch—a sugar storage compound in plants. Oxygen bridges link the glucose subunits.

b Structure of cellulose. In cellulose fibers, chains of glucose monomers stretch side by side and hydrogen-bond at —OH groups. Together the bonds stabilize the chains in bundles that are organized in fibers. Like many other organisms, humans lack the enzymes required to digest cellulose, which is a component of plant-derived products such as cotton thread used in clothing.

c Glycogen, the form in which excess glucose is stored in the human body (and other animals). It is especially abundant in the muscles and liver.

Figure 2.16 *Animated!*   Starch, cellulose, and glycogen. All three carbohydrates are built only of glucose monomers.

POLYSACCHARIDES ARE SUGAR CHAINS THAT STORE ENERGY

The "complex" carbohydrates, or polysaccharides, are straight or branched chains of sugar monomers. Often thousands have been joined by dehydration synthesis. A great deal of energy is stored in the many chemical bonds in polysaccharides. The energy is released to cells when these sugars are digested. Most of the carbohydrates humans eat are in the form of polysaccharides. The most common ones—glycogen, starch, and cellulose—consist only of glucose.

When you eat meat you are consuming glycogen (Figure 2.16c). Glycogen is one form in which animals store sugar, most notably in their muscles and the liver. When a person's blood-sugar levels fall, liver cells break down glycogen and release glucose to the blood. When you exercise, your muscle cells tap into their glycogen stores for quick access to energy.

Foods such as potatoes, rice, wheat, and corn are all rich in starch (Figure 2.16a), which is a storage form of glucose in plant cells. In starch the glucose subunits are arranged in a linear fashion. Plants also store glucose in the form of cellulose (Figure 2.16b). We humans lack digestive enzymes that can break down the cellulose in vegetables, whole grains, and other plant tissues. We do benefit from it, however, as undigested "fiber" that adds bulk and so helps move wastes through the lower part of the digestive tract.

Carbohydrates range from simple sugars (such as glucose) to molecules composed of many sugar units.

In order of their structural complexity, the three types of carbohydrates are monosaccharides, oligosaccharides, and polysaccharides.

The body uses carbohydrates in building cell parts and also packages them for energy in forms that can be stored or transported from one site to another.

2.10 Lipids: Fats and Their Chemical Kin

LINKS TO
SECTIONS
2.3, 2.4, AND 2.8

Cells use lipids to store energy, as structural materials (as in cell membranes), and as signaling molecules. Greasy or oily to the touch, major lipids in the body include fats, phospholipids, and sterols.

Oil and water don't mix. Why? Oils are a type of lipid, and a **lipid** is a nonpolar hydrocarbon. A lipid's large nonpolar region makes it hydrophobic, so it tends not to dissolve in water. Lipids easily dissolve in other nonpolar substances. For example, you can dissolve melted butter in olive oil. Here we focus on fats and phospholipids, both of which have chemical "tails" called fatty acids, and on sterols, which have a backbone of four carbon rings.

FATS ARE ENERGY-STORING LIPIDS

The lipids called **fats** have as many as three fatty acids, all attached to glycerol. Each **fatty acid** has a backbone of up to thirty-six carbons and a carboxyl group (—COOH) at one end. Hydrogen atoms occupy most or all of the remaining bonding sites. A fatty acid typically stretches out like a flexible tail (Figure 2.17). An *unsaturated* tail has one or more double bonds in its backbone. A *saturated* tail has only single bonds.

Most animal fats have lots of saturated fatty acids, which are held packed together by weak bonds. Like uncooked bacon fat, or lard, they are solid at room temperature. Most plant fats—"vegetable oils" such as canola, peanut oil, corn oil, and olive oil—stay liquid at room temperature. They stay pourable because the packing interactions in plant fats are not as stable due to rigid kinks in their fatty acid tails.

Butter, lard, plant oils, and other dietary fats consist mostly of **triglycerides**, so-called "neutral" fats that have three fatty acid tails attached to a glycerol backbone (Figure 2.18). Triglycerides are the most abundant lipids in the body and its richest source of energy. Compared to complex carbohydrates, they yield more than twice as much energy, gram for gram, when they are broken down. This is because triglycerides have more removable electrons than do carbohydrates—and energy is released when electrons are removed. In the body, cells of fat-storing tissues stockpile triglycerides as fat droplets.

The *trans fatty acids* are "hydrogenated," or partially saturated. They often are the main ingredient in solid margarines and occur in many packaged foods as well. Many people limit the amount of trans fatty acids in their diet because trans fatty acids have been implicated in the development of some types of heart disease.

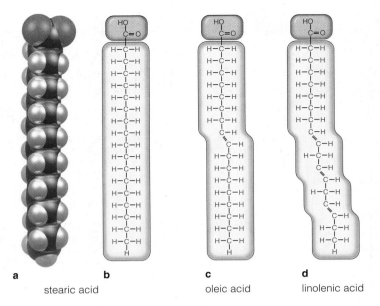

a   b   c   d

stearic acid   oleic acid   linolenic acid

Figure 2.17 *Animated!* Three fatty acids. (**a,b**) A space-filling model of stearic acid is shown next to its structural formula. Its carbon backbone is fully saturated with hydrogens. (**c**) Oleic acid, with its double bond in the carbon backbone, is unsaturated. (**d**) Linolenic acid, with three double bonds, is a "polyunsaturated" fatty acid.

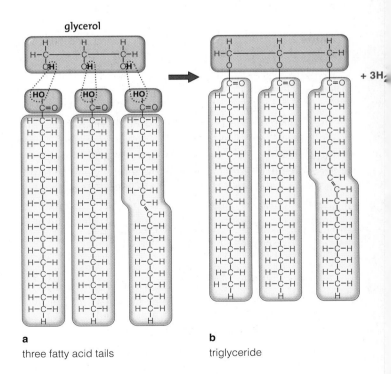

glycerol

a   three fatty acid tails

b   triglyceride

Figure 2.18 *Animated!* Condensation of (**a**) three fatty acids and a glycerol molecule into (**b**) a triglyceride.

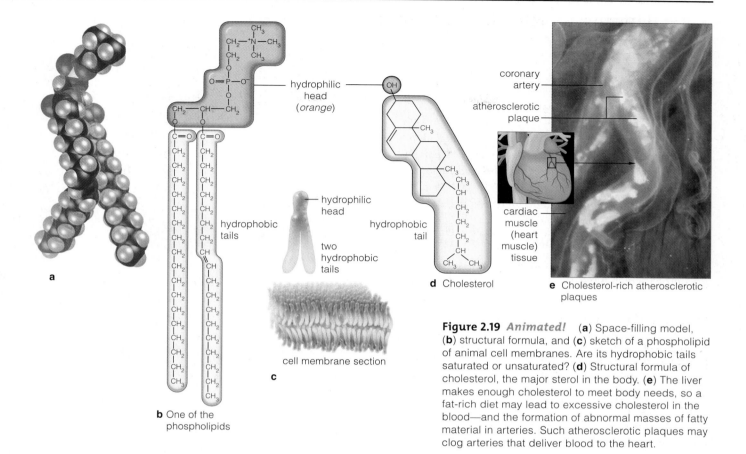

hydrophilic head (*orange*)

hydrophobic tails

a

b One of the phospholipids

hydrophilic head

two hydrophobic tails

cell membrane section

c

hydrophilic head

hydrophobic tail

d Cholesterol

coronary artery

atherosclerotic plaque

cardiac muscle (heart muscle) tissue

e Cholesterol-rich atherosclerotic plaques

Figure 2.19 *Animated!* (**a**) Space-filling model, (**b**) structural formula, and (**c**) sketch of a phospholipid of animal cell membranes. Are its hydrophobic tails saturated or unsaturated? (**d**) Structural formula of cholesterol, the major sterol in the body. (**e**) The liver makes enough cholesterol to meet body needs, so a fat-rich diet may lead to excessive cholesterol in the blood—and the formation of abnormal masses of fatty material in arteries. Such atherosclerotic plaques may clog arteries that deliver blood to the heart.

PHOSPHOLIPIDS ARE KEY BUILDING BLOCKS OF CELL MEMBRANES

A **phospholipid** has a glycerol backbone, two fatty acid tails, and a hydrophilic "head" with a phosphate group—a phosphorus atom bonded to four oxygen atoms—and another polar group (Figure 2.19*a*). Phospholipids are the main materials of cell membranes, which have two layers of lipids. The heads of one layer are dissolved in the cell's fluid interior, while the heads of the other layer are dissolved in the surroundings. Sandwiched between the two are all the fatty acid tails, which are hydrophobic.

STEROLS ARE BUILDING BLOCKS OF CHOLESTEROL AND STEROIDS

Sterols are among the lipids that have no fatty acid tails. Sterols differ in the number, position, and type of their functional groups, but they all have a rigid backbone of four fused-together carbon rings:

sterol backbone

Many people associate the sterol cholesterol (Figure 2.19*b* and 2.19*c*) with heart and artery disease. However, normal amounts of this sterol are crucial to the structure and proper functioning of cells. For instance, cholesterol is a vital component of membranes of every cell in your body. Important derivatives of cholesterol include vitamin D (essential for bone and tooth development), bile salts (which help with fat digestion in the small intestine), and steroid hormones such as estrogen and testosterone. Later chapters will look more closely at the ways steroid hormones influence reproduction, development, growth, and some other body functions.

Lipids are hydrophobic, greasy or oily compounds. Important lipids in the human body include:

- *Triglycerides (neutral fats), which are major reservoirs of energy*
- *Phospholipids, the main components of cell membranes*
- *Sterols (such as cholesterol), which are components of membranes and precursors of steroid hormones and other vital molecules.*

BIOLOGICAL MOLECULES

2.11 Proteins: Biological Molecules with Many Roles

Of all the large biological molecules, proteins are the most diverse. Those called enzymes speed up chemical reactions. Structural proteins are building blocks of your bones, muscles, and other body elements. Transport proteins help move substances, while the regulatory proteins, including some hormones, help adjust cell activities. They help make possible activities such as waking, sleeping, and engaging in sex, to cite just a few. Still other proteins function as weapons against harmful bacteria and other invaders.

PROTEINS ARE BUILT FROM AMINO ACIDS

Amazingly, our body cells build thousands of different **proteins** from only twenty kinds of amino acids. An **amino acid** is a small organic compound that consists of an amino group, a carboxyl group (an acid), an atom of hydrogen, and one or more atoms called its R group. As you can see from the structural formula in Figure 2.20, these parts generally are covalently bonded to the same carbon atom. Figure 2.21 shows several amino acids that we will consider later in the book.

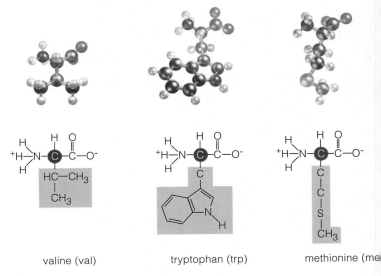

valine (val)　　　　tryptophan (trp)　　　　methionine (me

Figure 2.21 Three amino acids shown as ball-and-stick models with structural formulas of their common ionized form. Green boxes indicate R groups, which are side chains that include functional groups. A side chain helps determine an amino acid's chemical and physical properties.

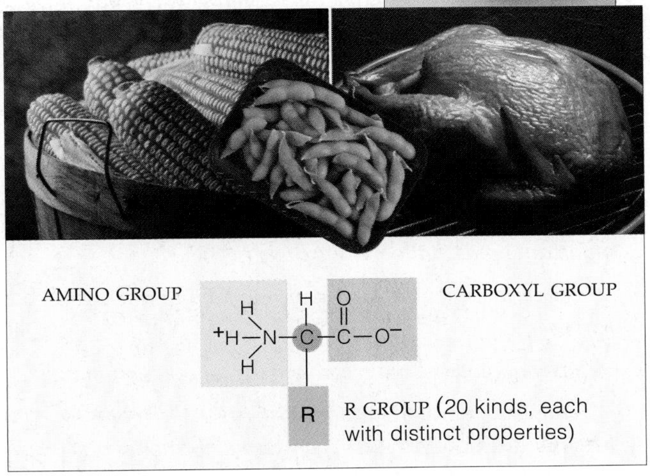

Figure 2.20 *Animated!* Generalized structural formula for amino acids, along with soybeans and a few other dietary sources of these small organic compounds.

AMINO GROUP　　　CARBOXYL GROUP

R GROUP (20 kinds, each with distinct properties)

THE SEQUENCE OF AMINO ACIDS IS A PROTEIN'S PRIMARY STRUCTURE

When a cell makes a protein, amino acids become linked, one after the other, by *peptide* bonds. As Figure 2.22 shows, this is the type of covalent bond that forms between one amino acid's amino group (NH_3^+) and the carboxyl group ($—COO^-$) of the next amino acid.

When peptide bonds join two amino acids together, we have a dipeptide. When they join three or more amino acids, we have a **polypeptide chain**. The backbone of each chain incorporates nitrogen atoms in this regular pattern: —N—C—C—N—C—C—.

For each kind of protein, different amino acids are added in a specific order, one at a time, from the twenty kinds available. As a later chapter describes more fully, DNA determines the order in which amino acids are "chosen" to be added to the growing chain. Once the chain is completed, the order of its linked amino acids is the unique sequence for that particular kind of protein (Figure 2.22*e*). Every other kind of protein in the body will have its own sequence of amino acids, linked one to the next like the links of a chain. This sequence is the *primary* structure of a protein. A large number of amino acids can be linked up this way. The primary structure of the largest known protein, which is a component of human muscle, is a string of some 27,000 amino acids!

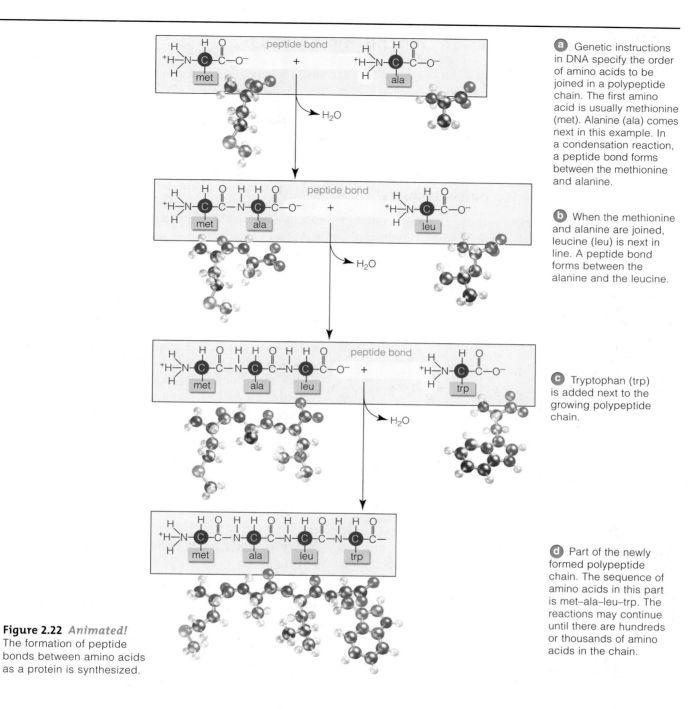

a Genetic instructions in DNA specify the order of amino acids to be joined in a polypeptide chain. The first amino acid is usually methionine (met). Alanine (ala) comes next in this example. In a condensation reaction, a peptide bond forms between the methionine and alanine.

b When the methionine and alanine are joined, leucine (leu) is next in line. A peptide bond forms between the alanine and the leucine.

c Tryptophan (trp) is added next to the growing polypeptide chain.

d Part of the newly formed polypeptide chain. The sequence of amino acids in this part is met–ala–leu–trp. The reactions may continue until there are hundreds or thousands of amino acids in the chain.

Figure 2.22 *Animated!* The formation of peptide bonds between amino acids as a protein is synthesized.

Different cells make thousands of different proteins. Many of the proteins are fibrous, with polypeptide chains organized as strands or sheets. They contribute to the shape and internal organization of cells. Other proteins are globular: They have one or more polypeptide chains folded into compact, rounded shapes. Most enzymes are globular proteins. So are the proteins that help cells, and cell parts, move.

As you will see next, a protein's final shape and chemical behavior arise from its primary structure. Said another way, information built into a protein's amino acid sequence determines its structure and function.

A protein consists of one or more polypeptide chains of amino acids. A sequence of amino acids makes up each kind of protein; this sequence is the protein's primary structure. It determines the protein's final structure, its chemical behavior, and its function.

2.12 A Protein's Function Depends on Its Shape

A key take-home message in this book is that in biology, structure equals function. Proteins are a prime example. How a protein functions (or malfunctions) depends on events that take place after a polypeptide has formed—that is, once the primary structure is in place—and the chain then bends, folds, and coils.

MANY PROTEINS FOLD TWO OR THREE TIMES

For the most part, a protein's primary structure guides its final shape in two ways. First, it allows hydrogen bonds to form between different amino acids in the chain. Second, it puts R groups in positions where they can interact. The interactions force the chain to bend and twist, as diagrammed in Figure 2.23.

Hydrogen bonds form at regular, short intervals along a new polypeptide chain. They give rise to a coiled or extended pattern known as the *secondary structure* of a protein. Think of a polypeptide chain as a set of rigid playing cards joined by links that can swivel a bit. Each "card" is a peptide group (Figure 2.23*a*). Atoms on either side of it can rotate slightly around their covalent bonds and form bonds with neighboring atoms. For instance, in many chains a hydrogen bond forms after every third amino acid. The bonding pattern forces the peptide groups to coil helically, like a spiral staircase (Figure 2.23*b*). In other proteins, the hydrogen bonds hold two or more chains side by side, like sections of a folded sheet of paper.

The coils, sheets, and loops of a protein fold up even more, much like an overly twisted rubber band. This is the third level of organization, or *tertiary* structure, of a protein (Figure 2.23*c*). Tertiary structure is what makes a protein a molecule that can perform a particular function. For instance, some proteins fold into a hollow "barrel" that provides a channel through cell membranes.

Figure 2.24*a* shows how a polypeptide chain was folded into the tertiary structure of the protein globin. Functional groups along the chain caused the folding when hydrogen bonds formed between certain ones.

PROTEINS CAN HAVE MORE THAN ONE POLYPEPTIDE CHAIN

Imagine that bonds form between *four* molecules of globin and that an iron-containing functional group, a heme group, nestles near the center of each. The result is hemoglobin, an oxygen-transporting protein. At this moment, each of the millions of red blood cells in your body is transporting a billion molecules of oxygen, bound to 250 million molecules of hemoglobin.

With its four globin molecules, hemoglobin is a good example of a protein that is built of more than one polypeptide chain. The hormone insulin, which consists of two chains, is another. Proteins that are constructed this way are said to have *quaternary* structure (Figure 2.24*b*). Their polypeptide chains are joined by weak interactions (such as hydrogen bonds) and sometimes by covalent bonds between sulfur atoms of R groups. These bonds between two sulfur atoms are called disulfide bridges (di = two).

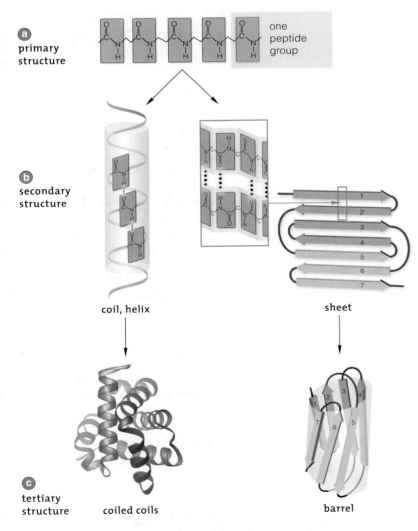

a primary structure

one peptide group

b secondary structure

coil, helix

sheet

c tertiary structure

coiled coils

barrel

Figure 2.23 *Animated!* The first three levels of protein structure. (**a**) Primary structure is a chain of amino acids. (**b**) Hydrogen bonds (dotted lines) along a polypeptide chain form a coiled or sheetlike secondary structure. (**c**) Coils and sheets pack together to form the protein's third level of structure, which suits it for its particular function.

Disulfide bridges

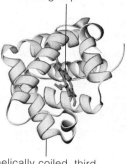

heme, an iron-containing, oxygen-transporting functional group

helically coiled, third structural level of one globin molecule

a third level

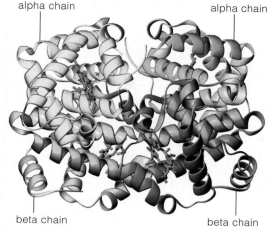

alpha chain

alpha chain

beta chain

beta chain

b fourth level of protein structure

Figure 2.24 *Animated!* (**a**) A globin molecule. This coiled polypeptide chain attracts heme, a functional group containing iron. (**b**) Hemoglobin, an oxygen-transporting pigment in red blood cells. It has four globin chains and four heme groups. The two alpha chains and two beta chains have slightly different amino acid sequences. To make it easier to tell the four chains apart, here the coiled regions are color-coded. The heme groups are shown in red. Each one can bind a molecule of oxygen (O_2), and this is how red blood cells transport oxygen to cells.

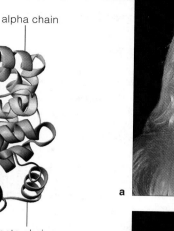
a

b

Figure 2.25 The hair of actress Nicole Kidman (**a**) before and (**b**) after a permanent wave.

Hemoglobin and insulin are globular proteins; so are most enzymes. Many other proteins with quaternary structure are fibrous. Collagen, the most common protein in the body, is an example of this. (Your skin, bones, corneas, and other body parts depend on collagen's strength.) Keratin, a structural protein of hair, is another example. The chemicals used in a permanent wave break hydrogen bonds in disulfide bridges in the keratin chains in hair. After the hair is wrapped around curlers that hold polypeptide chains in new positions, a second chemical causes disulfide bridges to form between *different* sulfur-bearing amino acids. The rearranged bonding locks the hair in curls (Figure 2.25).

GLYCOPROTEINS HAVE SUGARS ATTACHED AND LIPOPROTEINS HAVE LIPIDS

Some proteins have other organic compounds attached to their polypeptide chains. For example, **lipoproteins** form when certain proteins circulating in blood combine with cholesterol, triglycerides, and phospholipids that were consumed in food. Most **glycoproteins** (from *glukus*, the Greek word for sweet) have oligosaccharides bonded to them. Most of the proteins found at the surface of cells are glycoproteins, as are many proteins in blood and those that cells secrete (such as protein hormones).

DISRUPTING A PROTEIN'S SHAPE DENATURES IT

When a protein or any other large molecule loses its normal three-dimensional shape, it is *denatured*. For example, hydrogen bonds are sensitive to increases or decreases in temperature and pH. If the temperature or pH exceeds a protein's tolerance, its hydrogen bonds break, polypeptide chains unwind or change shape, and the protein no longer functions. Cooking an egg destroys weak bonds that contribute to the three-dimensional shape of the egg white protein albumin. Some denatured proteins can resume their shapes when normal conditions are restored—but not albumin. There is no way to uncook a cooked egg white.

Proteins have a secondary structure, a coil or an extended sheet. It results from hydrogen bonds located at short, regular intervals along a polypeptide chain.

At the third level of protein structure, bonding at certain amino acids makes a coiled chain bend and loop. Interactions among R groups in the chain hold the loops in the proper positions.

We see a fourth level of structure in proteins that consist of more than one polypeptide chain. Hydrogen bonds and other interactions join the chains.

2.13 Nucleotides and Nucleic Acids

The fourth and final class of biological molecules consists of nucleotides and nucleic acids. Since nucleotides are the subunits (monomers) of which nucleic acids (polymers) are built, we begin with them.

NUCLEOTIDES ARE ENERGY CARRIERS AND HAVE OTHER ROLES

A **nucleotide** (NOO-klee-oh-tide) is a small organic compound with a sugar, at least one phosphate group, and a base. The sugar is ribose or deoxyribose; both have a five-carbon ring structure. The only difference is that ribose has an oxygen atom attached to carbon 2 in the ring and deoxyribose does not. The bases have a single or double carbon ring structure that incorporates nitrogen.

One nucleotide, **ATP** (for adenosine triphosphate), has three phosphate groups attached to its sugar, as you can see in Figure 2.26. In cells, ATP molecules link chemical reactions that *release* energy with other reactions that *require* energy. How? ATP can readily transfer a phosphate group to many other molecules in the cell, providing the acceptor molecules with the energy they need to enter into a reaction.

In later chapters, you'll read about other nucleotides. For instance, some are subunits of coenzymes. A **coenzyme** is a molecule that accepts hydrogen atoms and electrons that are being removed from other molecules and transfers them to sites where they can be used for other reactions. Some other nucleotides act as chemical messengers inside

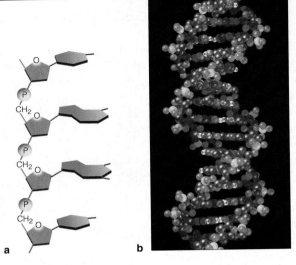

Figure 2.27 *Animated!* (**a**) Bonds between the bases in nucleotides. (**b**) Model of DNA, which has two strands of nucleotides joined by hydrogen bonds and twisted into a double helix. Here the nucleotide bases are blue.

and between cells. One of these is a nucleotide called cAMP (for cyclic adenosine monophosphate). It is a major player in events by which some hormones act.

NUCLEIC ACIDS INCLUDE DNA AND RNA

Nucleotides are building blocks for **nucleic acids**, which are single- or double-stranded molecules. In the backbones of the strands, each nucleotide's sugar is covalently bonded to a phosphate group of the neighboring nucleotides (Figure 2.27*a*). In this book you will read often about the nucleic acid **DNA** (deoxyribonucleic acid), which contains the sugar deoxyribose. DNA consists of two strands of nucleotides, twisted together in a double helix (Figure 2.27*b*). Hydrogen bonds between the nucleotide bases hold the strands together, and the sequence of bases encodes genetic information. In some parts of the molecule, the bases occur in a sequence that is unique to each species. Unlike DNA, **RNA** (short for ribonucleic acid) is usually a single strand of nucleotides. There are different kinds of RNA, but all have the sugar ribose. RNAs have crucial roles in processes that use genetic information to build proteins.

> *A nucleotide is an organic compound with a sugar, one or more phosphate groups, and a base. Nucleotides are building blocks for DNA and RNA. Some, including ATP, have key roles in energy transfers.*
>
> *DNA is a double-stranded nucleic acid. Its sequence of nucleotide bases carries genetic information. RNAs are single-stranded nucleic acids with roles in the processes by which DNA's genetic information is used to build proteins.*

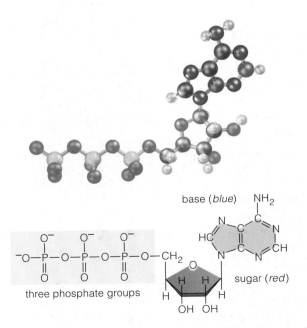

base (*blue*)

sugar (*red*)

three phosphate groups

Figure 2.26 *Animated!* A ball-and-stick model and structural formula for ATP, the energy-carrying nucleotide in cells.

2.14 Food Production and a Chemical Arms Race

The next time you shop for groceries, consider what it takes to provide you with your daily supply of organic compounds. For example, the lettuce for your salad most likely grew in fertilized cropland, and the grower may well have been concerned about invading weeds and attacks by insects. Each year, these food pirates and others ruin or eat nearly half of the food that people all over the world try to grow.

People—and plants—marshal various chemical defenses against the attackers (Figure 2.28). For instance, the tissues of many plants contain toxins that repel or kill harmful organisms. Humans encounter natural plant toxins in a wide range of foods—chili peppers, potatoes, figs, celery, and alfalfa sprouts, for instance. By and large, our bodies seem to be able to cope with those chemicals just fine—possibly because we have evolved our own biochemical ways of neutralizing them.

In 1945, the human race took a cue from the plant world as chemists began developing synthetic toxins that could improve our ability to protect crop yields, stored grains, ornamental plants, and even our pets. Since then researchers have developed a wide array of herbicides to kill weeds, insecticides to eradicate unwanted insects, and fungicides against harmful molds and other fungi.

Although extremely useful in some applications, pesticides are powerful chemicals and have become more so with the passing years. Some of them kill natural enemies of the targeted pest and others harm wildlife such as birds. Some, such as DDT, stay active for years. (DDT is banned in the United States, although not in many other countries.) When people are exposed to unsafe doses, either by accident or misuse, some pesticides can trigger rashes, hives, headaches, asthma, and joint pain. According to some authorities, young children who are exposed to pesticides applied to keep a lawn thick and green may be at risk of developing behavior problems, learning disabilities, and other problems. Although manufacturers dispute these claims, it is worth noting that according to the U.S. Environmental Protection Agency, homeowners in the United States use 10 times more pesticides on their lawns than farmers do in agricultural fields.

On the other hand, many studies show that used properly, modern pesticides increase food supplies and profits for farmers. They also save lives by killing disease-causing insects and other pathogens. And despite the natural worries of consumers, for now there is little evidence that the usual amounts of pesticides in or on food pose a significant health risk.

Figure 2.28 A low-flying crop duster with its rain of pesticides. Such pesticides may leave harmful residues in food.

Summary

Introduction An element is a fundamental substance that cannot be broken down to other substances by ordinary chemical means. The four main elements in the body are oxygen, carbon, hydrogen, and nitrogen. Small amounts of trace elements are also vital to many bodily functions.

Section 2.1 An atom is the smallest unit that has the properties of an element. Atoms are composed of protons, neutrons, and electrons. An element's atoms may vary in how many neutrons they contain. These various forms are isotopes. Whether an atom interacts with others depends on the number of electrons it has and how they are arranged in the atom.

 Learn how radioisotopes are used in a PET scan.

Section 2.3 We can think of electrons as moving in orbitals that are arranged in a series of shells around an atom's nucleus. An atom with one or more unfilled orbitals in its outer shell will tend to take part in chemical bonds.

A chemical bond is a union between the electron structures of atoms. Bonds join atoms into molecules. A chemical compound is a molecule that consists of atoms of two or more elements in proportions that do not vary. In a mixture, two or more kinds of molecules mingle, and their proportions *can* vary.

 Investigate electrons and the shell model.

Section 2.4 Atoms normally have no net charge. However, if an atom gains or loses one or more electrons it becomes an ion, which has a positive or negative charge.

In an ionic bond, positive and negative ions stay together by the mutual attraction of their opposite charges. In a covalent bond, atoms share one or more electrons. A hydrogen bond is a weak bond between polar molecules. At least one of the molecules contains a hydrogen atom that is part of a polar covalent bond.

Compare the types of chemical bonds found in biological molecules.

Section 2.6 Water is crucial for the shape, internal organization, and chemical activities of cells. Hydrogen bonds between its molecules give water special properties, such as the ability to resist temperature changes and to dissolve other polar substances. A dissolved substance is a solute. Polar molecules are hydrophilic (attracted to water). Nonpolar substances, such as oils, are hydrophobic (repelled by water).

Explore the structure and properties of water.

Section 2.7 The pH scale measures the concentration of hydrogen ions in a fluid. Acids release hydrogen ions (H^+), and bases release hydroxide ions (OH^-) that can combine with H^+. At pH 7, the H^+ and OH^- concentrations in a solution are equal; this is a neutral pH. A buffer system maintains pH values of blood, tissue fluids, and the fluid inside cells. A salt is a compound that releases ions other than H^+ and OH^-.

Investigate the pH of common solutions.

Section 2.8 A carbon atom forms up to four covalent bonds with other atoms. Carbon atoms bonded together in linear or ring structures are the backbone of organic compounds. The chemical and physical properties of many of those compounds depend largely on functional groups of atoms attached to the carbon backbone.

Cells assemble and break apart most organic compounds by way of five kinds of reactions: transfers of functional groups, electron transfers, internal rearrangements, condensation reactions (dehydration synthesis), and cleavage reactions such as hydrolysis. Enzymes speed all these reactions. A polymer is a molecule built of three or more subunits; each subunit is called a monomer.

Cells have pools of dissolved sugars, fatty acids, amino acids, and nucleotides. These are small organic compounds with no more than about twenty carbon atoms. They are building blocks for the larger biological molecules—the carbohydrates, lipids, proteins, and nucleic acids (Table 2.3).

Learn more about functional groups and watch animations that explain condensation, hydrolysis, and how a triglyceride forms.

Section 2.9 Cells use carbohydrates for energy or to build cell parts. Monosaccharides, or single sugar units, are the simplest ones. Chains of sugars linked by covalent bonds are oligosaccharides; common ones, such as glucose, are disaccharides built of two sugar units. Polysaccharides are longer chains that store energy in the bonds between the sugar units (Table 2.3).

Section 2.10 The body uses lipids for energy, to build cell parts, and as signaling molecules. The most important dietary fats are triglycerides. Phospholipids are building blocks of cell membranes; sterols also are constituents of membranes and various key molecules.

Table 2.3   Summary of the Main Carbon Compounds in the Human Body

Category	Main Subcategories	Examples	Functions
Carbohydrates *contain an aldehyde or a ketone group and one or more hydroxyl groups*	**Monosaccharides (simple sugars)** **Oligosaccharides** **Polysaccharides** **(complex carbohydrates)**	Glucose Sucrose (a disaccharide) Starch Cellulose	Structural roles, energy source Form of sugar transported in plants Energy storage Structural roles
Lipids *are largely hydrocarbon, generally do not dissolve in water but dissolve in nonpolar solvents*	**Lipids with fatty acids:** *Glycerides:* one, two, or three fatty acid tails attached to glycerol backbone *Phospholipids:* phosphate group, another polar group, and (often) two fatty acids attached to glycerol backbone **Lipids with no fatty acids:** *Sterols:* four carbon rings; the number, position, and type of functional groups vary	Fats (e.g., butter) Oils (e.g., corn oil) Phosphatidylcholine Cholesterol	Energy storage Key component of cell membranes Component of animal cell membranes, can be rearranged into other steroids (e.g., vitamin D, sex hormones)
Proteins *are polypeptides (up to several thousand amino acids, covalently linked)*	**Fibrous proteins:** Individual polypeptide chains, often linked into tough, water-insoluble molecules **Globular proteins:** One or more polypeptide chains folded and linked into globular shapes; many roles in cell activities	Keratin Collagen Enzymes Hemoglobin Insulin Antibodies	Structural element of hair, nails Structural element of bones and cartilage Increase in rates of reactions Oxygen transport Control of glucose metabolism Tissue defense
Nucleic Acids (and Nucleotides) *are chains of units (or individual units) that each consist of a five-carbon sugar, phosphate, and a nitrogen-containing base*	**Adenosine phosphates** **Nucleotide coenzymes** **Nucleic acids:** Chains of thousands to millions of nucleotides	ATP NAD^+, $NADP^+$ DNA, RNAs	Energy carrier Transport of protons (H^+) and electrons from one reaction site to another Storage, transmission, translation of genetic information

Sections 2.11, 2.12   Proteins are built of amino acids and have many roles in the body; each one's function depends on its structure. Three or more amino acids (linked by peptide bonds) form a polypeptide chain. The linear sequence of the amino acids is a protein's primary structure. A protein's final shape comes about as the polypeptide chain bends, folds, and coils. Many proteins consist of more than one polypeptide chain. Some have other organic compounds bonded to them; examples are glycoproteins, which have oligosaccharides attached, and lipoproteins, which have lipids attached.

A protein becomes denatured, losing its ability to function normally, when some factor changes its normal three-dimensional shape.

 Learn more about amino acids and how peptide bonds form a polypeptide chain.

Section 2.13   Nucleic acids such as DNA and RNA are built of nucleotides. A nucleotide consists of a sugar (such as deoxyribose, the sugar in DNA), one or more phosphate groups, and a base. The nucleotide

ATP transfers energy that powers chemical reactions in cells; coenzymes are nucleotides that assist in energy transfers.

 Explore the structure of DNA.

Review Questions

1. Distinguish between an element, an atom, and a molecule.

2. Explain the difference between an ionic bond and a covalent bond.

3. Ionic and covalent bonds join atoms into molecules. What do hydrogen bonds do?

4. Name three vital properties of water in living cells.

5. Which small organic molecules make up carbohydrates, lipids, proteins, and nucleic acids?

6. Which of the following is the carbohydrate, the fatty acid, the amino acid, and the polypeptide?
   a. $^+NH_3\text{—}CHR\text{—}COO^-$ c. $(glycine)_{20}$
   b. $C_6H_{12}O_6$ d. $CH_3(CH_2)_{16}COOH$

7. Describe the four levels of protein structure. How do a protein's side groups influence its interactions with other substances? What is denaturation?

8. Distinguish among the following:
   a. monosaccharide, polysaccharide, disaccharide
   b. peptide bond, polypeptide
   c. glycerol, fatty acid
   d. nucleotide, nucleic acid

Self-Quiz

Answers in Appendix V

1. The backbone of organic compounds forms when _____ atoms are covalently bonded.

2. Each carbon atom can form up to _____ bonds with other atoms.
a. four	c. eight
b. six	d. sixteen

3. All of the following except _____ are small organic molecules that serve as the main building blocks or energy sources in cells.
a. fatty acids	d. amino acids
b. simple sugars	e. nucleotides
c. lipids	

4. Which of the following is not a carbohydrate?
a. glucose molecule	c. margarine molecule
b. simple sugar	d. polysaccharide

5. _____, a class of proteins, make metabolic reactions proceed much faster than they would on their own.
a. Nucleic acids	c. Fatty acids
b. Amino acids	d. Enzymes

6. Examples of nucleic acids are _____.
a. polysaccharides	c. proteins
b. DNA and RNA	d. simple sugars

7. Which phrase best describes what a functional group does?
   a. assembles large organic compounds
   b. influences the behavior of organic compounds
   c. splits molecules into two or more parts
   d. speeds up metabolic reactions

8. In _____ reactions, small molecules are linked by covalent bonds, and water can also form.
a. hydrophilic	c. condensation
b. hydrolysis	d. ionic

9. Match each type of molecule with its description.
____ chain of amino acids	a. carbohydrate
____ energy carrier	b. phospholipid
____ glycerol, fatty acids, phosphate	c. protein
____ chain of nucleotides	d. DNA
____ one or more sugar units	e. ATP

10. What kinds of bonds often control the shape (or tertiary form) of large molecules such as proteins?
a. hydrogen	d. inert
b. ionic	e. single
c. covalent	

Critical Thinking

1. Black coffee has a pH of 5, and milk of magnesia has a pH of 10. Is coffee twice as acidic as milk of magnesia?

2. Your cotton shirt has stains from whipped cream and strawberry syrup, and your dry cleaner says that two separate cleaning agents will be needed to remove the stains. Explain why two agents are needed and what different chemical characteristic each would have.

3. A store clerk tells you that vitamin C extracted from rose hips is better for you than synthetic vitamin C. Based on what you know of the structure of organic compounds, does this claim seem credible? Why or why not?

4. Use the Internet to find three examples of acid rain damage and efforts to combat the problem. You might start with the United States Environmental Protection Agency's acid rain home page.

5. Carbonated drinks get that way when pressurized carbon dioxide gas is forced into flavored water. A chemical reaction between water molecules and some of the CO_2 molecules creates hydrogen ions (H^+) and bicarbonate, which is a buffer. In your opinion, is this reaction likely to raise the pH of a soda above 7, or lower it? Give your reasoning.

Explore on Your Own

It's easy to demonstrate the practical consequences of differences between hydrophilic and hydrophobic molecules. Just try this little kitchen experiment. Take two identical clean plates. Smear one with grease (such as margarine) and pour syrup over the other.

Next run moderately warm water over both plates for thirty seconds and observe the results. Which plate got cleaner, and why? The companies that make dishwashing detergents manipulate them chemically so that their molecules have both hydrophobic and hydrophilic regions. Given what you know about the ability of water by itself to dissolve hydrophilic and hydrophobic substances, why might this be?

When Mitochondria Spin Their Wheels

In the early 1960s, Swedish physician Rolf Luft was treating a young patient who felt weak and too hot all the time. Even on the coldest winter days, she couldn't stop sweating, and her skin was flushed. She was thin in spite of a huge appetite.

Luft inferred that his patient's symptoms pointed to a metabolic disorder. Her cells seemed to be spinning their wheels—a lot of their activity was being dissipated as metabolic heat. Working body cells use oxygen, and tests showed that her cells were consuming oxygen at the highest rate ever recorded.

A cell's energy powerhouses are called mitochondria, which are pictured in the microscope image at right. Mitochondria are specialized compartments, or organelles, that make the cellular fuel ATP. A sample of Dr. Luft's patient's muscle contained too many mitochondria, and their shape was abnormal. In addition, too little ATP was forming inside them.

What is now known as *Luft's syndrome* was the first human disease to be linked directly to a defective cell organelle. A person with this disorder is like a city with half of its power plants shut down.

Skeletal and heart muscles, the brain, and other hardworking body parts with the greatest energy needs are hurt the most.

More than a hundred other mitochondrial disorders are now known. Some of them run in families. These diseases generally affect only a small number of people. While this is good news from one standpoint, it also means that there is relatively little demand for drugs that might help save the lives of affected persons. There isn't much financial incentive for pharmaceutical companies to develop such so-called orphan drugs.

In this chapter we look at how cells are built and operate—bringing in some substances, releasing or keeping out others, and conducting their activities with the proverbial "Swiss watch" precision. As you read, keep in mind that all the body's living cells are adapted to function in the internal steady state called homeostasis.

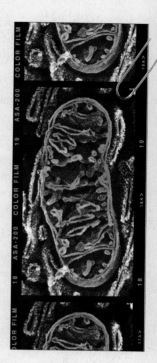

 How Would You Vote? Should pharmaceutical companies receive financial incentives (such as tax breaks) to search for cures for diseases that affect only a small number of people? Cast your vote online at www.thomsonedu.com/biology/starr/humanbio.

Key Concepts

BASIC CELL FEATURES
Cells have an outer plasma membrane, a semifluid interior called cytoplasm, and an inner region of DNA. Most cells are too small to be visible without the aid of a microscope.

CELLS AND THEIR PARTS
All cells except bacteria are eukaryotic: Their cytoplasm contains a nucleus and other organelles, which are compartments that have specialized functions. The DNA is in the nucleus.

HOW CELLS GAIN ENERGY
Cells use organic compounds to make a chemical called ATP, which fuels life processes. The major pathway for making ATP starts in the cytoplasm and ends in organelles called mitochondria.

Links to Earlier Concepts

The living cell is one of the earliest levels of organization in nature (1.3).

In this chapter, you will learn how lipids are organized to form cell membranes (2.10). You will also see where DNA and RNA are found in cells (2.13) and which cell structures use amino acids and carbohydrates as building blocks for other molecules, such as proteins (2.9, 2.11, 2.12).

The chapter explains principles that govern the movement of water and solutes into and out of cells (2.6). It also considers how cells make and use the nucleotide ATP to fuel their activities (2.13).

3.1 What Is a Cell?

LINKS TO
SECTIONS
.1, 1.3, AND 2.10

From its size and shape to the structure of its parts, a cell is built to allow it to carry out life functions efficiently.

There are trillions of cells in your body, and each one is a highly organized bit of life. A desire to understand cells led early biologists to develop the **cell theory**:

1. **Every organism is composed of one or more cells.**
2. **The cell is the smallest unit having the properties of life.**
3. **All cells come from pre-existing cells.**

These basic ideas still hold true, and they provide the foundation for everything that modern researchers have learned about cells.

ALL CELLS ARE ALIKE IN THREE WAYS

All living cells have three things in common. They have an outer **plasma membrane**, they contain DNA, and they contain cytoplasm.

THE PLASMA MEMBRANE This thin outer covering encloses the cell's internal parts, so that the cell's life-sustaining activities can go on apart from events that may be taking place outside the cell. The plasma membrane does not completely isolate the cell interior. Substances still can move across it, as you will read later in this chapter.

DNA A cell has DNA somewhere inside it, along with molecules that can copy or read the inherited genetic instructions DNA carries.

CYTOPLASM Cytoplasm (sy-toe-plasm) is everything between the plasma membrane and the region of DNA. It consists of a thick, jellylike fluid, the **cytosol**, and various other components.

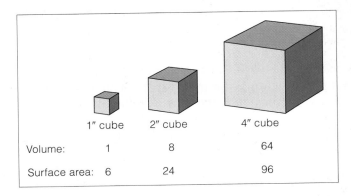

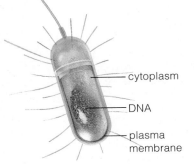

cytoplasm

DNA

plasma membrane

a Bacterial cell (prokaryotic)

b Animal cell (eukaryotic)

Figure 3.1 The two basic types of cells. (**a**) A prokaryotic cell. (**b**) Eukaryotic cells. These are kidney cells and are shown here in cross section. A dye makes the nucleus look reddish.

Figure 3.2 The relationship between surface area and volume. Here, the "cells" are boxes, which have six sides. If the linear dimensions of a box double, the volume increases 8 times but the surface area increases only 4 times. As in the text example, if the linear dimensions increase by 4 times, the volume is 64 times greater but the surface area is only 16 times larger.

	1" cube	2" cube	4" cube
Volume:	1	8	64
Surface area:	6	24	96

THERE ARE TWO BASIC KINDS OF CELLS

Cells are classified into two basic kinds, depending on how they are organized internally (Table 3.1). In a **prokaryotic cell** (prokaryotic means "before the nucleus") nothing separates the cell's DNA from other internal cell parts. Bacteria, like the one diagrammed in Figure 3.1*a*, are the only prokaryotic cells.

By contrast, all other cells are **eukaryotic cells** ("true nucleus"). In their cytoplasm are tiny compartments and sacs called **organelles** ("little organs"). One organelle, the nucleus, contains the DNA of a eukaryotic cell. Nuclei are clearly visible in the cells pictured in Figure 3.1*b*.

WHY ARE CELLS SMALL?

You may be wondering how small cells really are. Can any be observed with the unaided eye? There are a few, including the yolks of bird eggs and the fish eggs we call caviar. These cells can be large because when they are fully developed their metabolism is fairly sluggish. They are mainly storehouses for substances that will nourish developing young. Cells that are more active typically are

Table 3.1	Eukaryotic and Prokaryotic Cells Compared	
	Eukaryotic	Prokaryotic
Plasma membrane	yes	yes
DNA-containing region	yes	yes
Cytoplasm	yes	yes
Nucleus inside a membrane	yes	no

BASIC CELL FEATURES

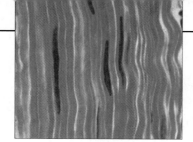

a Smooth muscle cell

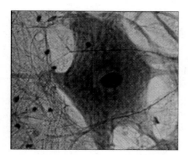

b Motor neuron

Figure 3.3 Two types of cells in the human body. (**a**) Smooth muscle cells, found in the walls of hollow organs such as the stomach, have an elongated shape. (**b**) A motor neuron, a type of nerve cell, has threadlike extensions.

so small that they can only be seen with a microscope. For instance, a human red blood cell is about 8 millionths of a meter across, so tiny that you could line up 2,000 of them across your thumbnail.

The **surface-to-volume ratio** is responsible for the small size of cells. This ratio is a physical relationship. It dictates that as the linear dimensions of a three-dimensional object increase, the volume of the object increases faster than its surface area does (Figure 3.2). For instance, if a round cell grew like an inflating balloon so that its diameter increased to 4 times the starting girth, the volume inside the cell would be 64 times more than before, but the cell's surface would be just 16 times larger. The cell would not have enough surface area to allow nutrients to flow inward rapidly, or for wastes or cell products to move rapidly outward. In short order the cell would die.

A large, round cell also would have trouble moving materials through its cytoplasm. In small cells, though, random, tiny motions of molecules easily distribute materials. If a cell isn't small, it probably is long and thin or has folds that increase its surface area relative to its volume. The smaller or narrower or more frilly the cell, the more efficiently materials can cross its surface and disperse inside it. Figure 3.3 shows two of the many shapes of cells in your own body. Part *a* depicts long, slender cells in a type of muscle called smooth muscle. The cells of muscle that attaches to the skeleton also are

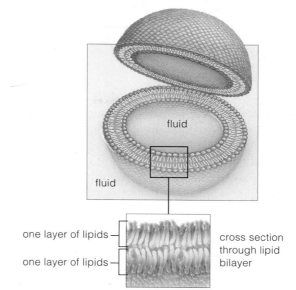

Figure 3.4 *Animated!* Phospholipids arranged in a lipid bilayer.

slender. In the biceps of your upper arm they are many inches long—as long as the muscle itself.

MEMBRANES ENCLOSE CELLS AND ORGANELLES

A eukaryotic cell and its organelles are enclosed by membranes. Most of the molecules in cell membranes are phospholipids, which were introduced in Section 2.10. You may remember that a phospholipid has a hydrophilic (water-loving) head and two fatty acid tails, which are hydrophobic (water-dreading). When a large number of phospholipids are immersed in water, they interact with the water molecules and with one another. They may spontaneously organize into two layers with all the hydrophobic tails sandwiched between all the heads (Figure 3.4). This heads-out, tails-in arrangement is called a **lipid bilayer**. All cell membranes have the lipid bilayer structure. The hydrophilic heads of the phospholipids are dissolved in the watery fluids inside and outside cells.

A cell has an outer plasma membrane, which encloses its jellylike cytoplasm and its DNA. The cells of humans, like those of other complex organisms, are eukaryotic: Their DNA is contained in an organelle, the nucleus.

In prokaryotic cells, the bacteria, the DNA is not contained inside a nucleus.

Most cells are small and have a large surface area relative to their volume. These features permit the efficient inward flow of nutrients and outward flow of wastes.

A cell's membranes are built mostly of phospholipids arranged in a bilayer.

3.2 The Parts of a Eukaryotic Cell

The interior of a cell is divided into organelles, each of which has one or more special functions.

In every eukaryotic cell, at any given moment, a vast number of chemical reactions are going on. Many of the reactions would conflict if they occurred in the same cell compartment. For example, a molecule of fat can be built by some reactions and taken apart by others, but a cell gains nothing if both sets of reactions proceed at the same time on the same fat molecule.

In eukaryotic cells, including those of the human body, organelles (Table 3.2) solve this problem. Their outer membrane physically separates the inside of an organelle from the rest of the cytoplasm. It also controls the types and amounts of substances that enter or leave the organelle. For example, organelles called lysosomes contain enzymes that break down various unwanted substances. If the enzymes escaped from the organelle, they could destroy the entire cell.

Organelles also may serve as "way stations" for operations that occur in steps. Proteins are assembled and modified in steps involving several organelles.

Figure 3.5 shows where organelles and some other structures might be located in a body cell. This is only a general picture of cells. There are major differences in the structures and functions of cells in different tissues.

Table 3.2 Common Features of Eukaryotic Cells	
ORGANELLES AND THEIR MAIN FUNCTIONS:	
Nucleus	Contains the cell's DNA
Endoplasmic reticulum (ER)	Routes and modifies newly formed polypeptide chains; also, where lipids are assembled
Golgi body	Modifies polypeptide chains into mature proteins; sorts and ships proteins and lipids for secretion or for use inside cell
Various vesicles	Transport or store a variety of substances; break down substances and cell structures in the cell; other functions
Mitochondria	Produce ATP
OTHER STRUCTURES AND THEIR FUNCTIONS:	
Ribosomes	Assemble polypeptide chains
Cytoskeleton	Gives overall shape and internal organization to cell; moves the cell and its internal parts

Organelles physically isolate chemical reactions inside cells. They also provide separate locations for activities that occur in a sequence of steps.

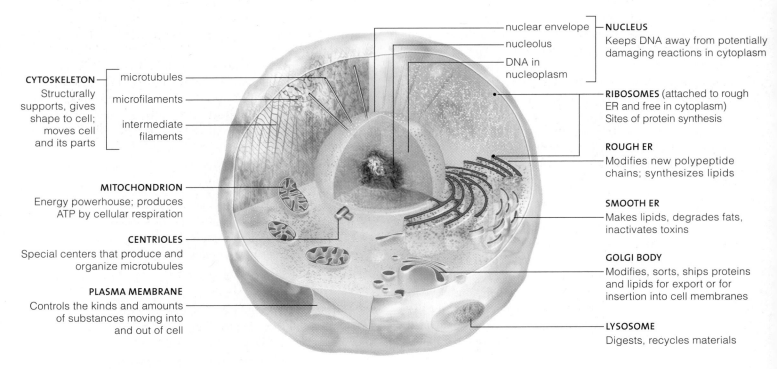

CYTOSKELETON — microtubules — microfilaments — intermediate filaments
Structurally supports, gives shape to cell; moves cell and its parts

MITOCHONDRION — Energy powerhouse; produces ATP by cellular respiration

CENTRIOLES — Special centers that produce and organize microtubules

PLASMA MEMBRANE — Controls the kinds and amounts of substances moving into and out of cell

nuclear envelope — nucleolus — DNA in nucleoplasm

NUCLEUS Keeps DNA away from potentially damaging reactions in cytoplasm

RIBOSOMES (attached to rough ER and free in cytoplasm) Sites of protein synthesis

ROUGH ER — Modifies new polypeptide chains; synthesizes lipids

SMOOTH ER — Makes lipids, degrades fats, inactivates toxins

GOLGI BODY — Modifies, sorts, ships proteins and lipids for export or for insertion into cell membranes

LYSOSOME — Digests, recycles materials

Figure 3.5 *Animated!* Typical parts of an animal cell. This cutaway diagram corresponds roughly to the micrograph in Figure 3.6.

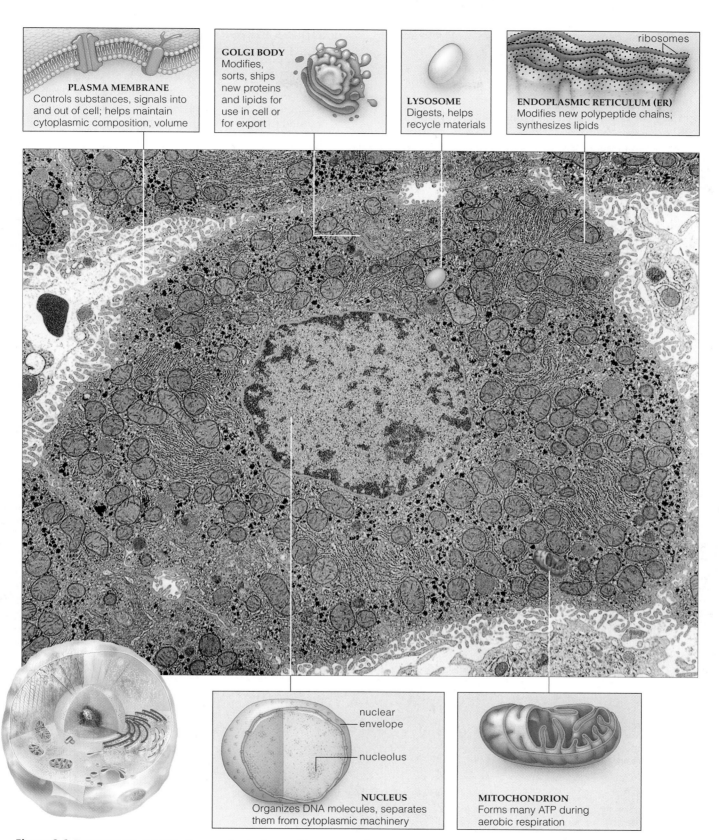

PLASMA MEMBRANE
Controls substances, signals into and out of cell; helps maintain cytoplasmic composition, volume

GOLGI BODY
Modifies, sorts, ships new proteins and lipids for use in cell or for export

LYSOSOME
Digests, helps recycle materials

ribosomes

ENDOPLASMIC RETICULUM (ER)
Modifies new polypeptide chains; synthesizes lipids

nuclear envelope

nucleolus

NUCLEUS
Organizes DNA molecules, separates them from cytoplasmic machinery

MITOCHONDRION
Forms many ATP during aerobic respiration

Figure 3.6 Transmission electron micrograph of a liver cell in cross section. Although this is a rat liver cell, liver cells in humans are not much different.

3.3 The Plasma Membrane: A Double Layer of Lipids

LINKS TO SECTIONS 2.8 AND 2.10

The plasma membrane isn't a solid, rigid wall between a cell's cytoplasm and the fluid outside. If it were, needed substances couldn't enter the cell and wastes couldn't leave it. Instead, the plasma membrane has an oily, fluid quality, something like cooking oil. The membrane also is extremely thin. A thousand stacked like pancakes would be about as thick as this page.

THE PLASMA MEMBRANE IS A MIX OF LIPIDS AND PROTEINS

In Figure 3.4 you've already seen a simple picture of a plasma membrane lipid bilayer with its "sandwich" of phospholipids. Figure 3.7 below gives a more complete idea of how biologists visualize this structure. It is often described as a "mosaic" of proteins and various lipids: phospholipids, glycolipids, and, in human cells (and those of other animals), the lipid cholesterol. The proteins are embedded in the bilayer or attach to its outer or inner surface, where they have specific functions.

What makes the membrane fluid? For one thing, the molecules that make it up move. Most phospholipids can spin on their long axis like a chicken on a rotisserie. They also move sideways and flex their tails—movements that help keep neighboring molecules from packing into a solid layer. The short or kinked hydrophobic tails of lipids in the bilayer also give the membrane a fluid quality.

PROTEINS PERFORM MOST OF THE FUNCTIONS OF CELL MEMBRANES

The proteins that are embedded in or attached to a lipid bilayer carry out most of a cell membrane's functions. Many of these proteins are enzymes; you may recall from Chapter 2 that enzymes speed chemical reactions in cells. Other membrane proteins serve a range of functions. Some are channels through the membrane, while others are transporters that move substances across it. Still others are receptors; they are like docks for signaling molecules, such as hormones, that trigger changes in cell activities. Recognition proteins that wave like flags on the surface of a cell are "fingerprints" that identify the cell as being of a specific type. You will read more about membrane proteins in upcoming chapters.

Before we examine the internal parts of cells, read the *Science Comes to Life* feature on the facing page, which describes how biologists use microscopes to study these tiny bits of life.

The plasma membrane is a lipid bilayer. It is a mix of various lipids and proteins and has a fluid quality. Proteins of the bilayer carry out most of the membrane's functions, such as moving substances across the membrane, binding substances, and serving as identity tags.

Figure 3.7 *Animated!* Cutaway view of a plasma membrane, based on the fluid mosaic model of membrane structure. Some of the proteins in the plasma membrane are drawn as ribbons to suggest the intricate folding of long polypeptide chains. Section 2.12 discusses how the chains form.

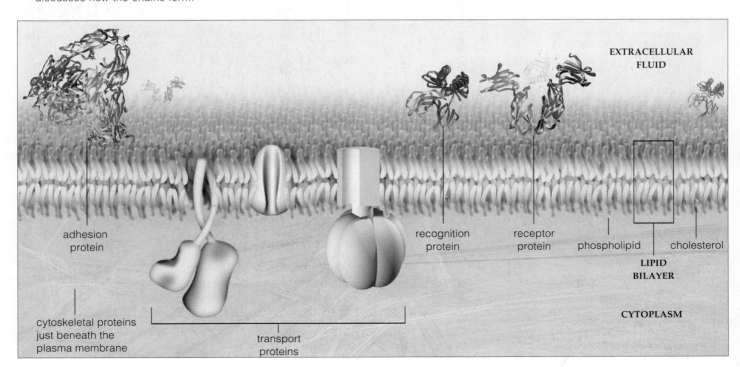

adhesion protein

cytoskeletal proteins just beneath the plasma membrane

transport proteins

recognition protein

receptor protein

phospholipid

cholesterol

EXTRACELLULAR FLUID

LIPID BILAYER

CYTOPLASM

3.4 How Do We See Cells?

Microscopy has allowed us to learn a great deal about cells in the human body. A photograph formed using a microscope is called a micrograph.

The micrographs in Figure 3.8 compare the sorts of detail different types of microscopes can reveal. For example, the red blood cells in Figure 3.8*a* were viewed using a compound light microscope, in which two or more glass lenses bend (refract) incoming light rays to form an enlarged image of a specimen. With this method, the cell must be small or thin enough for light to pass through, and its parts must differ in color or optical density from their surroundings. Unfortunately, most cell parts are nearly colorless and they have about the same density. For this reason, before viewing cells through a light microscope, researchers expose the cells to dyes that react with some cell parts but not with others. Even with the best glass lens system, however, light microscopes only provide sharp images when the diameter of the object being viewed is magnified by 2,000 times or less.

Electron microscopes use magnetic lenses to bend beams of electrons. They reveal smaller details than even the best light microscopes can. There are several types, with new innovations occurring often.

A transmission electron microscope uses a magnetic field as the "lens" that bends a stream of electrons and focuses it into an image, which then is magnified. With a scanning electron microscope, a beam of electrons is directed back and forth across a specimen thinly coated with metal. The metal emits some of its own electrons, and then the electron energy is converted into an image of the specimen's surface on a television screen. Most of the images have fantastic depth (Figure 3.8*b*, right).

A scanning tunneling microscope magnifies objects up to 100 million times (Figure 3.8*c*). The scope's needlelike probe has a single atom at its tip. As an electrical current passes between the tip and a specimen's surface, electrons "tunnel" from the probe to the specimen. A computer analyzes the tunneling motion and makes a 3-D view of the surface.

Figure 3.8 *Animated!* Human red blood cells viewed with different types of microscopes. (**a**) Red blood cells inside a small blood vessel, as revealed by a light microscope. (**b**) Electron micrographs. *Top:* This transmission electron micrograph (TEM) shows the inside of mature red blood cells, which are packed with hemoglobin. *Bottom:* A scanning electron micrograph (SEM) with color added shows the "doughnut without a hole" shape of red blood cells. (**c**) The green-colored image is a micrograph of DNA obtained with a scanning tunneling microscope.

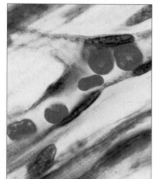

Compound light microscope   **a**

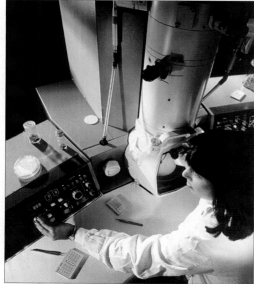

Transmission electron microscope

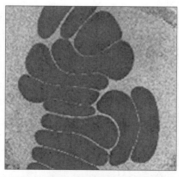
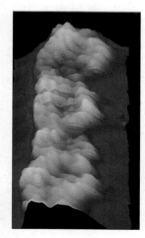
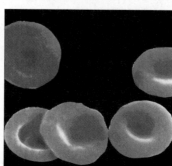

b

c

3.5 The Nucleus

The nucleus is often described as a cell's master control center. It also is a protective "isolation chamber" for the genetic material DNA.

The **nucleus** encloses the DNA of a eukaryotic cell. DNA contains instructions for building a cell's proteins and, through those proteins, for determining a cell's structure and function. In a human cell there are forty-six DNA molecules that would stretch more than 6 feet if they were stretched out end to end.

Figure 3.9 shows the structure of the nucleus, and Table 3.3 lists its five main components. The nucleus has several key functions. First, it prevents DNA from getting entangled with structures in the cytoplasm. When a cell divides, its DNA molecules must be copied so that each new cell receives a full set. Keeping the DNA separate makes it easier to copy and organize these hereditary instructions. In addition, outer membranes of the nucleus are a boundary where cells control the movement of substances to and from the cytoplasm.

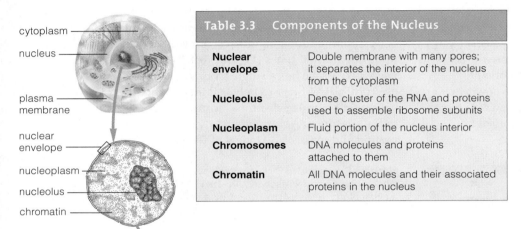

Table 3.3	Components of the Nucleus
Nuclear envelope	Double membrane with many pores; it separates the interior of the nucleus from the cytoplasm
Nucleolus	Dense cluster of the RNA and proteins used to assemble ribosome subunits
Nucleoplasm	Fluid portion of the nucleus interior
Chromosomes	DNA molecules and proteins attached to them
Chromatin	All DNA molecules and their associated proteins in the nucleus

A NUCLEAR ENVELOPE ENCLOSES THE NUCLEUS

Unlike the cell itself, a nucleus has two outer lipid bilayers, one pressed against the other. This double-membrane system is called a **nuclear envelope** (Figure 3.10). The bilayers surround the fluid part of the nucleus (the nucleoplasm), and many proteins are embedded in them. The outer section of the nuclear envelope merges with the membrane of ER, an organelle in the cytoplasm, which you will read more about in Section 3.6.

Threadlike bits of protein attach to the inner surface of the nuclear envelope. They anchor DNA molecules to the envelope and help keep them organized.

Membrane proteins that span both bilayers have a wide variety of functions. Some are receptors or transporters. Others form pores, as you can see in Figure 3.10*b*. The pores are passageways for small ions and for molecules dissolved in the watery fluid inside and outside the nucleus to cross the nuclear membrane.

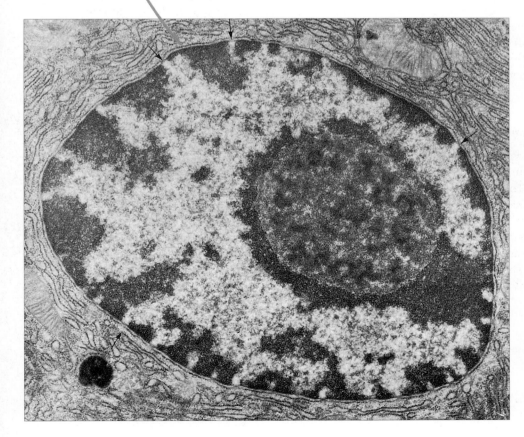

Figure 3.9 The nucleus of an animal cell. The small arrows on this micrograph (a photograph taken with an electron microscope) point to pores where substances can move through the nuclear envelope in controlled ways.

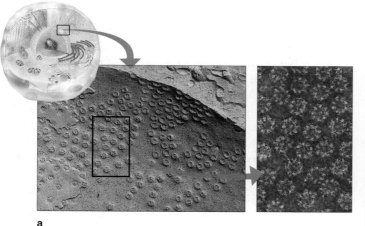

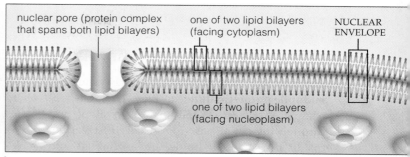

nuclear pore (protein complex that spans both lipid bilayers)

one of two lipid bilayers (facing cytoplasm)

NUCLEAR ENVELOPE

one of two lipid bilayers (facing nucleoplasm)

a

b

Figure 3.10 *Animated!* (**a**) Part of the outer surface of a nuclear envelope. *Left:* This specimen was prepared so as to show the layering of its two lipid bilayers. *Right:* Nuclear pores. Each pore across the envelope is a cluster of membrane proteins. It permits the selective transport of substances into and out of the nucleus. (**b**) Sketch of the nuclear envelope's structure.

THE NUCLEOLUS IS WHERE CELLS MAKE THE UNITS OF RIBOSOMES

As a cell grows, one or more dense masses appear inside its nucleus. Each mass is a **nucleolus** (noo-KLEE-uh-luhs; plural: nucleoli), a construction site where certain RNAs and proteins are combined to make the various parts of ribosomes. These subunits eventually will cross through nuclear pores to the cytoplasm. There, they join briefly to form ribosomes, the "workbenches" where amino acids are assembled into proteins.

DNA IS ORGANIZED IN CHROMOSOMES

When a eukaryotic cell is not dividing, you cannot see individual DNA molecules, nor can you see that each consists of two strands twisted together. The nucleus just looks grainy, as in Figure 3.9. When a cell is preparing to divide, however, it copies all of its DNA so that each new cell will get all the required hereditary instructions. Soon the duplicated DNA molecules are visible as long threads. They then fold and twist into a compact structure:

Early microscopists named the seemingly grainy substance in the nucleus *chromatin*, and they called the compact structures *chromosomes* ("colored bodies"). Today we define **chromatin** as the cell's DNA along with the proteins associated with it. We also understand that chromatin makes up each **chromosome**—a double-stranded DNA molecule that carries genetic information. A key point to remember is that a chromosome can look different at different times, being grainy or compact depending on whether the cell is dividing or is in some other part of its life cycle.

EVENTS THAT BEGIN IN THE NUCLEUS CONTINUE TO UNFOLD IN THE CELL CYTOPLASM

Outside the nucleus, new polypeptide chains for proteins are assembled on ribosomes. Many of them are used at once or stockpiled in the cytoplasm. Others enter the endomembrane system. As you'll read in the next section, this system includes various structures. It is where many proteins get their final form and where lipids are assembled and packaged.

The nucleus, an organelle with two outer membranes, keeps a cell's DNA molecules separated from the cytoplasm.

The separation makes it easier to organize the DNA and to copy it before a cell divides.

Pores across the nuclear envelope control the passage of many substances between the nucleus and the cytoplasm.

one chromosome (one dispersed DNA molecule + proteins; not duplicated)

one chromosome (threadlike and now duplicated; two DNA molecules + proteins)

one chromosome (duplicated and also condensed tightly)

3.6 The Endomembrane System

Some organelles assemble lipids, modify new polypeptide chains into final proteins, and then sort and ship these products to various destinations. These organelles are part of the cell's endomembrane system.

ER IS A PROTEIN AND LIPID ASSEMBLY LINE

The functions of the **endomembrane system** begin with **endoplasmic reticulum**, or **ER**. The ER is a flattened channel that starts at the nuclear envelope and snakes through the cytoplasm (Figure 3.11). At various points inside the channel, lipids are assembled and "raw" polypeptide chains are modified into final proteins. In different places the ER looks rough or smooth, depending mainly on whether the organelles called **ribosomes** are attached to the side of the membrane that faces the cytoplasm. Like a workbench, a ribosome is a platform for building a cell's proteins.

Rough ER is studded with ribosomes (Figure 3.11*b*). Newly forming polypeptide chains that have a built-in signal (a string of amino acids) can enter the space inside rough ER or be incorporated into ER membranes. Once the chains are in rough ER, enzymes in the channel may attach side chains to them. Body cells that secrete finished proteins have extensive rough ER. For example, in your pancreas, ER-rich gland cells make and secrete enzymes that end up in your small intestine and help you digest your meals.

Smooth ER has no ribosomes and curves through the cytoplasm like flat connecting pipes (Figure 3.11*c*). Many cells assemble most lipids inside these pipes. In liver cells, smooth ER inactivates certain drugs and harmful by-products of metabolism. In skeletal muscle cells a type of smooth ER called sarcoplasmic reticulum stores and releases calcium ions essential for muscles to contract.

GOLGI BODIES "FINISH, PACK, AND SHIP"

A **Golgi body** is a series of flattened sacs that often resemble a stack of pancakes (Figure 3.11*d*). Enzymes in the sacs put the finishing touches on proteins and lipids, then sort and package the completed molecules in vesicles

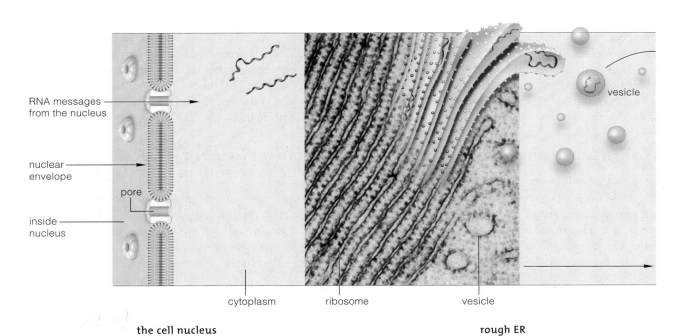

RNA messages from the nucleus

nuclear envelope

pore

inside nucleus

cytoplasm

ribosome

vesicle

vesicle

the cell nucleus

rough ER

a RNA messages are translated into polypeptide chains on ribosomes. Many chains are stockpiled in the cytoplasm or used at once. Others enter the rough ER.

b Flattened sacs of rough ER form one continuous channel between the nucleus and smooth ER. Polypeptide chains that enter the channel are modified. They will be inserted into organelle membranes or will be secreted from the cell.

Figure 3.11 *Animated!* The endomembrane system. With this system's components, many proteins are processed, lipids are assembled, and both products are sorted and shipped to destinations in the cell or to the plasma membrane to be exported out of the cell.

for shipment to specific locations. A **vesicle** is a tiny sac that moves through the cytoplasm or takes up positions in it. For example, an enzyme in one Golgi region might attach a phosphate group to a new protein and then "pack" the protein into a vesicle, thereby giving it a "mailing tag" to its proper destination. The top pancake of a Golgi body is the organelle's "shipping gate" for molecules to be exported. Here, vesicles form as patches of the membrane bulge out and then break away into the cell's cytoplasm.

A VARIETY OF VESICLES MOVE SUBSTANCES INTO AND THROUGH CELLS

Many kinds of vesicles shuttle substances around cells. A common type, the lysosome, buds from the membranes of Golgi bodies. A **lysosome** is specialized for digestion: It contains a potent stew of enzymes that speed the breakdown of proteins, complex sugars, nucleic acids, and some lipids. Lysosomes may even digest whole cells or cell parts. Often, lysosomes fuse with vesicles that have formed at a cell's plasma membrane. The vesicles usually contain molecules, bacteria, or other items that attached to the plasma membrane. White blood cells of the immune system take in foreign material in vesicles and dispose of it.

Peroxisomes, another type of vesicle, are tiny sacs of enzymes that break down fatty acids and amino acids. The reactions produce hydrogen peroxide, a potentially harmful substance. But before hydrogen peroxide can injure the cell, another enzyme in peroxisomes converts it to water and oxygen or uses it to break down alcohol. After someone drinks alcohol, nearly half of it is broken down in peroxisomes of liver and kidney cells.

In the ER and Golgi bodies of the cytomembrane system, many proteins take on final form, and lipids are assembled.

Lipids, proteins, and other substances are packaged in vesicles to be exported, stored, used to build membranes, and carry out other cell activities. Unwanted materials may be broken down in lysosomes and peroxisomes.

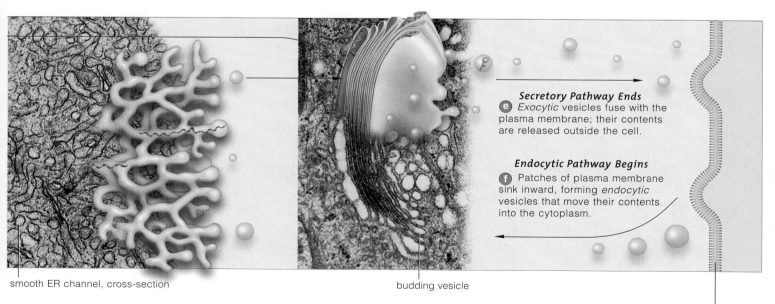

smooth ER channel, cross-section

budding vesicle

Secretory Pathway Ends
(e) *Exocytic* vesicles fuse with the plasma membrane; their contents are released outside the cell.

Endocytic Pathway Begins
(f) Patches of plasma membrane sink inward, forming *endocytic* vesicles that move their contents into the cytoplasm.

smooth ER

(c) Some proteins in the channel continue on, to smooth ER. Many become smooth ER enzymes or membrane proteins. The enzymes make lipids, inactivate toxins, and mediate other tasks.

Golgi body

(d) A Golgi body receives, processes, and then packages substances that arrive in vesicles from the ER. Other vesicles transport the substances to the plasma membrane or other parts of the cell.

plasma membrane

(g) Exocytic vesicles release cell products and wastes to the outside. Endocytic vesicles move nutrients, water, and other substances into the cytoplasm from outside.

3.7 Mitochondria: The Cell's Energy Factories

LINK TO
SECTION
2.13

For as long as a cell lives, it hums with chemical reactions. Nearly all those reactions require energy, which is provided by ATP—a life-sustaining molecule that is made in the cell's sausage-shaped mitochondria.

MITOCHONDRIA MAKE ATP

Section 2.13 introduced the main energy carrier in cells, ATP. Because ATP can deliver energy to nearly all the reaction sites in a cell, ATP drives nearly all of a cell's activities. ATP forms during reactions that break down organic compounds to carbon dioxide and water in a **mitochondrion** (plural: mitochondria).

Only eukaryotic cells contain mitochondria. The one shown in Figure 3.12 gives you an idea of their structure. The kind of ATP-forming reactions that occur in mitochondria extract far more energy from organic compounds than can be obtained by any other means. The reactions cannot be completed without an ample supply of oxygen. Every time you inhale, you are taking in oxygen mainly for mitochondria in your cells.

ATP FORMS IN AN INNER COMPARTMENT OF THE MITOCHONDRION

A mitochondrion has a double-membrane system. As shown in the sketch at the upper right, the outer membrane faces the cell's cytoplasm. The inner one generally folds back on itself, accordion-fashion. Each fold is a crista (KRIS-tuh; plural: cristae). This membrane system is the key to the mitochondrion's function, because it forms two separate compartments inside the organelle. In the outer one, enzymes and other proteins stockpile hydrogen ions. This process is fueled by energy from electrons. As electrons are depleted of energy, oxygen binds and removes them. When the stockpiled hydrogen ions later flow out of the compartment, energy inherent in the flow (as in a flowing river) powers the reactions that form ATP.

Look back at Figure 3.6 and you can see mitochondria all through the cytoplasm of that one thin slice from one liver cell. The large number of mitochondria indicate that the liver is a highly active, energy-demanding organ.

Mitochondria have intrigued biologists because they are about the same size as bacteria and function like them in many ways as well. Mitochondria even have their own DNA and some ribosomes, and they divide independently of the cell they are in. Many biologists believe mitochondria evolved from ancient bacteria that were consumed by another ancient cell, yet did not die. Perhaps they were able to reproduce inside the predatory cell and its descendants. If they became permanent,

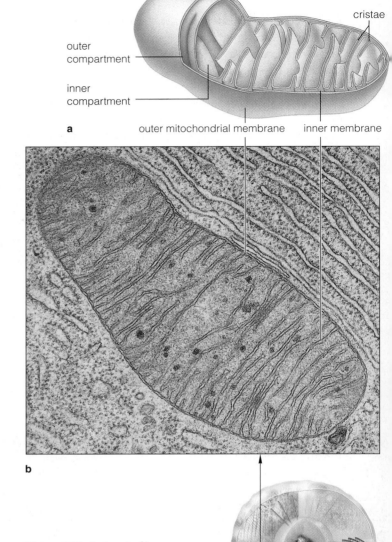

Figure 3.12 *Animated!*
(**a**) Sketch and (**b**) transmission electron micrograph of a thin slice through a typical mitochondrion. Reactions inside this organelle produce ATP, the major energy carrier in cells.

protected residents, they might have lost structures and functions required for independent life while they were becoming mitochondria, the ATP-producing organelles without which we humans could not survive.

The organelles called mitochondria are the ATP-producing powerhouses of eukaryotic cells.

ATP is produced by reactions that take place in the inner compartment formed by a mitochondrion's double-membrane system. These reactions require oxygen.

3.8 The Cell's Skeleton

A cell's internal framework is called the cytoskeleton. It is not permanently rigid, however. Its elements assemble and disassemble as needed for cell activities.

The **cytoskeleton** is a system of interconnected fibers, threads, and lattices in the cytosol (Figure 3.13). It gives cells their shape and internal organization, as well as their ability to move. **Microtubules** are the largest cytoskeleton elements. Their main function is to spatially organize the interior of the cell, although microtubules also help move cell parts.

Microfilaments often reinforce some part of a cell, such as the plasma membrane. Some membrane proteins are anchored in place by microfilaments.

Some kinds of cells also have **intermediate filaments** that add strength much as steel rods strengthen concrete pillars. Intermediate filaments also anchor the filaments of two other proteins, called actin and myosin, which interact in muscle cells and enable the muscle to contract. Chapter 6 looks at this process.

Some types of cells move about by **flagella** (singular: flagellum) or **cilia** (singular: cilium). In both structures nine pairs of microtubules ring a central pair; a system of spokes and links holds this "9 + 2 array" together (Figure 3.14). The flagellum or cilium bends when microtubules in the ring slide over each other. Whiplike flagella propel human sperm (Figure 3.13*b*).

Cilia are shorter than flagella, and there may be more of them per cell. In your respiratory tract, thousands of

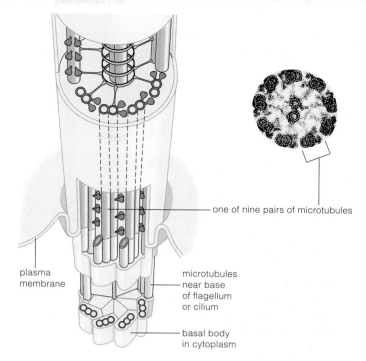

one of nine pairs of microtubules

plasma membrane

microtubules near base of flagellum or cilium

basal body in cytoplasm

Figure 3.14 *Animated!* How microtubules are arranged inside cilia and flagella.

ciliated cells whisk out mucus laden with dust or other undesirable material. The microtubules of cilia and flagella arise from **centrioles**, which remain at the base of the completed structure as a "basal body." As you will read in a later chapter, centrioles have an important role when a cell divides.

The cytoskeleton gives each cell its shape, internal structure, and capacity for movement. Its main elements are microtubules, microfilaments, and intermediate filaments.

Certain types of cells move their bodies or parts by way of flagella or cilia.

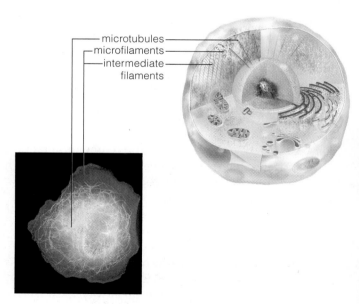

microtubules
microfilaments
intermediate filaments

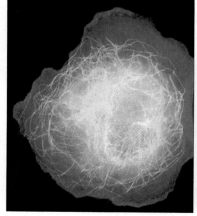

a

b

Figure 3.13 (**a**) The cytoskeleton of a human pancreas cell. The blue region is DNA. (**b**) The "tails" of sperm cells are whiplike flagella.

3.9 How Diffusion and Osmosis Move Substances across Membranes

LINKS TO
SECTIONS
2.10 AND 2.12

There is fluid on both sides of a cell's plasma membrane. The kinds and amounts of dissolved substances in the fluid are not the same on the two sides. A cell must maintain those differences—a task of the plasma membrane.

THE PLASMA MEMBRANE IS "SELECTIVE"

As you already know, a cell's plasma membrane is a bilayer containing lipids and proteins. These molecules give the membrane **selective permeability**. They allow some substances but not others to enter and leave a cell (Figure 3.15). They also control *when* a substance can cross and how much crosses at a given time. Lipids in the bilayer are mostly nonpolar, so they let small, nonpolar molecules such as carbon dioxide and oxygen slip across. Water molecules are polar, but some can slip through gaps that briefly open up in the bilayer. Ions, and large polar molecules such as glucose, cross the bilayer through the interior of its transport proteins. Why does a solute move one way or another at any given time? The answer starts with concentration gradients.

IN DIFFUSION, A SOLUTE MOVES DOWN A CONCENTRATION GRADIENT

"Concentration" refers to the number of molecules of a substance in a certain volume of fluid. "Gradient" means that the number of molecules in one region is not the same as in another. Therefore, a **concentration gradient** is a difference in the number of molecules or ions of a given substance in two neighboring regions. Molecules are always randomly moving between the two regions, but on balance, unless other forces come into play, they tend to move into the region where they are less concentrated.

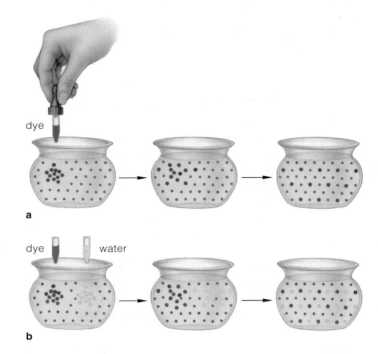

Figure 3.16 *Animated!* Two examples of diffusion. (**a**) A drop of dye enters a bowl of water. Gradually the dye molecules become evenly dispersed through the molecules of water. (**b**) The same thing happens with the water molecules. Here, red dye and yellow dye are added to the same bowl. Each substance will move down its own concentration gradient.

The net movement of like molecules or ions down a concentration gradient is called **diffusion**. In living organisms, the diffusion of a substance across a cell membrane is called **passive transport**, "passive" because a cell does not have to draw energy from ATP, the cell's chemical fuel, to make it happen. Diffusion moves substances to and from cells, and into and out of the fluids bathing them. Diffusion also moves substances through the cytoplasm of a cell.

If a solution contains more than one kind of solute, each kind diffuses down its own concentration gradient. For example, if you put a drop of dye in one side of a bowl of water, the dye molecules diffuse to the region where they are less concentrated. Likewise, the water molecules move in the opposite direction, to the region where *they* are less concentrated (Figure 3.16).

Molecules diffuse faster when the gradient is steep. Where molecules are most concentrated, more of them move outward, compared to the number that are moving in. As the gradient smooths out, there is less difference in the number of molecules moving either way. Even when the gradient disappears, molecules are still moving, but the total number going one way or the other during a given interval is about the same. For charged molecules,

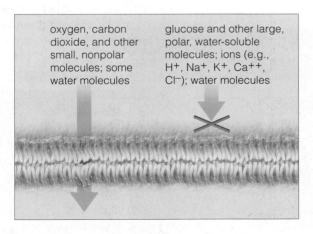

oxygen, carbon dioxide, and other small, nonpolar molecules; some water molecules

glucose and other large, polar, water-soluble molecules; ions (e.g., H^+, Na^+, K^+, Ca^{++}, Cl^-); water molecules

Figure 3.15 *Animated!* The selective permeability of cell membranes.

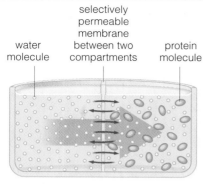

water molecule · selectively permeable membrane between two compartments · protein molecule

Figure 3.17 *Animated!* How a solute concentration gradient affects osmotic movement of water.

Start with a container divided by a membrane that water but not proteins can cross. Pour water into the left side and pour the same volume of a protein-rich solution into the right side. There, proteins occupy some of the space. The net diffusion of water in this example is from left to right (large gray arrow).

transport is influenced by both the concentration gradient and the *electric gradient*—a difference in electric charge across the cell membrane. As you will read in a later chapter, nerve impulses depend on electric gradients.

WATER CROSSES MEMBRANES BY OSMOSIS

Because the plasma membrane is selectively permeable, the concentration of a solute can increase on one side of the membrane but not on the other. For example, the cytoplasm of most cells usually contains solutes (such as proteins) that cannot diffuse across the plasma membrane. When solutes become more concentrated on one side of the plasma membrane, the resulting solute concentration gradients affect how water diffuses across the membrane. **Osmosis** is the name for the diffusion of water across a selectively permeable membrane in response to solute concentration gradients (Figure 3.17).

Tonicity is the ability of a solution to draw water into or out of a cell. When solute concentrations in the fluids on either side of a cell membrane are the same, the fluids are *isotonic* (*iso-* means same) and there is no net flow of water in either direction across the membrane. When the solute concentrations are not equal, one fluid is *hypotonic*—it has fewer solutes. The other has more solutes and it is *hypertonic*. Figure 3.18 shows how the tonicity of a fluid affects red blood cells. A key point to remember: Water always tends to move from a hypotonic solution to a hypertonic one because it moves down its concentration gradient.

If too much water enters a cell by osmosis, in theory the cell will swell up until it bursts. This is not a danger for most body cells because they can selectively move solutes out—and as solutes leave, so does water. Also, the cytoplasm exerts pressure against the plasma membrane. When this pressure counterbalances the tendency of water to follow its concentration gradient, osmosis stops.

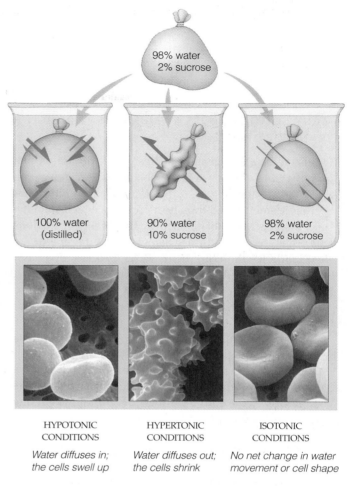

98% water 2% sucrose

100% water (distilled) · 90% water 10% sucrose · 98% water 2% sucrose

HYPOTONIC CONDITIONS · HYPERTONIC CONDITIONS · ISOTONIC CONDITIONS

Water diffuses in; the cells swell up · *Water diffuses out; the cells shrink* · *No net change in water movement or cell shape*

Figure 3.18 *Animated!* Tonicity and the diffusion of water. In the sketches, membrane-like bags through which water but not sucrose can move are placed in hypotonic, hypertonic, and isotonic solutions. In each container, arrow width represents the relative amount of water movement. The sketches show what happens when red blood cells—which cannot actively take in or expel water—are placed in similar solutions.

Moment to moment, cell activities and other events change the factors that affect the solute concentrations of body fluids and water movements between them. Cells that are not equipped to adjust to such differences shrivel or burst, as Figure 3.18 illustrates. In a later chapter we will discuss ways in which osmotic water movements help maintain the body's proper water balance.

The net movement of like molecules (or ions) from a region of higher concentration to a region of lower concentration is called diffusion.

Osmosis is the net diffusion of water across a selectively permeable membrane. Most body cells have mechanisms for adjusting the movement of water and solutes into and out of the cell.

3.10 Other Ways Substances Cross Cell Membranes

Substances also cross cell membranes by mechanisms called facilitated diffusion, active transport, exocytosis, and endocytosis.

MANY SOLUTES CROSS MEMBRANES THROUGH TRANSPORT PROTEINS

Diffusion directly through a plasma membrane is just one of three ways by which substances can move into and out of a cell (Figure 3.19). You may remember that Section 3.3 mentioned transport proteins, which span the lipid bilayer. Many of them provide a channel for ions and other solutes to diffuse across the membrane down their concentration gradients. The process does not require ATP energy, so it is a form of passive transport (Figure 3.20). It is called **facilitated diffusion** because the transport proteins provide a route for the solute that is crossing the cell membrane.

Two features allow a transport protein to fulfill its role. First, its interior can open to both sides of a cell membrane. Second, when the protein interacts with a solute, its shape changes, then changes back again. The changes move the solute through the protein, from one side of the lipid bilayer to the other. Transport proteins are "choosy" about which solutes pass through them. For example, the protein that transports amino acids will not carry glucose.

As cells use and produce substances, the concentrations of solutes on either side of their membranes are constantly changing. A cell also must actively move certain solutes in, out, and through its cytoplasm. Action requires energy, and so cells have mechanisms called "membrane pumps" that move substances across membranes *against*

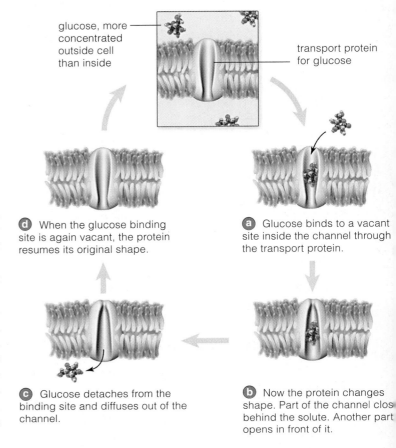

glucose, more concentrated outside cell than inside

transport protein for glucose

d When the glucose binding site is again vacant, the protein resumes its original shape.

a Glucose binds to a vacant site inside the channel through the transport protein.

c Glucose detaches from the binding site and diffuses out of the channel.

b Now the protein changes shape. Part of the channel clos[es] behind the solute. Another part opens in front of it.

Figure 3.20 *Animated!* Facilitated diffusion, a form of passive transport. In this mechanism, a solute can move in both directions through transport proteins. The solute moves down its concentration gradient. In this example the solute is the sugar glucose.

concentration gradients. This pumping is called **active transport** (Figure 3.21). ATP provides most of the energy for active transport, and membrane pumps can continue working until the solute is *more* concentrated on the side of the membrane where it is being pumped. For example, a calcium pump helps keep the concentration of calcium inside cells at least a thousand times lower than it is outside. This difference lays the chemical foundation for muscle contraction, which we will discuss in Chapter 6.

VESICLES TRANSPORT LARGE SOLUTES

Transport proteins can only move small molecules and ions into or out of cells. To bring in or expel larger molecules or particles, cells use vesicles that form through exocytosis and endocytosis.

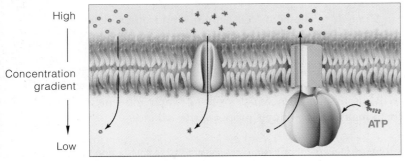

High

Concentration gradient

Low

| Diffusion of lipid-soluble substances across bilayer | Passive transport of water-soluble substances through channel protein; no energy input needed | Active transport through ATPase; requires energy input from ATP |

Figure 3.19 Membrane-crossing mechanisms.

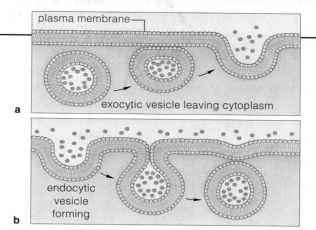

Figure 3.22 (**a**) Exocytosis. Cells can release substances when a vesicle's membrane fuses with the plasma membrane. (**b**) Endocytosis. A bit of plasma membrane balloons inward beneath water and solutes outside, then pinches off as a vesicle that moves into the cytoplasm.

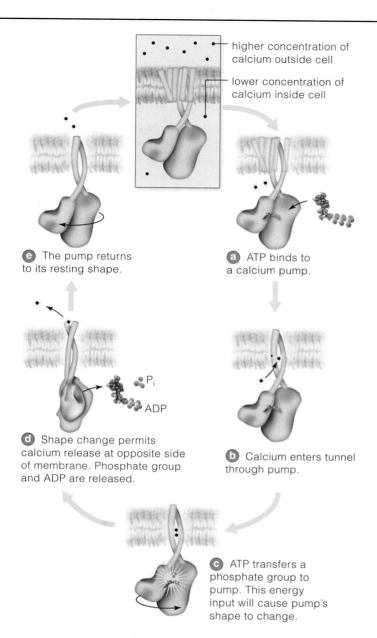

- higher concentration of calcium outside cell
- lower concentration of calcium inside cell

e The pump returns to its resting shape.

a ATP binds to a calcium pump.

d Shape change permits calcium release at opposite side of membrane. Phosphate group and ADP are released.

P$_i$

ADP

b Calcium enters tunnel through pump.

c ATP transfers a phosphate group to pump. This energy input will cause pump's shape to change.

Figure 3.21 *Animated!* Active transport across a cell membrane.

In **exocytosis** ("moving out of a cell"), a vesicle moves to the cell surface and the protein-studded lipid bilayer of its membrane fuses with the plasma membrane (Figure 3.22*a*). Its contents are then released to the outside.

In **endocytosis** ("coming inside a cell"), a cell takes in substances next to its surface. A small indentation forms at the plasma membrane, balloons inward, and pinches off. The resulting vesicle transports its contents or stores them in the cytoplasm (Figure 3.22*b*). When endocytosis brings organic matter into the cell, the process is called **phagocytosis**, or "cell eating."

Transport proteins carry many solutes across cell membranes. In passive transport, a solute diffuses down its concentration gradient. In active transport, membrane pumps move solutes against their gradient. ATP provides much of the needed energy. Exocytosis and endocytosis move large molecules or particles across the membrane.

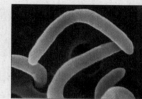

Vibrio cholerae, the cause of cholera

In places where there is little or no proper public sanitation, people run the risk of getting cholera because drinking water and some foods are contaminated by human sewage. Cholera's main symptom is sudden, massive diarrhea that can literally drain a person's body of water in less than 24 hours. The cause is a poison, cholera exotoxin, produced by the bacterium *Vibrio cholerae*. The toxin causes cells to pump out chloride ions, and other solutes follow. As solutes leave, cells lose their water by osmosis. Cholera is a common, deadly threat in parts of Africa, Asia, and South America, and after Hurricane Katrina, officials feared it would strike the U.S. Gulf Coast as well. In developed nations cholera can be treated with antibiotics. Elsewhere patients may recover if they are quickly rehydrated.

3.11 Metabolism: Doing Cellular Work

LINKS TO
SECTIONS
.5, 2.8, AND 2.13

The 65 trillion living cells in your body need energy for their operations. The raw energy for this cellular work comes from organic compounds in food, which a cell's mitochondria convert to ATP—a chemical form the cell can use.

ATP IS THE CELL'S ENERGY CURRENCY

The chemical reactions in cells are called **metabolism**. Some reactions release energy and others require it. ATP links the two kinds of reactions, carrying energy from one reaction to another. You may remember that ATP is short for adenosine triphosphate, one of the nucleotides. A molecule of ATP consists of the five-carbon sugar ribose to which adenine (a nucleotide base) and three phosphate groups are attached (Figure 3.23a). ATP's stored energy is contained in the bond between the second and third phosphate groups.

Enzymes can break the bond between the second and third phosphate groups of the ATP molecule. The enzymes then can attach the released phosphate group to another molecule. When a phosphate group is moved from one molecule to another, stored energy goes with it.

Cells use ATP constantly, so they must renew their ATP supply. In many metabolic processes, phosphate (symbolized by P_i) or a phosphate group that has been split off from some substance, is attached to ADP, adenosine diphosphate (the prefix *di-* indicates that *two* phosphate groups are present). Now the molecule, with three phosphates, is ATP. And when ATP transfers a phosphate group elsewhere, it reverts to ADP. In this way it completes the **ATP/ADP cycle** (Figure 3.23b).

Like money earned at a job and then spent to pay the rent, ATP is earned in reactions that produce energy and spent in reactions that require it. That is why textbooks often use a cartoon coin to symbolize ATP.

THERE ARE TWO MAIN TYPES OF METABOLIC PATHWAYS

At this moment thousands of reactions are transforming thousands of substances inside each of your cells. Most of these reactions are part of **metabolic pathways**, steps in which reactions take place one after another. There are two main types of metabolic pathways, called anabolism and catabolism.

In **anabolism**, small molecules are put together into larger ones. In these larger molecules, the chemical bonds hold more energy. Anabolic pathways assemble complex carbohydrates, proteins, and other large molecules. The energy stored in their bonds is a major reason why we can use these substances as food.

In **catabolism**, large molecules are broken down to simpler ones. Catabolic reactions disassemble complex carbohydrates, proteins, and similar molecules, releasing their components for use by cells. For example, when a complex carbohydrate is catabolized, the reactions release the simple sugar glucose, the main fuel for cells.

Any substance that is part of a metabolic reaction is called a *reactant*. A substance that forms between the beginning and the end of a metabolic pathway is an *intermediate*. Substances present at the end of a reaction or a pathway are the *end products*.

Many metabolic pathways advance step-by-step from reactants to end products:

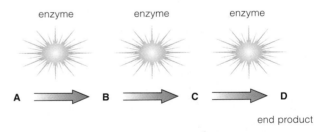

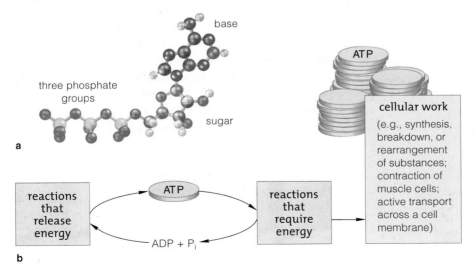

a

three phosphate groups

base

sugar

b

reactions that release energy → ATP → reactions that require energy → ADP + P_i

ATP

cellular work
(e.g., synthesis, breakdown, or rearrangement of substances; contraction of muscle cells; active transport across a cell membrane)

Figure 3.23 *Animated!* (**a**) Structure of the energy carrier ATP. (**b**) ATP connects energy-releasing reactions with energy-requiring ones. In the ATP/ADP cycle, the transfer of a phosphate group turns ATP into ADP, then back again to ATP.

HOW CELLS GAIN ENERGY

In other pathways the steps occur in a cycle, with the end products serving as reactants to start things over.

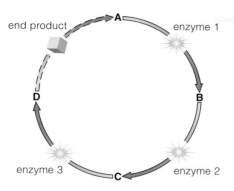

ENZYMES PLAY A VITAL ROLE IN METABOLISM

The metabolic reactions that keep all of us alive require **enzymes**, which you first read about in Section 2.8. Most enzymes are proteins, and they have several key features. Most importantly enzymes are catalysts: they speed up chemical reactions. In fact, enzymes usually make reactions occur hundreds to millions of times faster than would be possible otherwise. Enzymes are not used up in reactions, so a given enzyme molecule can be used over and over.

Each kind of enzyme can only interact with specific kinds of molecules, which are called its **substrates**. The enzyme can chemically recognize a substrate, bind it, and change it in some way. An example is thrombin, one of the enzymes required to clot blood. It only recognizes a side-by-side alignment of two particular amino acids in a protein. When thrombin "sees" this arrangement, it breaks the peptide bond between the amino acids.

An enzyme and its substrate interact at a surface crevice on the enzyme, called an **active site**. Figure 3.24 shows how enzyme action can combine two substrate molecules into a new, larger product molecule.

Powerful as they are, enzymes only work well within a certain temperature range. For example, if a person's body temperature rises too high, the increased heat energy breaks bonds holding an enzyme in its three-dimensional shape. The shape changes, substrates can't bind to the active site as usual, and chemical reactions are disrupted. People usually die if their internal temperature reaches 44°C (112°F).

Enzymes also function best within a certain pH range—in the body, from pH 7.35 to 7.4. Above or below this range most enzymes cannot operate normally.

Organic molecules called **coenzymes** assist with many reactions. Lots of coenzymes, including **NAD⁺** (nicotinamide adenine dinucleotide) and **FAD** (flavin adenine dinucleotide), are derived from vitamins, which is one reason why vitamins are important in the diet.

To maintain homeostasis the body must have ways of controlling the activity of enzymes. Some of these controls boost or slow the action of existing enzymes. Others adjust how fast enzyme molecules are made, and thus how many are available for a metabolic pathway. For example, when you eat, food arriving in your stomach causes gland cells there to secrete the hormone gastrin into your bloodstream. Stomach cells with receptors for gastrin respond in several ways, such as secreting the ingredients of "gastric juice"—including enzymes that break down food proteins.

Two enzymes, superoxide dismutase and catalase, help keep free radicals and some other toxic substances from building up in cells. As we age, our cells make less of both enzymes, so rogue molecules have free rein to damage cells. The age spots on this man's skin are visible evidence of this reduced enzyme activity.

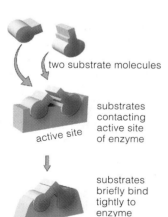

two substrate molecules

active site

substrates contacting active site of enzyme

substrates briefly bind tightly to enzyme active site

product molecule

enzyme unchanged by the reaction

Figure 3.24 *Animated!* How enzymes and substrates fit together. When substrate molecules contact an enzyme's active site, they bind to the site for a brief time and a product molecule forms. When the product molecule is released, the enzyme goes back to its previous shape. It is not changed by the reaction it catalyzed.

Most chemical reactions in cells are organized in the orderly steps of metabolic pathways.

Enzymes speed the rate of chemical reactions, but each one acts only on specific substrates. Enzymes function best within certain ranges of temperature and pH.

3.12 How Cells Make ATP

LINK TO SECTION 2.9

The chemical reactions that sustain the body depend on energy that cells capture when they produce ATP.

CELLULAR RESPIRATION MAKES ATP

To make ATP, cells break apart carbohydrates, especially glucose, as well as lipids and proteins. The reactions remove electrons from intermediate compounds, then energy associated with the electrons powers the formation of ATP. Human cells typically form ATP by **cellular respiration**. In large, complex organisms like ourselves, this process usually is aerobic, which means that it uses oxygen. Glucose is the most common raw material for cellular respiration, so it will be our example here.

STEP 1: GLYCOLYSIS BREAKS GLUCOSE DOWN TO PYRUVATE

Cellular respiration starts in the cell's cytoplasm, in a set of reactions called **glycolysis**—literally, "splitting sugar." You may recall that glucose is a simple sugar. Each glucose molecule consists of six carbon atoms, twelve hydrogens, and six oxygens, all joined by covalent bonds. During glycolysis, a glucose molecule is broken into two **pyruvate** molecules, each with three carbons (Figure 3.25).

When glycolysis begins, two ATPs each transfer a phosphate group to glucose, donating energy to it. This kind of transfer is called **phosphorylation**. It adds enough energy to glucose to begin the energy-releasing steps of glycolysis.

The first energy-releasing step breaks the glucose into two molecules of **PGAL** (for phosphoglyceraldehyde), which are converted to intermediates. These molecules then each donate a phosphate group to ADP, forming ATP. The same thing happens with the next intermediate in the sequence, and the end result is two molecules of pyruvate and four ATP. However, because two ATP were invested to start the reactions, the *net* energy yield is only two ATP.

Notice that glycolysis does not use oxygen. If oxygen is not available for the following aerobic steps of cellular respiration, for a short time a cell can still form a small amount of ATP by a process of fermentation, which also does not use oxygen. You will read more about this "back-up" process for forming ATP later in the chapter.

STEP 2: THE KREBS CYCLE PRODUCES ENERGY-RICH TRANSPORT MOLECULES

The pyruvate molecules formed by glycolysis move into a mitochondrion. There the oxygen-requiring phase of cellular respiration will be completed. Enzymes catalyze each reaction, and the intermediate molecules formed at one step become substrates for the next.

In preparatory steps, an enzyme removes a carbon atom from each pyruvate molecule. A coenzyme called coenzyme A combines with the remaining two-carbon fragment and becomes a compound called **acetyl-CoA**. This substance enters the **Krebs cycle**. For each turn of the cycle, six carbons, three from each pyruvate, enter and six also leave, in the form of carbon dioxide. The bloodstream then transports this CO_2 to the lungs where it is exhaled.

Reactions in mitochondria before and during the Krebs cycle have three important functions. First, they produce two molecules of ATP. Second, they regenerate intermediate compounds required to keep the Krebs cycle going. And in a third, crucial step, a large number of the coenzymes called NAD^+ and FAD pick up H^+ and electrons, in the process becoming NADH and $FADH_2$. Loaded with energy, NADH and $FADH_2$ will now move to the site of the third and final stage of reactions that make ATP.

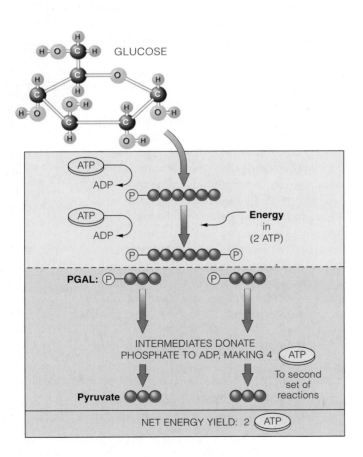

Figure 3.25 *Animated!* Overview of glycolysis.

STEP 3: ELECTRON TRANSPORT PRODUCES MANY ATP MOLECULES

ATP production goes into high gear during the final stage of cellular respiration. In the production "assembly line" chains of reactions capture and use energy released by electrons. Each chain is called an **electron transport system**. It includes enzymes inside the membrane that divides the mitochondrion into two compartments (Figure 3.26). As electrons flow through the system, each step transfers a bit of energy to a molecule that briefly stores it. This gradual releasing of energy reduces the amount of energy that is lost (as heat) while a cell is generating ATP.

As you can see at the bottom left of Figure 3.26, an electron transport system uses electrons and hydrogen ions delivered by NADH and $FADH_2$. The electrons are transferred from one molecule of the transport system to the next in line. When molecules in the chain accept and then donate electrons, they also pick up hydrogen ions in the inner compartment, then release them to the outer compartment. The blue arrows in Figure 3.26 represent this process. At the end of an electron transport system, oxygen accepts electrons in a reaction that forms water.

As the system moves hydrogen ions into the outer compartment, an H^+ concentration gradient develops. As the ions become more concentrated in the outer compartment, they follow the gradient back into the inner compartment, crossing the inner membrane through the interior of enzymes that can catalyze the formation of ATP from ADP and phosphate (P_i). This step is shown at the far right of Figure 3.26.

In glycolysis, a carbohydrate such as glucose is broken down to two molecules of pyruvate. The net energy yield of glycolysis is two ATP molecules.

When the two pyruvate molecules from glycolysis enter a mitochondrion, each gives up a carbon atom and the rest of the molecule enters the Krebs cycle. The carbon atoms end up in carbon dioxide. The Krebs cycle and its preparatory steps yield two more ATP molecules.

In the final stage of cellular respiration, electrons and H^+ move through transport systems inside mitochondria. ATP forms when hydrogen ions flow through membrane enzymes that add a phosphate group to ADP.

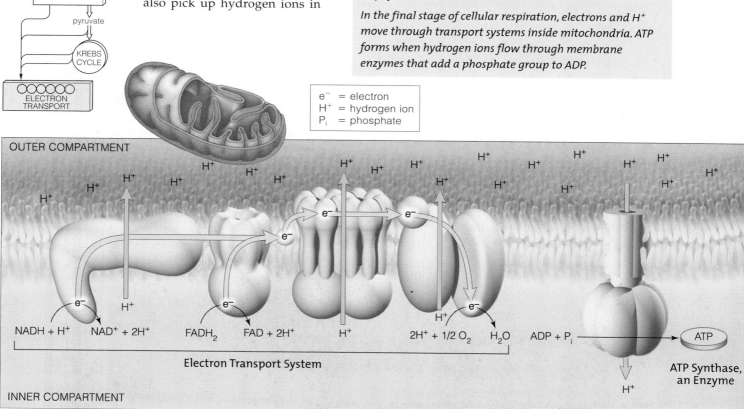

e^-	= electron
H^+	= hydrogen ion
P_i	= phosphate

a At the inner mitochondrial membrane, NADH and $FADH_2$ give up electrons to transfer chains. When electrons are transferred through the chains, hydrogen (H^+) is shuttled across the membrane to the outer compartment.

b Oxygen accepts electrons at the end of the transfer chain.

c There are now H^+ concentration and electric gradients across the membrane. H^+ follows the gradients through the interior of enzymes, to the inner compartment. This flow drives the formation of ATP from ADP and phosphate (P_i).

Figure 3.26 *Animated!* How electron transport forms ATP.

3.13 Summary of Cellular Respiration

Figure 3.27 below reviews the steps and ATP yield from cellular respiration. Only this aerobic pathway delivers enough energy to build and maintain a large, active, multicellular organism such as a human. In many types of cells, the third stage of reactions forms thirty-two ATP. When we add these to the final yield from the preceding stages, the total harvest is thirty-six ATP from one glucose molecule. This is a very efficient use of our cellular resources!

While aerobic cellular respiration typically yields thirty-six ATP, the actual amount may vary, depending on conditions in a cell at a given moment—for instance, if a cell requires a particular intermediate elsewhere and pulls it out of the reaction sequence. If you would like to learn more about these metabolic events, see Appendix I at the back of this book.

Cellular respiration begins with glycolysis in the cytoplasm and ends with electron transport systems in mitochondria. From start to finish this aerobic process typically has a net yield of thirty-six ATP for every glucose molecule.

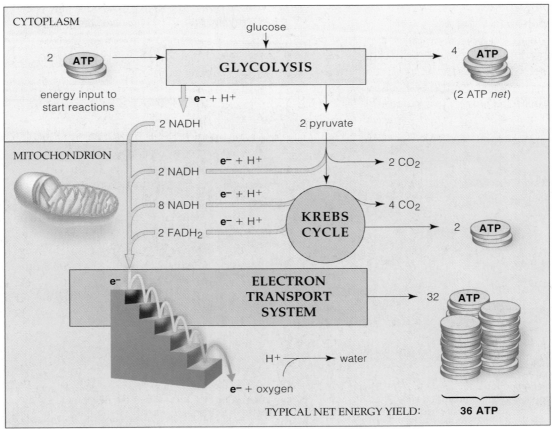

Figure 3.27 *Animated!* Summary of aerobic cellular respiration.

3.14 Alternative Energy Sources in the Body

Glucose from complex carbohydrates is the body's main energy source. When conditions warrant, however, other substances can supply needed fuel for making ATP.

HOW THE BODY USES CARBOHYDRATES AS FUEL

When glucose from food moves into your bloodstream, a rise in the glucose level in blood prompts an organ, the pancreas, to release insulin. This hormone makes cells take up glucose faster.

If you consume more glucose than your cells need for the moment, one of the intermediates of glycolysis is diverted into an anabolic pathway that makes a storage sugar called glycogen. The detour halts glycolysis, so for the time being no more ATP forms. This switch occurs quite often in muscle and liver cells, which store most of the body's glycogen. Other kinds of cells tend to store excess glucose as fat.

Sudden, intense exercise, such as weightlifting or a sprint, may call on cells in skeletal muscles (which attach to our bones) that use a different kind of ATP-forming mechanism, a process called *lactate fermentation* (Figure 3.28). The process converts pyruvate from glycolysis to lactic acid. It does not use oxygen and produces ATP quickly but not for very long. Muscles feel sore when lactic acid builds up in them.

Between meals, glucose is not moving into your bloodstream and its level in the blood falls. The decline must be offset because nerve cells in the brain use glucose as their preferred energy source. Accordingly, the pancreas responds to falling blood glucose by secreting a hormone that makes liver cells convert glycogen back to glucose and release it to the blood. Thus, hormones control whether the body's cells use glucose as an energy source or store it for future use.

Only about 1 percent of the body's total energy reserves consists of glycogen, however. Of the total energy stores in a typical adult American, 78 percent is in body fat and 21 percent in proteins.

FATS AND PROTEINS ALSO PROVIDE ENERGY

Most of the body's stored fat consists of triglycerides, which accumulate inside the fat cells in certain tissues (called *adipose* tissues) of the buttocks and other locations beneath the skin.

Between meals or during exercise, the body may tap triglycerides as energy alternatives to glucose. Enzymes in fat cells break apart triglycerides into glycerol and fatty acids, which enter the bloodstream. When glycerol reaches the liver, enzymes convert it to PGAL, the intermediate of glycolysis mentioned in Section 3.12. Most body cells take up the circulating fatty acids. Enzymes convert them to acetyl-CoA, which can enter the Krebs cycle. Each fatty acid tail has many more carbon-bound hydrogen atoms than glucose does, so breaking down a fatty acid yields much more ATP. In fact, this pathway can supply about half the ATP required by your muscle, liver, and kidney cells.

The body stores excess fats but not proteins. Enzymes dismantle unneeded proteins into amino acids. Then they remove the molecule's amino group ($-NH_3^+$) and ammonia (NH_3) forms. The cell's metabolic machinery may use leftover carbons to make fats or carbohydrates. Or the carbons may enter the Krebs cycle, where coenzymes can pick up hydrogen as well as electrons removed from the carbon atoms. These can be used to make ATP in electron transport systems in mitochondria. The ammonia is converted to urea, a waste that is excreted in urine.

IMPACTS, ISSUES

Due to an inherited defect in the functioning of their mitochondria, some people have *lactic acidosis*—their cells make far too much lactic acid. High levels of lactate make the blood dangerously acidic and cause muscle weakness, abdominal pain, nausea, fatigue, and, in extreme cases, death.

Figure 3.28 Sprinters, drawing on muscle cells that use lactate fermentation to generate ATP.

Complex carbohydrates, fats, and proteins all can serve as energy sources in the human body.

Certain muscle cells can make a small amount of ATP by the process of lactate fermentation.

Summary

Section 3.1 A living cell has a plasma membrane surrounding an inner region of cytoplasm. The cytoplasm consists of a jellylike cytosol and other components. In a eukaryotic cell, including human cells, membranes divide the cell into functional compartments called organelles. Organelle membranes separate metabolic reactions in the cytoplasm and allow different kinds to proceed in an orderly way.

 Investigate the physical limits on cell size and learn how different types of microscopes function.

Section 3.3 Cell membranes consist mostly of lipids and proteins. The lipids are mainly phospholipids, arranged as a double layer called a lipid bilayer. Various kinds of proteins in the bilayer, or at one of its surfaces, perform most membrane functions.

Some membrane proteins are transport proteins that allow water-soluble substances to cross the membrane. Others are receptors for hormones or other substances. Still other proteins have carbohydrate chains that serve as a cell's identity tags. Adhesion proteins help cells stay together in their proper tissues.

 Learn more about the functions of receptor proteins.

Section 3.5 The largest organelle is the nucleus, where the genetic material DNA is located. The nucleus is surrounded by a double membrane, the nuclear envelope. Pores in the envelope help control the movement of substances into and out of the nucleus. A nucleolus is a dense mass inside the nucleus; nucleoli are where the subunits of ribosomes are constructed.

A cell's DNA and proteins associated with it are called chromatin. Each chromosome in the nucleus is one DNA molecule with its associated proteins.

 Introduce yourself to the major types of organelles and take a close-up look at the nuclear membrane.

Section 3.6 The endomembrane system includes the endoplasmic reticulum, Golgi bodies, and different kinds of vesicles. In this system new proteins are modified into final form and lipids are assembled. Unwanted materials may be broken down in vesicles called lysosomes and peroxisomes.

 Follow a path through the endomembrane system.

Section 3.7 Mitochondria carry out the oxygen-requiring reactions that make ATP, the cell's energy currency. These reactions take place in the inner compartment formed by a mitochondrion's double-membrane system.

Section 3.8 The cytoskeleton consists mainly of microtubules and microfilaments; some types of cells also have intermediate filaments. The cytoskeleton gives a cell its shape and internal structure. In some kinds of cells microtubules are the framework for cilia or flagella, which are used in movement. Cilia and flagella develop from structures called centrioles.

 Learn more about elements of the cytoskeleton and what they do.

Section 3.9 A cell's plasma membrane is selectively permeable—the membrane allows some substances but not others to cross it, according to the cell's needs. Substances cross cell membranes by several transport mechanisms. Diffusion is the random movement of solutes down a concentration gradient. Osmosis is the movement of water across a selectively permeable membrane in response to concentration gradients, a pressure gradient, or both.

 Investigate how substances diffuse across membranes and how water crosses by osmosis.

Section 3.10 In passive transport, a solute moves down its concentration gradient through a membrane transport protein. In active transport, a solute is pumped through a membrane protein *against* its concentration gradient. Active transport requires an energy boost, as from ATP.

Cells use vesicles to take in or expel large molecules or particles. In exocytosis, a vesicle moves to the cell surface and fuses with the plasma membrane. In endocytosis, a vesicle forms at the surface and moves inward. When an endocytic vesicle brings organic matter into a cell, the process is called phagocytosis (cell eating).

 Compare the processes of passive and active transport, and see how vesicles move substances into and out of cells.

Section 3.11 The chemical reactions in a cell are collectively called its metabolism. A metabolic pathway is a stepwise sequence of chemical reactions catalyzed by enzymes—catalytic molecules that speed up the rate of metabolic reactions. Each enzyme interacts only with a specific substrate, linking with it at one or more active sites.

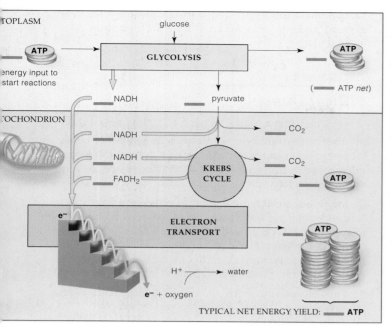

CYTOPLASM

glucose → GLYCOLYSIS

ATP → energy input to start reactions

ATP

(▬ ATP *net*)

NADH   pyruvate

MITOCHONDRION

NADH → CO_2

NADH → CO_2

FADH$_2$ → KREBS CYCLE

ATP

e⁻ → ELECTRON TRANSPORT → ATP

H⁺ → water

e⁻ + oxygen

TYPICAL NET ENERGY YIELD: ▬ ATP

Table 3.4	Summary of Energy Sources in the Human Body	
Starting Molecule	**Subunit**	**Entry Point into the Aerobic Pathway**
Complex carbohydrate	Simple sugars (e.g., glucose)	Glycolysis
Fat	Fatty acids	Preparatory reactions for Krebs cycle
	Glycerol	Raw material for key intermediate in glycolysis (PGAL)
Protein	Amino acids	Carbon backbones enter Krebs cycle or preparatory reactions

Anabolism builds large, energy-rich organic compounds from smaller molecules. Catabolism breaks down molecules to smaller ones. Various cofactors, such as the coenzymes NAD⁺ and FAD, assist enzymes or carry electrons, hydrogen, or functional groups from a substrate to other sites.

 Investigate how enzymes facilitate chemical reactions.

Section 3.12 The reactions of most anabolic pathways run on energy from ATP. In body cells, cellular respiration produces most ATP molecules. This pathway releases chemical energy from glucose and other organic compounds. ATP is replenished by way of the ATP/ADP cycle.

Section 3.13 In aerobic cellular respiration, oxygen is the final acceptor of electrons removed from glucose. The pathway has three stages: glycolysis (in the cytoplasm), the Krebs cycle, and electron transport, which generates a large amount of ATP in mitochondria. The typical net energy yield of cellular respiration is thirty-six ATP.

Thomson NOW! *Take a step-by-step journey through glycolysis and cellular respiration.*

Section 3.14 The body can extract energy from carbohydrates, fats, and proteins. Complex carbohydrates are broken down to the simple sugar glucose, the body's main metabolic fuel. Alternatives to glucose include fatty acids and glycerol from triglycerides and, in certain circumstances, amino acids from proteins (Table 3.4).

Thomson NOW! *Learn more about how cells can use different kinds of organic molecules as energy sources.*

Review Questions

1. Describe the general functions of the following in a eukaryotic cell: the plasma membrane, cytoplasm, DNA, ribosomes, organelles, and cytoskeleton.

2. Which organelles are part of the cytomembrane system?

3. Distinguish between the following pairs of terms:
   a. diffusion; osmosis
   b. passive transport; active transport
   c. endocytosis; exocytosis

4. What is an enzyme? Describe the role of enzymes in metabolic reactions.

5. In aerobic cellular respiration, which reactions occur only in the cytoplasm? Which ones occur only in a cell's mitochondria?

6. For the diagram of the aerobic pathway shown above, fill in the number of molecules of pyruvate and the net ATP formed at each stage.

1. The plasma membrane _____.
   a. surrounds the cytoplasm
   b. separates the nucleus from the cytoplasm
   c. separates the cell interior from the environment
   d. both a and c are correct

2. The _____ is responsible for a eukaryotic cell's shape, internal organization, and cell movement.

3. Cell membranes consist mainly of a _____.
   a. carbohydrate bilayer and proteins
   b. protein bilayer and phospholipids
   c. phospholipid bilayer and proteins

4. _____ carry out most membrane functions.
   a. Proteins   c. Nucleic acids
   b. Phospholipids   d. Hormones

5. The passive movement of a solute through a membrane protein down its concentration gradient is an example of _____.
   a. osmosis   c. endocytosis
   b. active transport   d. diffusion

6. Match each organelle with its correct function.
   ____ protein synthesis   a. mitochondrion
   ____ movement   b. ribosome
   ____ intracellular digestion c. smooth ER
   ____ modification of proteins d. rough ER
   ____ lipid synthesis   e. nucleolus
   ____ ATP formation   f. lysosome
   ____ ribosome assembly   g. flagellum

7. Which of the following statements is *not* true? Metabolic pathways _____.
   a. occur in stepwise series of chemical reactions
   b. are speeded up by enzymes
   c. may break down or assemble molecules
   d. always produce energy (such as ATP)

8. Enzymes _____.
   a. enhance reaction   c. act on specific
      rates   substrates
   b. are affected by pH   d. all of the above
                                 are correct

9. Match each substance with its correct description.
   ____ a coenzyme or metal ion a. reactant
   ____ formed at end of a   b. enzyme
        metabolic pathway   c. cofactor
   ____ mainly ATP   d. energy carrier
   ____ enters a reaction   e. end product
   ____ catalytic protein

10. Cellular respiration is completed in the _____.
    a. nucleus   c. plasma membrane
    b. mitochondrion   d. cytoplasm

11. Match each type of metabolic reaction with its function:
    ____ glycolysis   a. many ATP, NADH, FADH$_2$,
    ____ Krebs cycle   and CO$_2$ form
    ____ electron   b. glucose to two pyruvate
         transport   molecules and some ATP
                          c. H$^+$ flows through channel
                             proteins, ATP forms

12. In a mitochondrion, where are the electron transport systems and enzymes required for ATP formation located?

Critical Thinking

1. Using Section 3.4 as a reference, suppose you want to observe the surface of a microscopic section of bone. Would you benefit most from using a compound light microscope, a transmission electron microscope, or a scanning electron microscope?

2. Jogging is considered aerobic exercise because the cardiovascular system (heart and blood vessels) can adjust to supply the oxygen needs of working cells. In contrast, sprinting the 100-meter dash might be called "anaerobic" (lacking oxygen) exercise, and golf "nonaerobic" exercise. Explain these last two observations.

3. The cells of your body never use nucleic acids as an energy source. Can you suggest a reason why?

Explore on Your Own

In this chapter you learned that an enzyme can only act on certain substrates. Because your saliva contains enzymes that can use some substances as substrates but not others, you can easily gain some insight into practical impacts of this concept (Figure 3.29). Start by holding a bite of plain cracker in your mouth for thirty seconds, without chewing it. What happens to the cracker, which is mostly starch (carbohydrate)? Repeat the test with a dab of butter or margarine (lipid), then with a piece of meat, fish, or even scrambled egg (protein). Based on your results, what type of biological molecules do your salivary enzymes act upon?

Figure 3.29 Putting enzymes to work digesting the different kinds of biological molecules in foods.

Stem Cells

Each year tens of thousands of people severely injure their spinal cords. In 1995 actor Christopher Reeve, the movies' Superman, suffered a fall from a horse that left him paralyzed. Until his death in 2004 he was a strong supporter of stem cell research.

Stem cells are the first to form when a fertilized egg starts dividing, and they are plentiful in developing embryos and fetuses.

Adults also have them in some tissues, including bone marrow and adipose (fat) tissue. Stem cells are like blank slates. Under the proper conditions, they can give rise to a range of different cell types, including blood cells, cartilage, muscle, and nerve cells.

Stem cells from adults have shown quite a bit of promise for regenerating some kinds of tissues, such as missing cartilage and heart muscle damaged by a heart attack.

Embryonic stem cells are more controversial. In theory, embryonic stem cells can give rise to every kind of cell in the body. Many scientists feel they are the best alternative for research leading to therapies that can replace the damaged or dead nerve cells responsible for paralysis or disorders such as Alzheimer's disease. Other people believe it's unethical to use embryonic cells for any reason, because doing so destroys the embryo. Currently, the United States government funds only research that uses existing embryonic stem cell lines.

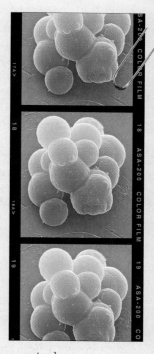

Stem cells start us thinking about how the human body and its parts are put together (anatomy) and how the body functions (physiology). This chapter is an overview of body tissues, organs, and organ systems. A **tissue** is a group of similar cells that perform a particular function. Various tissues combine in certain proportions and patterns to form an organ, such as the heart. An organ system is two or more organs that work together in performing a common task.

As you know by now, homeostasis is the name for stable operating conditions inside the body. This chapter also considers the controls that help maintain this stability.

 How Would You Vote? Should researchers be allowed to start embryonic stem cell lines from human embryos that are not used for in vitro fertilization? Cast your vote online at www.thomsonedu.com/biology/starr/humanbio.

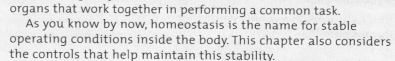

Key Concepts

FOUR TYPES OF TISSUES
Four types of tissues make up the body. Epithelial tissues line body surfaces. Connective tissues bind, support, strengthen, and insulate other tissues. Muscle tissues contract and move the body. Nervous tissue detects stimuli, integrates the information, and governs responses to it.

ORGANS AND ORGAN SYSTEMS
Organs consist of different tissues organized in specific proportions and patterns. Organs are the components of the body's organ systems. Each organ system has specialized functions, but all interact and contribute to the survival of the body as a whole.

Links to Earlier Concepts

In this chapter we reach the tissue, organ, and organ system levels of biological organization (1.3). As you learn about the differences among different types of tissues, you will also get a look at some of the many variations on basic cell structure (3.1–3.8) that occur in your body. The variations are a reminder that cells which perform different functions must be built to carry out those specialized tasks.

4.1 Epithelium: The Body's Covering and Linings

LINK TO
SECTION
3.8

Like other complex animals, we humans are built of just four basic types of tissues. Epithelial tissues cover the body surface or line its cavities and tubes.

Your skin. The rosy lining of your mouth. Each of these is an example of **epithelium** (plural: epithelia). Epithelium is a sheetlike tissue with one surface that faces the outer environment or a body fluid (Figure 4.1*a*). The tissue's other surface rests on a **basement membrane** that is sandwiched between it and the tissue below (Figure 4.1*a*). A basement membrane has no cells but is packed with proteins and polysaccharides.

The cells in epithelium nestle closely together and they are arranged in one or more layers. The cells also are linked by junctions that perform specific structural or functional tasks. Cells in some epithelia are specialized to absorb substances, others to secrete them.

THERE ARE TWO BASIC TYPES OF EPITHELIA

Epithelium may be "simple," with just one layer of cells, or it may be "stratified" and have several layers. Simple epithelium lines the body's cavities, ducts, and tubes—for example, the chest cavity, tear ducts, and the tubes in the kidneys where urine is formed (Figure 4.1*b–d*). In general, the cells in a simple epithelium function in the diffusion, secretion, absorption, or filtering of substances across the layer.

Some simple epithelia have a single cell layer that looks like several layers when it is viewed from the side because the nuclei of neighboring cells don't line up evenly. Most of the cells also have cilia. This type of simple epithelium is termed *pseudostratified* (*pseudo-* means false). It lines the throat, nasal passages, reproductive tract, and other sites in the body where cilia sweep mucus or some other fluid across the surface of the tissue.

Stratified epithelium has two or more layers of cells, and its typical function is protection. For example, this is the tissue at the surface of your skin, which is exposed to nicks, bumps, scrapes, and so forth.

The two basic types of epithelium are subdivided into categories depending on the shape of cells at the tissue's free surface. A *squamous epithelium* has flattened cells, a *cuboidal epithelium* has cube-shaped cells, and a *columnar epithelium* has tall, elongated cells. The different shapes correlate with different functions. For instance, oxygen and carbon dioxide easily diffuse across the thin simple squamous epithelium that makes up the walls of fine blood vessels, as in Figure 4.1*b*. The plumper cells of cuboidal and columnar epithelia secrete substances. Table 4.1 summarizes the types of epithelium and their roles.

GLANDS DEVELOP FROM EPITHELIUM

A **gland** is a structure that makes and releases specific products, such as saliva or mucus. Some glands consist of a single cell, while others are multicellular. Regardless, each gland develops from epithelial tissue and often stays connected to it. Mucus-secreting goblet cells, for instance, are embedded in epithelium that lines the trachea (your windpipe) and other tubes leading to the lungs. The stomach's epithelial lining contains gland cells that secrete protective mucus and digestive juices.

Glands often are classified according to how their secretions reach the place where they are used. **Exocrine glands** release substances through ducts or tubes. Mucus, saliva, earwax, oil, milk, and digestive enzymes all are exocrine secretions. Many exocrine glands simply release the substance they are specialized to make; salivary glands and most sweat glands are like this. In other cases, a gland's secretions include bits of the gland cells. For instance, milk secreted from a nursing woman's mammary glands contains bits of the glandular epithelial tissue. In still other cases, such as sebaceous (oil) glands in your skin, whole cells full of the material to be secreted are actually shed into the duct, where they burst and their contents spill out.

In contrast to exocrine glands, **endocrine glands** do not release substances through tubes or ducts. They make hormones that directly enter the extracellular fluid bathing the glands. Typically, the bloodstream picks up hormones and carries them to target cells somewhere else in the body. Examples of endocrine glands include the pituitary gland, the thyroid, and other glands that are discussed in Chapter 15.

Table 4.1	Major Types of Epithelium	
Type	**Shape**	**Typical Locations**
Simple (one layer)	Squamous	Linings of blood vessels, lung alveoli (sites of gas exchange)
	Cuboidal	Glands and their ducts, surface of ovaries, pigmented epithelium of eye
	Columnar	Stomach, intestines, uterus
Pseudostratified	Columnar	Throat, nasal passages, sinuses, trachea, male genital ducts
Stratified (two or more layers)	Squamous	Skin (keratinized), mouth, throat, esophagus, vagina (nonkeratinized)
	Cuboidal	Ducts of sweat glands
	Columnar	Male urethra, ducts of salivary glands

FOUR TYPES OF TISSUES

free surface
of epithelium

simple
squamous
epithelium

basement
membrane

connective
tissue

a

Figure 4.1 *Animated!* Some basic characteristics of epithelium. (**a**) All epithelia have a free surface. A basement membrane is sandwiched between the opposite surface and underlying connective tissue. The diagram shows simple epithelium, a single layer of cells. The micrograph shows the upper portion of stratified squamous epithelium, which has more than one cell layer. The cells are more flattened toward the surface. (**b–d**) Examples of simple epithelium, showing the three basic cell shapes in this type of tissue.

Epithelia are sheetlike tissues with one free surface. Simple epithelium lines body cavities, ducts, and tubes. Stratified epithelium, like that at the skin surface, typically protects the underlying tissues.

Glands make and secrete substances. They are derived from epithelium, and often remain connected to it. Some glands are single cells, while others are multicellular.

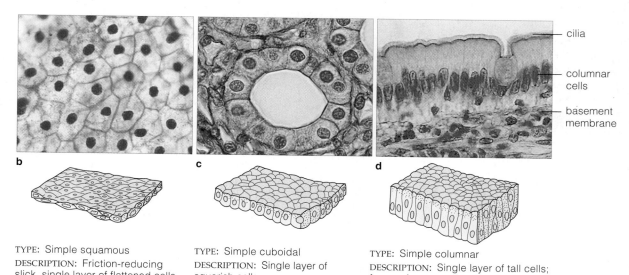

cilia

columnar
cells

basement
membrane

b

TYPE: Simple squamous
DESCRIPTION: Friction-reducing slick, single layer of flattened cells
COMMON LOCATIONS: Lining of blood and lymph vessels, heart; air sacs of lungs; peritoneum
FUNCTION: Diffusion; filtration; secretion of lubricants

c

TYPE: Simple cuboidal
DESCRIPTION: Single layer of squarish cells
COMMON LOCATIONS: Ducts, secretory part of small glands; retina; kidney tubules; ovaries, testes; bronchioles
FUNCTION: Secretion; absorption

d

TYPE: Simple columnar
DESCRIPTION: Single layer of tall cells; free surface may have cilia, mucus-secreting glandular cells, microvilli
COMMON LOCATIONS: Glands, ducts; gut; parts of uterus; small bronchi
FUNCTION: Secretion; absorption; ciliated types move substances

FOUR TYPES OF TISSUES

4.2 Connective Tissue: Binding, Support, and Other Roles

Connective tissue binds together, supports, and anchors body parts. In some cases, it provides metabolic support as well.

Connective tissue is the most abundant body tissue. There are two general groups: fibrous connective tissues and specialized types, which include cartilage, bone, blood, and adipose (fat) tissue (Table 4.2). In most kinds of connective tissues cells secrete fiberlike structural proteins and a "ground substance" of polysaccharides. Together these ingredients make up a **matrix** around the cell. The matrix can range from hard to liquid, and it gives each kind of connective tissue its specialized properties.

FIBROUS CONNECTIVE TISSUES ARE STRONG AND STRETCHY

Fibrous connective tissue is subdivided into several categories, with several forms within each category. All the different kinds have cells, fibers, and a matrix, but in different proportions that make each one well-suited to perform its special function.

For example, the various forms of **loose connective tissue** have few fibers and cells, and they are loosely arranged in a jellylike ground substance, as pictured in Figure 4.2a. This structure makes loose connective tissue flexible. The example in Figure 4.2a wraps many organs and helps support the skin. A "reticular" (netlike) form of loose connective tissue is the framework for soft organs such as the liver, spleen, and lymph nodes.

Dense connective tissue is packed with more collagen fibers than we see in loose connective tissue, so it is less flexible but much stronger. It also comes in several forms. The one pictured in Figure 4.2b helps support the skin's lower layer, the dermis. It also wraps around muscles and organs that do not need to stretch much, such as kidneys. In another version of this connective tissue, large bundles of collagen fibers are aligned in the same plane (Figure 4.2c). This tissue occurs in tendons, which attach skeletal muscle to bones, and in ligaments, which attach bones to one another. Its structure allows a tendon to resist being torn, and in ligaments the tissue's elastic fibers allow the ligament to stretch so bones can move at joints such as the knee.

Elastic connective tissue is a form of dense connective tissue in which most of the fibers are the protein elastin. As a result, this tissue is elastic and is found in organs that must stretch, such as the lungs, which expand and recoil as air moves in and out.

CARTILAGE, BONE, ADIPOSE TISSUE, AND BLOOD ARE SPECIALIZED CONNECTIVE TISSUES

Like rubber, **cartilage** is both solid and pliable and is not easily compressed. Its matrix is a blend of collagen and

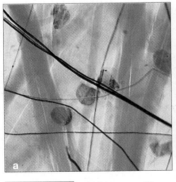
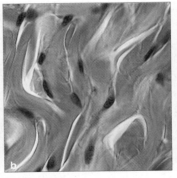
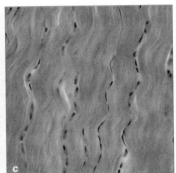
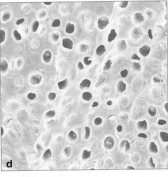

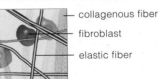
— collagenous fiber
— fibroblast
— elastic fiber

TYPE: Loose connective tissue
DESCRIPTION: Fibroblasts, other cells, plus fibers loosely arranged in semifluid matrix
COMMON LOCATIONS: Under the skin and most epithelia
FUNCTION: Elasticity, diffusion

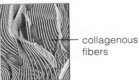
collagenous fibers

TYPE: Dense, irregular connective tissue
DESCRIPTION: Collagenous fibers, fibroblasts, less matrix
COMMON LOCATIONS: In skin and capsules around some organs
FUNCTION: Support

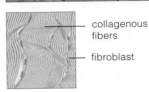
collagenous fibers
fibroblast

TYPE: Dense, regular connective tissue
DESCRIPTION: Collagen fibers in parallel bundles, long rows of fibroblasts, little matrix
COMMON LOCATIONS: Tendons, ligaments
FUNCTION: Strength, elasticity

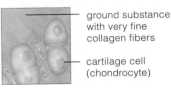
ground substance with very fine collagen fibers
cartilage cell (chondrocyte)

TYPE: Cartilage
DESCRIPTION: Cells embedded in pliable, solid matrix
COMMON LOCATIONS: Ends of long bones, nose, parts of airways, skeleton of embryos
FUNCTION: Support, flexibility, low-friction surface for joint movement

Figure 4.2 *Animated!* Characteristics of connective tissues.

Table 4.2 Connective Tissues at a Glance

Fibrous Connective Tissues

Loose	Collagen and elastin loosely arranged in ground substance; quite flexible and fairly strong
Dense	Mainly collagen; somewhat flexible and quite strong. Collagen fibers are aligned in parallel in the dense connective tissue of tendons and ligaments
Elastic	Mainly elastin; easily stretches and recoils

Special Connective Tissues

Cartilage	Mainly collagen in a watery matrix; resists compression
Bone	Mineral-hardened matrix; very strong
Adipose tissue	Mainly cells filled with fat; soft matrix
Blood	Matrix is the fluid blood plasma, which contains blood cells and other substances

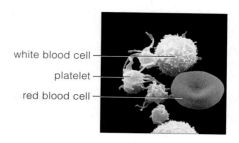

white blood cell
platelet
red blood cell

Figure 4.3 Some components of human blood. This tissue's straw-colored, liquid matrix (plasma) is mostly water in which a variety of substances are dissolved.

elastin fibers in a rubbery ground substance, and the end result is a tissue that can withstand a great deal of physical stress. The collagen-producing cells become trapped inside small cavities in the matrix (Figure 4.2d). Lacking blood vessels, injured cartilage heals slowly.

Most cartilage in the body is whitish, glistening *hyaline cartilage* (hyalin = "glassy"). Hyaline cartilage at the ends of bones reduces friction in movable joints. It also makes up parts of your nose, windpipe (trachea), and ribs. An early embryo's skeleton consists of hyaline cartilage.

Elastic cartilage has both collagen and elastin fibers and it occurs in places where a flexible yet rigid structure is required, such as the flexible outer flaps of your ears. Sturdy and resilient *fibrocartilage* is packed with thick bundles of collagen fibers. It can withstand tremendous pressure, and it forms the cartilage "cushions" in joints such as the knee and in the disks between the vertebrae in the spinal column.

Bone tissue is the main tissue in bones. It is hard because its matrix includes not only collagen fibers and ground substance but also calcium salts (Figure 4.2e). As part of the skeleton our bones serve the body in many ways that you will learn about in Chapter 5.

Adipose tissue stores fat—the way the body deals with carbohydrates and proteins that are not immediately used for metabolism. It is mostly cells packed with fat droplets, with just a little matrix between them (Figure 4.2f). Most of our adipose tissue is located just beneath the skin, where it provides insulation and cushioning.

Blood is classified as connective tissue even though it does not "connect" or bind other body parts. Instead blood's role is transport. Its matrix is the fluid plasma, which contains proteins (blood's "fibers") as well as a variety of blood cells and cell fragments called platelets (Figure 4.3). Chapter 8 discusses this complex tissue.

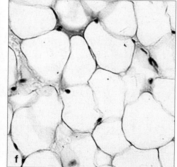

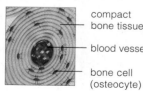

compact bone tissue
blood vessel
bone cell (osteocyte)

nucleus
cell bulging with fat droplet

TYPE: Bone tissue

DESCRIPTION: Collagen fibers, matrix hardened with calcium

COMMON LOCATIONS: Bones of skeleton

FUNCTION: Movement, support, protection

TYPE: Adipose tissue

DESCRIPTION: Large, tightly packed fat cells occupying most of matrix

COMMON LOCATIONS: Under skin, around heart, kidneys

FUNCTION: Energy reserves, insulation, padding

Connective tissue binds together, supports, strengthens, protects, and insulates other body tissues. All connective tissues consist of cells in a matrix that contains protein fibers and a ground substance.

Fibrous connective tissues include loose, dense, and elastic types, depending on the amount and arrangements of collagen and elastin fibers.

Cartilage, bone, blood, and adipose tissue are specialized connective tissues. Cartilage and bone are both structural materials. Blood is specialized to transport substances. Adipose tissue is a reservoir of stored energy.

4.3 Muscle Tissue: Movement

Muscle tissue, another of the four basic tissue types, has contractile cells that are specialized for moving body parts.

The cells in **muscle tissue** contract, or shorten, when they are stimulated by an outside signal; then they relax and lengthen. Muscle tissue has long, cylindrical cells lined up in parallel. This shape is why muscle cells are often called "muscle fibers." Muscle layers—and muscular organs—contract and relax in a coordinated way. This is how the action of muscles maintains and changes the positions of body parts, movements that range from walking to blinking your eyes. The three types of muscle tissue are skeletal, smooth, and cardiac muscle tissues.

Skeletal muscle is located in muscles that attach to your bones (Figure 4.4*a*). In a typical muscle, such as the biceps, skeletal muscle cells are bundled closely together, in parallel. This arrangement makes them look striped, or *striated*. The bundles, called fascicles, are enclosed by a sheath of dense connective tissue. This arrangement of muscle and connective tissue makes up the organs we call "muscles." The structure and function of skeletal muscle tissue are topics we will consider in Chapter 6.

Smooth muscle cells taper at both ends (Figure 4.4*b*). Junctions hold the cells together (Section 4.5), and they are bundled inside a connective tissue sheath. This type of muscle tissue is specialized for steady, controlled contraction. It is found in the walls of internal organs—including blood vessels, the stomach, and the intestines. The contraction of smooth muscle is said to be "involuntary" because we usually cannot make it contract just by thinking about it (as we can with skeletal muscle).

Cardiac muscle (Figure 4.4*c*) is found only in the wall of the heart and its sole function is to pump blood. As you will read in Chapter 9, special junctions fuse the plasma membranes of cardiac muscle cells. In places, communication junctions allow the cells to contract as a unit. When one cardiac muscle cell is signaled to contract, the cells around it contract, too.

Muscle tissue can contract (shorten) in response to stimulation. It helps move the body and its parts.

Skeletal muscle is attached to bones. Smooth muscle is found in internal organs. Cardiac muscle makes up the walls of the heart.

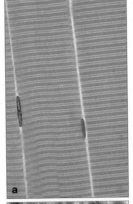

TYPE: Skeletal muscle
DESCRIPTION: Bundles of cylindrical, long, striated contractile cells; many mitochondria; often reflex-activated but can be consciously controlled
LOCATIONS: Partner of skeletal bones, against which it exerts great force
FUNCTION: Locomotion, posture; head, limb movements

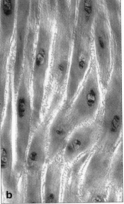

TYPE: Smooth muscle
DESCRIPTION: Contractile cells tapered at both ends; not striated
LOCATIONS: Wall of arteries, sphincters, stomach, intestines, urinary bladder, many other soft internal organs
FUNCTION: Controlled constriction; motility (as in gut); arterial blood flow

TYPE: Cardiac muscle
DESCRIPTION: Unevenly striated, fused-together cylindrical cells that contract as a unit owing to signals at gap junctions between them
LOCATIONS: Heart wall
FUNCTION: Pump blood forcefully through circulatory system

Figure 4.4 *Animated!* Characteristics and examples of skeletal muscle, smooth muscle, and cardiac muscle tissues.

4.4 Nervous Tissue: Communication

Of the four types of tissues in the body, nervous tissue has the most control over how the body responds to changing conditions, both internal and external.

The body's **nervous tissue** consists mostly of cells. They include **neurons**, the "nerve cells," as well as other cells that serve various support functions. There are tens of thousands of neurons in the brain and spinal cord, and millions more are present throughout the body. Because neurons transmit signals called nerve impulses, they make up the body's communication lines.

NEURONS CARRY MESSAGES

Like other kinds of cells, a neuron has a cell body that contains the nucleus and cytoplasm. It also has two types of extensions, or cell "processes." Branched processes called dendrites pick up incoming chemical messages. Outgoing messages are conducted by an axon. Depending on the type of neuron, its axon may be very short, or it may be as long as three or four feet. Figure 4.5a shows cell processes of a motor neuron, which carries signals to muscles and glands.

A cluster of processes from several neurons forms a **nerve**. Nerves conduct messages from the central nervous system (the brain and spinal cord) to muscles and glands. They also carry messages from specialized sensory receptors back to the central nervous system.

NEUROGLIA ARE SUPPORT CELLS

About 90 percent of the cells in the nervous system are **glial cells** (also called **neuroglia**). The word *glia* means glue, and glial cells were once thought to simply be the "mortar" that physically supported neurons. Today we know that they also have other functions. In the central nervous system, glia called astrocytes ("astro" because they are star-shaped; Figure 4.5b) help bring nutrients to neurons and provide physical support. Another type removes debris, microorganisms, or other foreign matter. Outside the brain and spinal cord glia called Schwann cells provide insulation—an extremely important function that helps speed nerve impulses through the body, as described in Chapter 13.

Neurons are the basic units of communication in nervous tissue. Different kinds detect specific stimuli, integrate information, and issue or relay commands for response.

Neuroglia lend structural support to neurons, help nourish and protect them, or provide insulation.

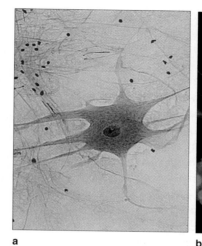
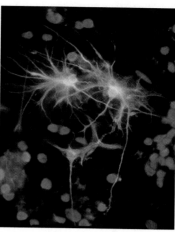

a   b

Figure 4.5 A sampling of the millions of cells in nerve tissue. (**a**) A motor neuron. This type of nerve cell relays signals from the brain or spinal cord to muscles and glands. (**b**) Astrocytes, a type of neuroglia. These and other kinds of neuroglia make up well over half the volume of nerve tissue and provide vital support and other services for neurons.

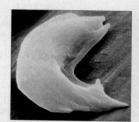

4.5 Cell Junctions: Holding Tissues Together

LINKS TO
SECTIONS
3.3, 3.7, AND 3.8

Junctions between the cells in a tissue have various functions, from stopping leaks, holding a tissue's cells firmly together, and serving as channels for chemical communication.

Our tissues and organs would fall into disarray if there were not some way for individual cells to "stick together" and to communicate. Cell junctions meet these needs, and they can be found in all tissues. These cell-to-cell contacts are particularly common where substances must not leak from one body compartment to another.

Figure 4.6 shows some examples of cell junctions. **Tight junctions** (Figure 4.6*a*) are strands of protein that help stop substances from leaking across a tissue. The strands form gasketlike seals that prevent molecules from moving easily across the junction. In epithelium, for example, tight junctions allow the epithelial cells to control what enters the body. For instance, while food is being digested, various types of nutrient molecules can diffuse into epithelial cells or enter them selectively by active transport, but tight junctions keep those needed molecules from slipping *between* cells. Tight junctions also prevent the highly acidic gastric fluid in your stomach from leaking out and digesting proteins of your own body instead of those you consume in food. Actually, that kind of leakage is what happens in people who have peptic ulcers (Section 7.3).

Adhering junctions (Figure 4.6*b*) cement cells together. One type, sometimes called desmosomes, are like spot welds at the plasma membranes of two adjacent cells. They are anchored to the cytoskeleton in each cell and help hold cells together in tissues that are subject to stretching, such as epithelium of the skin, the lungs, and the stomach. Another type of adhering junction (also called zonula adherens junctions) forms a tight collar around epithelial cells.

Gap junctions (Figure 4.6*c*) are channels that connect the cytoplasm of neighboring cells. They help cells communicate by promoting the rapid transfer of ions and small molecules between them. Gap junctions are most plentiful in smooth muscle and cardiac muscle. As you will read in Chapter 9, ions moving through them from muscle cell to muscle cell play a key role in contraction of whole muscles. In other kinds of tissues gap junctions are the conduits for many kinds of signaling molecules.

Tight junctions between cells help stop leaks in a tissue. Adhering junctions cement cells in a tissue together. Gap junctions serve as channels through which ions and small molecules can move from cell to cell.

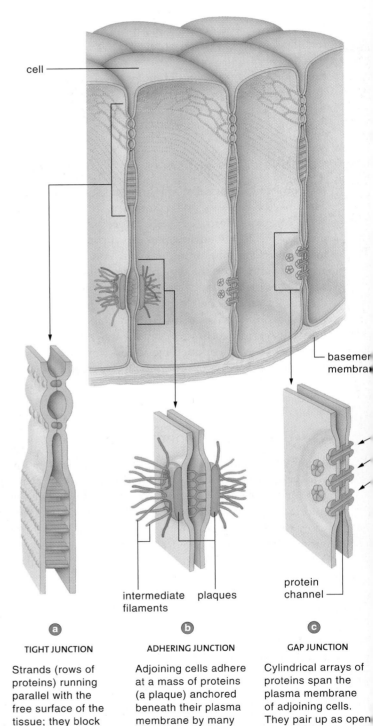

a TIGHT JUNCTION
Strands (rows of proteins) running parallel with the free surface of the tissue; they block leaking between adjoining cells.

b ADHERING JUNCTION
Adjoining cells adhere at a mass of proteins (a plaque) anchored beneath their plasma membrane by many intermediate filaments of the cytoskeleton.

c GAP JUNCTION
Cylindrical arrays of proteins span the plasma membrane of adjoining cells. They pair up as open channels for signals between cells.

Figure 4.6 *Animated!* Cell junctions.

4.6 Tissue Membranes: Thin, Sheetlike Covers

The body's surfaces and cavities are covered by different kinds of thin, sheetlike membranes. Some mainly provide protection, while others both protect and lubricate organs.

A membrane is assigned to one of two categories, depending on its structure. In one group are *epithelial membranes*, while in the second group are *connective tissue membranes*. Here we'll consider some examples of each.

EPITHELIAL MEMBRANES PAIR WITH CONNECTIVE TISSUE

Epithelial membranes consist of a sheet of epithelium atop connective tissue. For instance, consider the body's *mucous membranes*, sometimes called mucosae (singular: mucosa). These are the pink, moist membranes lining the tubes and cavities of your digestive, respiratory, urinary, and reproductive systems (Figure 4.7a). Most mucous membranes are specialized to absorb substances, secrete them, or both. And as you might guess, most mucous membranes, like the lining of the stomach, contain glands, including mucous glands that secrete mucus. Not all do, though. For instance, the mucous membrane lining the urinary tract (including the tubes that carry urine out) has no glands. Later chapters will provide many examples of how mucous membranes protect other tissues and secrete or absorb substances.

Serous membranes are another type of epithelial membrane. These membranes occur in paired sheets; imagine one paper sack inside another, with a narrow space between them, and you'll get the idea. Serous membranes don't have glands, but the layers do secrete a fluid that fills the space between them. Examples include the membranes that line the chest (thoracic) cavity and enclose the heart and lungs. Among other functions, serous membranes help anchor internal organs in place and provide lubricated smooth surfaces that prevent chafing between adjacent organs or between organs and the body wall.

A third type of epithelial membrane is the *cutaneous membrane* (Figure 4.7c). You know this hardy, dry membrane as your skin. Its tissues also are part of one of the body's major organ systems, the integumentary system, which we examine in some detail in Section 4.8.

MEMBRANES IN JOINTS CONSIST OF CONNECTIVE TISSUE

A few membranes in the body have no epithelial cells, only connective tissue. These *synovial membranes* (Figure 4.7d) line the sheaths of tendons and the capsules around certain joints. Cells in the membranes secrete fluid that lubricates the ends of moving bones or prevents friction between a moving tendon and the bone it is attached to.

Epithelial membranes consist of epithelium overlying connective tissue. They line body surfaces, cavities, ducts, and tubes. Different types include mucous and serous membranes and the cutaneous membrane of skin. Most epithelial membranes contain glands and epithelial cells specialized for secretion, absorption, or both.

Connective tissue membranes consist only of connective tissue. They line joint cavities.

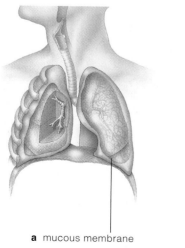

a mucous membrane

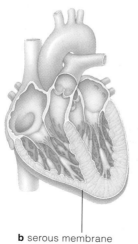

b serous membrane

c cutaneous membrane (skin)

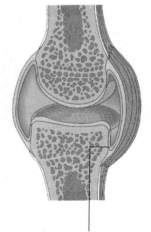

d synovial membrane

Figure 4.7 Examples of membranes in the human body.

4.7 Organs and Organ Systems

LINK TO
SECTION
1.3

Tissues begin to develop in the tiny embryo that arises after conception. With time, development produces organs in eleven organ systems.

An **organ** is a combination of two or more kinds of tissue which together perform one or more functions. The heart, for example, contains all four of the tissue types you have read about in previous sections. Much of the heart's wall is cardiac muscle, and several nerves help regulate the heart's life-sustaining beat. Tough dense connective tissue provides a sturdy outer wrapping, while the heart's chambers are lined with connective tissue and epithelium.

The heart and many other major organs are located inside body cavities shown in Figure 4.8. The figure also lists some terms biologists and medical professionals use to describe the positions of various organs. The **cranial cavity** and **spinal cavity** house your brain and spinal cord—the central nervous system. Your heart and lungs reside in the **thoracic cavity**—essentially, inside your chest. The diaphragm muscle separates the thoracic cavity from the **abdominal cavity**, which holds your stomach, liver, most of the intestine, and other organs. Reproductive organs, the bladder, and the rectum are located in the **pelvic cavity**.

Two or more organs combine to make up each of the body's eleven **organ systems**. Each organ system in turn contributes to the survival of all living cells in the body (Figure 4.9). Does this statement seem like a stretch? After all, how could, say, bones and muscles help each microscopically small cell to stay alive? Yet, interactions between your skeletal and muscular systems allow you to move about—toward sources of nutrients and water, for example. Parts of those systems help keep your blood circulating to cells, as when contractions of leg muscles help move blood in veins back to your heart. Blood inside the circulatory system rapidly carries nutrients and other substances to cells and transports products and wastes away from them. Your respiratory system swiftly delivers oxygen from air to your circulatory system and takes up carbon dioxide wastes from it, skeletal muscles assist the respiratory system—and so it goes, throughout the entire body.

> *The body's organ systems each serve a specialized function that contributes to the survival of all living body cells.*

IMPACTS, ISSUES

Is it possible to grow new organs as replacement parts? Give cells the structural model and nutrients they need, and the tissues they form will assemble into the desired organ—one that will function properly. One success to date is a small artificial bladder, which was grown using cultured muscle and epithelial cells (for the bladder lining). For now, such artificial organs are only experimental, but they are the first steps toward a time when we may be able to grow replacements for aging or diseased hearts and other vital body parts.

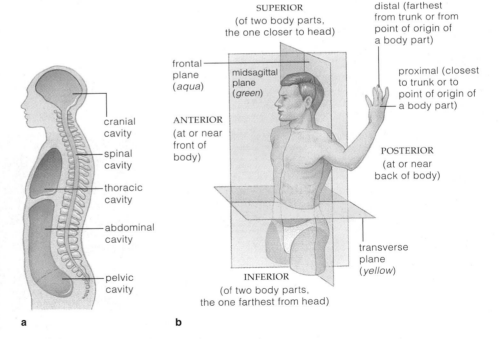

Figure 4.8 *Animated!* (**a**) The major cavities in the human body. (**b**) Directional terms and planes of symmetry for the human body. Notice how the midsagittal plane divides the body into right and left halves. The transverse plane divides it into superior (top) and inferior (bottom) parts. The frontal plane divides it into anterior (front) and posterior (back) parts.

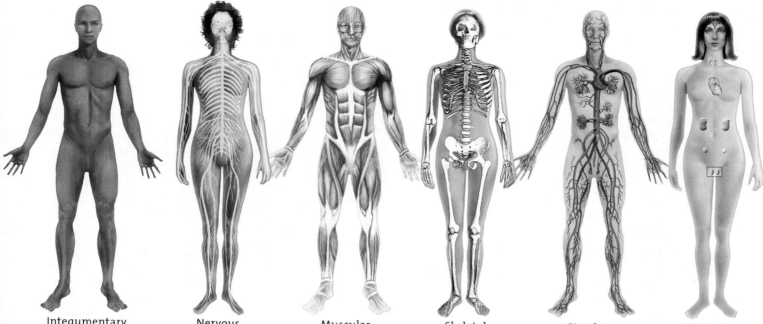

Integumentary System

Protects body from injury, dehydration, and some microbes; controls body temperature; excretes some wastes; receives some sensory information.

Nervous System

Detects external and internal stimuli; controls and coordinates the responses to stimuli; integrates all organ system activities.

Muscular System

Moves body and its parts; maintains posture; generates heat by increasing metabolic activity.

Skeletal System

Supports and protects body parts; provides muscle attachment sites; produces red blood cells; stores calcium, phosphorus.

Circulatory System

Rapidly transports many materials to and from cells; helps stabilize internal pH and temperature.

Endocrine System

Hormonally controls body functioning; works with nervous system to integrate short-term and long-term activities.

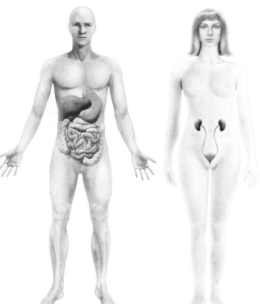

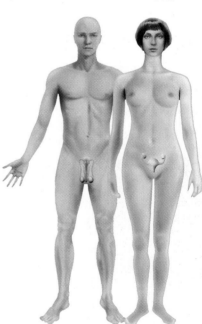

Lymphatic System

Collects and returns tissue fluid to the blood; defends the body against infection and tissue damage.

Respiratory System

Delivers oxygen to all living cells; removes carbon dioxide wastes of cells; helps regulate pH.

Digestive System

Ingests food and water; mechanically, chemically breaks down food and absorbs small molecules into internal environment; eliminates food residues.

Urinary System

Maintains the volume and composition of blood and tissue fluid; excretes excess fluid and blood-borne wastes.

Reproductive System

Female: Produces eggs; after fertilization, affords a protected, nutritive environment for the development of a fetus. *Male:* Produces and transfers sperm to the female. Hormones of both systems also influence other organ systems.

Figure 4.9 *Animated!* Overview of human organ systems and their functions.

 ORGANS AND ORGAN SYSTEMS

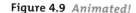

4.8 The Integument—Example of an Organ System

Our integument includes the skin and several other components. The skin itself is the body's largest organ, weighing about 9 pounds in an average-sized adult.

The organ system called the **integument** (from Latin *integere*, "to cover") consists of the skin, oil and sweat glands, hair, and nails. As coverings go, skin is pretty amazing. It holds its shape after years of washing and being stretched, blocks harmful solar radiation, is a barrier to many microbes, holds in moisture, and fixes small cuts and burns. Skin also helps regulate body temperature, and signals from sensory receptors in skin help the brain assess what's going on in the outside world. Yet except for places subjected to regular abrasion (such as the palms of the hands and soles of the feet), your skin is generally not much thicker than a piece of construction paper. It is even thinner in some places, such as the eyelids.

Human skin also makes cholecalciferol, a precursor of vitamin D. Vitamin D is a generic name for steroid-like compounds that help the body absorb calcium from food. When vitamin D made in skin is released into the bloodstream in a hormone-like action, skin exposed to sunlight acts like an endocrine gland.

Figure 4.10 *Animated!* (**a**) The structure of human skin. The dark spots in the epidermis are cells to which melanocytes have passed pigment. (**b**, right): A section through human skin.

EPIDERMIS AND DERMIS ARE THE TWO LAYERS OF SKIN

Skin has an outer **epidermis** and an underlying **dermis**. Sweat glands, oil glands, hair follicles, and toenails and fingernails develop from the epidermal tissue (Figure 4.10). The dermis is mainly dense connective tissue, so it contains elastin fibers that make skin resilient and collagen fibers that make it strong. Together, the epidermis and dermis form the cutaneous membrane you read about in Section 4.6. Below the dermis is a subcutaneous ("under the skin") layer, the hypodermis. This is a loose connective tissue that anchors the skin while allowing it to move a bit. Fat stored in the hypodermis helps insulate the body and cushions some of its parts.

The outer part of the epidermis is a stratified squamous epithelium. Its cells arise in deeper layers and are pushed toward the skin's surface as new cells arise beneath them. (This efficient replacement is one reason why the skin can mend minor damage so quickly.) Due to pressure from the ever-growing cell mass and from normal wear and tear at the surface, older cells are dead and flattened by the time they reach the outer layers. There, they are rubbed off or flake away.

Most cells of the epidermis are **keratinocytes**. These cells make keratin, a tough, water-insoluble protein. By the time they reach the skin surface and have died, all that remain are the keratin fibers inside plasma membranes. This helps make the skin's outermost layer—the stratum corneum—tough and waterproof.

In the deepest layer of epidermis, cells called **melanocytes** produce a brown-black pigment called melanin. The pigment is transferred to keratinocytes and helps give skin its color. A yellow-orange pigment in the dermis, called carotene, also contributes some color. In general, all humans have the same number of melanocytes, but skin color varies due to differences in the distribution and activity of those cells. For example, the pale skin of Caucasians contains only a little melanin, so the pigment hemoglobin inside red blood cells shows through thin-walled blood vessels and the epidermis itself, both of which are transparent. There is more melanin in naturally brown or black skin.

Researchers dream of one day using stem cells to grow organs such as kidneys and hearts. But lab-grown epidermis is a reality. Artificial skin is already available to treat burns and cover unhealed open sores on legs and feet.

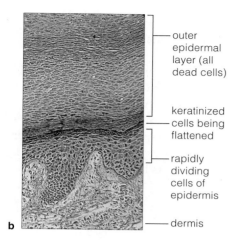

— outer epidermal layer (all dead cells)

— keratinized cells being flattened

— rapidly dividing cells of epidermis

b — dermis

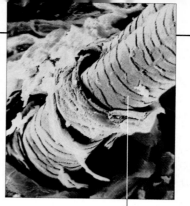

dead, flattened cells of a shaft of hair

Figure 4.11 Close-up of a hair. Dead, flattened hair cells form a tubelike cuticle around the hair shaft.

The epidermis also contains two cell types that help protect the body. *Langerhans cells* are phagocytes ("cell eaters") that engulf bacteria or virus particles, a process that mobilizes the immune system. *Granstein cells* may help control immune responses in the skin.

The dense connective tissue of the dermis makes it quite tough, but this protection has limits. For example, ongoing abrasion—as might happen if you wear a too-tight shoe—separates the epidermis from the dermis, the gap fills with a watery fluid, and you get a blister.

The dermis is laced with small blood vessels and sensitive nerve endings, and hair follicles, sweat glands, and oil glands are embedded in it. On the palms of the hands and soles of the feet it also has ridges that push up corresponding ridges on the epidermis. These ridges loop and curve in the intricate patterns we call fingerprints. The pattern is determined by a person's genes and is different for each of us, even identical twins.

SWEAT GLANDS AND OTHER STRUCTURES ARE DERIVED FROM EPIDERMIS

The body has about 2.5 million sweat glands. The fluid they secrete is 99 percent water; it also contains dissolved salts, traces of ammonia and other wastes, vitamin C, and other substances. A type of sweat gland that is plentiful in the palms of the hands, soles of the feet, forehead, and armpits functions mainly in temperature regulation. Another type is abundant in skin around the genitals. Stress, pain, and sexual foreplay all can increase the amount of sweat they secrete.

Oil glands (or *sebaceous glands*) are everywhere except on the palms and the soles of the feet. The oily substance they release softens and lubricates the hair and skin. Other secretions kill many harmful bacteria. *Acne* is a skin inflammation that develops after bacteria infect the ducts of oil glands.

A **hair** is a flexible structure of mostly keratinized cells, rooted in skin with a shaft above its surface. As cells divide near the base of the root, older cells are pushed upward, then flatten and die. The outermost layer of the shaft consists of flattened cells that overlap like roof shingles (Figure 4.11). These dead cells are what frizz out as "split ends." An average human scalp has about 100,000 hairs. However, the growth and the density of a person's hair are influenced by genes, nutrition, hormones, and stress.

SUNLIGHT PERMANENTLY DAMAGES THE SKIN

Ultraviolet (UV) radiation stimulates the melanin-producing cells of the epidermis. With prolonged sun exposure, melanin levels increase and light-skinned people become tanned. Tanning gives some protection against UV radiation, but over the years, it causes elastin fibers in the dermis to clump together. The skin loses its resiliency and begins to look leathery.

Ultraviolet radiation from sunlight or from the lamps of tanning salons also can activate proto-oncogenes in skin cells (Section 23.2). These genes can trigger cancer, like the squamous cell carcinoma, a common form of skin cancer, shown at right.

Until recently, ozone in the stratosphere intercepted much of the potentially damaging UV radiation that reaches Earth. Today, however—due in large part to human activities described in Chapter 25— the ozone layer over ever-larger regions of the globe is being destroyed faster than natural processes can replace it. The rate of skin cancers now is rapidly increasing.

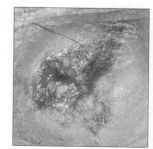

Squamous cell carcinoma

With its layers of keratinized and melanin-shielded epidermal cells, skin helps the body conserve water, limit damage from ultraviolet radiation, and resist mechanical stress. Hairs, oil glands, sweat glands, and other structures associated with skin are derived from epidermis.

4.9 Homeostasis: The Body in Balance

LINKS TO
SECTIONS
1.1 AND 2.7

Cells, tissues, and organs can function properly only when conditions inside the body are stable. Maintaining this stable internal state—homeostasis—demands finely tuned controls.

THE INTERNAL ENVIRONMENT IS A POOL OF EXTRACELLULAR FLUID

The trillions of cells in your body all are bathed in fluid—about 15 liters, or a little less than four gallons. This fluid, called **extracellular** ("outside the cell") **fluid**, is what we mean by the term "internal environment." Much of the extracellular fluid is *interstitial*, meaning that it fills spaces between cells and tissues. The rest is

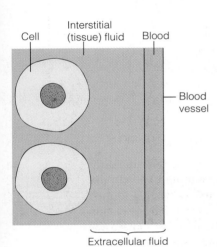

Cell
Interstitial (tissue) fluid
Blood
Blood vessel
Extracellular fluid

blood plasma, the fluid portion of blood. Substances constantly enter and leave interstitial fluid as cells draw nutrients from it and dump their metabolic waste products into it. Those substances can include ions, compounds such as water, and other materials.

All this chemical traffic means that the chemical makeup and volume of extracellular fluid change from moment to moment. If the changes are drastic, they can have drastic effects on cell activities. The number and type of ions in extracellular fluid (such as H^+) are especially crucial, because they must be kept at levels that allow metabolism to continue normally. As you read in Chapter 1, **homeostasis** means "staying the same." The mechanisms of homeostasis operate to maintain stability in the volume and chemical makeup of extracellular fluid.

In maintaining homeostasis, all components of the body work together in the following general way:

- Each cell engages in metabolic activities that ensure its own survival.

- Tissues, which consist of cells, perform one or more activities that contribute to the survival of the whole body.

- Together, the operations of individual cells, tissues, organs, and organ systems help keep the extracellular fluid in a stable state—a state of homeostasis that allows cells to survive.

HOMEOSTASIS REQUIRES THE INTERACTION OF SENSORS, INTEGRATORS, AND EFFECTORS

Three "partners" must interact to maintain homeostasis. They are sensory receptors, integrators, and effectors. **Sensory receptors** are cells or cell parts that can detect a **stimulus**—a specific change in the environment. For a simple example, if someone taps you on the shoulder, there is a change in pressure on your skin. Receptors in the skin translate the stimulus into a signal, which can be sent to the brain. Your brain is an **integrator**, a control point where different bits of information are pulled together in the selection of a response. It can send signals to muscles, glands, or both. Your muscles and glands are **effectors**—they carry out the response, which in this case might include turning your head to see if someone is there. Of course, you cannot keep your head turned indefinitely, because eventually you must eat, use the bathroom, and perform other tasks that maintain body operating conditions.

So how does the brain deal with physiological change? Receptors inform it about how things *are* operating, but the brain also maintains information about how things *should be* operating—that is, information from "set points." When conditions deviate sharply from a set point, the brain brings them back within proper operating range. It does this by sending signals that cause specific muscles and glands to step up or reduce their activity. Set points are important in many physiological mechanisms, including those that influence eating, breathing, thirst, and urination, to name a few.

FEEDBACK MECHANISMS ARE IMPORTANT HOMEOSTATIC CONTROLS

Mechanisms for feedback help keep physical and chemical aspects of the body within tolerable ranges. In

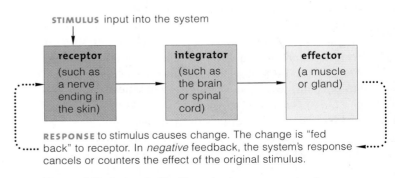

STIMULUS input into the system

| **receptor** (such as a nerve ending in the skin) | **integrator** (such as the brain or spinal cord) | **effector** (a muscle or gland) |

RESPONSE to stimulus causes change. The change is "fed back" to receptor. In *negative* feedback, the system's response cancels or counters the effect of the original stimulus.

Figure 4.12 *Animated!* Three basic components of negative feedback at the organ level.

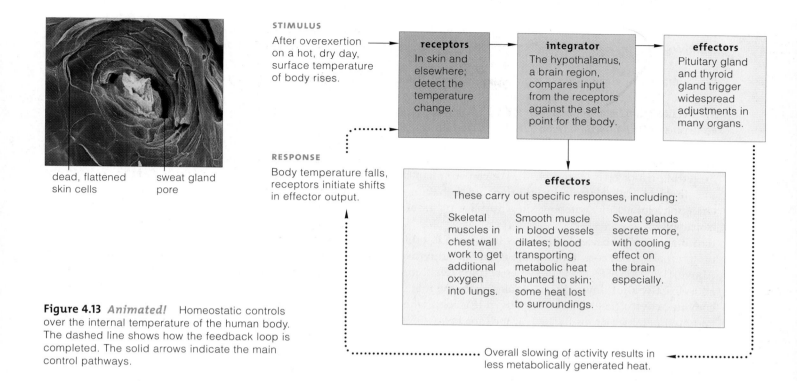

After overexertion on a hot, dry day, surface temperature of body rises.

receptors
In skin and elsewhere; detect the temperature change.

integrator
The hypothalamus, a brain region, compares input from the receptors against the set point for the body.

effectors
Pituitary gland and thyroid gland trigger widespread adjustments in many organs.

RESPONSE
Body temperature falls, receptors initiate shifts in effector output.

effectors
These carry out specific responses, including:

| Skeletal muscles in chest wall work to get additional oxygen into lungs. | Smooth muscle in blood vessels dilates; blood transporting metabolic heat shunted to skin; some heat lost to surroundings. | Sweat glands secrete more, with cooling effect on the brain especially. |

dead, flattened skin cells

sweat gland pore

Figure 4.13 *Animated!* Homeostatic controls over the internal temperature of the human body. The dashed line shows how the feedback loop is completed. The solid arrows indicate the main control pathways.

Overall slowing of activity results in less metabolically generated heat.

negative feedback, an activity alters a condition in the internal environment, and this triggers a response that reverses the altered condition (Figure 4.12). By analogy, think of a furnace with a thermostat. The thermostat senses the air temperature and mechanically compares it to a preset point on a thermometer built into the furnace control system. When the temperature falls below the preset point, the thermostat signals a switch that turns on the heating unit. When the air warms enough to match the preset level, the thermostat signals the switch to shut off the heating unit.

In a similar way, negative feedback helps keep body temperature within a normal range (Figure 4.13). For example, when sensors indicate that the skin is getting too hot while you work outside in the sun, mechanisms kick in that slow both the metabolic activity of cells *and* overall activity levels. You may move less and look for shade. At the same time, blood flow to the skin increases and your sweat glands secrete more sweat. As water in sweat evaporates, your body loses more heat. These and other changes curb the body's heat-producing activities and release excess heat to the surroundings.

In a few situations **positive feedback** operates. In this type of mechanism, a chain of events *intensify* a change from an original condition—and after a limited time, the intensifying feedback reverses the change. There are not many instances of positive feedback in body functions, but one familiar example is childbirth. During labor a fetus exerts pressure on the walls of its mother's uterus. The pressure stimulates the production and secretion of a hormone (oxytocin) that causes the mother's uterine muscles to contract and exert pressure on the fetus, which exerts more pressure on the uterine wall, and so on until the fetus is expelled.

As the body monitors and responds to information about the external world and the internal environment, its organ systems must operate in a coordinated way. In upcoming chapters we will be asking four important questions about how organ systems function:

1. What physical or chemical aspect of the internal environment is each organ system working to maintain as conditions change?

2. How is each organ system kept informed of changes?

3. How does each system process incoming information?

4. What are the responses?

As you will see, all organ systems operate under precise controls of the nervous system and the endocrine system.

Homeostatic control mechanisms maintain the physical and chemical characteristics of the internal environment within ranges that are favorable for cell operations.

4.10 How Homeostatic Feedback Maintains the Body's Core Temperature

Controls over the body's core temperature provide good examples of negative feedback loops.

We humans are **endotherms**, which means "heat from within." The body's **core temperature**—the temperature of the head and torso—is about 37°C, or 98.6°F. It is controlled mainly by metabolic activity, which produces heat, and by negative feedback loops. These homeostatic controls adjust physiological responses for conserving or getting rid of heat (Figure 4.14). We can supplement the physiological controls by altering our behavior—changing clothes or switching on a furnace or an air-conditioner.

Metabolism produces heat. If that heat were to build up internally, your core temperature would steadily rise. Above 41°C (105.8°F), some enzymes become denatured and virtually shut down. By the same token, the rate of enzyme activity generally *decreases* by at least half when body temperature drops by 10°F. If it drops below 35°C (95°F), you are courting danger. As enzymes lose their ability to function, your heart will not beat as often or as effectively, and heat-generating mechanisms such as shivering stop. At this low core temperature breathing

slows, so you may lose consciousness. Below 80°F the human heart may stop beating entirely. Given these stark physiological facts, humans require mechanisms that help maintain the core body temperature within narrow limits.

RESPONSES TO COLD STRESS

Table 4.3 summarizes the major responses to cold stress. They are governed by the **hypothalamus**, a centrally located structure in the brain that includes both neurons and endocrine cells. When the outside temperature drops, thermoreceptors (*thermo-* means heat) at the body surface detect the decrease. When their signals reach the hypothalamus, neurons command smooth muscle in the walls of arterioles in the skin to contract. The resulting **peripheral vasoconstriction** reduces blood flow to capillaries near the body surface, so your body retains heat. For example, when your fingers or toes get cold, as much as 99 percent of the blood that would otherwise flow to your skin is diverted.

In the **pilomotor response** to a drop in outside temperature, your body hair can "stand on end." This

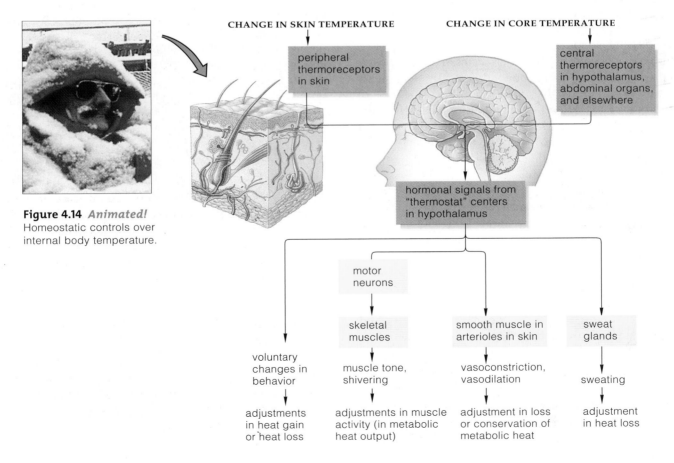

Figure 4.14 *Animated!*
Homeostatic controls over internal body temperature.

Table 4.3	Summary of Human Responses to Cold Stress and to Heat Stress		
Environmental Stimulus	**Main Responses**	**Outcome**
Drop in temperature	Vasoconstriction of blood vessels in skin; pilomotor response; behavior changes (e.g., putting on a sweater)	Heat is conserved
	Increased muscle activity; shivering; nonshivering heat production	More heat is produced
Rise in temperature	Vasodilation of blood vessels in skin; sweating; changes in behavior; heavy breathing	Heat is dissipated from body
	Reduced muscle activity	Less heat is produced

happens because smooth muscle controlling the erection of body hair is stimulated to contract. This creates a layer of still air close to the skin that reduces heat losses. (This response is most effective in mammals with more body hair than humans!) Heat loss can be restricted even more by behaviors that reduce the amount of body surface exposed for heat exchange, as when you put on a sweater or hold your arms tightly against your body.

When other responses can't counteract cold stress, signals from the hypothalamus step up skeletal muscle contractions, similar to the low-level contractions that produce muscle tone. The result? You start shivering. Your skeletal muscles contract ten to twenty times per second, boosting heat production throughout the body.

Prolonged or severe exposure to cold can lead to a hormonal response that elevates the rate of metabolism in cells. This *nonshivering heat production* is especially notable in a specialized type of adipose tissue called "brown fat." Heat is generated as the lipid molecules are broken down. Babies (who can't shiver) have this tissue in the neck and armpits and near their kidneys; adults have little brown fat unless they are cold-adapted.

In *hypothermia*, body core temperature falls below the normal range. A drop of only a few degrees leads to mental confusion; further cooling can lead to coma and death. Some victims of extreme hypothermia, mainly children, have survived prolonged immersion in ice-cold water. One reason is that mammals, including humans, have a dive reflex. When the body is submerged, the heart rate slows and blood is shunted to the brain and other vital organs.

Freezing often destroys tissues, a condition we call *frostbite*. Frozen cells may be saved if thawing is precisely controlled. This sometimes can be done in a hospital.

RESPONSES TO HEAT STRESS

Table 4.3 also summarizes the main responses to heat stress. When core temperature rises above a set point, the hypothalamus again orders key responses. In **peripheral vasodilation**, its signals cause blood vessels in the skin to dilate. More blood flows to the skin, where the excess heat that the blood carries is dissipated.

Evaporative heat loss also can be influenced by the hypothalamus, which can activate sweat glands. There are roughly 2.5 million sweat glands in skin, and lots of heat is dissipated when the water in sweat evaporates. With prolonged heavy sweating the body also loses key salts, especially sodium chloride. Losing too many electrolytes can make you feel woozy. People who exercise heavily may consume "sports drinks" that replenish electrolytes.

Sometimes peripheral blood flow and evaporative heat loss can't adequately counter heat stress. The result is *hyperthermia*, in which the core temperature rises above normal. If the increase isn't too great, a person can suffer *heat exhaustion*, in which blood pressure drops due to vasodilation and water losses from heavy sweating. The skin feels cold and clammy, and the person may collapse.

When heat stress is severe enough to completely break down the body's temperature controls, *heat stroke* occurs. Sweating stops, the skin becomes dry, and the core body temperature rapidly rises to a level that can be lethal.

When someone has a fever, the hypothalamus has reset the "thermostat" that dictates what the body's core temperature will be. The normal response mechanisms are brought into play, but they are carried out to maintain a higher temperature.

When a fever starts, heat production increases, heat loss drops, and the person feels chilled. When a fever "breaks," peripheral vasodilation and sweating increase as the body tries to restore the normal core temperature; then you feel warm. The controlled increase in core temperature during a fever seems to enhance the body's immune response, so using fever-reducing drugs such as aspirin or ibuprofen may actually interfere with fever's beneficial effects. A severe fever, however, requires medical supervision because of the dangers it poses.

The hypothalamus governs responses that regulate the body's core temperature.

Physiological responses to cold stress include constriction of blood vessels near the body surface, the pilomotor response, shivering, and sometimes nonshivering heat production.

Responses to heat stress include dilation of peripheral blood vessels and evaporative heat loss.

Summary

Introduction A tissue is a group of similar cells that perform a common function (Table 4.4). Different tissues combine in certain proportions and patterns to form an organ. In an organ system, two or more organs interact in ways that contribute to the body's survival.

Section 4.1 Epithelial tissues cover external body surfaces and line internal cavities and tubes. Each kind of epithelium has one surface exposed to body fluids or the external environment; the opposite surface rests on a basement membrane sandwiched between it and an underlying connective tissue.

Glands are derived from epithelium. A gland is a cell or a multicellular structure that makes and secretes a specific substance such as saliva. Exocrine glands release substances onto the surface of an epithelium through ducts or tubes. This contrasts with endocrine glands, which secrete substances (hormones) directly into extracellular fluid.

Section 4.2 Connective tissues bind together, support, strengthen, protect, and insulate other tissues. Most have fibers of structural proteins (especially collagen), fibroblasts, and other cells within a matrix. They include fibrous connective tissue and specialized connective tissues such as cartilage, bone, adipose tissue, and blood.

Section 4.3 Muscle tissue contracts (shortens) and then returns to the resting position. It helps move the body or its parts. The three types of muscle tissue are skeletal muscle, smooth muscle, and cardiac muscle.

Section 4.4 Nervous tissue receives and integrates information from inside and ouside the body and sends signals for responses. Neurons are the basic units of the nervous system; they have extensions (axons) that form nerves. Neuroglia (glial cells) are accessory cells of the nervous system. They physically support and help nourish neurons, among other functions.

Section 4.5 Tight junctions help prevent substances from leaking across a tissue. Adhering junctions bind cells together in tissues. Gap junctions link the cytoplasm of neighboring cells.

 Compare the structure and functions of the main types of cell junctions.

Section 4.6 Membranes cover body surfaces and cavities. Those made of epithelium include mucous and serous membranes. Most mucous membranes have glands that secrete mucus; serous membranes help anchor organs and secrete lubricating fluid onto their surfaces. Connective tissue membranes include the synovial membranes of certain joints. The skin is a cutaneous membrane.

Section 4.7 Body organs are located in five major cavities: the cranial cavity (brain); spinal cavity (spinal cord); thoracic cavity (heart and lungs); abdominal cavity (stomach, liver, most of the intestine, other organs); and pelvic cavity (reproductive organs, bladder, rectum). The various organs in the body are arranged into eleven organ systems. Each system performs a specific function, such as transporting blood (cardiovascular system) or reproduction.

 Investigate the function of organ systems and learn about terms used to describe their locations.

Section 4.8 An example of an organ system is the integument, or skin. Skin has an outer epidermis and an underlying dermis. Most epidermal cells are keratinocytes, which make the protein keratin. Keratin makes the skin's outer layer tough and waterproof. Melanocytes in the epidermis produce pigment that gives skin its color. Hair, nails, sweat glands, and oil glands are derived from the epidermis.

Skin protects the rest of the body from abrasion, invading bacteria, ultraviolet radiation, and dehydration. It helps control internal temperature, contains cells that synthesize vitamin D, and serves as a blood reservoir for the rest of the body. Receptors in skin are essential for detecting environmental stimuli.

 Explore the structure of skin and hair.

Section 4.9 Extracellular fluid, which consists of blood and tissue fluid, is the body's internal environment. Tissues, organs, and organ systems work together to maintain the stable state of homeostasis in this fluid environment. Maintaining homeostasis requires sensory receptors, which can detect a stimulus, integrators, and effectors.

Feedback controls help maintain internal conditions. In negative feedback, a change in a condition triggers a response that reverses the change. In positive feedback, a response reverses a change in a condition by intensifying the change for a limited time.

Section 4.10 Physiological responses that govern temperature rely on negative feedback controls that respond to heat stress and cold stress.

 See how negative feedback helps regulate body temperature.

Table 4.4   Summary of Basic Tissue Types in the Human Body

Tissue	Function	Characteristics
Epithelium	Covers body surface; lines internal cavities and tubes	One free surface; opposite surface rests on basement membrane supported by connective tissue
Connective tissue	Binds, supports, adds strength; some provide protection or insulation	Cells surrounded by a matrix (ground substance) containing structural proteins except in blood
FIBROUS CONNECTIVE TISSUES		
Loose	Elasticity, diffusion	Cells and fibers loosely arranged
Dense	Support. elasticity	Several forms. One has collagen fibers in various orientations in the matrix; it occurs in skin and as capsules around some organs Another form has collagen fibers in parallel bundles; it occurs in ligaments, tendons
Elastic	Elasticity	Mainly elastin fibers; occurs in organs and that must stretch
SPECIALIZED CONNECTIVE TISSUES		
Cartilage	Support, flexibility, low-friction surface	Matrix solid but pliable; no blood supply
Bone	Support, protection, movement	Matrix hardened by minerals
Adipose tissue	Insulation, padding, energy storage	Soft matrix around large, fat-filled cells
Blood	Transport	Liquid matrix (plasma) containing blood cells, many other substances
Muscle tissue	Movement of the body and its parts	Made up of arrays of contractile cells
Nervous tissue	Communication between body parts; coordination, regulation of cell activity	Made up of neurons and support cells (neuroglia)

Review Questions

1. List the general characteristics of epithelium, and then describe the various types of epithelial tissues in terms of specific characteristics and functions.

2. List the major types of connective tissues; add the names and characteristics of their specific types.

3. Identify and describe the tissues shown below.

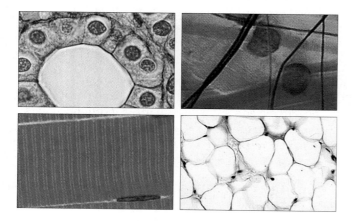

4. List the types of cell junctions and their functions.

5. List the basic types of membranes in the body.

6. What is the difference between a tissue, an organ, and an organ system? From memory, try to make a list of the eleven major organ systems of the human body.

7. What are some functions of skin?

8. Define homeostasis.

9. What is extracellular fluid, and how does the concept of homeostasis pertain to it?

10. What is the difference between negative feedback and positive feedback? What role do these mechanisms play in maintaining homeostasis?

Self-Quiz

Answers in Appendix V

1. _____ tissues have closely linked cells and one free surface.
   - a. Muscle
   - b. Nerve
   - c. Connective
   - d. Epithelial

2. Most _____ has collagen and elastin fibers.
   - a. muscle tissue
   - b. nervous tissue
   - c. connective tissue
   - d. epithelial tissue

3. _____, a specialized connective tissue, is mostly plasma with cellular components and various dissolved substances.
   - a. Irregular connective tissue
   - b. Blood
   - c. Cartilage
   - d. Bone

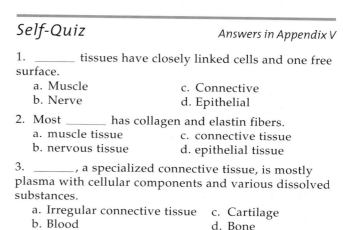

4. _____ tissue detects and integrates information about changes and controls responses to changes.
   a. Muscle   c. Connective
   b. Nervous   d. Epithelial

5. _____ can shorten (contract).
   a. Muscle tissue   c. Connective tissue
   b. Nervous tissue   d. Epithelial tissue

6. After you eat too many carbohydrates and proteins, your body converts the excess to storage fats, which accumulate in _____.
   a. loose connective tissue   c. adipose tissue
   b. dense connective tissue   d. both b and c

7. In _____, physical and chemical aspects of the body are being kept within tolerable ranges by controlling mechanisms.
   a. positive feedback   c. homeostasis
   b. negative feedback   d. metastasis

8. Fill in the blanks: _____ detect specific environmental changes, an _____ pulls different bits of information together in the selection of a response, and _____ carry out the response.

9. Match the concepts:
   ____ muscles and glands   a. integrating center
   ____ positive feedback   b. reverses an altered condition
   ____ sites of body receptors
   ____ negative feedback   c. eyes and ears
   ____ brain   d. effectors
       e. intensifies the original condition

Critical Thinking

1. In people who have the genetic disorder anhidrotic ectodermal dysplasia, patches of tissue have no sweat glands. What kind of tissue are we talking about?

2. The disease called scurvy results from a deficiency of vitamin C, which the body uses to synthesize collagen. Explain why scurvy sufferers tend to lose teeth, and why any wounds heal much more slowly than normal, if at all.

3. The man pictured in Figure 4.15 wears several dozen ornaments in his skin, nearly all of them applied by piercing. Among the skin's many functions, it serves as a

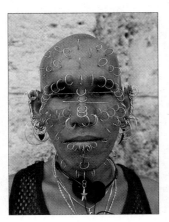

Figure 4.15 An example of heavy body piercing.

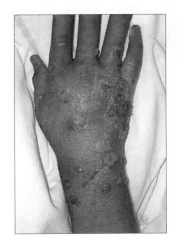

Figure 4.16 Ulcers and blisters that form on the skin of a person affected by porphyria after exposure to sunlight.

barrier to potentially dangerous bacteria, and some people object to extensive body piercing on the grounds that it opens the door to infections. Explain why you do or don't agree with this objection.

4. Porphyria, a genetic disorder, occurs in about 1 in 25,000 individuals. Affected people lack enzymes of a metabolic pathway that forms heme, the iron-containing group in hemoglobin. Accumulating porphyrins, which are intermediates in the pathway, cause awful symptoms, especially after exposure to sunlight. Lesions and scars form on the skin (Figure 4.16). Thick hair grows on the face and hands. The gums retreat and the canine teeth can begin to look like fangs. Symptoms worsen if the affected person consumes alcohol or garlic. Individuals with porphyria can avoid sunlight and aggravating substances. They also can get injections of heme from normal red blood cells. If you are familiar with vampire stories, which date from even before the Middle Ages, can you think of a reason why they may have evolved among people who knew nothing of the cause of porphyria?

Explore on Your Own

As epithelium, your skin contains fibers of collagen and elastin. These structural proteins have different properties that you can see in action when you pull on a patch of skin, such as on the back of your hand. Notice that even if you pull firmly, the skin doesn't tear; which type of protein fiber gives it that tensile strength? Which type returns the skin to its original shape when you let go?

5 THE SKELETAL SYSTEM

Creaky Joints

Whether you're 18 or 80, you probably have or will develop some degree of osteoarthritis—a disorder in which joints become painfully stiff because their cartilage lining is breaking down or bone spurs have formed there. Disease, sports injuries, obesity, and simple aging cause creaky joints, and common remedies range from nonprescription pain relievers and cartilage-building supplements to injections of steroid drugs. Severely affected joints often are replaced with high-tech artificial ones.

A lot of arthritis sufferers also are exploring less conventional "treatments." Gullible ones eat ground-up cartilage from sharks or baby chicks. Botanicals—herbs and exotic plant extracts—also are finding customers eager to find relief for their symptoms.

There is a long menu of nontraditional, plant-based arthritis remedies, including evening primrose oil, ginger, devil's claw, feverfew, and an Indian herb called ashwaghanda. Do such substances work? Well, in 1998 researchers at a meeting of the American College of Rheumatology reported the results of a carefully designed study of 90 people with

osteoarthritis. Of patients who used botanicals suggested by Ayurveda, the traditional medicine of India, half improved, compared to only one-fifth of patients who received a placebo. Findings were similar in a study that tested the same herbal formula on patients with rheumatoid arthritis.

Critics pointed out that this research was sponsored by a company that sells the herbs. Also, the two types of arthritis involved have different causes and symptoms. How could one "therapy" treat both? In general, no authoritative scientific basis has been established for the purported health effects of many herbal remedies.

Arthritis research introduces this chapter's topic, the **skeletal system**—the skeleton along with cartilages, joints, and straplike ligaments that hold our bones together. As you will learn, your bones are not just a sturdy framework for your soft flesh. They partner with muscles to bring about movement and have an essential role in maintaining the body's calcium balance.

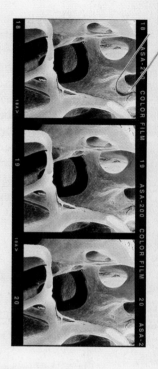

☑ *How Would You Vote?* Should claims about "medicinal" exotic plant extracts have to be backed up by independent scientific testing? Cast your vote online at www.thomsonedu.com/biology/starr/humanbio.

 ## Key Concepts

THE STRUCTURE AND FUNCTIONS OF BONES
Bones are built of bone tissue. They store minerals, protect and support soft organs, and function in body movement. Some bones contain marrow where blood cells develop.

THE SKELETON
The skeleton's key function is to serve as the body's strong internal framework. Its 206 bones are organized into two parts, the axial skeleton and the appendicular skeleton.

JOINTS
At joints, different bones touch or are in close contact. Some of these connections permit adjoining bones to move in ways that in turn move body parts, such as the limbs.

BONES UNDER SIEGE
Disorders that affect our bones can upset homeostasis by impairing normal bone functions, such as aiding movement.

 ## Links to Earlier Concepts

With this chapter we begin a survey of the body's eleven organ systems. As you study the skeletal system, you will learn more about the structure and functions of bone tissue, cartilage, and some other connective tissues (4.2) that are major components of the system.

Chapter 1 introduced the concept of homeostasis, and Section 4.9 gave you an overview of mechanisms that help maintain this internal stability. Although courses in human biology usually consider each organ system in turn, it is important to keep in mind that at every moment all of your organ systems are contributing to the survival of the amazingly complex whole that is you.

5.1 Bone—Mineralized Connective Tissue

LINK TO
SECTION
4.2

We begin our look at the skeletal system with bone tissue, the hardened connective tissue that makes up our bones.

Bone is a connective tissue, so it is a blend of living cells and a matrix that contains fibers. Bones are covered by a sturdy two-layer membrane called the periosteum (meaning "around the bone"). The membrane's outer layer is dense connective tissue and the inner layer contains bone cells called **osteoblasts** ("bone formers"). As bone develops, the osteoblasts secrete collagen and some elastin, as well as carbohydrates and other proteins. With time, this matrix around osteoblasts hardens when salts of the mineral calcium are deposited in it. The osteoblasts are trapped in spaces, or lacunae, in the matrix (*lacuna* = hole). At this point their bone-forming function ends and they are called **osteocytes** (*osteo* = bone; *cyte* = cell).

The minerals in bone tissue make it hard, but it is the collagen that gives our bones the strength to withstand the mechanical stresses associated with activities such as standing, lifting, and tugging.

THERE ARE TWO KINDS OF BONE TISSUE

Bones contain two kinds of tissue, compact bone and spongy bone. Figure 5.1 shows where these tissues are in a long bone such as the femur (thighbone). As its name suggests, **compact bone** is a dense tissue that looks solid and smooth. In a long bone, it forms the bone's shaft and the outer part of its two ends. A cavity inside the shaft contains bone marrow.

Compact bone tissue forms in thin, circular layers around small central canals. Each set of layers is called an **osteon** (or sometimes a *Haversian system*). The canals connect with each other and serve as channels for blood vessels and nerves that transport substances to and from osteocytes. Osteocytes also extend slender cell processes into narrow channels called canaliculi that run between lacunae. These "little canals" allow nutrients to move through the hard matrix from osteocyte to osteocyte. Wastes can be removed the same way.

The bone tissue *inside* a long bone's shaft and at its ends looks like a sponge. Tiny, flattened struts are fused together to make up this **spongy bone** tissue, which looks lacy and delicate but actually is quite firm and strong.

A BONE DEVELOPS ON A CARTILAGE MODEL

An early embryo has a rubbery skeleton that consists of cartilage and membranes. Yet, after only about two months of life in the womb, this flexible framework is transformed into a bony skeleton. Once again, we can look at the development of a long bone as an example.

As you can see at the top of Figure 5.2, a cartilage "model" provides the pattern for each long bone. Once the outer membrane is in place on the model, the bone-forming osteoblasts become active and a bony "collar" forms around the cartilage shaft. Then the cartilage inside the shaft calcifies, and blood vessels, nerves, and elements including osteoblasts begin to infiltrate the forming bone. Soon, the marrow cavity forms and osteoblasts produce the matrix that will become mineralized with calcium.

Each end of a long bone is called an epiphysis (e-PIF-uh-sis). As long as a person is growing, each epiphysis is separated from the bone shaft by an *epiphyseal plate* of cartilage. Human growth hormone (GH) prevents the plates from calcifying, so the bone can lengthen. When

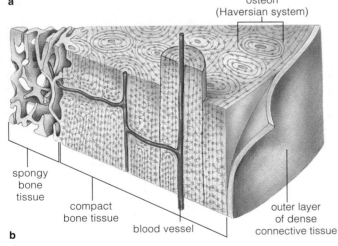

space occupied by living bone cell

blood vessel

compact bone tissue

spongy bone tissue

a

osteon (Haversian system)

spongy bone tissue

compact bone tissue

blood vessel

outer layer of dense connective tissue

b

Figure 5.1 *Animated!* (**a**) Spongy and compact bone tissue in a femur. (**b**) Thin, dense layers of compact bone tissue form interconnected arrays around canals that contain blood vessels and nerves. Each array is an osteon (Haversian system). The blood vessel threading through it transports substances to and from osteocytes, living bone cells in small spaces (lacunae) in the bone tissue. Small tunnels called canaliculi connect neighboring spaces.

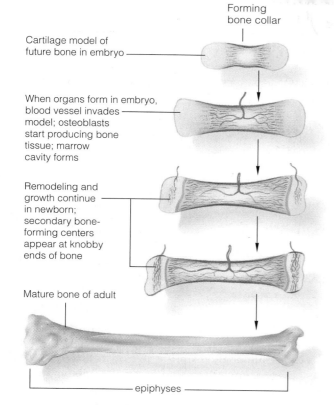

Forming bone collar

Cartilage model of future bone in embryo

When organs form in embryo, blood vessel invades model; osteoblasts start producing bone tissue; marrow cavity forms

Remodeling and growth continue in newborn; secondary bone-forming centers appear at knobby ends of bone

Mature bone of adult

epiphyses

Figure 5.2 *Animated!* How a long bone forms. First, osteoblasts begin to function in a cartilage model in the embryo. The bone-forming cells are active first in the shaft, then at the knobby ends. In time, cartilage is left only in the epiphyses at the ends of the shaft.

growth stops, usually in the late teens or early twenties, bone replaces the cartilage plates.

BONE TISSUE IS CONSTANTLY "REMODELED"

Calcium is constantly entering and leaving a person's bones. Calcium is deposited when osteoblasts form bone, and it is withdrawn when "bone breaker" cells called **osteoclasts** break down the matrix of bone tissue. This ongoing calcium recycling is called **bone remodeling**, and it has several important functions.

Regularly breaking down "old" bone and replacing it with fresh tissue helps keep bone resilient, so it is less likely to become brittle and break. When a bone is subjected to mechanical stress, such as load-bearing exercise, the remodeling process is adjusted so that more bone is deposited than removed. That is why the bones of regular exercisers are denser and stronger than the bones of couch potatoes. On the other hand, when the body must heal a broken bone, osteoclasts release more calcium than usual from bone matrix. Osteoblasts then use the calcium to repair the injured bone tissue.

A child's body requires lots of calcium to meet the combined demands of bone growth and other needs for the calcium stored in bones. Along with dietary calcium, remodeling helps meet the demand. For example, the diameter of a growing child's thighbones increases as

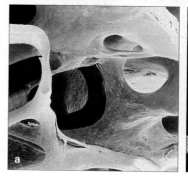
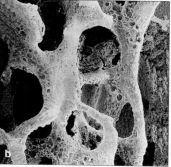

Figure 5.3 Osteoporosis. (**a**) Normal bone tissue. (**b**) After the onset of osteoporosis, replacements of mineral ions lag behind withdrawals. In time the tissue erodes, and the bone becomes hollow and brittle.

osteoblasts form bone at the surface of each shaft. At the same time, however, osteoclasts break down a small amount of bone tissue *inside* the shaft. Thus the child's thighbones become thicker and stronger to support the increasing body weight, but they don't get too heavy.

Bone remodeling also plays a key role in maintaining homeostasis of the blood level of calcium. Neither our nervous system nor our muscles can function properly unless the blood level of calcium stays within a narrow range. When the level falls below this range, a hormone called PTH stimulates osteoclasts to break down bone and release calcium to the blood. If the level rises too high, another hormone, calcitonin, stimulates osteoblasts to *deposit* calcium in bone tissue. Notice that this control mechanism is an example of negative feedback. You will read more about it in Chapter 15, when we take a closer look at hormones.

As we age, bone tissue may break down faster than it is renewed. This progressive deterioration is called *osteoporosis* (Figure 5.3). When it occurs, the backbone, pelvis (hip bones), and other bones lose mass. Osteoporosis is most common in women past menopause, although men can be affected, too. Deficiencies of calcium and sex hormones, smoking, and a sedentary lifestyle all may contribute to osteoporosis. On the other hand, getting lots of exercise (to stimulate bone deposits) and taking in plenty of calcium can help minimize bone loss. Drug treatments can slow or even help reverse the bone loss.

IMPACTS, ISSUES

Mechanical stress prompts the body to form new bone. Hence, regular load-bearing exercise can help stave off osteoporosis. New experiments with mice have shown that osteoblasts that have a particular type of estrogen receptor slow or boost their bone-forming activity depending on the loads a bone bears. Now studies are probing whether osteoporosis in aging humans may be related to the loss of these estrogen receptors. If so, finding a way to replace them is a promising target for future research.

Bone tissue, including both compact bone and spongy bone, consists of living cells and a nonliving mineralized matrix.

Bones grow, become strong, and are repaired through the process of bone remodeling.

5.2 The Skeleton: The Body's Bony Framework

LINKS TO
SECTIONS
4.3 AND 5.1

We associate body movements with muscles, but muscles can't do the job alone. The force of contraction must be applied against something else. The skeleton fills the bill.

The skeleton consists mainly of bones. From ear bones no larger than a watch battery to massive thighbones, bones vary in size and shape. Some bones, like the thighbone in Figure 5.4, are long and slender. Other bones, like the ankle bones, are short. Still other bones, including the sternum (breastbone), are flat, and still others, such as spinal vertebrae, are "irregular." All bones are alike in some ways, however. They all contain bone tissue and other connective tissue that lines their surfaces and internal cavities. At joints there is cartilage where one bone meets or "articulates" with another. Other tissues associated with bones include nervous tissue and epithelium, which occurs in the walls of blood vessels that carry substances to and from bones.

Long bones and some other bones have cavities that contain **bone marrow**, a connective tissue where blood cells are formed. With time, the red marrow in most long bones is replaced by fatty yellow marrow. For this reason, most of an adult's blood cells form in red bone marrow in irregular bones, such as the hip bone, and in flat bones, such as the sternum. If a person loses a great deal of blood, yellow marrow in long bones can convert to red marrow, which makes red blood cells.

Table 5.1 Functions of Bone
1. **Movement**. Bones interact with skeletal muscles to maintain or change the position of body parts.
2. **Support**. Bones support and anchor muscles.
3. **Protection**. Many bones form hard compartments that enclose and protect soft internal organs.
4. **Mineral storage**. Bones are a reservoir for calcium and phosphorus. Deposits and withdrawals of these mineral ions help to maintain their proper concentrations in body fluids.
5. **Blood cell formation**. Some bones contain marrow where blood cells are produced.

THE SKELETON: A PREVIEW

A fully formed human skeleton has 206 bones, which grow by way of remodeling until a person is about twenty. The bones are organized into an **axial skeleton** and an **appendicular skeleton** (Figure 5.5). The bones of the axial skeleton form the body's vertical, head-to-toe axis. The appendicular ("hanging") skeleton includes bones of the limbs, shoulders, and hips. **Ligaments** connect bones at joints. Ligaments are composed of elastic connective tissue, so they are stretchy and resilient like thick rubber bands. **Tendons** are cords or straps that attach muscles to bones or to other muscles. They are built of connective tissue packed with collagen fibers, which make tendons strong.

BONE FUNCTIONS ARE VITAL IN MAINTAINING HOMEOSTASIS

It can be easy to take our bones for granted simply as girders that support our soft, rather squishy flesh, but in fact bones are complex organs that contribute to homeostasis in many ways (Table 5.1). For instance, bones that support and anchor skeletal muscles help maintain or change the positions of our body parts. Some form hard compartments that enclose and protect other organs; for example, the skull encloses and protects the brain, and the rib cage protects the lungs. As noted in Section 5.1, bones also serve as a "pantry" where the body can store calcium. Because the calcium in bone is in the form of the compound calcium phosphate, bone also is a storage depot for phosphorus.

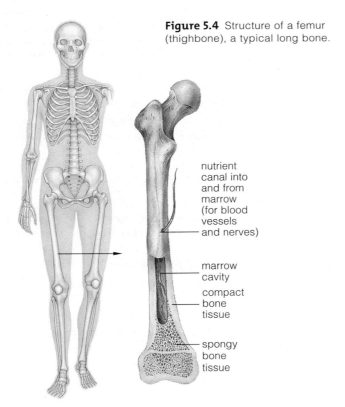

Figure 5.4 Structure of a femur (thighbone), a typical long bone.

nutrient canal into and from marrow (for blood vessels and nerves)

marrow cavity

compact bone tissue

spongy bone tissue

The fully formed human skeleton consists of 206 bones, in axial and appendicular divisions.

Bones contribute to homeostasis by providing body support, enabling movement, storing minerals, and in some cases, producing blood cells in marrow.

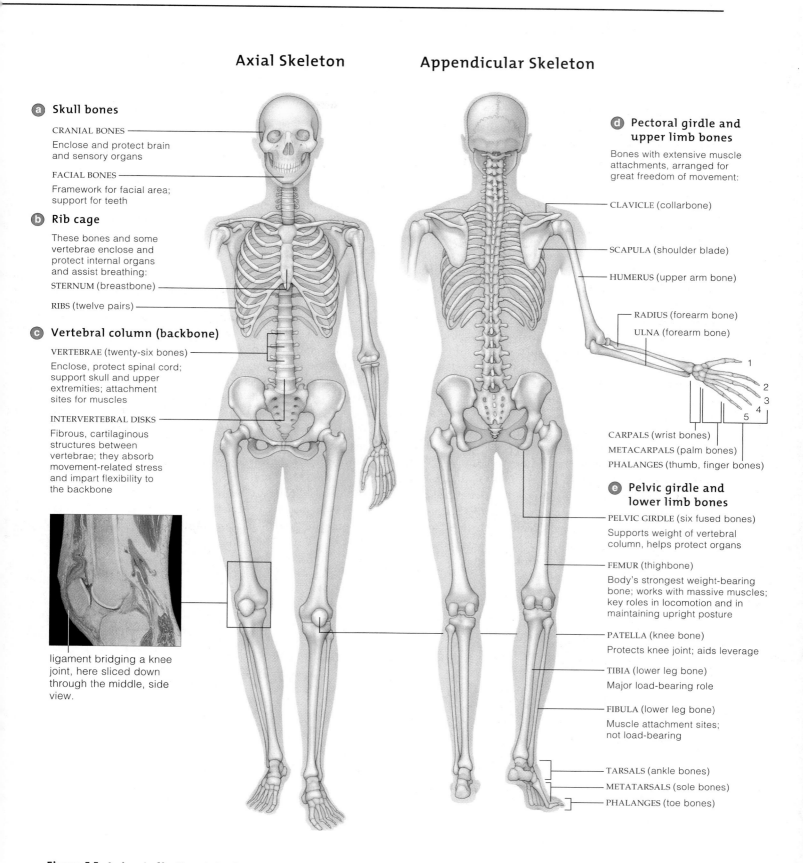

Axial Skeleton

Appendicular Skeleton

a) Skull bones

CRANIAL BONES —

Enclose and protect brain and sensory organs

FACIAL BONES —

Framework for facial area; support for teeth

b) Rib cage

These bones and some vertebrae enclose and protect internal organs and assist breathing:

STERNUM (breastbone) —

RIBS (twelve pairs) —

c) Vertebral column (backbone)

VERTEBRAE (twenty-six bones) —

Enclose, protect spinal cord; support skull and upper extremities; attachment sites for muscles

INTERVERTEBRAL DISKS —

Fibrous, cartilaginous structures between vertebrae; they absorb movement-related stress and impart flexibility to the backbone

ligament bridging a knee joint, here sliced down through the middle, side view.

d) Pectoral girdle and upper limb bones

Bones with extensive muscle attachments, arranged for great freedom of movement:

CLAVICLE (collarbone)

SCAPULA (shoulder blade)

HUMERUS (upper arm bone)

RADIUS (forearm bone)

ULNA (forearm bone)

1
2
3
4
5

CARPALS (wrist bones)

METACARPALS (palm bones)

PHALANGES (thumb, finger bones)

e) Pelvic girdle and lower limb bones

PELVIC GIRDLE (six fused bones)

Supports weight of vertebral column, helps protect organs

FEMUR (thighbone)

Body's strongest weight-bearing bone; works with massive muscles; key roles in locomotion and in maintaining upright posture

PATELLA (knee bone)

Protects knee joint; aids leverage

TIBIA (lower leg bone)

Major load-bearing role

FIBULA (lower leg bone)

Muscle attachment sites; not load-bearing

TARSALS (ankle bones)

METATARSALS (sole bones)

PHALANGES (toe bones)

Figure 5.5 *Animated!* The skeletal system. The blue-tinged areas are cartilage.

5.3 The Axial Skeleton

The axial skeleton supports much of our body weight and protects many internal organs.

We begin our tour of the skeleton with bones of the axial skeleton—the skull, vertebral column (backbone), ribs, and sternum (the breastbone).

THE SKULL PROTECTS THE BRAIN

Did you know that your skull consists of more than two dozen bones? These bones are divided into several groups, and while by tradition many of them have names derived from Latin, their roles are simple to grasp. For example, one grouping, the "cranial vault," or **brain case**, includes eight bones that together surround and protect your brain. As Figure 5.6*a* shows, the *frontal bone* makes up the forehead and upper ridges of the eye sockets. It contains **sinuses**, which are air spaces lined with mucous membrane. Sinuses make the skull lighter, which translates into less weight for the spine and neck muscles to support. But passages link them to the upper respiratory tract—and their ability to produce mucus can mean misery for anyone who has a head cold or pollen allergies. Bacterial infections in the nasal passages can spread to the sinuses, causing *sinusitis*. Figure 5.6*c* shows sinuses in the cranial and facial bones.

Temporal bones form the lower sides of the cranium and surround the ear canals, which are tunnels that lead to the middle and inner ear. Inside the middle ear are tiny bones that function in hearing (Chapter 14). On either side of your head, in front of each temporal bone, a *sphenoid bone* extends inward to form part of the inner eye socket.

The *ethmoid bone* also contributes to the inner socket and helps support the nose. Two *parietal bones* above and behind the temporal bones form a large part of the skull; they sweep upward and meet at the top of the head. An *occipital bone* forms the back and base of the skull and also encloses a large opening, the *foramen magnum* ("large hole"). Here, the spinal cord emerges from the base of the brain and enters the spinal column (Figure 5.6*b*). Several passageways run through and between various skull bones for nerves and blood vessels, especially at the base of the skull. For instance, the jugular veins, which carry blood leaving the brain, pass through openings between the occipital bone and each temporal bone.

FACIAL BONES SUPPORT AND SHAPE THE FACE

Figure 5.6 also shows facial bones, many of which you can easily feel with your fingers. The largest is your lower jaw, or **mandible**. The upper jaw consists of two *maxillary bones*. Two *zygomatic bones* form the middle of the hard bumps we call "cheekbones" and the outer parts of the eye sockets. A small, flattened *lacrimal bone* fills out the inner eye socket. Tear ducts pass between this bone and the maxillary bones and drain into the nasal cavity—one reason why your nose runs when you cry. Tooth sockets in the upper and lower jaws also contain the teeth.

Palatine bones make up part of the floor and side wall of the nasal cavity. (Extensions of these bones, together with the maxillary bones, form the back of the hard palate, the "roof" of your mouth.) A *vomer bone* forms part of the nasal septum, a thin "wall" that divides the nasal cavity into two sections.

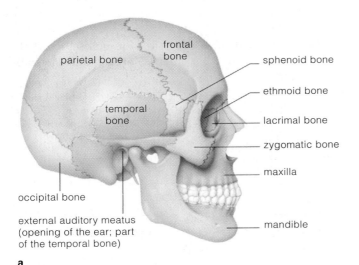

a

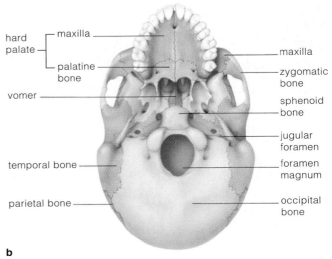

b

Figure 5.6 The skull. (**a**) The irregular junctions between different bones are called sutures. (**b**) An "inferior," or bottom-up, view of the skull. The large foramen magnum is situated atop the uppermost cervical vertebra. (**c**) Sinuses in bones in the skull and face.

THE VERTEBRAL COLUMN IS THE BACKBONE

The flexible, curved human vertebral column—your backbone or spine—extends from the base of the skull to the hip bones (pelvic girdle). This arrangement transmits the weight of a person's torso to the lower limbs. As a result, people who gain a large amount of excess weight may develop problems with their knees and ankles because those joints are not designed to bear such a heavy load. The **vertebrae** are stacked one on top of the other. They have bony projections that form a protected channel for the delicate spinal cord. As sketched in Figure 5.7, humans have seven *cervical* vertebrae in the neck, twelve thoracic vertebrae in the chest area, and five *lumbar* vertebrae in the lower back. During the course of human evolution, five other vertebrae have become fused to form the sacrum, and another four have become fused to form the coccyx, or "tailbone." Counting these, there are thirty-three vertebrae in all.

Roughly a quarter of your spine's length consists of **intervertebral disks**—compressible pads of fibrocartilage sandwiched between vertebrae. The disks serve as shock absorbers and flex points. They are thickest between cervical vertebrae and between lumbar vertebrae. Severe or rapid shocks, as well as changes due to aging, can cause a disk to *herniate* or *"slip."* If the slipped disk ruptures, its jellylike core may squeeze out, making matters worse. And if the changes compress neighboring nerves or the spinal cord, the result can be excruciating pain and the loss of mobility that often comes with pain. Depending on the situation, treatment can range from bed rest and use of painkilling drugs to surgery.

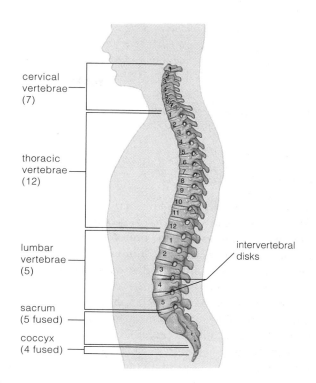

Figure 5.7 Side view of the vertebral column or backbone. The cranium balances on the column's top vertebra.

cervical vertebrae (7)
thoracic vertebrae (12)
lumbar vertebrae (5)
intervertebral disks
sacrum (5 fused)
coccyx (4 fused)

THE RIBS AND STERNUM SUPPORT AND HELP PROTECT INTERNAL ORGANS

In addition to protecting the spinal cord, absorbing shocks, and providing flexibility, the vertebral column also serves as an attachment point for twelve pairs of **ribs**, which in turn function as a scaffolding for the body cavity of the upper torso. The upper ribs also attach to the paddle-shaped **sternum** (see Figure 5.5). As you will read in later chapters, this rib cage helps protect the lungs, heart, and other internal organs and is vitally important in breathing.

While the axial skeleton provides basic body support and helps protect internal organs, many movements depend on interactions of skeletal muscles with the bones of the appendicular skeleton—the skeletal component we turn to next.

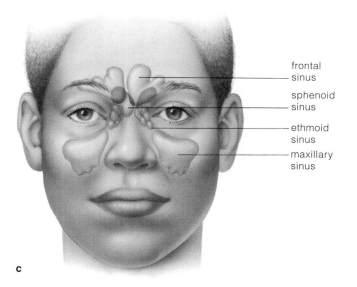

frontal sinus
sphenoid sinus
ethmoid sinus
maxillary sinus

c

> Bones of the axial skeleton make up the body's vertical axis. They include the skull (and facial bones), the vertebral column, and the ribs and sternum.
>
> Intervertebral disks between the vertebrae absorb shocks and serve as flex points.

5.4 The Appendicular Skeleton

"Append" means to hang, and the appendicular skeleton includes the bones of body parts that we sometimes think of as dangling from the main body frame.

The bones of your arms, hands, legs, and feet are all parts of the appendicular skeleton. It also includes a pectoral girdle at each shoulder and the pelvic girdle at the hips.

THE PECTORAL GIRDLE AND UPPER LIMBS PROVIDE FLEXIBILITY

Each **pectoral girdle** (Figure 5.8) has a large, flat shoulder blade—a **scapula**—and a long, slender collarbone, or **clavicle,** that connects to the breastbone (sternum). The rounded shoulder end of the **humerus**, the long bone of the upper arm, fits into an open socket in the scapula. Your arms can move in a great many ways; they can swing in wide circles and back and forth, lift objects, or tug on a rope. Such freedom of movement is possible because muscles only loosely attach the pectoral girdles and upper limbs to the rest of the body. Although the arrangement is sturdy enough under normal conditions, it is vulnerable to strong blows. Fall on an outstretched arm and you might fracture your clavicle or dislocate your shoulder. The collarbone is the bone most frequently broken.

Each of your upper limbs includes thirty separate bones. The humerus connects with two bones of the forearm—the **radius** (on the thumb side) and the **ulna** (on the "pinky finger" side). The upper end of the ulna joins the lower end of the humerus to form the elbow joint. The bony bump sometimes (mistakenly) called the "wrist bone" is the lower end of the ulna.

The radius and ulna join the hand at the wrist joint, where they meet eight small, curved *carpal* bones. Ligaments attach these bones to the long bones. Blood vessels, nerves, and tendons pass in sheaths over the wrist; when a blow, constant pressure, or repetitive movement (such as typing) damages these tendons, the result can be a painful disorder called *carpal tunnel syndrome* (Section 5.6). The bones of the hand, the five *metacarpals*, end at the knuckles. *Phalanges* are the bones of the fingers.

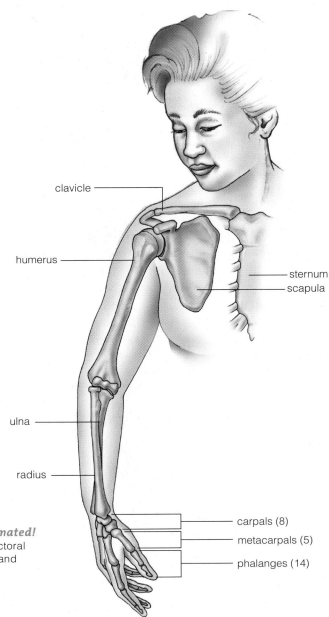

Figure 5.8 *Animated!*
Bones of the pectoral girdle, the arm, and the hand.

clavicle

humerus

sternum

scapula

ulna

radius

carpals (8)

metacarpals (5)

phalanges (14)

THE PELVIC GIRDLE AND LOWER LIMBS SUPPORT BODY WEIGHT

For most of us, our shoulders and arms are much more flexible than our hips and legs. Why? Although there are similarities in the basic "design" of both girdles, this lower part of the appendicular skeleton is adapted to bear the body's entire weight when we are standing. The **pelvic girdle** (Figure 5.9) is much more massive than the combined pectoral girdles, and it is attached to the axial skeleton by extremely strong ligaments. It forms an open basin: A pair of *coxal bones* attach to the lower spine (sacrum) in back, then curve forward and meet at the *pubic arch*. ("Hipbones" are actually the upper *iliac* regions of the coxal bones.) This combined structure is the *pelvis*. In females the pelvis is broader than in males, and it shows other structural differences that are evolutionary adaptations for childbearing. A forensic scientist or paleontologist examining skeletal remains can easily establish the sex of the deceased if a pelvis is present.

The legs contain the body's largest bones. In terms of length, the thighbone, or **femur**, ranks number one. It is also extremely strong. When you run or jump, your femurs routinely withstand stresses of several tons per square inch (aided by contracting leg muscles). The femur's ball-like upper end fits snugly into a deep socket in the coxal (hip) bone. The other end connects with one of the bones of the lower leg, the thick, load-bearing *tibia* on the inner (big toe) side. A slender *fibula* parallels the tibia on the outer (little toe) side. The tibia is your shinbone. A triangular kneecap, the patella, helps protect the knee joint. In spite of this protection, knees are among the joints most often damaged by athletes, both amateur and professional.

The ankle and foot bones correspond closely to those of the wrist and hand. *Tarsal* bones make up the ankle and heel, and the foot contains five long bones, the *metatarsals*. The largest metatarsal, leading to the big toe, is thicker and stronger than the others to support a great deal of body weight. Like fingers, the toes contain phalanges.

> The appendicular skeleton includes bones of the limbs, a pectoral girdle at the shoulders, and a pelvic girdle at the hips.
>
> The thighbone (femur) is the largest bone in the body and one of the strongest. The wrists and hands and ankles and feet have corresponding sets of bones known respectively as carpals and metacarpals and tarsals and metatarsals.

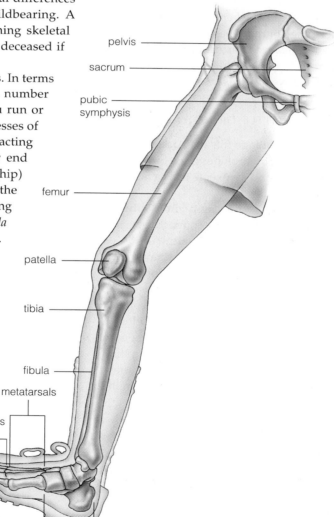

pelvis

sacrum

pubic symphysis

femur

patella

tibia

fibula

metatarsals

phalanges

tarsals

Figure 5.9 *Animated!*
Bones of the pelvic girdle, the leg, and the foot.

IMPACTS, ISSUES

A common sports-related knee injury is tearing of the ACL—the anterior cruciate ligament, which connects the tibia to the femur at the center of the knee. At Tufts University, researchers are developing a new process for repairing the damage. Using a bioreactor, they coax stem cells from the patient's bone marrow into developing into ligament tissue, which forms as the cells infiltrate a strand of silk. The new ligament can then be transplanted. Recovery time is less than half that of standard ACL repair procedures.

5.5 Joints—Connections between Bones

Joints are areas of contact or near contact between bones. Each of the various types of joints has some form of connective tissue that bridges the gap between bones.

SYNOVIAL JOINTS MOVE FREELY

In the most common type of joint, called a **synovial joint**, adjoining bones are separated by a cavity (Figure 5.10). The articulating ends of the bones are covered with a cushioning layer of cartilage, and they are stabilized by ligaments. A capsule of dense connective tissue surrounds the bones of a synovial joint. Cells that line the inner surface of the capsule secrete a lubricating *synovial fluid* into the joint cavity.

Synovial joints are built to allow movement. In hinge-like synovial joints such as the knee and elbow, the motion is limited to simple flexing and extending (straightening). The ball-and-socket joints at the hips are capable of a wider range of movements: They can rotate and move in different planes—for instance, up-down or side-to-side. Figure 5.11 shows these and some other ways body parts can move at joints.

OTHER JOINTS MOVE LITTLE OR NOT AT ALL

In a **cartilaginous joint**, cartilage fills the space between bones, so only slight movement is possible. Such joints occur between vertebrae and between the breastbone and some of the ribs.

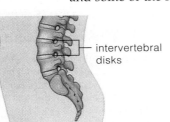

intervertebral disks

There is no cavity in a **fibrous joint**, and fibrous connective tissue unites the bones. An adult's fibrous joints generally don't allow movement. Examples are the fibrous joints that hold your teeth in their sockets. In a fetus, fibrous joints loosely connect the flat skull bones. During childbirth, these loose connections allow the bones to slide over each other, preventing skull fractures. A newborn baby's skull still has fibrous joints and soft areas called fontanels. With time the joints harden into *sutures*. Much later in life the skull bones may fuse completely.

> *A joint connects one bone to another. In all joints, connective tissue bridges the gap between bones.*
>
> *Freely movable (synovial) joints include the hinge-like knee joint and the ball-and-socket joints at the hips.*
>
> *Cartilaginous joints have cartilage in the space between bones. They allow only slight movement. In fibrous joints fibrous connective tissue joins the bones.*

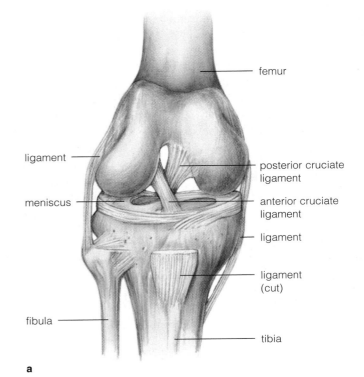

ligament —
meniscus —
fibula —

femur
posterior cruciate ligament
anterior cruciate ligament
ligament
ligament (cut)
tibia

a

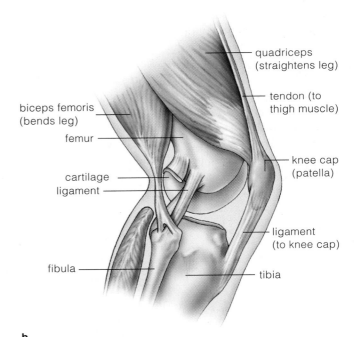

biceps femoris (bends leg)
femur
cartilage
ligament
fibula

quadriceps (straightens leg)
tendon (to thigh muscle)
knee cap (patella)
ligament (to knee cap)
tibia

b

Figure 5.10 The knee joint, an example of a synovial joint. The knee is the largest and most complex joint in the body. Part (**a**) shows the joint with muscles stripped away; in (**b**) you can see where muscles such as the quadriceps attach.

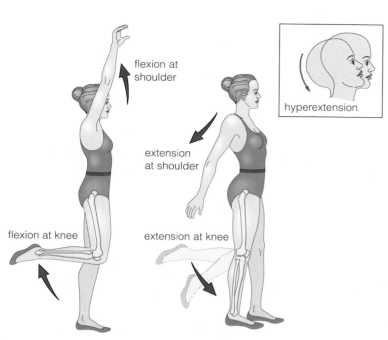

a **flexion and extension**
Flexion reduces the angle between two bones, while extension increases it. Hyperextension, as when you tip your head back, increases the angle beyond 180°.

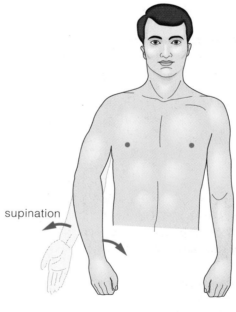

b **circumduction** (*above*) **and rotation** (*right*)
In circumduction a limb traces an imaginary cone. Rotation moves a body part around its axis.

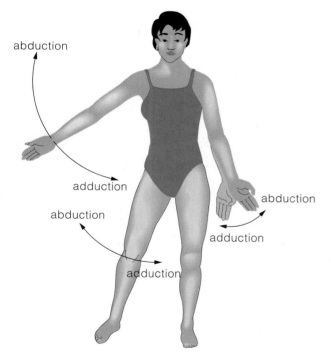

c **abduction and adduction**
Abduction moves a limb away from the body's midline; adduction moves a limb toward the midline or beyond it.

d **supination and pronation**
In supination forearm bones rotate so that the palms face outward; in pronation the rotation turns the palms to the rear.

e gliding movement between carpals

Figure 5.11 (**a–e**) Ways body parts move at synovial joints. The synovial joint at the shoulder permits the greatest range of movement.

5.6 Disorders of the Skeleton

When a part of the skeleton is injured or affected by disease, impaired movement is the likely result.

INFLAMMATION IS A FACTOR IN SOME SKELETAL DISORDERS

Excessive wear on a joint is the hallmark of *osteoarthritis*. This kind of wear happens when years of use, mechanical stress, or disease wears away the cartilage covering the bone ends of freely movable joints. Often, the arthritic joint is painfully inflamed, and surgeons now routinely replace seriously arthritic hips, knees, and shoulders. Another degenerative joint condition, *rheumatoid arthritis*, results when a person's immune system malfunctions and mounts an attack against tissues in the affected joint. Then, the synovial membrane becomes inflamed and thickens, cartilage is eroded away, and the bones fall out of proper alignment (Figure 5.12). With time the bone ends may even fuse together.

Repetitive movements also can cause inflammation when they damage the soft tissue associated with joints. *Tendinitis*, the underlying cause of conditions such as "tennis elbow," develops when tendons and synovial membranes around joints such as the elbow, shoulders, and fingers become inflamed.

Today one of the most common repetitive motion injuries is *carpal tunnel syndrome*. The "carpal tunnel" is a slight hollow between a wrist ligament and the underside of the wrist's eight carpal bones (see Figure 5.8). Squeezed into this tunnel are several tendons and a nerve that services parts of the hand. Chronic overuse, such as long hours typing at a computer keyboard, can inflame the tendons. When the swollen tendons press on the nerve, the result can be pain, numbness, and tingling in fingers. Simply avoiding the offending motion can help relieve carpal tunnel syndrome. In more serious cases injections of an anti-inflammatory drug are helpful. Sometimes, however, the wrist ligament must be surgically cut to relieve the pressure.

JOINTS ALSO ARE VULNERABLE TO STRAINS, SPRAINS, AND DISLOCATIONS

Synovial joints such as our knees, hips, and shoulders get a lot of use, so it's not surprising that they are vulnerable to mechanical stresses. Stretch or twist a joint suddenly and too far, and you *strain* it. Do something that makes a small tear in its ligaments or tendons and you will have a *sprain*. In fact, a sprained ankle is the most common joint injury. Sprains hurt mainly because of swelling and bleeding from broken small blood vessels. Applying cold (such as an ice pack, 30 minutes on, then 30 minutes off) for the first 24 hours will minimize these effects; after that, doctors usually advise applying heat, such as a hot

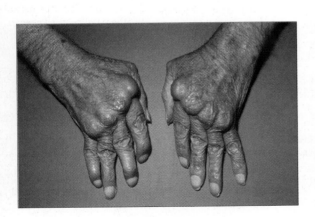

Figure 5.12 Hands affected by rheumatoid arthritis.

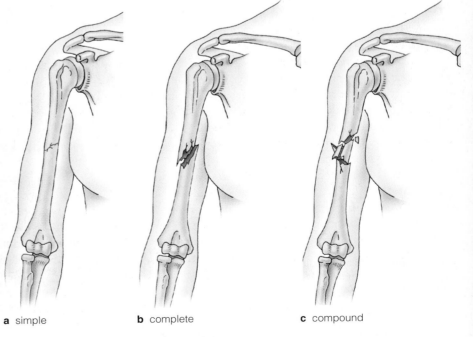

a simple **b** complete **c** compound

Figure 5.13 Three types of bone fractures.

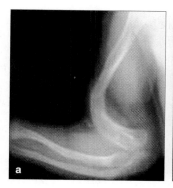

Figure 5.14 Effects of *osteogenesis imperfecta* (OI). (**a**) An X-ray of an arm bone deformed by OI. (**b**) Tiffany has OI. She was born with multiple fractures in her arms and legs. By age six, she had undergone surgery to correct more than 200 bone fractures and to place steel rods in her legs. Every three months she receives intravenous infusions of an experimental drug that may help strengthen her bones.

pad. The warmth speeds tissue repair by increasing blood circulation to the injured tissue.

A blow can *dislocate* a joint—that is, the two bones will no longer be in contact. During collision sports such as football, a blow to a knee often tears a ligament. If the torn part is not reattached within ten days, phagocytic cells in the knee joint's synovial fluid will attack and destroy the damaged tissue.

IN FRACTURES, BONES BREAK

Injuries severe enough to dislocate a joint also often break one or both of the bones involved. Regardless of the cause, most breaks can be classed as either a simple fracture, a complete fracture, or a compound fracture. As you can probably tell from the drawings in Figure 5.13, a simple fracture is the least serious injury; it is really only a crack in a bone. A complete fracture, in which the bone separates into two pieces and the surrounding soft tissue is damaged, is more serious. Even worse is a compound fracture, in part because broken ends or shards of bone puncture the skin, creating an open wound and the chance of infection. It also may be difficult or impossible for a surgeon to reattach all the pieces of a bone that has been shattered in this way.

When a bone breaks into pieces, the situation demands prompt medical attention. Unless the pieces are soon reset into their normal alignment, it's unlikely that the bone will heal properly. Its functioning may be impaired for the rest of a person's life. Today, in addition to the pins and casts that may be used to hold healing bones in place, the injured area may be stimulated with electricity, a procedure that speeds healing.

Overall, injuries to joints and bones tend to heal faster when we're younger. Aging, and bad habits such as smoking cigarettes, slow the body's ability to repair itself.

OTHER BONE DISORDERS INCLUDE GENETIC DISEASES, INFECTIONS, AND CANCER

Some skeleton disorders are inherited, and a few cause lifelong difficulties for affected people. An example is *osteogenesis imperfecta* or OI (Figure 5.14). In this disease the collagen in bone tissue is defective. As a result, the bones are exceptionally brittle and break easily. Children with OI often have stunted growth and must endure repeated hospitalizations to have fractures set. In some cases where the disease has not been detected early, an affected child's parents have been wrongly suspected of child abuse. Unfortunately, there is no cure for OI, but researchers are looking for ways to improve bone strength in affected individuals.

Our bones and bone marrow also can become infected by bacteria when an infection elsewhere spreads (via the bloodstream) or when the microbe enters an open wound. A heavy dose of antibiotics usually can cure the problem, although severe cases may require surgery to clean out the affected bone tissue.

Bone cancer, or *osteosarcoma*, can strike people young and old. It usually occurs in a long bone in an arm or leg, or in a joint such as the hip or knee. Unfortunately, bone cancer spreads rapidly to other organs. The first sign may be a painful swelling, and the most common treatment is to remove the affected bone tissue by amputating the limb involved. Like many other cancers, however, if caught early bone cancer often is curable.

IMPACTS, ISSUES

In this replacement knee joint a projection of the joint has been fitted into the end of the patient's femur (*center*) and another projection has been fitted into the tibia below. The hatlike disk at the upper left attaches to the patella—the kneecap. With technological advances, today it may take only about 2 hours to replace a knee joint, even less for a hip. After surgery, walking and standing put stress on the new joint, so the patient's osteoblasts generate new bone that grows into pits on the prosthesis. With normal use and proper care, a new knee or hip may last decades.

Summary

Section 5.1 Bones are organs. In addition to bone tissue, they include other types of connective tissue, nervous tissue, and epithelial tissue (in the walls of blood vessels).

A bone develops as osteoblasts secrete collagen fibers and a matrix of protein and carbohydrate. The matrix eventually surrounds each osteoblast and hardens (mineralizes) as calcium salts are deposited in it. The mature living bone cells, osteocytes, are located inside spaces (lacunae) in the bone tissue.

Bone tissue has both compact bone and spongy bone. Denser compact bone is organized as thin, circular layers called osteons. Small canals through the layers are channels for nerves and blood vessels. In spongy bone, needlelike struts are fused together in a latticework.

A cartilage model provides the pattern for a developing bone. Long bones lengthen at their ends (epiphyses). This process stops by early adulthood. Until then, a cartilage plate separates each epiphysis from the bone shaft. The plates are replaced by bone when growth ends.

Bones grow, gain strength, and are repaired by bone remodeling. In this process, osteoblasts deposit bone and osteoclasts break it down. Hormones largely control bone remodeling.

 Look inside a human femur.

Section 5.2 Bones are the main elements of the skeleton and function in movement by interacting with skeletal muscles. Bones also store minerals and help protect and support other body parts. Ligaments connect bones at joints; tendons attach muscles to bones or to other muscles.

Some bones, including the sternum, hip bones, and femur, contain bone marrow. Blood cells are produced in red bone marrow.

Section 5.3 The skeleton is divided into an axial portion and an appendicular portion (Table 5.2). The axial skeleton forms the body's vertical axis and is a central support structure. In the spine, intervertebral disks of fibrocartilage are shock pads and flex points.

Eight skull bones form the brain case, which protects the brain. The skull's frontal bone contains sinuses—air spaces that make the skull lighter in weight. The mandible (lower jaw) is the largest facial bone.

 Explore the parts of the human skeleton.

Section 5.4 The appendicular skeleton—including limb bones, the pelvic girdle, and pectoral girdles—

Table 5.2 Review of the Skeleton

FUNCTIONS OF BONE:

1. *Movement.* Interact with skeletal muscles to maintain or change the position of body parts.

2. *Support.* Support and anchor muscles.

3. *Protection.* Many bones form hard compartments that enclose and protect soft internal organs.

4. *Mineral storage.* Reservoir for mineral ions, which are deposited or withdrawn and so help maintain ion concentrations in body fluids.

5. *Blood cell formation.* Some bones contain red marrow, where blood cells are produced.

PARTS OF THE SKELETON:

Appendicular portion
Pectoral girdles: clavicle and scapula
Arm: humerus, radius, ulna
Wrist and hand: carpals, metacarpals, phalanges (of fingers)
Pelvic girdle (6 fused bones at the hip)
Leg: femur (thighbone), patella, tibia, fibula
Ankle and foot: tarsals, metatarsals, phalanges (of toes)

Axial portion
Skull: cranial bones and facial bones
Rib cage: sternum (breastbone) and ribs (12 pairs)
Vertebral column: vertebrae (26)

provides support for upright posture and interacts with skeletal muscles in most movements. Major bones of each pectoral girdle are a scapula (shoulder blade) and a clavicle (collarbone). The long bone of the upper arm, the humerus, connects at its top end with the scapula. The other end of the humerus connects with the two major bones of the lower arm, the radius and ulna.

At the hips, bones of the pelvic girdle form the pelvis. Each coxal bone of the pelvis articulates with the upper end of the femur, the longest bone in the body. Major bones of the lower leg are the tibia and fibula. The wrists and hands and ankles and feet have corresponding sets of bones.

Section 5.5 Together with skeletal muscles, the skeleton works like a system of levers in which rigid rods (bones) move about at fixed points (joints). In a synovial joint, a fluid-filled cavity separates adjoining bones. Such joints are freely movable. In cartilaginous joints, cartilage fills the space between bones and allows only slight movements. In fibrous joints, there is no cavity, and fibrous connective tissue unites the bones.

Section 5.6 Diseases and disorders that affect the skeletal system can impair movement and hamper other functions of bones that help maintain homeostasis.

Review Questions

1. Describe the basic elements of bone tissue.

2. What are the two types of bone tissue, and how are they different?

3. Describe how bone first develops.

4. Explain why bone remodeling is important, and give its steps.

5. How do bones contribute to homeostasis?

6. Name the two main divisions of the skeleton.

7. How does a tendon differ from a ligament?

8. What is the function of intervertebral disks? What are they made of?

9. What is a joint?

10. Name at least two different synovial joints. What is the defining feature of this type of joint?

Self-Quiz

Answers in Appendix V

1. The _____ and _____ systems work together to move the body and specific body parts.

2. Bone tissue contains _____ .
   a. living cells
   b. collagen fibers
   c. calcium and phosphorus
   d. all of these
   e. only a and b

3. _____ are shock pads and flex points.
   a. Vertebrae
   b. Cervical bones
   c. Lumbar bones
   d. Intervertebral disks

4. The hollow center of an osteon (Haversian system) provides space for what vital part of compact bone tissue?
   a. marrow
   b. collagen fibers
   c. a blood vessel
   d. osteocytes

5. _____ is a type of connective tissue; _____ form(s) in it.
   a. An osteon; collagen
   b. Bone marrow; blood cells
   c. Bone; an osteocyte
   d. A sinus; bone marrow

6. Mineralization of bone tissue requires _____ .
   a. calcium ions
   b. osteoclasts
   c. elastin
   d. all of the above

7. The axial skeleton consists of the _____ , while the appendicular skeleton consists of the _____ .

8. Match the terms and definitions.
   ___ bone
   ___ collagen
   ___ synovial fluid
   ___ osteocyte
   ___ marrow
   ___ metacarpals
   ___ mandible
   ___ sinuses
   a. in certain skull bones
   b. all in the hands
   c. blood cell production
   d. a fibrous protein
   e. mature bone cell
   f. lubrication
   g. mineralized connective tissue
   h. the lower jaw

Critical Thinking

1. Hormones and vitamins play important roles in the formation of bones. In particular, vitamin D is needed for bone tissue to mineralize properly. Children who develop the disorder called rickets (Figure 5.15) have suffered from a deficiency of vitamin D, so their bones are abnormally soft and become deformed. Based on your reading in this chapter, which cells in bone tissue are affected by the vitamin deficiency? Do you think bone remodeling might be affected?

2. Growth hormone, or GH, is used clinically to spur growth in children who are unusually short because they have a GH deficiency. However, it is useless for a short but otherwise normal 25-year-old to request GH treatment from a physician. Why?

3. If bleached human bones found lying in the desert were carefully examined, which of the following would not be present? Haversian canals, a marrow cavity, osteocytes, calcium.

4. For young women, the recommended daily allowance (RDA) of calcium is 800 milligrams. During Hilde's pregnancy, the RDA is 1,200 milligrams a day. What might happen to a pregnant woman's bones without the larger amount, and why?

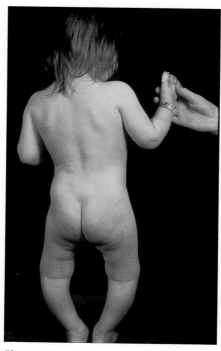

Figure 5.15 A child with rickets. The medical name for this disease is *osteomalacia*.

Explore on Your Own

When it comes to the skeleton and joints, your body can be a great learning tool.

- Feel along the back of your neck beginning at your hairline. Can you feel any lumps made by the bony processes of your spinal vertebrae? In the figure below, locate the C7 vertebra, which in most people is the most prominent. Can you feel it at the base of your neck?

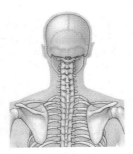

- While seated, feel your kneecap—the patella—move as you flex and extend your lower leg. Just below the patella you should also be able to feel a ligament that attaches it to your tibia.

  Can you find the upper protuberance of your tibia? Moving your fingers around to outside of the joint, can you feel the knobby upper part of the fibula?

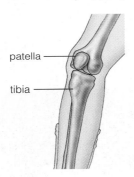

patella

tibia

- Using the diagram below as a guide, see if you can locate the ridges of your frontal bone above your eyebrows; the arching part of your zygomatic bone, which forms your "cheekbones"; and the joint where your lower jaw articulates with the temporal bone.

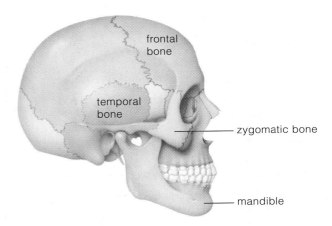

frontal bone

temporal bone

zygomatic bone

mandible

A series of horizontal cartilage rings support the trachea, your windpipe. Rest your fingers on this area and swallow. Can you feel the rings? What happens to them when you swallow? As described in Chapter 7, this movement is part of a mechanism that normally prevents swallowed food or drink from "going down the wrong way" into your lungs.

Pumping Up Muscles

Want to "bulk up" your muscles and be stronger, with more endurance? Just swallow a pill. That is the message to bodybuilders and other athletes from the sellers of substances like "andro"—androstenedione—and THG (tetrahydrogestrinone). Andro made news when Mark McGwire said he used it during his successful effort to break major league baseball's home-run record. An international track star admitted using THG, as did some professional football players. Several American professional baseball players were called before a grand jury investigating a nutritional supplement company that makes THG. Tests have shown that this "food supplement" actually is a chemical cousin of two anabolic (tissue-building) steroids prohibited in sports competitions. The federal Food and Drug Administration has forced THG off the market.

Androstenedione occurs naturally when the body synthesizes the sex hormone testosterone. Studies suggest, however, that andro is not an effective muscle-builder, because it only raises the testosterone level for a few hours. On the other hand, andro does have side effects, including a risk of liver damage. In 2004

the FDA issued an advisory warning of these problems, and companies were ordered to stop distributing the drug.

Creatine is an easy-to-obtain performance enhancer. The body normally produces this substance and gets more from food. Muscle cells use it as a quick energy source when they must contract hard and fast. Controlled studies show that creatine supplements do improve performance during brief, high-intensity exercise. Long-term effects are not known, although there is evidence that in large amounts creatine puts a strain on the kidneys. No regulatory agency checks to see how much creatine is actually present in any commercial product.

With this chapter we look at why we have muscles in the first place. We will begin by reviewing the three types of muscle tissue in the body, and then focus on skeletal muscles, which make up the **muscular system**. As you will read, their coordinated interactions with the skeleton underlie the movements and position changes required for the full range of a person's daily activities.

 How Would You Vote? *Dietary supplements are largely unregulated. Should they be subject to more stringent testing for effectiveness and safety? Cast your vote online at www.thomsonedu.com/biology/starr/humanbio.*

Key Concepts

WHAT SKELETAL MUSCLES DO
Like all muscle tissue, the tissue of skeletal muscles contains long muscle cells, often called muscle fibers, lined up in parallel arrays. Skeletal muscles attach to and pull on bones to move the body and its parts. Skeletal muscles also work with one another.

HOW MUSCLES WORK
A muscle cell is divided into units called sarcomeres. A sarcomere contracts—that is, it shortens—due to sliding interactions between filaments of two proteins, actin and myosin. When sarcomeres shorten, muscle cells shorten, and so does the whole muscle.

Links to Earlier Concepts

Building on what you learned about the skeleton in Chapter 5, this chapter explains how muscles partner with bones to bring about movements of the body and its parts.

You will learn how two proteins, actin and myosin, work together in ways that allow muscle cells to contract (3.8). Our discussion also will draw on your knowledge of how ATP fuels cell activities (3.7), and how active transport moves substances into and out of cells (3.10).

6.1 The Body's Three Kinds of Muscle

LINKS TO
SECTIONS
4.3 AND 4.6

A full 50 percent of the body is muscle tissue. Three different kinds of muscle perform different functions, but in all of them groups of cells contract to produce movement.

THE THREE KINDS OF MUSCLE ARE BUILT AND FUNCTION IN DIFFERENT WAYS

In Chapter 4 we introduced the three basic kinds of muscle tissue—skeletal muscle, smooth muscle, and cardiac muscle. In all of them, cells specialized to contract bring about some type of movement.

Most of the body's muscle tissue is **skeletal muscle**, which interacts with the skeleton to move body parts. Its long, thin cells are often called muscle "fibers" (Figure 6.1*a*). And unlike other body cells, skeletal muscle fibers have more than one nucleus. As you will read later on, their internal structure gives them a striated, or striped, appearance, and bundles of them form skeletal muscles.

Smooth muscle is found in the walls of hollow organs and of tubes, such as blood vessels (Figure 6.1*b*). Its cells are smaller than skeletal muscle cells, and they do not look striped—hence the "smooth" name for this muscle tissue. Junctions link smooth muscle cells, which often are organized into sheets.

You may recall that **cardiac muscle** is found only in the heart (Figure 6.1*c*). It looks striated, like skeletal muscle. Unlike skeletal and smooth muscle, however, cardiac muscle can contract on its own, without stimulation by the nervous system. Special junctions between its cells allow contraction signals to pass between them so fast that for all intents and purposes the cells contract as a single unit.

We do not have conscious control over the contractions of cardiac muscle and smooth muscle, so they are considered to be "involuntary" muscles. We *can* control many of our skeletal muscles, so they are "voluntary" muscles. Figure 6.2 shows the major skeletal muscles in the body. Some are close to the surface, others deep in the body wall. Some, such as facial muscles, attach to the skin. The trunk has muscles of the thorax (chest), spine, abdominal wall, and pelvic cavity. And of course, other muscle groups attach to limb bones.

When we speak of the body's "muscular system," we're talking about skeletal muscle, and so it is the focus of the rest of this chapter. Only skeletal muscle interacts with the skeleton to move the body, its limbs, or other parts. Those movements range from delicate adjustments that help us keep our balance to the cool moves you might execute on a dance floor. Our skeletal muscles also help stabilize joints between bones, and while we won't focus on it in this chapter, muscles also generate body heat.

> The body's three kinds of muscle—skeletal, smooth, and cardiac—each have a specific function in the body. Skeletal muscle makes up the muscular system, which partners with the skeleton to produce movement.

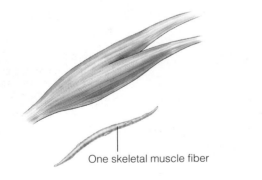

One skeletal muscle fiber

a   Skeletal muscle

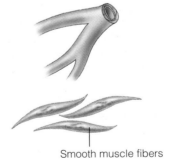

Smooth muscle fibers

b   Smooth muscle

Cardiac muscle fibers

c   Cardiac muscle

Figure 6.1 The three kinds of muscle in the body and where each type is found.

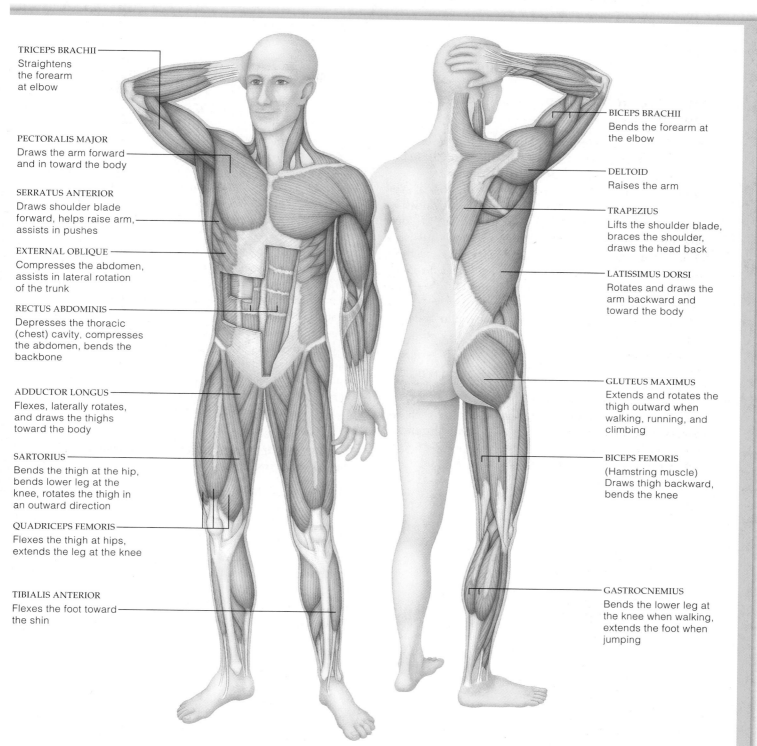

TRICEPS BRACHII
Straightens
the forearm
at elbow

PECTORALIS MAJOR
Draws the arm forward
and in toward the body

SERRATUS ANTERIOR
Draws shoulder blade
forward, helps raise arm,
assists in pushes

EXTERNAL OBLIQUE
Compresses the abdomen,
assists in lateral rotation
of the trunk

RECTUS ABDOMINIS
Depresses the thoracic
(chest) cavity, compresses
the abdomen, bends the
backbone

ADDUCTOR LONGUS
Flexes, laterally rotates,
and draws the thighs
toward the body

SARTORIUS
Bends the thigh at the hip,
bends lower leg at the
knee, rotates the thigh in
an outward direction

QUADRICEPS FEMORIS
Flexes the thigh at hips,
extends the leg at the knee

TIBIALIS ANTERIOR
Flexes the foot toward
the shin

BICEPS BRACHII
Bends the forearm at
the elbow

DELTOID
Raises the arm

TRAPEZIUS
Lifts the shoulder blade,
braces the shoulder,
draws the head back

LATISSIMUS DORSI
Rotates and draws the
arm backward and
toward the body

GLUTEUS MAXIMUS
Extends and rotates the
thigh outward when
walking, running, and
climbing

BICEPS FEMORIS
(Hamstring muscle)
Draws thigh backward,
bends the knee

GASTROCNEMIUS
Bends the lower leg at
the knee when walking,
extends the foot when
jumping

Figure 6.2 *Animated!* Some of the major
muscles of the muscular system.

6.2 The Structure and Function of Skeletal Muscles

Muscle cells generate force by contracting. After a muscle contracts, it can relax and lengthen. As their name suggests, skeletal muscles attach to and interact with bones.

A SKELETAL MUSCLE IS BUILT OF BUNDLED MUSCLE CELLS

A skeletal muscle contains bundles of muscle cells, which look like long, striped fibers (Figure 6.3). Inside each cell are threadlike **myofibrils**, which you'll read more about in Section 6.3. There may be hundreds, even thousands, of cells in a muscle, all bundled together by connective tissue that extends past them to form tendons. A **tendon** is a strap of dense connective tissue that attaches a muscle to bone. Tendons make joints more stable by helping keep the adjoining bones properly aligned. Tendons often rub against bones, but they slide inside fluid-filled sheaths that help reduce the friction (Figure 6.4). Your knees, wrists, and finger joints all have tendon sheaths.

BONES AND SKELETAL MUSCLES WORK LIKE A SYSTEM OF LEVERS

You have more than 600 skeletal muscles, and each one helps produce some kind of body movement. In general,

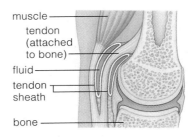

muscle
tendon (attached to bone)
fluid
tendon sheath
bone

Figure 6.4 A tendon sheath. Notice the lubricating fluid inside each of the sheaths sketched here.

one end of a muscle, called the **origin**, is attached to a bone that stays relatively motionless during a movement. The other end of the muscle, called the **insertion**, is attached to the bone that moves most (Figure 6.5). In effect, the skeleton and the muscles attached to it are like a system of levers in which bones (rigid rods) move near joints (fixed points). When a skeletal muscle contracts, it pulls on the bones it attaches to. Because muscles attach very close to most joints, a muscle only has to contract a short distance to produce a major movement.

MANY MUSCLES ARE ARRANGED AS PAIRS OR IN GROUPS

Many muscles are arranged as pairs or groups. Some work in opposition (that is, antagonistically) so that the action of one opposes or reverses the action of the other. Figure 6.5 shows an antagonistic muscle pair, the biceps and triceps of the arm. Try extending your right arm in front of you, then place your left hand over the biceps in the upper arm and slowly "bend the elbow." Can you feel the biceps contract? When the biceps relaxes and its partner (the triceps) contracts, your arm straightens. This kind of coordinated action comes partly from *reciprocal innervation* by nerves from the spinal cord. When one muscle group is stimulated, no signals are sent to the opposing group, so it does not contract.

Other muscles work in a synergistic, or support, role. Their contraction adds force or helps stabilize another contracting muscle. If you make a fist while keeping your wrist straight, synergist muscles are stabilizing your wrist joint while muscles in your hand are doing the "heavy lifting" of closing your fingers.

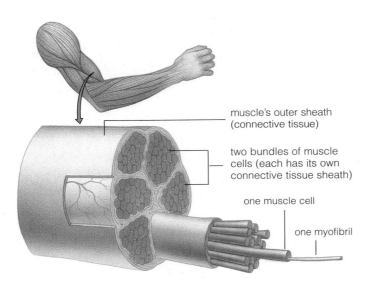

muscle's outer sheath (connective tissue)

two bundles of muscle cells (each has its own connective tissue sheath)

one muscle cell

one myofibril

Figure 6.3 Structure of skeletal muscle. The muscle's cells are bundled together inside a wrapping of connective tissue.

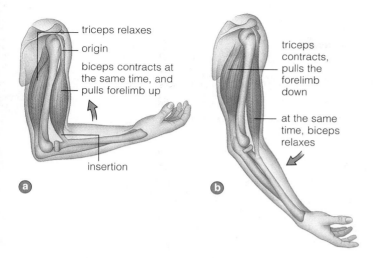

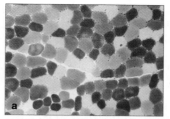

Figure 6.5 *Animated!* Two opposing muscle groups in human arms. (**a**) When the triceps relaxes and its opposing partner (biceps) contracts, the elbow joint flexes and the forearm bends up. (**b**) When the triceps contracts and the biceps relaxes, the forearm is extended down.

Figure 6.6 Fast and slow skeletal muscle. (**a**) This micrograph shows a cross section of the different kinds of cells in a skeletal muscle. The lighter, "white fibers" are fast muscle. They have little myoglobin and fewer mitochondria than the dark red fibers, which are slow muscle. (**b**) A distance swimmer can work her shoulder muscles for extended periods due to the many well-developed slow muscle cells they contain.

"FAST" AND "SLOW" MUSCLE

Your body has two basic types of skeletal muscle (Figure 6.6*a*). "Slow" or "red" muscle appears crimson because its cells are packed with myoglobin, a reddish protein that binds oxygen for the cell's use in making ATP. Red muscle also is served by larger numbers of the tiny blood vessels called capillaries. (Red muscle is the dark meat in chicken and turkey.) Red muscle contracts fairly slowly, but because its cells are so well equipped to make lots of ATP, the contractions can be sustained for a long time. For example, some muscles of the back and legs—called postural muscles because they aid body support—must contract for long periods when a person is standing. They have a high proportion of red muscle cells. By contrast, the muscles of your hand have fewer capillaries and relatively more "fast" or "white" muscle cells, in which there are fewer mitochondria and less myoglobin. Fast muscle can contract rapidly and powerfully for short periods, but it can't sustain contractions for long periods. This is why you get writer's cramp if you write long-hand for an hour or two.

When an athlete trains rigorously, one goal is to increase the relative size and contractile strength of fast or slow fibers in muscles. The type of sport determines which type of fiber is targeted. A sprinter will benefit from larger, stronger fast muscle cells in the thighs, while a distance swimmer (Figure 6.6*b*) will train to increase the number of mitochondria in his or her shoulder muscle cells.

A skeletal muscle consists of hundreds or thousands of muscle cells bundled together by connective tissue. When a skeletal muscle contracts, it pulls on a bone to produce movement.

Tendons strap skeletal muscles to bone.

In many movements, the action of one muscle opposes or reverses the action of another.

The cells in red or "slow" skeletal muscle have features that support slow, long-lasting contractions. The cells in white or "fast" skeletal muscle are specialized for rapid, strong bursts of contraction.

6.3 How Muscles Contract

Bones move—they are pulled in some direction—when the skeletal muscles attached to them contract. In turn, a skeletal muscle contracts when the individual muscle cells in it shorten.

A MUSCLE CONTRACTS WHEN ITS CELLS SHORTEN

When a muscle cell shortens, many units of contraction inside that cell are shortening. Each of these basic units of contraction is a **sarcomere**.

Figure 6.7*a* is a reminder of how bundles of cells in a skeletal muscle run parallel with the muscle. In Figure 6.7*b* you can see how each myofibril in a muscle cell is divided into bands, which show up as an alternating light–dark pattern when they are stained and viewed under a microscope. The bands of the myofibrils in the cells line up rather closely; this is why a skeletal muscle cell looks striped.

The dark bands, or Z bands, mark the ends of each sarcomere. Inside a sarcomere are many filaments, some thick, others thin. Each thin filament is like two strands of pearls, twisted together, with one end attached to a

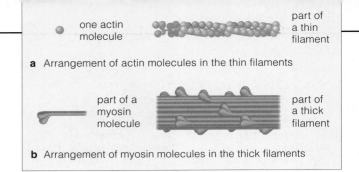

a Arrangement of actin molecules in the thin filaments

b Arrangement of myosin molecules in the thick filaments

Figure 6.8 Actin and myosin filaments.

Z band. The "pearls" are molecules of **actin** (Figure 6.8*a*), a globular protein that can contract. Other proteins are found near grooves on actin's surface.

Each thick filament is made of molecules of the protein **myosin**. Each myosin molecule has a tail and a double head. In a thick filament many of them are bundled together so that all the heads project outward (Figure 6.8*b*), away from the sarcomere's center.

As you can see in Figure 6.7, muscle bundles, muscle cells, myofibrils, and their filaments all run in the same direction. Why? This arrangement focuses the force of a contracting muscle onto a bone in a specific direction.

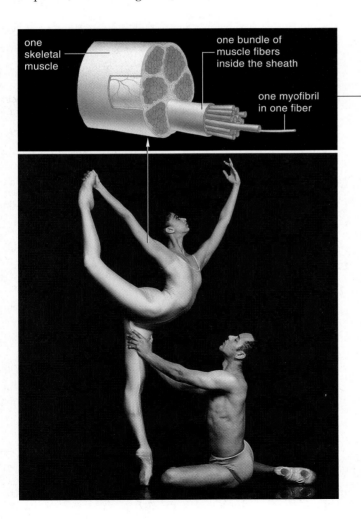

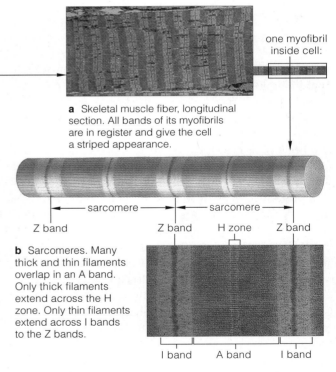

a Skeletal muscle fiber, longitudinal section. All bands of its myofibrils are in register and give the cell a striped appearance.

b Sarcomeres. Many thick and thin filaments overlap in an A band. Only thick filaments extend across the H zone. Only thin filaments extend across I bands to the Z bands.

Figure 6.7 *Animated!* Zooming down through skeletal muscle from a biceps to filaments of the proteins actin and myosin. These proteins can contract.

MUSCLE CELLS SHORTEN WHEN ACTIN FILAMENTS SLIDE OVER MYOSIN

Years of research have produced an explanation for how sarcomeres shorten and contract a muscle. According to the **sliding filament model**, all of the myosin filaments stay in place. They use short "power strokes" to slide the sets of actin filaments over them, toward the sarcomere's center. It's like two pocket doors closing—but pulling with them both walls to which they are attached. Pulling both sets shrinks the length of the sarcomere (Figure 6.9). Each power stroke is driven by energy from ATP.

Each myosin head connects repeatedly to binding sites on a nearby actin filament. The head is an ATPase, a type of enzyme. It binds ATP and catalyzes a phosphate-group transfer that powers the reaction.

A change in the concentration of calcium ions causes the myosin head to form a **cross-bridge** to the actin (Figure 6.9b). This link tilts the myosin head and pulls the actin filament toward the center of the sarcomere. Next, with the help of energy from ATP, the myosin head's grip on actin is broken and the head returns to its starting position (Figure 6.9c–e). Each contraction of a sarcomere requires hundreds of myosin heads making a series of short strokes down the length of actin filaments.

When a person dies, body cells stop making ATP. In muscle fibers this means that the myosin cross-bridges with actin can't break apart after a power stroke. As a result skeletal muscles "lock up," a stiffening called **rigor mortis** ("stiffness of death"). Rigor mortis lasts for 24 to 60 hours, or until the natural decomposition of dead tissues gets under way. Crime investigators can use this kind of information to help pinpoint the time when a suspicious death occurred.

> *A skeletal muscle cell contracts when its sarcomeres shorten. Thus sarcomeres are the basic units of muscle contraction.*
>
> *Powered by ATP, interactions between myosin and actin filaments shorten the sarcomeres of a muscle cell.*

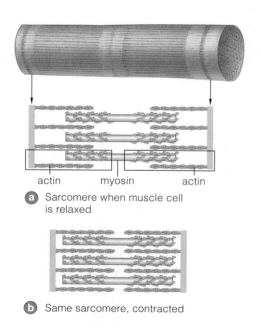

actin   myosin   actin

a Sarcomere when muscle cell is relaxed

b Same sarcomere, contracted

Figure 6.9 *Animated!* (**a**) Actin and myosin filaments in a sarcomere. Interactions between the two kinds of filaments shorten the sarcomere. (**b–e**) Sliding filament model of contraction in the sarcomeres of muscle cells.

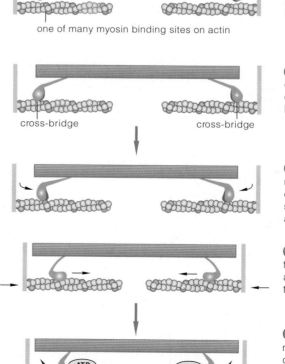

myosin head

one of many myosin binding sites on actin

cross-bridge   cross-bridge

ATP   ATP

c A myosin filament in a resting muscle. All the myosin heads were energized earlier by the binding of ATP.

d Calcium released from a cellular storage system allows cross-bridges to form; myosin binds to actin filaments.

e Binding makes each myosin head tilt toward the center of the sarcomere and slide the actin filaments along with it.

f Using energy from ATP, the myosin heads drag the actin filaments inward, pulling the Z lines closer together.

g New ATP binds to the myosin heads and they detach from actin. The myosin heads return to their original orientation, ready to act again.

6.4 How the Nervous System Controls Muscle Contraction

LINK TO
SECTION
3.6

In response to signals from the nervous system, contracting skeletal muscles move the body and parts of it at certain times, in certain ways.

CALCIUM IONS ARE THE KEY TO CONTRACTION

The nervous system controls the contraction of skeletal muscle cells. Its "orders" reach the muscles by way of motor neurons that stimulate or inhibit contraction of the sarcomeres in muscle cells (Figure 6.10).

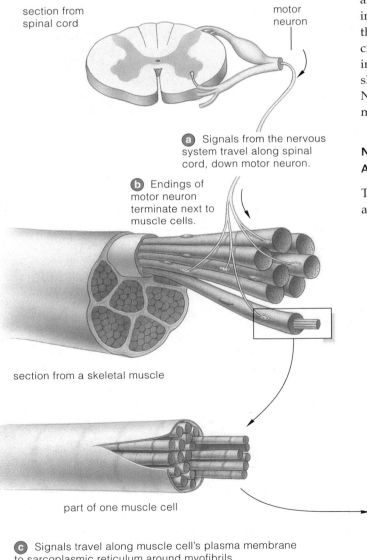

section from spinal cord

motor neuron

a Signals from the nervous system travel along spinal cord, down motor neuron.

b Endings of motor neuron terminate next to muscle cells.

section from a skeletal muscle

part of one muscle cell

c Signals travel along muscle cell's plasma membrane to sarcoplasmic reticulum around myofibrils.

Figure 6.10 *Animated!* Pathway for signals from the nervous system that stimulate contraction of skeletal muscle.

When neural signals arrive at a muscle cell, they spread rapidly and eventually reach small extensions of the cell's plasma membrane. These **T tubules** connect with a membrane system that laces around the cell's myofibrils (Figure 6.10*d*). The system, called the **sarcoplasmic reticulum** (SR), is a modified version of the endoplasmic reticulum described in Chapter 3. SR takes up and releases calcium ions (Ca^{++}). An incoming nerve impulse triggers the release of calcium ions from the SR. The ions diffuse into myofibrils, and when they reach actin filaments the stage is set for contraction.

Two proteins, troponin and tropomyosin, are found along the surface of actin filaments (Figure 6.11). When incoming calcium binds to troponin, the binding site on the actin filament is uncovered. This allows myosin cross-bridges to attach to the site, and the cycle described in Section 6.3 continues. When nervous system signals shut off, calcium is actively transported back into the SR. Now the binding site on actin is covered up again, myosin can't bind to actin, and the muscle cell relaxes.

NEURONS ACT ON MUSCLE CELLS AT NEUROMUSCULAR JUNCTIONS

The nerve impulses that stimulate a skeletal muscle cell arrive at **neuromuscular junctions**. A motor neuron has

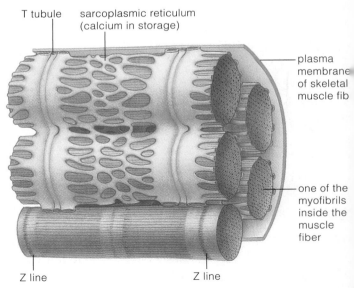

T tubule   sarcoplasmic reticulum (calcium in storage)

plasma membrane of skeletal muscle fib

one of the myofibrils inside the muscle fiber

Z line   Z line

d Signals trigger the release of calcium ions from sarcoplasmic reticulu threading among the myofibrils. The calcium allows actin and myosin filaments in the myofibrils to interact and bring about contraction.

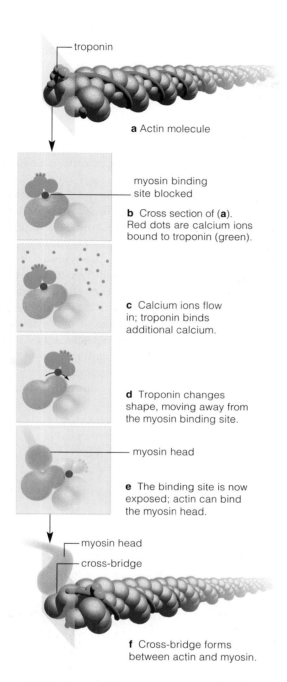

— troponin

a Actin molecule

myosin binding
— site blocked

b Cross section of (**a**).
Red dots are calcium ions
bound to troponin (green).

c Calcium ions flow
in; troponin binds
additional calcium.

d Troponin changes
shape, moving away from
the myosin binding site.

— myosin head

e The binding site is now
exposed; actin can bind
the myosin head.

— myosin head
— cross-bridge

f Cross-bridge forms
between actin and myosin.

Figure 6.11 *Animated!* The interactions of actin, tropomyosin,
and troponins in a skeletal muscle cell.

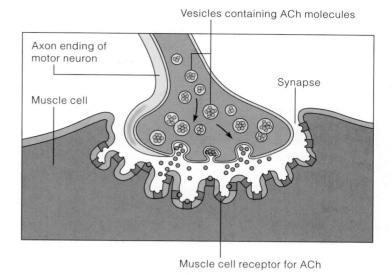

Vesicles containing ACh molecules

Axon ending of
motor neuron

Synapse

Muscle cell

Muscle cell receptor for ACh

Figure 6.12 How a chemical messenger called a
neurotransmitter carries a signal across a neuromuscular
junction.

of chemical messenger, a *neurotransmitter* called ACh (for acetylcholine) carries the signal from a motor neuron across the gap.

This signaling between a neuron and a muscle cell takes place in several steps. When the motor neuron is stimulated, calcium channels open in the plasma membrane of the neuron's axon endings that are in the neuromuscular junction. Then, calcium ions from the extracellular fluid flow inside the axon endings, and vesicles in each ending release ACh. When ACh binds to receptors on the muscle cell membrane, it may set in motion the events that cause the muscle cell to contract. ACh can excite or inhibit muscle and gland cells, as well as some cells in the brain and spinal cord.

extensions called *axons*; neuromuscular junctions are places where the branched endings of axons abut the muscle cell membranes, as you can see in Figure 6.10*b* and Figure 6.12. The neuron endings don't touch a muscle cell; between them there is a gap called a *synapse*. A type

The nervous system controls the contraction of muscle cells by way of signals that spark the release of calcium ions from a membrane system around a muscle cell's myofibrils. Nerve impulses pass from a neuron to a muscle cell across neuromuscular junctions.

6.5 How Muscle Cells Get Energy

LINKS TO
SECTIONS
3.11 AND 3.14

In resting muscle cells the demand for ATP can skyrocket quickly when the muscle is ordered to contract.

When a resting muscle cell is stimulated to contract, ATP must become available twenty to one hundred times faster than before. A muscle cell has only a little ATP when contraction starts, so a fast reaction forms more of it. An enzyme transfers phosphate from **creatine phosphate** to ADP. Because a cell has about five times as much creatine phosphate as ATP, this reaction can fuel contractions until a slower ATP-forming pathway can kick in (Figure 6.13).

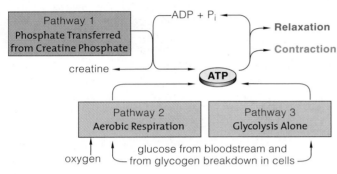

Figure 6.13 *Animated!* Three metabolic pathways by which ATP forms in muscles in response to the demands of physical exercise.

Normally, most of the ATP for muscle contraction comes from the oxygen-using reactions of cellular respiration. It's the same with the first five to ten minutes of moderate exercise. For the next half hour or so of steady activity, that muscle cell depends on glucose and fatty acids delivered by the blood. Beyond that time, fatty acids are the main fuel source (Section 3.14).

If you exercise hard, your respiratory and circulatory systems may not deliver enough oxygen for aerobic cellular respiration in some muscles. Then, glycolysis (which does not use oxygen) will contribute more of the ATP being formed. Although glycolysis doesn't yield much ATP, muscle cells use this metabolic backup as long as stored glycogen can provide glucose—or at least until **muscle fatigue** sets in. This is a state in which a muscle cannot contract, even if it is being stimulated. Fatigue probably is due to an **oxygen debt** that results when your muscles use more ATP than cellular respiration can deliver. The switch to glycolysis produces lactic acid. Along with the already low ATP supply, the rising acidity hampers the contraction of muscle cells. Deep, rapid breathing helps repay the oxygen debt.

How much ATP is available inside muscle cells affects whether the fiber can contract, and for how long.

6.6 Properties of Whole Muscles

A muscle may contract weakly, strongly, or somewhere in between. A contraction may last a long time or only a few thousandths of a second. The properties of whole muscles relate to how individual muscle cells contract.

SEVERAL FACTORS DETERMINE THE CHARACTERISTICS OF A MUSCLE CONTRACTION

A **motor neuron** supplies a number of cells in a muscle. A motor neuron and the muscle cells it synapses with form a **motor unit** (Figure 6.14). The number of cells in a motor unit depends on how precise the muscle control must be. For instance, where precise control is required, as in the tiny muscles that move the eye, motor units have only four or five muscle cells. By contrast, motor units in some large leg muscles include hundreds of cells.

When a motor neuron fires, all the cells in its motor unit contract for a fleeting moment. This response is a **muscle twitch** (Figure 6.15*a*). If a new nerve impulse arrives before a twitch ends, the muscle twitches again. Repeating the stimulation of a motor unit in a short period of time makes all the twitches run together (Figure 6.15*b*). The result is a sustained contraction called **tetanus**

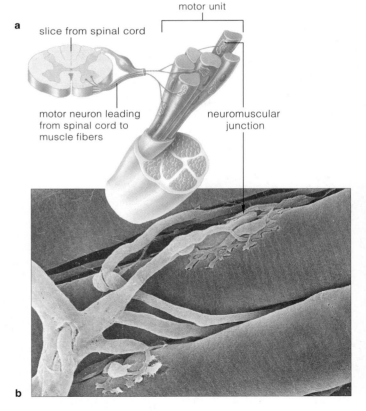

Figure 6.14 (**a**) Example of motor units present in muscles. (**b**) The micrograph shows the axon endings of a motor neuron that acts on individual muscle cells in the muscle.

(Figure 6.15c). Our muscles normally contract in this way, which generates three or four times the force of a single twitch. In the disease *tetanus*, muscles stay contracted, sometimes fatally (Figure 6.15d).

A skeletal muscle contains a large number of muscle cells, but not all of them contract at the same time. If a muscle is contracting only weakly—say, as your forearm muscles do when you pick up a pencil—it is because the nervous system is activating only a few of the muscle's motor units. In stronger contractions (when you heft a stack of books) more motor units are stimulated. Even when a muscle is relaxed, however, some of its motor units are contracted. This steady, low-level contracted state is called **muscle tone**. It helps maintain muscles in general good health and is important in stabilizing the skeleton's movable joints.

Muscle tension is the force that a contracting muscle exerts on an object, such as a bone. Opposing this force is a load, either the weight of an object or gravity's pull on the muscle. A stimulated muscle shortens only when muscle tension exceeds the opposing forces.

Isotonically contracting muscles shorten and move a load (Figure 6.16a). *Isometrically* contracting muscles develop tension but don't shorten. This is what happens when you attempt to lift an object that is too heavy (Figure 6.16b).

TIRED MUSCLES CAN'T GENERATE MUCH FORCE

When steady, strong stimulation keeps a muscle in a state of tetanus, the muscle eventually becomes fatigued. Muscle fatigue is a decrease in the muscle's ability to

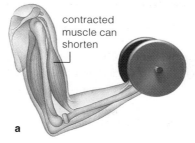
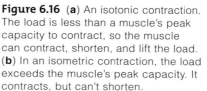
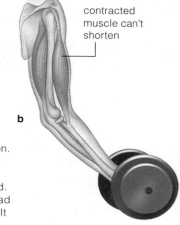

contracted muscle can shorten

a

contracted muscle can't shorten

b

Figure 6.16 (**a**) An isotonic contraction. The load is less than a muscle's peak capacity to contract, so the muscle can contract, shorten, and lift the load. (**b**) In an isometric contraction, the load exceeds the muscle's peak capacity. It contracts, but can't shorten.

generate force (that is, to develop tension). After a few minutes of rest, a fatigued muscle will be able to contract again. How long this recovery takes depends in part on how long and how often the muscle was stimulated before. Muscles trained by a pattern of brief, intense exercise fatigue and recover rapidly. This is what happens during weight lifting. Muscles used in prolonged, moderate exercise fatigue slowly but take longer to recover, often up to a day. Exactly what causes muscle fatigue is unknown, but one factor is depletion of glycogen, the form in which muscles hold glucose in reserve for energy. The build-up of lactic acid, which makes overused muscles sore, also contributes to fatigue.

A motor unit consists of a motor neuron and the muscle fibers it serves. The number of motor units in a muscle correlates with how precisely the nervous system must control a muscle's activity.

A muscle twitch is a brief muscle contraction following a stimulating nerve impulse. Body muscles normally contract in a sustained way called tetanus. Muscle tension is the force a contracting muscle exerts.

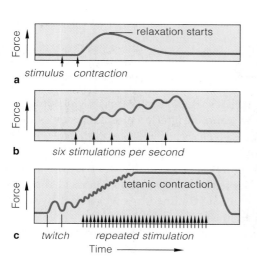

a relaxation starts

Force

stimulus contraction

b Force

six stimulations per second

c Force

twitch repeated stimulation

tetanic contraction

Time

d

Figure 6.15 *Animated!* Recordings of twitches in muscles artificially stimulated in different ways. (**a**) A single twitch. (**b**) Six per second cause a summation of twitches, and (**c**) about 20 per second cause tetanic contraction. (**d**) Painting of a soldier dying of the disease tetanus in a military hospital in the 1800s after the bacterium *Clostridium tetani* infected a battlefield wound.

6.7 Muscle Disorders

LINK TO SECTION 3.12

Every movement depends on skeletal muscles, so when an accident, disease, or disuse prevents them from functioning normally, nearly every aspect of life is affected.

If you have ever torn a muscle or known someone with a muscle-wasting disease, you are very well aware that any problem that impairs the ability of skeletal muscles to produce movement has a serious impact on activities that most of us take for granted. In general, ills that can befall our skeletal muscles fall into three categories: injuries, disease, and disuse.

STRAINS AND TEARS ARE MUSCLE INJURIES

Given that our muscular system gets almost constant use, it's not surprising that the most common disorders of skeletal muscles are injuries. Lots of people, and athletes especially, strain a muscle at some point in their lives (Figure 6.17). The injury happens when a movement stretches or tears muscle fibers. Usually, there is some bleeding into the damaged area, which causes swelling and a painful muscle spasm. The usual first aid is an ice pack, followed by resting the affected muscle and using anti-inflammatory drugs such as ibuprofen.

When a whole muscle is torn, the aftereffects can last a lifetime. If scar tissue develops while the tear mends, the healed muscle may be shorter than before. As a result it may not function as effectively.

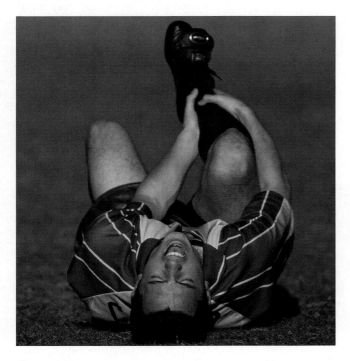

Figure 6.17 For athletes, muscle strains and tears often are "part of the game."

Figure 6.18 A child with Duchenne muscular dystrophy.

SOMETIMES A SKELETAL MUSCLE WILL CONTRACT ABNORMALLY

In a muscle *spasm*, a muscle suddenly and involuntarily contracts. A muscle *cramp* is a painful muscle spasm that doesn't immediately release. Any skeletal muscle can cramp, but the usual "victims" are calf and thigh muscles. In some cases the real culprit is a deficiency of potassium, which is needed for the proper transmission of nerve impulses to muscles and other tissues. Gentle stretching and massage may coax a cramped muscle to release.

Most people experience occasional muscle *tics*. These minor, involuntary twitches are common in muscles of the face and eyelids and may be triggered by anxiety or some other psycho-emotional cause.

MUSCULAR DYSTROPHIES DESTROY MUSCLE FIBERS

Muscular dystrophies are genetic diseases in which muscle fibers break down and the affected muscles progressively weaken and shrivel. *Duchenne muscular dystrophy* (DMD) is the most common form in children (Figure 6.18). It is caused by a single mutant gene that interferes with the ability of sarcomeres in muscle cells to contract. Affected youngsters usually are confined to a wheelchair by their teens, and die by their early twenties.

Myotonic muscular dystrophy is usually seen in adults. It generally affects only the hands and feet and is not life-threatening. "Myo" means muscle, and the name of this disorder indicates that affected muscles contract strongly but do not relax in the normal way.

Figure 6.19 Muscle-building alternatives. (**a**) Aerobic exercise builds endurance and improves overall muscle function. (**b**) Strength training builds larger, stronger muscles but does not improve endurance.

EXERCISE MAKES THE MOST OF MUSCLES

Muscle cells adapt to the activity demanded of them. When severe nerve damage or prolonged bed rest prevents a muscle from being used, the muscle will rapidly begin to waste away, or *atrophy*. Over time, affected muscles can lose up to three-fourths of their mass, with a corresponding loss of strength. More commonly, the skeletal muscles of a sedentary person stay basically healthy but cannot respond to physical demands in the same way that well-worked muscles can.

The best way to maintain or improve the work capacity of your muscles is to exercise them—that is, to increase the demands on muscle fibers to contract. To increase muscle endurance, nothing beats regular aerobic exercise—activities such as walking, biking, jogging, swimming, and aerobics classes (Figure 6.19a). Aerobic exercise works muscles at a rate at which the body can keep them supplied with oxygen. It affects muscle fibers in several ways:

1. There is an increase in the number and the size of mitochondria, the organelles that make ATP.

2. The number of blood capillaries supplying muscle tissue increases. This increased blood supply brings more oxygen and nutrients to the muscle tissue and removes metabolic wastes more efficiently.

3. Muscle tissues contain more of the oxygen-binding pigment myoglobin.

Together, these changes produce muscles that are more efficient metabolically and can work longer without becoming fatigued.

By contrast, strength training involves intense, short-duration exercise, such as weight lifting. It affects fast muscle fibers, which form more myofibrils and make more of the enzymes used in glycolysis (which forms some ATP). These changes translate into whole muscles that are larger and stronger (Figure 6.19b), but such bulging muscles fatigue rapidly so they don't have much endurance. Fitness experts recommend a workout plan that combines strength training and aerobic workouts.

Starting at about age 30, the tension, or physical force, a person's muscles can muster begins to decrease. This means that, once you enter your fourth decade of life, you may exercise just as long and intensely as a younger person but your muscles cannot adapt to the workouts to the same extent. Even so, being physically active is extremely beneficial. Aerobic exercise improves endurance and blood circulation, and even modest strength training slows the loss of skeletal muscle tissue that is an inevitable part of aging.

Summary

Section 6.1   Muscle tissue includes skeletal, smooth, and cardiac muscle. Although the cells of these different kinds of muscle tissue are structurally specialized for their particular functions, all muscle cells are specialized to generate force—that is, to contract or shorten.

Section 6.2   Skeletal muscle makes up the muscular system. There are more than 600 skeletal muscles, which transmit force to bones and move body limbs or other parts (Table 6.1). Skeletal muscles also help to stabilize joints and generate body heat. Each one contains bundles of muscle fibers (muscle cells) that are wrapped in connective tissue.

Tendons connect skeletal muscle to bones. The origin end of a skeletal muscle is attached to a bone that stays relatively motionless during a movement. The insertion end is attached to the bone that moves most. Some muscles work antagonistically, so the action of one opposes or reverses the action of the other. Other muscles are synergists that facilitate movements.

 Learn about the location and action of skeletal muscles.

Section 6.3   Bones move when they are pulled by the shortening, or contraction, of skeletal muscles. In turn, this shortening occurs because individual muscle fibers are shortening. Skeletal (and cardiac) muscle fibers contain threadlike myofibrils, which are divided lengthwise into sarcomeres, the basic units of contraction. Each sarcomere consists of an array of filaments of the proteins actin (thin) and myosin (thick):

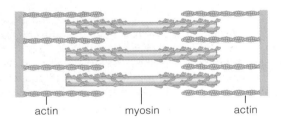

actin   myosin   actin

Interacting actin and myosin filaments shorten a sarcomere. The myosin head attaches to a neighboring actin filament (forming a cross-bridge); then the actin slides over the myosin. This movement is powered by ATP and is called the sliding filament mechanism of muscle contraction.

 Get an in-depth look at the structure and function of skeletal muscles.

Section 6.4   Nerve impulses cause skeletal muscle cells to contract. When the signals reach T tubules

Table 6.1   Review of Skeletal Muscle
FUNCTION OF SKELETAL MUSCLE: Contraction (shortening) that moves the body and its parts.
MAJOR COMPONENTS OF SKELETAL MUSCLE CELLS: **Myofibrils:** Strands containing filaments of the contractile proteins actin and myosin.   **Sarcomeres:** The basic units of muscle contraction.   *Other:*   **Motor unit:** A motor neuron and the muscle cells it controls.   **Neuromuscular junction:** Synapse between a motor neuron and muscle cells.

(extensions of the cell's plasma membrane) they trigger the release of calcium ions from sarcoplasmic reticulum, a membrane system that wraps around myofibrils in the muscle fiber. The binding of calcium affects proteins on the surface of actin filaments so that the heads of myosin molecules can bind to actin.

A neuromuscular junction is a synapse between a motor neuron and a muscle fiber. A nerve impulse triggers the release of a neurotransmitter called ACh into the synapse. This starts the events that cause the fiber to contract.

 See how the nervous system controls muscle contraction.

Section 6.5   The ATP required for muscle contraction can come from cellular respiration, from glycolysis alone, or from the generation of ATP from creatine phosphate. Glycolysis is used when muscles are exercised so intensively that the full aerobic pathway can't keep up with the demand for ATP. When muscles use more ATP than aerobic respiration can provide, an oxygen debt may develop in muscle tissue.

 Compare sources of energy for muscle contraction.

Section 6.6   A motor neuron and the muscle fibers it controls make up a motor unit. When a stimulus activates a certain number of motor units, it produces a brief muscle contraction called a muscle twitch. If a series of twitches occur close together, a sustained contraction called tetanus develops. Skeletal muscles normally operate near or at tetanus. Some of a muscle's motor units are contracted even when it is relaxed. This low-level state of contraction is called muscle tone and helps keep muscles healthy. Muscle tension is the force that a contracting muscle exerts on an object. When muscle fatigue sets in, a muscle cannot contract even if it is being stimulated.

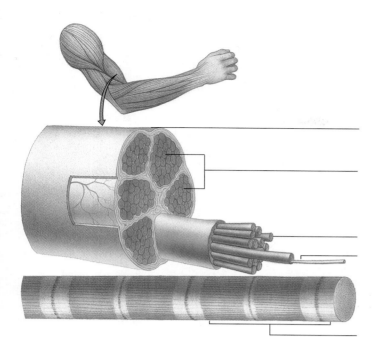

Section 6.7

Injuries are the most common disorders of skeletal muscles, and even healthy muscles may contract abnormally, such as when they cramp. Muscular dystrophies are a set of diseases that destroy muscle fibers and cause skeletal muscles to lose function. A combination of regular aerobic exercise and resistance training helps build muscle and increase its endurance.

Review Questions

1. In a general sense, how do skeletal muscles produce movement?

2. In the diagram above, label the fine structure of a muscle, down to one of its myofibrils. Identify the basic unit of contraction in a myofibril.

3. How do actin and myosin interact in a sarcomere to bring about muscle contraction? What roles do ATP and calcium play?

4. How does a muscle cell incur an oxygen debt? How is this "debt" different from muscle fatigue?

5. What is the function of the sarcoplasmic reticulum in muscle cell contraction?

6. Explain why (a) calcium ions and (b) ACh are vital for muscle contraction.

7. What is a motor unit? Why does a rapid series of muscle twitches yield a stronger overall contraction than a single twitch?

8. What are the structural and functional differences between "slow" and "fast" muscle?

Self-Quiz

Answers in Appendix V

1. The _____ and _____ systems work together to move the body and specific body parts.

2. The three types of muscle tissue are _____, _____, and _____.

3. _____ forms cross-bridges with myosin.
   a. A muscle fiber   c. Myoglobin
   b. A tendon   d. Actin

4. The _____ is the basic unit of muscle contraction.
   a. myofibril   c. muscle fiber
   b. sarcomere   d. myosin filament

5. Skeletal muscle contraction requires _____.
   a. calcium ions   c. arrival of a nerve impulse
   b. ATP   d. all of the above

6. Match the M words with their defining feature.
   ____ muscle   a. actin's partner
   ____ muscle twitch   b. delivers contraction signal
   ____ muscle tension   c. a muscle cannot contract
   ____ myosin   d. motor unit response
   ____ motor neuron   e. force exerted by cross-bridges
   ____ myofibrils   f. muscle cells bundled in connective tissue
   ____ muscle fatigue   g. threadlike parts in a muscle fiber

Critical Thinking

1. You are training athletes for the 100-meter dash. They need muscles specialized for speed and strength, *not* endurance. What muscle characteristics would your training regimen aim to develop? How would you alter it to train marathoners?

2. In 1989, explorer Will Steger and his dogsled team crossed Antarctica, traveling some 3,741 miles. Steger said later that his polar huskies worked the hardest and pulled all the weight. A husky's limb bones and skeletal muscles are suited for long-distance load-pulling. For example, the forelegs move freely, thanks to a deep but not-too-broad rib cage, and the dog also has a well-muscled chest. What kind of muscle fibers and muscle mass would you expect to find in a husky's *hind* legs, which provide much of the brute power to propel a loaded sled?

3. Curare, a poison extracted from a South American shrub, blocks the binding of ACh by muscle cells. What do you suppose would happen to your muscles, including the ones involved in breathing, if a toxic dose of curare entered your bloodstream?

4. At the gym Sean gets on a stair-climbing machine and "climbs" as fast as he can for fifteen minutes. At the end of that time he is breathing hard and his quadriceps and other leg muscles are aching. What is the physiological explanation for these symptoms?

5. In training for a marathon, Lydia plans to take creatine supplements because she heard that they boost an athlete's energy. What is your opinion on this plan?

Explore on Your Own

A good way to improve your understanding of your muscular system is to explore the movements of your own muscles. Try the following quick exercises.

Human hands don't contain many of the muscles that control hand movements. Instead, as you can see in Figure 6.20a, most of those muscles are in the forearm. Tendons extending from one muscle, the flexor digitorum superficialis (the "superficial finger flexer"), bend your fingers. Place one hand on the top of the opposite forearm, and then wiggle your fingers on that side or make a fist several times. Can you feel the "finger flexer" in action?

Place your fingers on the skin above your nose, between your eyebrows. Now frown. The muscle you feel pulling your eyebrows together is the corrugator supercilii. One effect of its contraction is to "corrugate" the skin of your forehead into vertical wrinkles.

A grin calls into action other facial muscles, including the zygomaticus major (Figure 6.20b). On either side of the skull, this muscle originates on the cheekbones and inserts at the corners of the mouth. To feel it contract, place the tips of your index fingers at the corners of your mouth, and then smile.

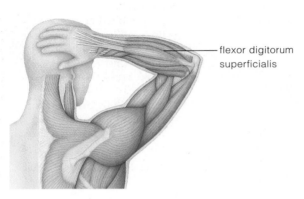

flexor digitorum superficialis

a The flexor digitorum superficialis, a forearm muscle that helps move the fingers.

Figure 6.20 Some muscles to explore.

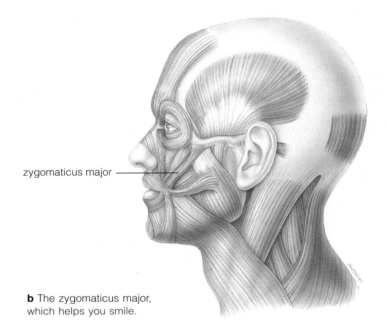

zygomaticus major

b The zygomaticus major, which helps you smile.

Hormones and Hunger

Americans are among the fattest people in the world, with 60 percent of adults overweight or obese. Excess weight is a risk factor for heart disease, diabetes, and some forms of cancer. So what should we do? The seemingly obvious answer is, "Lose the weight." But it's not that simple. Studies confirm what dieters have always thought. Once we put on extra pounds, they're hard to lose.

Like other mammals, we have fat-storing cells concentrated in adipose tissue. This energy warehouse evolved among our early ancestors, who could not always be sure where their next meal was coming from. Stored body fat helped them through the lean times. Once these cells form, however, they are in the body to stay. Take in more calories than you burn, and the cells plump up with fat droplets.

Adipose cells make leptin. This hormone acts on a part of the brain that deals with appetite. Researchers discovered that mutant mice that can't make leptin also eat nonstop. Does a lack of leptin also make overweight people eat too much? Unfortunately, no. Tests show that, if anything, overweight people have more leptin in their blood. It's possible that their leptin receptors aren't functioning

properly. Or perhaps their body cells just don't have enough of the receptors.

The stomach and brain also "weigh in" on our eating habits. Some of their cells secrete ghrelin, a hormone that sparks feelings of hunger. When a person's stomach is empty, more ghrelin is released. The level falls again after a meal.

In one experiment on ghrelin, obese volunteers ate a low-fat, low-calorie diet for six months. On average they lost 17 percent of their body weight. However, the level of ghrelin circulating in the subjects' blood had climbed 24 percent. The now-thinner dieters were hungrier than ever!

The topics of appetite, eating, and body weight take us into the world of digestion and nutrition. In this chapter you will learn how the digestive system brings into the body the nutrients living body cells need to survive. As it makes this key contribution to homeostasis, the digestive system interacts with other organ systems as well.

☑ *How Would You Vote?* Obesity may soon replace smoking as the main cause of preventable deaths in the United States. Fast food is contributing to the problem. Should fast-food items be required to carry health warnings? Cast your vote online at www.thomsonedu.com/biology/starr/humanbio.

 Key Concepts

THE DIGESTIVE SYSTEM
The digestive system mechanically and chemically breaks down food, absorbs nutrient molecules, and then eliminates the residues.

NUTRITION AND BODY WEIGHT
An ideal diet provides enough nutrients, vitamins, and minerals to support the metabolic activity of living cells. A given body weight can be maintained when the amount of energy used by the body balances energy inputs from food.

 Links to Earlier Concepts

This chapter shows how carbohydrates (2.9), proteins (2.11), and lipids (2.10) in food are broken down by digestion. Transport mechanisms, including diffusion and osmosis (3.9) and active transport (3.10) are essential to this process, for they provide the routes by which nutrient molecules enter the bloodstream. You will also build on what you have learned about different sources that can supply the body's energy needs (3.14).

7.1 The Digestive System: An Overview

LINKS TO
SECTIONS
4.1 AND 4.7

Stretched out, the gastrointestinal tract would be 6.5 to 9 meters long in an adult (21 to 30 feet). This long tube is where food processing takes place and nutrition begins.

Our **digestive system** is a tube with two openings and many specialized organs. It extends from the mouth to the anus and is also called the **gastrointestinal (GI) tract**.

An interesting fact about the GI tract is that while food or food residues are in it, technically the material is still *outside* the body. Nutrients don't "officially" enter the body until they move from the space inside the digestive tube—its *lumen*—into the bloodstream.

From beginning to end, epithelium lines the surfaces facing the lumen. The lining is coated with thick, moist mucus that protects the wall of the tube and enhances the diffusion of substances across it.

When we eat, food advances in one direction, from the mouth (the oral cavity) through the pharynx, the esophagus, stomach, small intestine, and large intestine. The large intestine ends in the rectum, anal canal, and anus. Figure 7.1 diagrams an adult's digestive system.

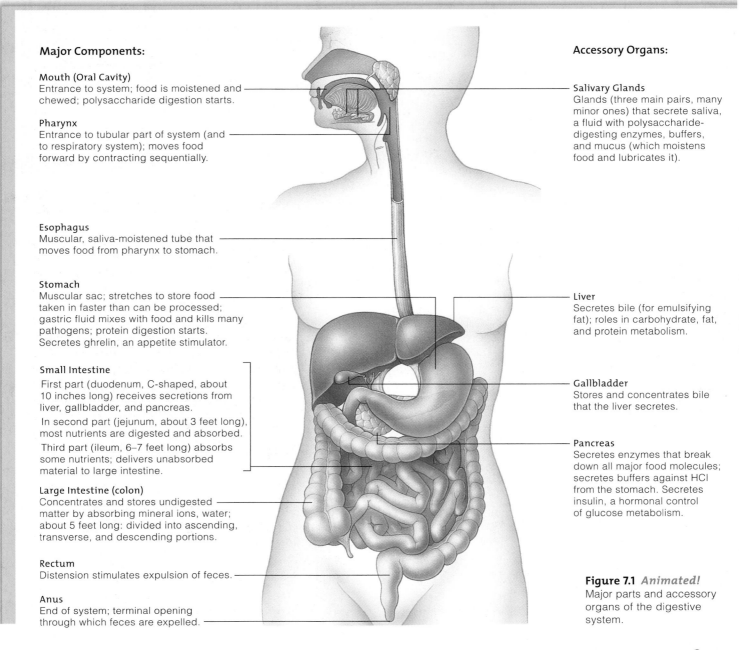

Major Components:

Mouth (Oral Cavity)
Entrance to system; food is moistened and chewed; polysaccharide digestion starts.

Pharynx
Entrance to tubular part of system (and to respiratory system); moves food forward by contracting sequentially.

Esophagus
Muscular, saliva-moistened tube that moves food from pharynx to stomach.

Stomach
Muscular sac; stretches to store food taken in faster than can be processed; gastric fluid mixes with food and kills many pathogens; protein digestion starts. Secretes ghrelin, an appetite stimulator.

Small Intestine
First part (duodenum, C-shaped, about 10 inches long) receives secretions from liver, gallbladder, and pancreas.
In second part (jejunum, about 3 feet long), most nutrients are digested and absorbed.
Third part (ileum, 6–7 feet long) absorbs some nutrients; delivers unabsorbed material to large intestine.

Large Intestine (colon)
Concentrates and stores undigested matter by absorbing mineral ions, water; about 5 feet long; divided into ascending, transverse, and descending portions.

Rectum
Distension stimulates expulsion of feces.

Anus
End of system; terminal opening through which feces are expelled.

Accessory Organs:

Salivary Glands
Glands (three main pairs, many minor ones) that secrete saliva, a fluid with polysaccharide-digesting enzymes, buffers, and mucus (which moistens food and lubricates it).

Liver
Secretes bile (for emulsifying fat); roles in carbohydrate, fat, and protein metabolism.

Gallbladder
Stores and concentrates bile that the liver secretes.

Pancreas
Secretes enzymes that break down all major food molecules; secretes buffers against HCl from the stomach. Secretes insulin, a hormonal control of glucose metabolism.

Figure 7.1 *Animated!*
Major parts and accessory organs of the digestive system.

THE DIGESTIVE TUBE HAS FOUR LAYERS

From the esophagus onward, the digestive tube wall has four layers (Figure 7.2). The *mucosa* (the innermost layer of epithelium) faces the lumen—the space through which food passes. The mucosa is surrounded by the *submucosa*, a layer of connective tissue with blood and lymph vessels and nerve cells. The next layer is *smooth muscle*—usually two sublayers, one circling the tube and the other oriented lengthwise. An outer layer, the *serosa*, is a very thin serous membrane (Section 4.7). Circular arrays of smooth muscle in sections of the GI tract are **sphincters**. Contractions of the sphincter muscles can close off a passageway. In your stomach, they help pace the forward movement of food and prevent backflow.

DIGESTIVE SYSTEM OPERATIONS CONTRIBUTE TO HOMEOSTASIS IN KEY WAYS

The following list summarizes the overall operations of the digestive system:

1. **Mechanical processing and motility**. Movements of various parts, such as the teeth, tongue, and muscle layers, break up, mix, and propel food material.

2. **Secretion**. Digestive enzymes and other substances are released into the digestive tube.

3. **Digestion**. Food is chemically broken down into nutrient molecules small enough to be absorbed.

4. **Absorption**. Digested nutrients and fluid pass across the tube wall and into blood or lymph.

5. **Elimination**. Undigested and unabsorbed residues are eliminated from the end of the GI tract.

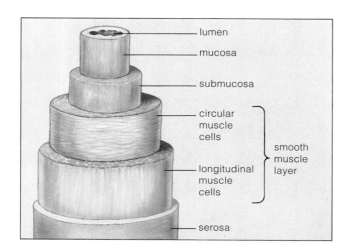

Figure 7.2 The four-layered wall of the gastrointestinal tract. The layers are not drawn to scale.

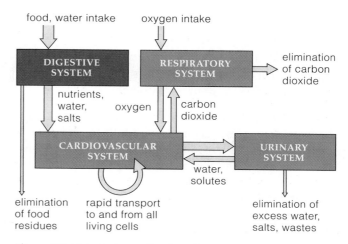

Figure 7.3 Links between the digestive system and other organ systems. As the text describes, it works together with the circulatory system, respiratory system, and urinary system to supply cells with raw materials and to eliminate wastes.

Various accessory structures secrete enzymes and other substances that are essential for different aspects of digestion and absorption. They include glands in the wall of the GI tract, the salivary glands, and the liver, gallbladder, and pancreas.

The "flow diagram" in Figure 7.3 gives a general idea of how the workings of the digestive system fit into the larger picture of homeostasis in the body. For instance, once nutrients from food have entered the bloodstream, the circulating blood carries them throughout the body. The respiratory system keeps all body cells, including those of digestive system tissues and organs, supplied with the oxygen they need for aerobic respiration, and removes carbon dioxide wastes. And although food residues are eliminated by the digestive system itself, the urinary system disposes of many other wastes or unneeded substances (such as excess salt) that enter the blood from the GI tract. Together these adjustments help maintain the proper volume and chemical makeup of the extracellular fluid. With this overview in mind, let's now see how each major component of the digestive system performs its functions.

The digestive tube extends from the mouth to the anus. For most of its length the tube wall consists of four layers, including smooth muscle.

The digestion and absorption of food make a vital contribution to homeostasis as interactions among the digestive, circulatory, respiratory, and urinary systems supply cells with raw materials and dispose of wastes.

7.2 Chewing and Swallowing: Food Processing Begins

LINK TO
SECTION
2.9

Food processing begins the moment food enters your mouth, where enzymes begin chemical digestion of starches.

PROCESSING STARTS WITH THE TEETH AND SALIVARY GLAND ENZYMES

In the **oral cavity**, or mouth, the food you eat begins to be broken apart by chewing. Most adults have thirty-two teeth (Figure 7.4*a*); young children have just twenty "primary teeth." A tooth's crown (Figure 7.4*b*) is coated with hardened calcium deposits, the tooth enamel—the hardest substance in the body. It covers a living, bonelike layer called dentin. Dentin and an inner pulp extend into the root. The pulp cavity contains blood vessels and nerves.

The shape of a tooth fits its function. Chisel-shaped incisors bite off chunks of food, and cone-shaped canines (cuspids) tear it. Premolars and molars, with broad crowns and rounded cusps, grind it.

Chewing mixes food with saliva from several **salivary glands** (Figure 7.4*c*). A large *parotid gland* nestles just in front of each ear. *Submandibular glands* lie just below the lower jaw in the floor of the mouth, and *sublingual glands*

are under your tongue. The tongue itself is skeletal muscle covered by a membrane. As described in Chapter 14, its taste receptors respond to dissolved chemicals.

Saliva is mostly water, but it includes other important substances. One, the enzyme **salivary amylase**, breaks down starch; chew on a soda cracker and you can feel it turning to mush as salivary amylase goes to work. A buffer, bicarbonate (HCO_3^-), keeps the pH of your mouth between 6.5 and 7.5, a range within which salivary amylase can function. Saliva also contains *mucins*, proteins that help bind food bits into a lubricated ball called a **bolus** (BOE-lus). Starch digestion continues in the stomach until acids there inactivate salivary amylase.

The roof of the mouth, a bone-reinforced section of the **palate**, provides a hard surface against which the tongue can press food as it mixes it with saliva. Tongue muscle contractions force the bolus into the **pharynx** (FARE-inks; throat). This passageway connects with the windpipe, or *trachea* (Figure 7.5), which leads to the lungs. It also connects with the **esophagus**, which leads to the stomach. Mucus secreted by the membrane lining the pharynx and esophagus lubricates the bolus, helping move food on its way.

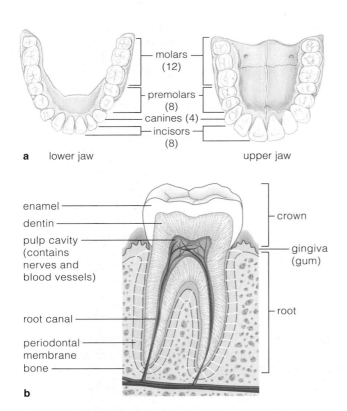

a lower jaw   upper jaw

molars (12)
premolars (8)
canines (4)
incisors (8)

enamel
dentin
pulp cavity (contains nerves and blood vessels)
root canal
periodontal membrane
bone
crown
gingiva (gum)
root

b

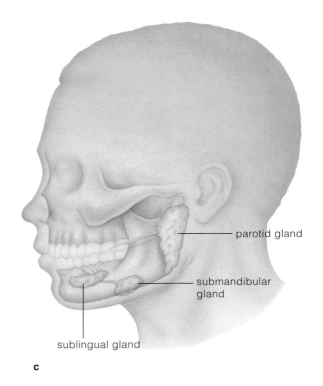

parotid gland
submandibular gland
sublingual gland

c

Figure 7.4 *Animated!* (**a**) Locations of the different types of teeth. (**b**) Anatomy of a human tooth. (**c**) Locations of the salivary glands.

THE DIGESTIVE SYSTEM

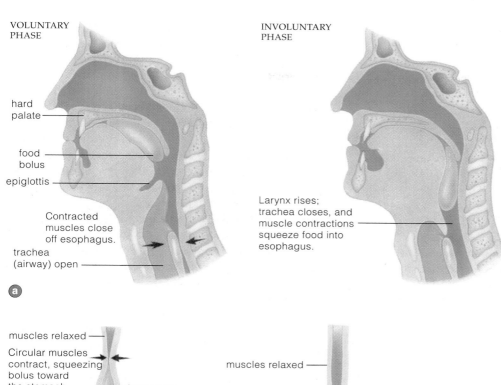

VOLUNTARY PHASE

INVOLUNTARY PHASE

hard palate

food bolus

epiglottis

Contracted muscles close off esophagus.

trachea (airway) open

Larynx rises; trachea closes, and muscle contractions squeeze food into esophagus.

a

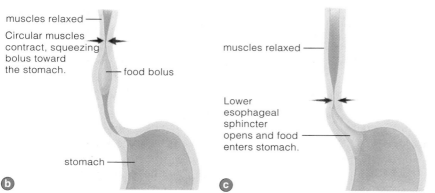

muscles relaxed

Circular muscles contract, squeezing bolus toward the stomach.

food bolus

stomach

b

muscles relaxed

Lower esophageal sphincter opens and food enters stomach.

c

Figure 7.5 *Animated!*
Swallowing and peristalsis. (**a**) Contractions of the tongue push the food bolus into the pharynx. Next, the vocal cords seal off the larynx, and the epiglottis bends downward, helping to keep the trachea closed. Contractions of throat muscles then squeeze the food bolus into the esophagus. (**b**,**c**) Finally, peristalsis in the esophagus moves the bolus through a sphincter, and food enters the stomach.

SWALLOWING HAS VOLUNTARY AND INVOLUNTARY PHASES

Swallowing a mouthful of food might seem simple, but it involves a sequence of events. Swallowing begins when voluntary skeletal muscle contractions push a bolus into the pharynx, stimulating sensory receptors in the pharynx wall. The receptors trigger a swallowing reflex in which involuntary muscle contractions keep food from moving up into your nose and down into the trachea. As this reflex gets under way, the vocal cords are stretched tight across the entrance to the larynx (your "voice box"). Then, the flaplike epiglottis is pressed down over the vocal cords as a secondary seal. For a moment,

breathing stops as food moves into the esophagus, so you normally don't choke when you swallow. When swallowed food reaches the lower end of the esophagus, it passes through a sphincter into the stomach (Figure 7.5*b*,*c*). Waves of muscle contractions called **peristalsis** (pair-uh-STALL-sis) help push the food bolus along.

As food is chewed, the teeth and tongue start breaking it up mechanically. Enzymes in saliva begin the chemical digestion of starches.

Swallowed food moves down the esophagus, through the lower esophageal sphincter, and into the stomach.

7.3 The Stomach: Food Storage, Digestion, and More

LINKS TO
SECTIONS
2.11, 4.6, AND 4.7

You may think of your stomach as simply a bag for holding food, but it really is a complex organ with multiple functions in processing the food you eat.

The **stomach** is a muscular, stretchable sac (Figure 7.6a) that has three functions:

1. It mixes and stores ingested food.

2. It produces secretions that help dissolve and break down food particles, especially proteins.

3. It helps control the passage of food into the small intestine.

The stomach wall surface facing the lumen is lined with glandular epithelium. Each day, gland cells in the lining release about two liters of hydrochloric acid (HCl), mucus, and other substances. These include pepsinogens, precursors of digestive enzymes called **pepsins**. Other gland cells secrete *intrinsic factor*, a protein required for vitamin B_{12} to be absorbed in the small intestine. Along with water, these substances make up the stomach's strongly acidic **gastric juice**. Combined with stomach contractions, the acidity converts swallowed boluses into a thick mixture called **chyme** (KIME). The acidity kills most microbes in food. It also can cause "heartburn" when gastric fluid backs up into the esophagus.

The digestion of proteins starts when the high acidity denatures proteins and exposes their peptide bonds. The acid also converts pepsinogens to active pepsins, which break the bonds, "chopping" the protein into fragments. Meanwhile, gland cells secrete the hormone *gastrin*, which stimulates cells that secrete HCl and pepsinogen.

Why don't HCl and pepsin break down the stomach lining? Usually, mucus and bicarbonate protect the lining. These protections, which form the "gastric mucosal barrier," can go awry, however. A common cause is the bacterium *Helicobacter pylori*. It produces a toxin that inflames the lining. Tight junctions that normally prevent HCl from passing between cells of the stomach lining break down, so hydrogen ions and pepsins diffuse into the lining—and that launches further damage. The resulting open sore is a *peptic ulcer*. Antibiotics can cure peptic ulcers caused by *H. pylori*, but about 20 percent of ulcers are related to factors such as chronic emotional stress, smoking, and excessive use of aspirin and alcohol.

Waves of peristalsis empty the stomach of food. These waves mix chyme and build force as they approach the pyloric sphincter at the stomach's base (Figure 7.6b). When a strong contraction arrives, the sphincter closes, squeezing most of the chyme back. Only a small amount moves into the small intestine at a given time. In this way the stomach regulates the rate at which food moves onward, so that food is not passed along faster than it can be processed. Depending mainly on the fat content and acidity of chyme, it can take from two to six hours for a full stomach to empty. When the stomach is empty, its walls crumple into folds called *rugae*.

Water and alcohol are two of a few substances that begin to be absorbed across the stomach wall. Liquids imbibed on an empty stomach pass rapidly to the small intestine, where further absorption occurs. When food is in the stomach, gastric emptying slows. This is why a person feels the effects of alcohol more slowly when drinking accompanies a meal.

The stomach's functions are storing food, initial digestion of proteins, and regulating passage of food (in the form of chyme) into the small intestine.

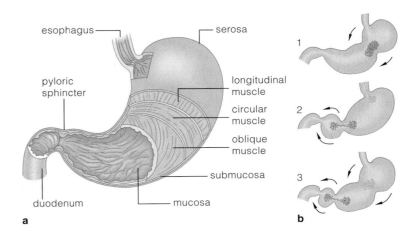

Figure 7.6 *Animated!*
(**a**) Structure of the stomach.
(**b**) A peristaltic wave down the stomach, produced by alternating contraction and relaxation of muscles in the stomach wall.

esophagus — serosa
pyloric sphincter
longitudinal muscle
circular muscle
oblique muscle
submucosa
duodenum — mucosa

a

b

1
2
3

7.4 The Small Intestine: A Huge Surface Area for Digestion and Absorption

Your small intestine—about an inch and a half in diameter and 6 meters (20 feet) long—absorbs most nutrients.

The key to the **small intestine**'s ability to absorb nutrients is the structure of its wall. Figure 7.7 shows how densely folded the mucosa is, and how the folds all project into the lumen. Each one of the folds has an amazing number of ever tinier projections. And the epithelial cells at the surface of these tiny projections have a brushlike crown of still *smaller* projections, all exposed to the lumen.

What is the benefit of so many folds and projections? Together, all the projections from the intestinal mucosa greatly increase the surface area for absorbing nutrients from chyme. Without that huge surface area, absorption would take place too slowly to sustain life.

Figure 7.7c shows a **villus** (plural: villi). Millions of villi, each one about a millimeter long, are the absorptive "fingers" on the folds of the intestinal mucosa. Their density makes the mucosa look velvety. Small blood vessels (an arteriole and a vein) in each villus and a lymph vessel move substances to and from the bloodstream (Figure 7.7d).

Most cells in the epithelium covering each villus bear microvilli (singular: microvillus). A **microvillus** is a threadlike projection of the epithelial cell's plasma membrane. Each epithelial cell has about 1,700 of them. This dense array gives the epithelium of villi its common name, the "brush border." Gland cells in the lining release digestive enzymes, and defensive cells called phagocytes ("cell eaters") patrol and help protect the lining.

> A folded mucosa, millions of villi, and hundreds of millions of microvilli give the small intestine a vast surface area for absorbing nutrients.

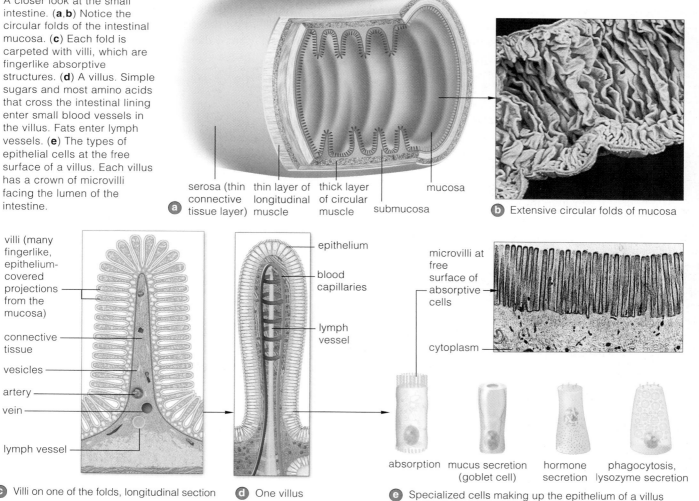

Figure 7.7 *Animated!*
A closer look at the small intestine. (**a**,**b**) Notice the circular folds of the intestinal mucosa. (**c**) Each fold is carpeted with villi, which are fingerlike absorptive structures. (**d**) A villus. Simple sugars and most amino acids that cross the intestinal lining enter small blood vessels in the villus. Fats enter lymph vessels. (**e**) The types of epithelial cells at the free surface of a villus. Each villus has a crown of microvilli facing the lumen of the intestine.

a serosa (thin connective tissue layer) — thin layer of longitudinal muscle — thick layer of circular muscle — submucosa — mucosa

b Extensive circular folds of mucosa

villi (many fingerlike, epithelium-covered projections from the mucosa)
connective tissue
vesicles
artery
vein
lymph vessel

c Villi on one of the folds, longitudinal section

epithelium
blood capillaries
lymph vessel

d One villus

microvilli at free surface of absorptive cells
cytoplasm

absorption — mucus secretion (goblet cell) — hormone secretion — phagocytosis, lysozyme secretion

e Specialized cells making up the epithelium of a villus

7.5 Accessory Organs: The Pancreas, Gallbladder, and Liver

LINKS TO
SECTIONS
2.7 AND 4.1

Before absorbed nutrients start moving throughout the body in the bloodstream, they make a key stop—the liver.

Figure 7.1 listed three important accessory organs of digestion: the pancreas, gallbladder, and liver. These organs are "accessory" because they assist digestion in some way but are outside the digestive tube.

THE PANCREAS PRODUCES A VARIETY OF DIGESTIVE ENZYMES

The long, slender **pancreas** nestles behind and below the stomach. It contains two kinds of gland cells: exocrine cells that make digestive enzymes and release them into the first section of the small intestine, and endocrine cells that make and release hormones into the bloodstream (Figure 7.8). The hormones help regulate blood sugar, and you will learn more about them in Chapter 15.

The pancreas produces four basic kinds of digestive enzymes, which can chemically dismantle the four major categories of food—complex carbohydrates, proteins, lipids, and nucleic acids. These enzymes work best when the pH is neutral or slightly alkaline, and so the pancreas also secretes fluid containing bicarbonate ($NaHCO_3^-$),

which neutralizes the acid in chyme arriving from the stomach. Depending on how often and what you eat, your pancreas may make as much as two quarts of this fluid each day!

THE GALLBLADDER STORES BILE

When the digestive system is processing food, along with pancreatic enzymes and bicarbonate-rich fluid, a fluid called *bile* also is released into the upper small intestine. The liver makes bile, as you will read shortly, and this yellowish fluid is stored in the **gallbladder**, a sausage-shaped, green-colored sac tucked behind the liver. As needed, the gallbladder contracts and empties bile into the small intestine where it aids in the digestion and absorption of fats. When there's no food moving through the GI tract, a sphincter closes off the main bile duct, and bile backs up into the gallbladder.

The gallbladder is one of our more "dispensible" organs. If it is surgically removed—usually due to the presence of gallstones, described in a moment—the duct that connects it to the small intestine enlarges and takes on the role of bile storage. This is why many millions of people today are walking around minus their gallbladder, with no ill effects.

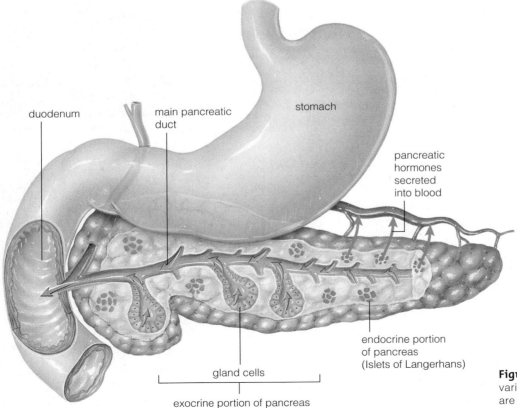

duodenum

main pancreatic duct

stomach

pancreatic hormones secreted into blood

endocrine portion of pancreas (Islets of Langerhans)

gland cells

exocrine portion of pancreas enzymes secreted into duodenum

Figure 7.8 The pancreas. The various regions of the pancreas are shown here much larger than their actual size.

THE DIGESTIVE SYSTEM

THE LIVER IS A MULTIPURPOSE ORGAN

The **liver** is one of the body's largest organs, and it serves a range of important functions (Table 7.1). Its role in digestion is to secrete bile—as much as 1,500 ml, or 1.5 quarts, every day. Bile contains bile salts, which the liver synthesizes from cholesterol. Bile salts help to emulsify fats in chyme—that is, to break up large fat globules into smaller bits.

The liver not only uses cholesterol to make bile salts, but also helps manage the level of this lipid in the body. Liver cells secrete cholesterol into bile, which bile salts emulsify along with other lipids in chyme. Some of this cholesterol becomes part of the food residues that eventually are excreted in feces. When there is chronically more cholesterol in bile than available bile salts can dissolve, the excess may separate out. Hard *gallstones*, which are mostly lumps of cholesterol, can develop in the gallbladder. They cause severe pain if they become lodged in bile ducts.

The liver also processes nutrient-bearing blood from the small intestine. This blood flows to the **hepatic portal vein**, which carries the blood through vessels in the liver. In the liver, excess glucose is taken up before a hepatic vein returns the blood to the general circulation (Figure 7.9). The liver converts and stores much of this glucose as glycogen.

Besides its digestive functions, the liver helps maintain homeostasis in other ways (Table 7.1). For instance, it processes incoming nutrient molecules into substances the body requires (such as blood plasma proteins) and

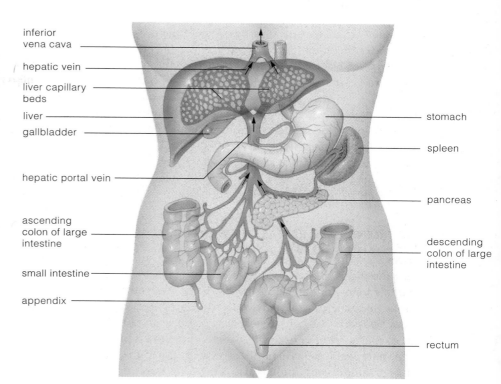

inferior vena cava
hepatic vein
liver capillary beds
liver
gallbladder
hepatic portal vein
ascending colon of large intestine
small intestine
appendix
stomach
spleen
pancreas
descending colon of large intestine
rectum

Figure 7.9 Hepatic portal system. Arrows show the direction of blood flow.

removes toxins ingested in food or already circulating in the bloodstream. It also inactivates many hormones and sends them to the kidneys for excretion (in urine). Ammonia (NH_3) that is produced when cells break down amino acids can be dangerously toxic to cells, especially in the nervous system. The circulatory system carries ammonia to the liver, where it is converted to a much less toxic waste product, urea, which also is excreted in urine.

Table 7.1	Ways the Liver Contributes to Homeostasis

1. Plays a role in carbohydrate metabolism
2. Partially controls synthesis of proteins in blood; assembles and disassembles certain other proteins
3. Forms urea from nitrogen-containing wastes
4. Assembles and stores some fats; forms bile to aid in fat digestion
5. Inactivates many chemicals (hormones, some drugs)
6. Detoxifies many poisons
7. Breaks down worn-out red blood cells
8. Aids immune response (removes some foreign particles)
9. Absorbs, stores factors needed for red blood cell formation

The pancreas, gallbladder, and liver are accessory organs of the digestive system.

The pancreas produces enzymes that can dismantle complex carbohydrates, protein, lipids, and nucleic acids.

The gallbladder stores bile, which is produced in the liver.

The liver also processes nutrient-bearing blood, storing excess glucose as glycogen, removing toxins, and other functions.

7.6 Digestion and Absorption in the Small Intestine

The small intestine's vast surface area is the stage for nutrients to be taken into the internal environment—tissue fluid and the bloodstream. Different kinds of nutrients are absorbed by way of several mechanisms.

On average, each day about 9 liters of fluid (roughly 10 quarts) enters the first section of the small intestine, the duodenum (doo-oh-DEE-num). This fluid includes chyme as well as digestive juices and other substances from the pancreas, liver, and gallbladder. All these chemicals have key roles in digestion.

NUTRIENTS ARE RELEASED BY CHEMICAL AND MECHANICAL MEANS

Chyme entering the duodenum triggers hormone signals that stimulate a brief flood of digestive enzymes from the pancreas. As part of "pancreatic juice," these enzymes act on carbohydrates, fats, proteins, and nucleic acids (Table 7.2). For example, like pepsin in the stomach, the pancreatic enzymes trypsin and chymotrypsin digest the polypeptide chains of proteins into peptide fragments. The fragments are then broken down to amino acids by different peptidases (present on the surface of the intestinal mucosa). As noted in Section 7.5, the pancreas also secretes bicarbonate, which buffers stomach acid and so maintains a chemical environment in which pancreatic enzymes can function.

Besides enzymes, fat digestion requires the bile salts in bile secreted by the liver and delivered via the gallbladder. You have already read that bile salts speed up fat digestion by breaking up large units of fat into smaller ones. How does this emulsification process work? Most fats in the average diet are triglycerides, which do not dissolve in water. Accordingly, in chyme they tend to clump into big fat globules. When peristalsis mixes chyme, the globules break up into droplets that become coated with bile salts (see Figure 7.10c). The salts bear a negative charge, so the coated droplets repel each other and stay separated. The droplets give fat-digesting enzymes a much greater surface area to act on. So, because triglycerides are emulsified, they can be broken down much more rapidly to monoglycerides and fatty acids, molecules that are small enough to be absorbed.

When a nutrient, water, or some other substance is absorbed, it crosses the intestine lining into the bloodstream. The vast absorptive surface area of the small intestine, with its villi and microvilli, helps make this process extremely efficient. **Segmentation** helps, too. In this process, rings of smooth muscle in the wall repeatedly contract and relax. This creates a back-and-forth movement that mixes digested material and forces it against the wall:

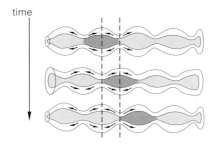

Table 7.2	Major Enzymes of Digestion and What They Do				
Enzyme	**Released by:**	**Active in:**	**Breaks down:**	**Resulting Products**	
DIGESTING CARBOHYDRATES:					
Salivary amylase	Salivary glands	Mouth, stomach	Polysaccharides	Disaccharides, oligosaccharides	
Pancreatic amylase	Pancreas	Small intestine	Polysaccharides	Disaccharides, monosaccharides	
Disaccharidases	Intestinal lining	Small intestine	Disaccharides	MONOSACCHARIDES* (e.g., glucose)	
DIGESTING PROTEINS:					
Pepsins	Stomach lining	Stomach	Proteins	Protein fragments	
Trypsin and chymotrypsin	Pancreas	Small intestine	Proteins	Protein fragments	
Carboxypeptidase	Pancreas	Small intestine	Peptides	AMINO ACIDS*	
Aminopeptidase	Intestinal lining	Small intestine	Peptides	AMINO ACIDS*	
DIGESTING FATS:					
Lipase	Pancreas	Small intestine	Triglycerides	FREE FATTY ACIDS, MONOGLYCERIDES*	
DIGESTING UCLEIC ACIDS:					
Pancreatic nucleases	Pancreas	Small intestine	DNA, RNA	NUCLEOTIDES*	
Intestinal nucleases	Intestinal lining	Small intestine	Nucleotides	NUCLEOTIDE BASES, MONOSACCHARIDES*	

*Products small enough to be absorbed into the internal environment.

THE DIGESTIVE SYSTEM

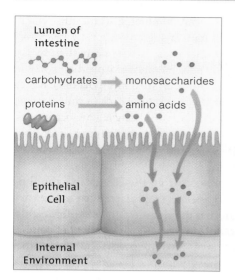
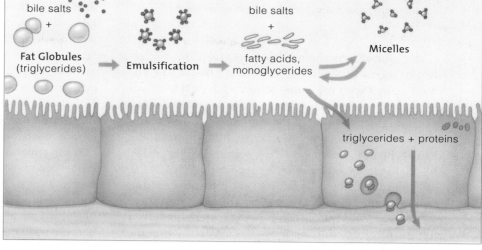

a Enzymes from the pancreas and from cells of the intestine lining complete the digestion of carbohydrates to monosaccharides and proteins to amino acids.

b Monosaccharides and amino acids are actively transported into epithelial cells, then move out of the cells and into the bloodstream.

c The constant movement of the intestine wall breaks up fat globules into small droplets (emulsification). Bile salts prevent the globules from re-forming. Pancreatic enzymes digest the droplets to fatty acids and monoglycerides.

d Micelles form as bile salts combine with nutrient molecules and phospholipids. Nutrients can easily slip into and out of the micelles.

e Concentrating monoglycerides and fatty acids in micelles creates steeper concentration gradients. Both substances then diffuse into cells of the intestine lining.

f Triglycerides re-form in cells of the intestine lining. They become coated with proteins, then are moved (by exocytosis) into the internal environment. They move into lacteals and then into the blood.

Figure 7.10 *Animated!* Digestion and absorption in the small intestine.

DIFFERENT NUTRIENTS ARE ABSORBED BY DIFFERENT MECHANISMS

By the time food is halfway through your small intestine, most of it has been broken apart and digested. Water crosses the intestine lining by osmosis, and cells in the lining also selectively absorb minerals. Figure 7.10 diagrams what happens with other kinds of nutrients.

For instance, transport proteins in the plasma membrane of brush border cells actively move some nutrients, such as the monosaccharide glucose and amino acids, across the lining. After glucose and amino acids are absorbed, they move directly into blood vessels.

By contrast, even after fat globules are emulsified, several more steps are required to move fatty acids and monoglycerides into the bloodstream (Figure 7.10d–f). Both of these kinds of molecules from digested lipids have hydrophobic regions, so they don't dissolve in watery chyme. Instead, the molecules clump with bile salts, along with cholesterol and other substances, and form tiny droplets. Each droplet is a *micelle* (my-CELL).

The molecules inside micelles constantly exchange places with those in chyme. However, the micelles concentrate them next to the intestine lining. When they are concentrated enough, nutrient molecules diffuse out of the micelles and into epithelial cells. Inside an epithelial cell, fatty acids and monoglycerides quickly reunite into triglycerides. Then triglycerides combine with proteins into particles that leave the cells by exocytosis and enter tissue fluid.

Unlike glucose and amino acids, when triglycerides are absorbed they do not move immediately into blood vessels. First they cross into lymph vessels called **lacteals**, which drain into the general circulation.

In the small intestine, most large organic molecules are digested to smaller molecules that can be absorbed.

Pancreatic enzymes secreted into the small intestine act on carbohydrates, fats, proteins, and nucleic acids in chyme. Bile salts emulsify fats (triglycerides), allowing them to be more easily digested.

Substances pass through brush border cells that line the surface of each villus by osmosis, active transport, or diffusion across plasma membranes.

7.7 The Large Intestine

Anything not absorbed in the small intestine moves into the large intestine, which absorbs water and some nutrients and eliminates wastes.

The **large intestine** is about 1.2 meters (5 feet) long (Figure 7.11). It begins as a blind pouch called the *cecum*. The cecum merges with the **colon**, which is divided into four regions in an inverted U-shape. The ascending colon travels up the right side of the abdomen, the transverse colon continues across to the left side, and the descending colon then turns downward. The sigmoid colon makes an S-curve and connects with the **rectum**.

Cells in the colon's lining actively transport sodium ions out of the tube. When the ion concentration there falls, water moves out by osmosis. As water is removed and returned to the bloodstream, the material left in the colon is gradually concentrated into *feces*, a mixture of undigested and unabsorbed matter, bacteria, and a little water. It is stored and finally eliminated. The typical brown color of feces comes mainly from bile pigments.

Bacteria make up about 30 percent of the dry weight of feces. Such microorganisms, including *Escherichia coli*, normally inhabit our intestines and are nourished by the food residues there. Their metabolism produces useful fatty acids and some vitamins (such as vitamin K), which are absorbed into the bloodstream. Feces of humans and other animals also can contain disease-causing organisms. Health officials use evidence of such "coliform bacteria," including *E. coli*, in water and food supplies as a measure of fecal contamination.

Your **appendix** projects from the cecum like the little finger of a glove. No one has ever discovered a digestive function for it, but, like the ileum of the small intestine, the appendix is colonized by defensive cells that combat bacteria you may have consumed in food. Feces that become wedged in the appendix can cause **appendicitis**. If an inflamed appendix isn't removed right away, it can burst and spew bacteria into the abdominal cavity where they can cause the life-threatening infection **peritonitis**.

Short, lengthwise bands of smooth muscle in the colon wall are gathered at their ends, like full skirts nipped in at elastic waistbands. As they contract and relax, material in the colon moves back and forth against the wall's absorptive surface. Shortly after you eat, hormone signals and nervous system commands direct large portions of the ascending and transverse colon to contract at the same time. Within a few seconds, residues in the colon may move as much as three-fourths of the colon's length and make way for incoming food. When feces distend the rectal wall, the stretching triggers defecation—elimination of feces from the body. From the rectum feces move into the **anal canal**. The nervous system also controls defecation. It can stimulate or inhibit contractions of sphincter muscles at the **anus**, the terminal opening of the GI tract.

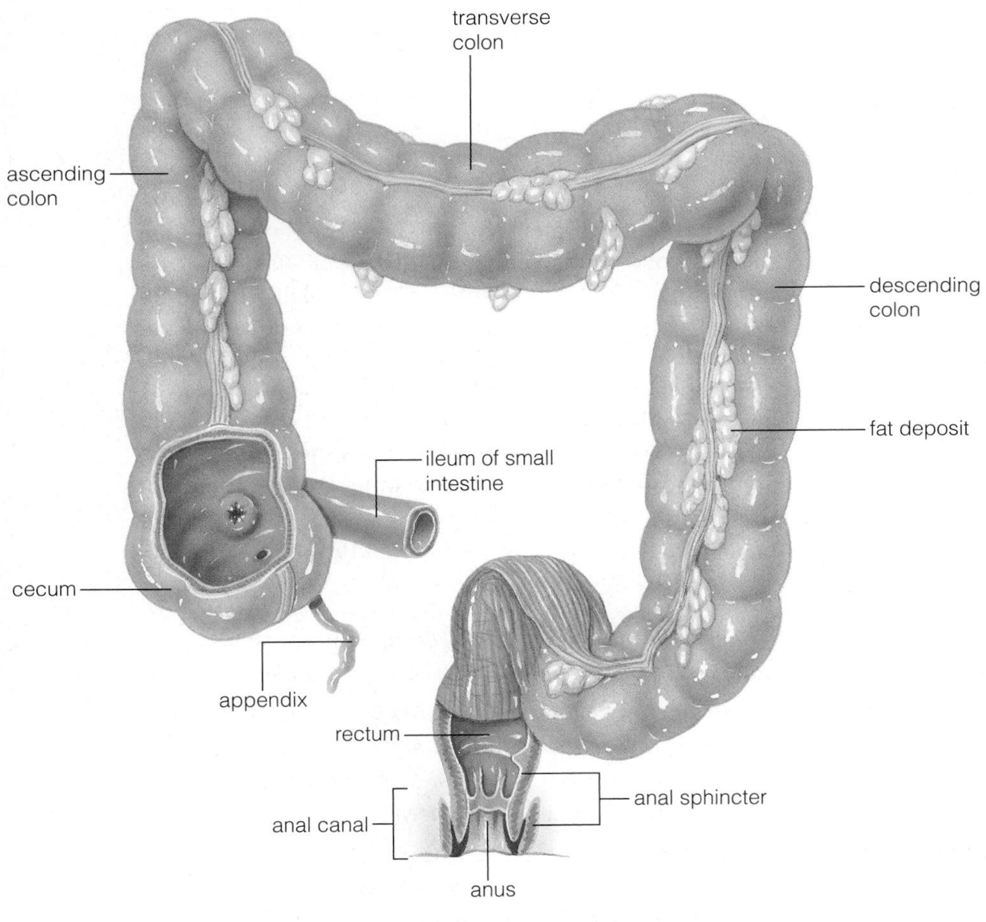

ascending colon
transverse colon
descending colon
fat deposit
ileum of small intestine
cecum
appendix
rectum
anal canal
anal sphincter
anus

Figure 7.11 *Animated!* The large intestine.

In the large intestine, water and salts are reabsorbed from food residues entering from the small intestine. The remaining concentrated residues are stored and later eliminated as feces.

7.8 Managing Digestion and the Processing of Nutrients

As you know, homeostatic controls counter shifts in the internal environment. In digestion, however, controls act in the GI tract, before digested nutrients enter the bloodstream.

NERVES AND HORMONES REGULATE DIGESTION

The nervous system and endocrine system jointly control digestion (Figure 7.12). These controls are sensitive to two factors: the amount of food in the GI tract and the food's chemical makeup.

Food entering the stomach stretches the stomach walls, and then those of the small intestine. This stretching triggers signals from sensory receptors in the walls. Some of the signals give you (by way of processing in your brain) that "full" feeling after you eat. Others can lead to the muscle contractions of peristalsis or the release of digestive enzymes and other substances. Centers in the brain coordinate these activities with factors such as how much blood is flowing to the small intestine, where nutrients are being absorbed.

There are several types of endocrine cells in the GI tract. For example, one type secretes the hormone gastrin into the bloodstream when the stomach contains protein. Gastrin mainly stimulates the release of hydrochloric acid (HCl), which you may recall is a key ingredient in gastric juice. After the stomach empties, the increased acidity there causes another type of endocrine cell to release somatostatin, which shuts down HCl secretion so that conditions in the stomach are less acid. Notice that this is an example of negative feedback.

Endocrine cells in the small intestine also release hormones. One of them, secretin, signals the pancreas to release bicarbonate when acid enters the duodenum. When fat enters the small intestine, a hormone called

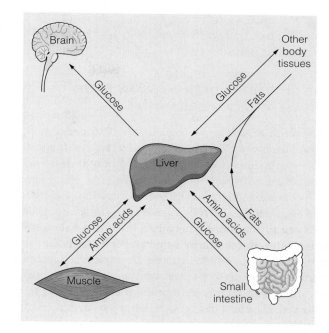

Figure 7.13 The liver's central role in managing nutrients.

CCK (for cholecystokinin) is released. CCK spurs the pancreas to release enzymes and triggers gallbladder contractions that deliver bile into the small intestine. Secretin and CCK also slow the rate at which the stomach empties—the mechanism mentioned in Section 7.3 that prevents food from entering the small intestine faster than it can be processed there. Yet another hormone, GIP (for glucose insulinotropic peptide) is released when fat and glucose are in the small intestine. Its roles include stimulating the release of insulin (from the pancreas), which is required for cells to take up glucose.

After nutrients are absorbed, the blood carries them to the liver, as described in Section 7.5. The liver is like a central shipping, storage, and receiving center. When glucose arrives from the small intestine, it is either shipped back out to the brain and other tissues, or stored as glycogen. Arriving fats may be stored, or used to make lipoproteins and other needed molecules. Liver cells also assemble amino acids into various proteins or process and reship them in a form cells can use to make ATP. Figure 7.13 is a simple visual summary of these activities. They are vital to maintain the body's supply of molecules cells can use as fuel, as building blocks, or in other ways.

Signals from the nervous system and the endocrine system control activity in the digestive system.

When absorbed nutrients reach the liver, they are sent on to the general circulation, stored, or converted to other forms for use in body cells.

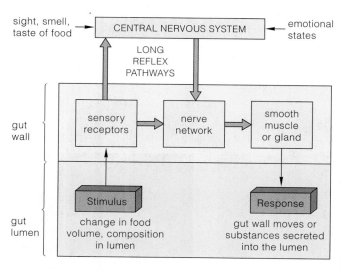

Figure 7.12 Controls over the digestive tract.

7.9 Digestive System Disorders

A disorder of the digestive system is a serious matter if it hampers processes that supply the body with nutrients or other needed substances.

THE GI TRACT IS OPEN TO MANY KINDS OF DISEASE-CAUSING ORGANISMS

The GI tract opens to the outside world, so it is a convenient portal into the body for bacteria, viruses, and other pathogens. Contaminated foods and water also can bring in harmful microorganisms.

A common effect of an intestinal infection is **diarrhea**, or watery feces. Diarrhea can develop when an irritant (such as a bacterial toxin) causes the lining of the small intestine to secrete more water and salts than the large intestine can absorb. It can also result when infections, stress, or other factors speed up peristalsis in the small intestine, so that there isn't time for enough water to be absorbed. Diarrheal diseases are dangerous in part because they dehydrate the body, depleting water and salts nerve and muscle cells need to function properly.

If you have ever had a case of "food poisoning," your stomach or intestines have been colonized by bacteria such as *Salmonella*, which can contaminate meat, poultry, and eggs (Figure 7.14*a*). Humans also are susceptible to several harmful strains of *E. coli* bacteria (Figure 7.14*b*). One of them, called O157:H7, inhabits the intestines of cattle. If a person eats ground beef or some other food that is contaminated with this microbe, it can cause a dangerous form of diarrhea that is coupled with anemia and may lead to kidney failure.

Bacteria that cause tooth decay (dental caries) flourish on food residues in the mouth, especially sugars (Figure 7.14*c*). Daily brushing and flossing are the best way to avoid a bacterial infection of the gums, which can lead to **gingivitis** (jin-juh-VY-tus). This inflammation can spread to the periodontal membrane that helps anchor a tooth in the jaw. Untreated periodontal disease can slowly destroy a tooth's bony socket, which can lead to loss of the tooth and other complications.

Section 7.3 mentioned **peptic ulcers**, open sores in the wall of the stomach or small intestine (Figure 7.14*d*) that are caused by the bacterium *Helicobacter pylori*. This microbe also is responsible for some cases of **gastritis** (inflammation of the GI tract), and even stomach cancer.

COLON DISORDERS RANGE FROM INCONVENIENT TO LIFE-THREATENING

It is normal to "move the bowels," or defecate, anywhere from three times a day to once a week. In **constipation**, food residues remain in the colon for too long, too much water is reabsorbed, and the feces become dry, hard, and difficult to eliminate. Constipation is uncomfortable, and it is a common cause of the enlarged rectal blood vessels known as hemorrhoids.

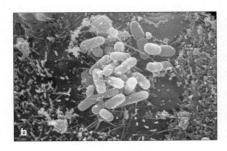

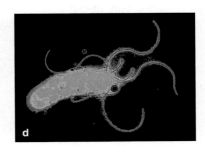

Figure 7.14 Some bacteria that infect the GI tract.
(**a**) Raw poultry may harbor *Salmonella*. Kitchen tools, and the cook's hands, should be thoroughly washed after handling raw poultry.
(**b**) A disease-causing strain of *E. coli* on an intestinal cell.
(**c**) Various bacteria on a human tooth.
(**d**) *Helicobacter pylori*.

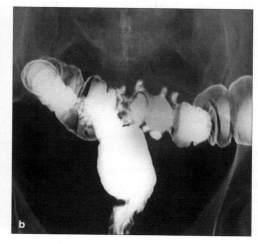

Figure 7.15 Fruits like grapes (**a**) are good sources of both soluble and insoluble fiber, which provides bulk in the diet and helps keep feces moving through the colon. (**b**) X-ray showing a colon in which knoblike diverticula (green areas) have developed.

Constipation is often due to a lack of bulk in the diet. *Bulk* is the volume of fiber (mainly cellulose from plant foods) and other undigested food material that is not decreased by absorption in the colon. Much of it consists of *insoluble fiber* such as cellulose and other plant compounds that humans cannot digest (we lack the required enzymes) and that does not easily dissolve in water. Wheat bran and the edible skins of fruits such as apples, plums, and grapes are just a few examples (Figure 7.15*a*). (*Soluble* fiber consists of plant carbohydrates such as fruit pectins that swell or dissolve in water.) If you chronically eat too little fiber, you are much more likely to be in the 50 percent of the U.S. population in whom the colon has formed diverticula—knoblike sacs where the inner colon lining protrudes through the intestinal wall. Inflammation of a diverticulum is called **diverticulitis**, and it can have quite serious complications, including peritonitis, if an inflamed diverticulum ruptures. A more common form of this disorder is **diverticulosis** (Figure 7.15*b*), in which diverticula are there but have not (yet) become inflamed.

Have you ever heard of someone having a "spastic colon"? This problematical condition also is known as **irritable bowel syndrome** (IBS), and it is the most common intestinal disorder. IBS often begins in early to mid-adulthood, and it affects twice as many women as men. Although the symptoms—abdominal pain and alternating diarrhea and constipation—are distressing, a medical examination rarely turns up signs of disease. While the direct cause of IBS symptoms is a disturbance in the smooth muscle contractions that move material through the colon, the reason for the change is not known.

Colon cancer is the #2 cancer diagnosis in the United States, second only to lung cancer, and it accounts for about 20 percent of all cancer deaths. Colon cancer often gets started when a growth called a polyp develops on the colon wall and becomes malignant. Fortunately, many cases of colon cancer and precancerous polyps can easily be detected by colonoscopy. After the patient is mildly sedated, a physician inserts a viewing tube into the colon and can examine it for polyps and other signs of disease.

The tendency to develop polyps, and colon cancer, can run in families, but usually there is no obvious genetic link. Because colon cancer is much more common in Western societies, some experts have proposed that the typical high-fat, low-fiber Western diet may be a factor, and there is a lot of active research on the issue. Chapter 23 looks in more detail at this and other forms of cancer.

MALABSORPTION DISORDERS PREVENT SOME NUTRIENTS FROM BEING ABSORBED

Anything that interferes with the ability of the small intestine to take up nutrients can lead to a *malabsorption disorder*. Many adults develop **lactose intolerance**, a mild disorder that results from deficiency of the enzyme lactase. It prevents normal breakdown and absorption of lactose, the sugar found in milk and many other milk products.

More serious malabsorption disorders are associated with some diseases that affect the pancreas, including the genetic condition **cystic fibrosis** (CF). Patients with CF don't make the necessary pancreatic enzymes for normal digestion and absorption of fats and other nutrients. (CF also affects the lungs, as you will read in later chapters.) **Crohn's disease** is an inflammatory disorder that can so severely damage the intestinal lining that much of the intestine must be removed.

7.10 The Body's Nutritional Requirements

LINKS TO
SECTIONS
2.9–2.11

Diet definitely has a profound effect on body functions. So, what is an average person "supposed" to eat?

What happens to the nutrients we absorb? As you've read, they are burned as fuel to provide energy and used as building blocks to build and replace tissues. In this section we focus on the three main classes of nutrients—carbohydrates, lipids, and proteins—and we take a look at new guidelines for what makes up a healthy diet.

COMPLEX CARBOHYDRATES ARE BEST

There are many views on the definition of a "proper" diet, but on one point just about all nutritionists can agree: The healthiest carbohydrates are the "complex" ones such as starch—the type of carbohydrate in fleshy fruits, cereal grains, and legumes, including peas and beans.

Complex carbohydrates are easily broken down to glucose, the body's chief energy source. Foods rich in complex carbohydrates also usually are high in fiber, including the insoluble fiber that adds needed bulk to feces and helps prevent constipation (see Section 7.9). By contrast, simple sugars don't have much fiber, and they lack the vitamins and minerals of whole foods.

The average American eats up to two pounds of refined sugars per week. In packaged foods, these sugars often are disguised as corn syrup, corn sweeteners, and dextrose. Refined sugars represent "empty calories" because they add to our caloric intake, but meet no other nutritional needs. Highly refined carbohydrates also have a high *glycemic index*. This means that within minutes of being absorbed, refined carbohydrates cause a surge in the blood levels of sugar and insulin.

Circulating insulin makes cells take up glucose quickly, and it also prevents cells from using stored fat as fuel. At the same time, glucose that is not needed as fuel for cells is stored as fat. When blood sugar levels later fall, we feel hungry. So we eat more, secrete more insulin, and keep storing fat, mainly in the form of triglycerides. Over time, high triglyceride levels increase the risk of heart disease and type 2 diabetes.

THERE ARE GOOD FATS AND BAD FATS

The body can't survive without fats and other lipids. The phospholipid lecithin and the sterol cholesterol both are building blocks of cell membranes. Fat stored in adipose tissue serves as an energy reserve, cushions organs such as the eyes and kidneys, and provides insulation beneath the

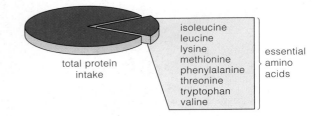

Figure 7.16 The eight essential amino acids.

skin. The brain of a young child won't develop properly without a supply of cholesterol and saturated fat. The body also stores fat-soluble vitamins in adipose tissues.

The liver can manufacture most fats the body needs, including cholesterol, from protein and carbohydrates. The ones it cannot produce are **essential fatty acids**, but whole foods and vegetable oils provide plenty of them. Linoleic acid is an example. You can get enough of it by consuming just one teaspoon a day of corn oil, olive oil, or some other polyunsaturated fat.

Animal fats—the fat in butter, cheese, and fatty meat—are rich in saturated fats and cholesterol. Eating too much of these kinds of foods increases the risk for heart disease and stroke, as well as for certain cancers. The *trans fatty acids*, or "trans fats," are also bad for the cardiovascular system. Food labels are now required to show the amounts of trans fats, saturated fats, and cholesterol per serving. Section 9.8 has more information on "good" and "bad" forms of cholesterol.

PROTEINS ARE VITAL TO LIFE

When the digestive system digests and absorbs proteins, their amino acids become available for protein synthesis in cells. Of the twenty common amino acids, eight are **essential amino acids**. Our cells cannot make them, so we must obtain them from food. The eight are isoleucine, leucine, lysine, methionine, phenylalanine, threonine, tryptophan, and valine (Figure 7.16).

Most animal proteins are *complete*, meaning their ratios of amino acids match human nutritional needs. Nearly all plant proteins are *incomplete*, meaning they lack one or more of the essential amino acids. The proteins of quinoa (KEEN-wah) are a notable exception. In parts of the world where animal protein is a luxury, traditional cuisines include combinations of plant proteins, such as beans with rice, cornbread with chili, tofu with rice, and lentils with wheat bread.

USDA Nutritional Guidelines	
Food Group	Amount Recommended
Vegetables	2.5 cups/day
Dark green vegetables	3 cups/week
Orange vegetables	2 cups/week
Legumes	3 cups/week
Starchy vegetables	3 cups/week
Other vegetables	6.5 cups/week
Fruits	2 cups/day
Milk Products	3 cups/day
Grains	6 ounces/day
Whole grains	3 ounces/day
Other grains	3 ounces/day
Fish, poultry, lean meat	5.5 ounces/day
Oils	24 grams/day

Figure 7.17 From the United States Department of Agriculture, a summary of nutritional guidelines as of 2006. The recommended proportions add up to a daily caloric intake of 2,000 kilocalories for sedentary females between ages ten and thirty. Recommended intake and serving sizes are larger for males and highly active females and less for older females. The USDA recommends varying protein choices (fish, poultry, lean red meats, eggs, beans, nuts, and seeds).

GUIDELINES FOR HEALTHY EATING

The United States Food and Drug Administration has issued a set of nutritional guidelines to replace its earlier "food pyramid." These guidelines are based on nutritional research. They are designed to educate consumers about how a healthy diet can help reduce the risk for chronic diseases, such as diabetes, heart disease, hypertension (high blood pressure), and certain cancers. Figure 7.17 shows the recommended number of servings of various food groups. In comparison with the diet of a typical American, the guidelines call for a reduced intake of refined grains (such as white flour and white rice), trans fats and saturated fats, and refined sugars. The guidelines also suggest eating more whole grains, legumes, dark green and orange vegetables, fruits, and milk products. The full report can be downloaded from www.health.gov.

The new USDA guidelines call for about 55 percent of daily calories to come from complex carbohydrates, and recommends limiting total fat intake to 20 to 30 percent of daily caloric intake. About 4 ounces of lean meat—the rough equivalent of a small hamburger—is enough to meet minimum daily protein requirements.

There are respected alternative diets, however. One of them is the *Mediterranean diet*, which is associated with lower risk of heart disease, among other chronic ills. It emphasizes grains first, and then fruits and vegetables. Its main fat is olive oil, an excellent antioxidant. It limits weekly intakes of animal protein, eggs, and refined sugars, and places red meat at the pyramid's tiny tip.

In recent years, highly promoted diet plans that strictly limit carbohydrates and load up on proteins (and, often, fats) have become wildly popular. Although low-carb diets are controversial and their long-term effects on organs such as the kidneys are not known, millions of dieters swear by them because they can lead to extremely rapid weight loss.

A healthy diet must provide essential nutrients in the proper proportions and amounts.

Complex carbohydrates provide nutrients and fiber without adding "empty" calories.

Fats and other lipids are used for building cell membranes, energy stores, and other needs. Food must provide the essential fatty acids, which the body cannot synthesize.

Proteins are the source of essential amino acids.

7.11 Vitamins and Minerals

Vitamins are organic substances that are essential for growth and survival. No other substances can play their metabolic roles. In the course of evolution, animal cells have lost the ability to synthesize these substances, so we must obtain vitamins from food.

At a minimum, our cells need the vitamins listed in Table 7.3. Each vitamin has specific metabolic functions. Many chemical reactions use several types, and the absence of one affects the functions of others.

Minerals are inorganic substances that are essential for growth and survival. For instance, all of your cells need iron for their electron transport chains. Your red blood cells can't function without iron in hemoglobin, the oxygen-carrying pigment in blood. And neurons stop functioning without sodium and potassium (Table 7.4).

In general, people who are in good health and who eat a balanced diet of whole foods may get most of the vitamins and minerals they need. According to the

Table 7.3 Vitamins: Sources, Functions, and Effects of Deficiencies or Excesses*

Vitamin	Common Sources	Main Functions	Signs of Severe Long-Term Deficiency	Signs of Extreme Excess
FAT-SOLUBLE VITAMINS:				
A	Its precursor comes from beta carotene in yellow fruits, yellow or green leafy vegetables; also in fortified milk, egg yolk, fish liver	Used in synthesis of visual pigments, bone, teeth; maintains epithelia	Dry, scaly skin; lowered resistance to infections; night blindness; permanent blindness	Malformed fetuses; hair loss; changes in skin; liver and bone damage; bone pain
D	D_3 formed in skin and in fish liver oils, egg yolk, fortified milk; converted to active form elsewhere	Promotes bone growth and mineralization; enhances calcium absorption	Bone deformities (rickets) in children; bone softening in adults	Retarded growth; kidney damage; calcium deposits in soft tissues
E	Whole grains, dark green vegetables, vegetable oils	Possibly inhibits effects of free radicals; helps maintain cell membranes; blocks breakdown of vitamins A and C in gut	Lysis of red blood cells; nerve damage	Muscle weakness, fatigue, headaches, nausea
K	Colon bacteria form most of it; also in green leafy vegetables, cabbage	Blood clotting; ATP formation via electron transport	Abnormal blood clotting; severe bleeding (hemorrhaging)	Anemia; liver damage and jaundice
WATER-SOLUBLE VITAMINS:				
B_1 (thiamine)	Whole grains, green leafy vegetables, legumes, lean meats, eggs	Connective tissue formation; folate utilization; coenzyme action	Water retention in tissues; tingling sensations; heart changes; poor coordination	None reported from food; possible shock reaction from repeated injections
B_2 (riboflavin)	Whole grains, poultry, fish, egg white, milk	Coenzyme action	Skin lesions	None reported
Niacin	Green leafy vegetables, potatoes, peanuts, poultry, fish, pork, beef	Coenzyme action	Contributes to pellagra (damage to skin, gut, nervous system, etc.)	Skin flushing; possible liver damage
B_6	Spinach, tomatoes, potatoes, meats	Coenzyme in amino acid metabolism	Skin, muscle, and nerve damage; anemia	Impaired coordination; numbness in feet
Pantothenic acid	In many foods (meats, yeast, egg yolk especially)	Coenzyme in glucose metabolism, fatty acid and steroid synthesis	Fatigue, tingling in hands, headaches, nausea	None reported; may cause diarrhea occasionally
Folate (folic acid)	Dark green vegetables, whole grains, yeast, lean meats; colon bacteria produce some folate	Coenzyme in nucleic acid and amino acid metabolism	A type of anemia; inflamed tongue; diarrhea; impaired growth; mental disorders	Masks vitamin B_{12} deficiency
B_{12}	Poultry, fish, red meat, dairy foods (not butter)	Coenzyme in nucleic acid metabolism	A type of anemia; impaired nerve function	None reported
Biotin	Legumes, egg yolk; colon bacteria produce some	Coenzyme in fat, glycogen formation, and amino acid metabolism	Scaly skin (dermatitis), sore tongue, depression, anemia	None reported
C (ascorbic acid)	Fruits and vegetables, especially citrus, berries, cantaloupe, cabbage, broccoli, green pepper	Collagen synthesis; possibly inhibits effects of free radicals; structural role in bone, cartilage, and teeth; role in carbohydrate metabolism	Scurvy, poor wound healing, impaired immunity	Diarrhea, other digestive upsets; may alter results of some diagnostic tests

*The guidelines for appropriate daily intakes are being worked out by the Food and Drug Administration.

Mineral	Common Sources	Main Functions	Signs of Severe Long-Term Deficiency	Signs of Extreme Excess
Calcium	Dairy products, dark green vegetables, dried legumes	Bone, tooth formation; blood clotting; neural and muscle action	Stunted growth; possibly diminished bone mass (osteoporosis)	Impaired absorption of other minerals; kidney stones in susceptible people
Chloride	Table salt (usually too much in diet)	HCl formation in stomach; contributes to body's acid–base balance; neural action	Muscle cramps; impaired growth; poor appetite	Contributes to high blood pressure in susceptible people
Copper	Nuts, legumes, seafood, drinking water	Used in synthesis of melanin, hemoglobin, and some electron transport chain components	Anemia, changes in bone and blood vessels	Nausea, liver damage
Fluorine	Fluoridated water, tea, seafood	Bone, tooth maintenance	Tooth decay	Digestive upsets; mottled teeth and deformed skeleton in chronic cases
Iodine	Marine fish, shellfish, iodized salt, dairy products	Thyroid hormone formation	Enlarged thyroid (goiter), with metabolic disorders	Goiter
Iron	Whole grains, green leafy vegetables, legumes, nuts, eggs, lean meat, molasses, dried fruit, shellfish	Formation of hemoglobin and cytochrome (electron transport chain component)	Iron-deficiency anemia, impaired immune function	Liver damage, shock, heart failure
Magnesium	Whole grains, legumes, nuts, dairy products	Coenzyme role in ATP-ADP cycle; roles in muscle, nerve function	Weak, sore muscles; impaired neural function	Impaired neural function
Phosphorus	Whole grains, poultry, red meat	Component of bone, teeth, nucleic acids, ATP, phospholipids	Muscular weakness; loss of minerals from bone	Impaired absorption of minerals into bone
Potassium	Diet provides ample amounts	Muscle and neural function; roles in protein synthesis and body's acid–base balance	Muscular weakness	Muscular weakness, paralysis, heart failure
Sodium	Table salt; diet provides ample to excessive amounts	Key role in body's acid–base balance; roles in muscle and neural function	Muscle cramps	High blood pressure in susceptible people
Sulfur	Proteins in diet	Component of body proteins	None reported	None likely
Zinc	Whole grains, legumes, nuts, meats, seafood	Component of digestive enzymes; roles in normal growth, wound healing, sperm formation, and taste and smell	Impaired growth, scaly skin, impaired immune function	Nausea, vomiting, diarrhea; impaired immune function and anemia

*The guidelines for appropriate daily intakes are being worked out by the Food and Drug Administration.

American Medical Association, however, many physicians now recommend that even healthy people can benefit from certain vitamin and mineral supplements, in moderation. For example, vitamins E, C, and A lessen some aging effects and can improve immune function by inactivating free radicals. (A free radical, remember, is an atom or group of atoms that is highly reactive because it has an unpaired electron.) Vitamin K supplements help older women retain calcium and diminish the loss of bone due to osteoporosis.

However, metabolism varies in its details from one person to the next, so no one should take massive doses of any vitamin or mineral supplement except under medical supervision. Also, excessive amounts of many vitamins and minerals can harm anyone. For example, very large doses of the fat-soluble vitamins A and D can accumulate in tissues, especially in the liver, and interfere with normal metabolism. And although sodium has roles in the body's salt–water balance, muscle activity, and nerve function, prolonged, excessive intake of sodium may contribute to high blood pressure in some people.

Severe shortages or self-prescribed, massive excesses of vitamins and minerals can disturb the delicate balances in body function that promote health.

7.12 Calories Count: Food Energy and Body Weight

Attitudes about body weight often are cultural, but excess weight also raises real health issues.

The "fat epidemic" described in this chapter's introduction is spreading around the world. In the United States alone, about 300,000 people die each year due to preventable, weight-related conditions. Lifestyles are becoming more sedentary, and many people simply are eating more: Studies show that since the 1970s portion sizes in most restaurants have doubled. This is one reason why the FDA guidelines noted in Section 7.10 don't say "servings" of food but specify amounts instead.

The scientific standard for body weight is based on the ratio of weight to height (Figure 7.18). A person who is overweight has a higher than desirable weight-for-height. **Obesity** is an excess of body fat—more than 20 percent for males, and 24 percent for females. The World Health Organization has declared obesity a major global health concern, in part because its harmful effects on health are so serious—increasing not only the risk of type 2 diabetes and heart disease, but also osteoarthritis, high blood pressure, kidney stones, and many other ailments.

One indicator of weight-related health risk is the *body mass index* (BMI). It is determined by the formula

$$BMI = \frac{weight\ (pounds) \times 700}{height\ (inches)^2}$$

If your BMI value is 27 or higher, the health risk rises dramatically. Other risk factors include smoking, a genetic predisposition for heart disease, and fat stored above the waist (having an "apple shape" or "beer belly").

When someone is overweight, the usual culprit is a chronically unbalanced "energy equation" in which too many food calories are taken in while too few calories are burned. We measure food energy in **kilocalories** (kcal). A kilocalorie is 1,000 calories of heat energy. (Calorie, with a capital "C," is shorthand for a kilocalorie.) A value called **basal metabolic rate** (BMR) measures the amount of energy needed to sustain basic body functions. As a general rule, the younger you are, the higher your BMR. But BMR also varies from person to person, and it is influenced by the amount of muscle tissue in the body, emotions, hormones, and differences in physical activity. Adding BMR to the kcal needed for other demands (such as body movements) gives the total amount of food energy you need to fuel your daily life.

To figure out how many kcal you should take in daily to maintain a desired weight, multiply that weight (in pounds) by 10 if you are sedentary, by 15 if you are fairly active, and by 20 if you are highly active. From the value you get this way, subtract the following amount:

Age	20–34	Subtract	0
	35–44		100
	45–54		200
	55–64		300
	Over 65		400

For instance, if you want to weigh 120 pounds and are very active, $120 \times 20 = 2,400$ kilocalories. If you are 35 years old and moderately active, then you should take in a total of $1,800 - 100$, or 1,700 kcal a day. Along with

Figure 7.18 How to estimate the "ideal" weight for an adult. The values given are consistent with a long-term Harvard study into the link between excessive weight and increased risk of heart disorders. Depending on certain factors, such as having a small, medium, or large skeletal frame, the "ideal" may vary by plus or minus 10 percent.

Weight Guidelines for Women

Starting with an ideal weight of 100 pounds for a woman who is 5 feet tall, add five additional pounds for each additional inch of height. Examples:

Height (feet)	Weight (pounds)
5' 2"	110
5' 3"	115
5' 4"	120
5' 5"	125
5' 6"	130
5' 7"	135
5' 8"	140
5' 9"	145
5' 10"	150
5' 11"	155
6'	160

Weight Guidelines for Men

Starting with an ideal weight of 106 pounds for a man who is 5 feet tall, add six additional pounds for each additional inch of height. Examples:

Height (feet)	Weight (pounds)
5' 2"	118
5' 3"	124
5' 4"	130
5' 5"	136
5' 6"	142
5' 7"	148
5' 8"	154
5' 9"	160
5' 10"	166
5' 11"	172
6'	178

Table 7.5   Calories Expended in Some Common Activities

Activity	Kcal/hour per pound of body weight	Hours needed to lose 1 lb. fat 120 lbs	155 lbs	185 lbs
Basketball	3.78	7.7	6.0	5.0
Cycling (9 mph)	2.70	10.8	8.4	7.0
Hiking	2.52	11.6	8.9	7.5
Jogging	4.15	7.0	5.4	4.5
Mowing lawn (push mower)	3.06	9.5	7.4	6.2
Racquetball	3.90	7.5	5.8	4.8
Running (9-minute mile)	5.28	5.5	4.3	3.6
Snow skiing (cross-country)	4.43	6.6	5.1	4.3
Swimming (slow crawl)	3.48	8.4	6.5	5.4
Tennis	3.00	9.7	7.5	6.3
Walking (moderate pace)	2.16	13.5	10.4	8.7

To calculate these values for your own body weight, first multiply your weight by the kcal/hour expended for an activity to determine total kcal you use during one hour of the activity. Then divide that number into 3,500 (kcal in a pound of fat) to obtain the number of hours you must perform the activity to burn a pound of body fat.

this rough estimate, factors such as height and gender also must be considered. Males tend to have more muscle and so burn more calories (they have a higher BMR); hence an active woman needs fewer kilocalories than an active man of the same height and weight. Nor does she need as many as another active woman who weighs the same but is several inches taller.

GENES, WEIGHT CONTROL, AND EXERCISE

You've probably noticed that some people have a lot more trouble keeping off excess weight than others do. Although various factors influence body weight, recent research has shown that genes play a major role. As you will read later in this textbook, there are different chemical versions of many genes, and each version may have a slightly different effect. Scientists have identified several dozen genes that govern hormones, such as leptin and ghrelin, that influence appetite, hunger, how the body stores fat, and other weight-related factors. It may be that differences among genes help explain why some people stay slim no matter what and how often they eat, while others wage a lifelong struggle with extra pounds.

Regardless of genes, for most people maintaining a healthy weight over the years requires balancing their "energy budget" so that energy in—calories in food— equals energy used by our cells. Losing a pound of fat requires expending about 3,500 kcal. Although weight-loss diets may accomplish this deficit temporarily, over the long haul keeping off excess weight means pairing a moderate reduction in caloric intake with an increase in physical activity (Table 7.5). Exercise also increases the mass of skeletal muscles, and even at rest muscle burns more calories than other types of tissues.

Emotions can influence weight gain and loss, sometimes to extremes. People who suffer from **anorexia nervosa** see themselves as fat no matter how thin they become. An anorexic purposely starves and may overexercise as well. Most common among younger women, anorexia can be fatal. Another extreme is the binge–purge disorder called **bulimia**. The term means "having an oxlike appetite." A bulimic might consume as much as 50,000 calories at one sitting and then purposely vomit, take a laxative, or both. Chronic vomiting can erode away the enamel from a person's teeth (due to stomach acid) and rupture the stomach. In severe cases it also can cause chemical imbalances that lead to heart and kidney failure.

To maintain an acceptable body weight, energy input (caloric intake) must be balanced with energy output in the form of metabolic activity and exercise.

Basal metabolic rate, physical activity, age, hormones, and emotions all influence the body's energy use.

Genes govern the hormones that influence appetite, hunger, and how the body stores and uses energy.

Summary

Section 7.1 The digestive system has five main activities.

a. Mechanical processing and motility: Chewing and muscle movements break up, mix, and propel ingested food through the system.

b. Secretion: Digestive enzymes and other substances are released from the salivary glands, pancreas, liver, and glandular epithelium into the digestive tube.

c. Digestion: Food is broken down into particles, then into nutrient molecules small enough to be absorbed.

d. Absorption: Digested organic compounds, fluid, and ions pass into the internal environment.

e. Elimination: Undigested and unabsorbed residues are expelled at the end of the system.

The gastrointestinal tract includes the mouth, pharynx, esophagus, stomach, small intestine, and large intestine. Its associated accessory organs include salivary glands, the liver, the gallbladder, and the pancreas (Table 7.6).

The GI tract is lined with mucous membrane. From the esophagus onward its wall consists of four layers: an innermost mucosa, then the submucosa, then smooth muscle, then the serosa. Sphincters at either end of the stomach and at other locations control the forward movement of ingested material.

 Tour the human digestive system.

Section 7.2 Starch digestion begins in the mouth or oral cavity, where the salivary glands secrete saliva, which contains salivary amylase. Chewed food mixes with saliva to form a bolus that is swallowed. Waves of peristalsis move each bolus down the esophagus to the stomach.

Section 7.3 Protein digestion begins in the stomach, where gastric fluid containing pepsins and other substances is secreted. The stomach contents are reduced to a watery chyme that passes through a sphincter into the small intestine.

Section 7.4 Digestion is completed and most nutrients are absorbed in the small intestine, which has a large surface area for absorption due to its many villi and microvilli.

Section 7.5 Enzymes and some other substances secreted by the pancreas, the liver, and the gallbladder aid digestion. Bile (secreted by the liver and then stored and released into the small intestine by the gallbladder) contains bile salts that speed up the digestion of fats. Micelles aid the absorption of fatty

acids and triglycerides. A hepatic portal vein carries nutrient-laden blood to the liver for processing.

Section 7.6 In the small intestine, a process of segmentation mixes material and forces it close to the absorptive surface. Absorbed glucose and amino acids move into blood vessels in intestinal villi. Triglycerides enter lacteals, then move into blood vessels.

Section 7.7 Peristalsis moves wastes into the large intestine. Water is reabsorbed in the colon; wastes (feces) move on to the rectum and into the anal canal and are eliminated via the anus. The appendix projects from the upper part of the large intestine. It may have a role in immunity.

Section 7.8 The nervous and endocrine systems govern the digestive system. Many controls operate in response to the volume and composition of food in the gut. They cause changes in muscle activity and in the secretion rates of hormones or enzymes.

Section 7.10 Complex carbohydrates are the body's preferred energy source. The diet also must provide

Table 7.6 Summary of the Digestive System

MOUTH (oral cavity)	Start of digestive system, where food is chewed, moistened, polysaccharide digestion begins
PHARYNX	Entrance to tubular parts of digestive and respiratory systems
ESOPHAGUS	Muscular tube, moistened by saliva, that moves food from pharynx to stomach
STOMACH	Sac where food mixes with gastric fluid and protein digestion begins; stretches to store food taken in faster than can be processed; gastric fluid destroys many microbes
SMALL INTESTINE	The first part (duodenum) receives secretions from the liver, gallbladder, and pancreas
	Most nutrients are digested, absorbed in second part (jejunum)
	Some nutrients absorbed in last part (ileum), which delivers unabsorbed material to colon
COLON (large intestine)	Concentrates and stores undigested matter (by absorbing mineral ions and water)
RECTUM	Distension triggers expulsion of feces
ANUS	Terminal opening of digestive system

Accessory Organs:	
SALIVARY GLANDS	Glands (three main pairs, many minor ones) that secrete saliva, a fluid with polysaccharide-digesting enzymes, buffers, and mucus (which moistens and lubricates ingested food)
PANCREAS	Secretes enzymes that digest all major food molecules and buffers against HCl from stomach
LIVER	Secretes bile (used in fat emulsification); role in carbohydrate, fat, and protein metabolism
GALLBLADDER	Stores and concentrates bile from the liver

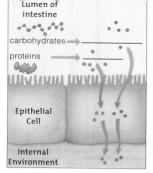

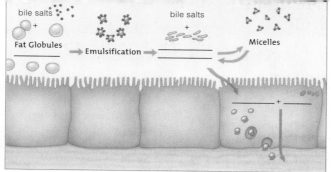

Figure 7.19 Fill in the blanks for substances that cross the lining of the small intestine.

eight essential amino acids, some essential fatty acids, vitamins, and minerals.

Section 7.11 Vitamins and minerals both are essential for normal body growth and functioning. Vitamins are organic substances; minerals are inorganic.

Section 7.12 Food energy is measured in kilocalories. The basal metabolic rate is the amount of kilocalories needed to sustain the body when a person is awake and resting. To maintain acceptable weight and overall health, a person's total energy output must balance caloric intake. Obesity is a health-threatening condition that increases the risk of type 2 diabetes, heart trouble, and some cancers, among other diseases and disorders.

Review Questions

1. What are the main functions of the stomach? The small intestine? The large intestine?

2. Using the sketch below, list the organs and accessory organs of the digestive system. On a separate piece of paper, list the main functions of each.

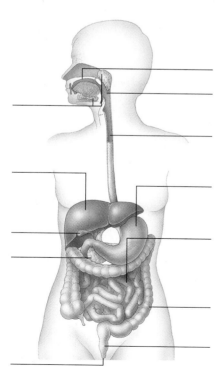

3. Define peristalsis, and list the regions of the GI tract where it occurs. Mention segmentation in your answer.

4. Using the black lines shown in Figure 7.19, name the types of molecules small enough to be absorbed across the small intestine's lining.

Self-Quiz

Answers in Appendix V

1. Different regions of the digestive system specialize in _____ and _____ food and in _____ unabsorbed food residues.

2. Maintaining normal body weight requires that _____ intake be balanced by _____ output.

3. The preferred energy sources for the body are _____.

4. The human body cannot produce its own vitamins or minerals, nor can it produce certain _____ and _____.

5. Which of the following is *not* associated with digestion?
   a. salivary glands   d. gallbladder
   b. thymus gland   e. pancreas
   c. liver

6. Digestion is completed and products are absorbed in the _____.
   a. mouth   c. small intestine
   b. stomach   d. large intestine

7. After absorption, triglycerides, fatty acids, and monoglycerides leave the cell and move into the _____.
   a. bloodstream   c. liver
   b. intestinal cells   d. lacteals

8. Excess carbohydrates and proteins are stored as _____.
   a. amino acids   c. fats
   b. starches   d. monosaccharides

9. Match the digestive system parts and functions.
   ____ liver
   ____ small intestine
   ____ salivary glands
   ____ stomach
   ____ large intestine

   a. secrete substances that moisten food, start polysaccharide breakdown
   b. where protein digestion begins
   c. where water is reabsorbed
   d. where most digestion is completed
   e. receives blood carrying absorbed nutrients

Critical Thinking

1. A glass of whole milk contains lactose, protein, triglycerides (in butterfat), vitamins, and minerals. Explain what happens to each component when it passes through your digestive tract.

2. Some nutritionists claim that the secret to long life is to be slightly underweight as an adult. If a person's weight is related partly to diet, partly to activity level, and partly to genetics, what underlying factors could be at work to generate statistics that support this claim?

3. As a person ages, the number of body cells steadily decreases and energy needs decline. If you were planning an older person's diet, what kind(s) of nutrients would you emphasize, and why? Which ones would you recommend less of?

4. Along the lines of question 3, formulate a healthy diet for an actively growing seven-year-old.

5. Raw poultry can carry *Salmonella* or *Campylobacter* bacteria, both of which produce toxins that can cause serious diarrhea, among other symptoms. Aside from the discomfort, why does such an infection require immediate medical attention?

6. Dutch cyclist Leontien Zijlaard, the young woman shown in Figure 7.20, won three Olympic gold medals. Four years earlier, she was suffering from anorexia and too weak and malnourished to compete. Many recovered anorexics lead normal—even extraordinary—lives, and researchers are uncovering a wealth of new information about the disorder. Do some research yourself and find answers to the following questions:

Are eating disorders common or rare?

How many people die each year from anorexia and bulemia?

Is there evidence that genes influence these conditions?

Explore on Your Own

This is an exercise you can eat when you're done. All you need is a food item like a hamburger or a salad and paper for jotting notes.

To begin, analyze your meal, noting the various kinds of biological molecules it includes. (For this exercise, ignore nucleic acids.) Then, beginning with your mouth and teeth, write what happens to your meal as it moves through your digestive system. Key questions to consider include: What kinds of enzymes act on the different components of the meal (such as lettuce or meat), and where do they act, as it is digested? What mechanical processes aid digestion? Which ones can you consciously control? Using the tables in Section 7.11, list the vitamins and minerals that your meal likely contains. Finally, analyze your meal in terms of its contribution (or not) to a balanced diet.

Figure 7.20 Dutch cyclist Leontien Zijlaard, who recovered from anorexia and went on to win Olympic gold.

8 BLOOD

Chemical Questions

In 2002 a team of scientists at the Centers for Disease Control in Atlanta reported finding 116 pollutants in the blood and urine of more than 2,500 healthy people who had volunteered to be tested for contaminated body fluids. The volunteers were selected to provide a statistically reliable cross section of the U.S. population. Many of the pollutants that turned up were substances known or strongly suspected to be harmful—toxic metals, chemicals in secondhand cigarette smoke, residues of pesticides and herbicides, and by-products of manufacturing processes.

A similar study by researchers at the Environmental Working Group in Washington, D.C., found a whopping 167 contaminants in the body fluids of volunteers who reported no unusual exposure to polluting chemicals.

Few of the chemicals tracked in the tests even existed when you were born. For the most part they are recent inventions designed to enhance products ranging from lipstick to telephone equipment or to improve agricultural productivity.

Many researchers are concerned that too little is known about the health impacts of many synthetic chemicals. For example, in the CDC study the majority of subjects, including children, had traces of phthalates in their fluids. These substances, which are used in cosmetics and plastics, are not regulated in the United States. Yet studies using laboratory animals have produced compelling evidence that phthalates cause cancer and abnormalities of the reproductive system.

How serious is the problem? In general, say environmental scientists, children and fetuses are most at risk, because many pollutants affect development. Also, little is known about the effect of long-term exposure to many synthetic chemicals. The metal lead is an example: Levels of lead in blood that were deemed safe in 1970 were later found to pose a serious health threat to children. Ultimately lead was banned for use in paints and some other products.

Our blood can transport substances good and not so good. In this chapter you will learn why blood truly is "the river of life"—and a key player in maintaining homeostasis.

 How Would You Vote? *Government regulation of substances such as lead seems to be effective: In recent years the levels of several pollutants in the general population have fallen. Should other suspect industrial chemicals be regulated? Cast your vote online at www.thomsonedu.com/ biology/starr/humanbio.*

 ## Key Concepts

COMPONENTS AND FUNCTIONS OF BLOOD
Blood consists of watery plasma, red blood cells, white blood cells, and platelets.

Red blood cells transport O_2 and CO_2, white blood cells are part of body defenses, and platelets help clot blood. Blood also helps maintain a stable pH and body temperature.

BLOOD TYPES
Red blood cells have "self" proteins on their surface that establish a person's blood type.

BLOOD CLOTTING
Mechanisms that clot blood help prevent blood loss.

Links to Earlier Concepts

This chapter is a prelude to our study of the cardiovascular system—the heart and blood vessels— in Chapter 9. It also expands on some topics you have already read about. For example, you will learn more about hemoglobin, the oxygen-carrying protein in red blood cells (2.12), and about the various kinds of blood cells that arise from stem cells in bone marrow (5.2).

This chapter's discussion of blood typing shows a key function of recognition proteins that are embedded in cell plasma membranes (3.3). Section 8.7 on blood clotting provides good examples of how enzymes catalyze chemical reactions that are vital to life.

8.1 Blood: Plasma, Blood Cells, and Platelets

LINKS TO
SECTIONS
2.6, 2.11, 3.9,
AND 7.5

As the old saying goes, human blood is thicker than water. It also flows more slowly, and it is rather sticky. But what exactly is this unusual liquid?

Blood consists of plasma, blood cells, and cell fragments called platelets. If you are an adult woman of average size, your body has about 4 to 5 liters of blood; males have slightly more. In all, blood amounts to about 6 to 8 percent of your body weight.

PLASMA IS THE FLUID PART OF BLOOD

If you fill a test tube with blood, treat it so it doesn't clot, and whirl it in a centrifuge, the tube's contents should look like what you see in Figure 8.1. About 55 percent of whole blood is **plasma**. Plasma is mostly water. It transports blood cells and platelets, and more than a hundred other substances. Most of these "substances" are different plasma proteins, which have a variety of functions.

Plasma proteins determine the fluid volume of the blood—how much of it is water. Two-thirds of plasma proteins are albumin molecules made in the liver. Because there is so much of it—that is, because its concentration is so high—albumin has a major influence on the osmotic movement of water into and out of blood. Albumin also carries many chemicals in blood, from metabolic wastes to therapeutic drugs. Too little albumin can be one cause of *edema*, swelling that occurs when water leaves the blood and enters tissues.

Other plasma proteins include protein hormones and proteins involved in immunity and blood clotting. Lipoproteins carry lipids, and still other plasma proteins transport fat-soluble vitamins.

Plasma also contains ions, glucose and other simple sugars, amino acids, various communication molecules, and dissolved gases—mostly oxygen, carbon dioxide, and nitrogen. The ions (such as Na^+, Cl^-, H^+, and K^+) help maintain the volume and pH of extracellular fluid.

RED BLOOD CELLS CARRY OXYGEN AND CO_2

About 45 percent of whole blood—the bottom portion in your centrifuged test tube—consists of erythrocytes, or **red blood cells**. Each red blood cell is a biconcave disk, like a thick pancake with a dimple on each side. The cell's red color comes from the iron-containing protein hemoglobin. Hemoglobin transports oxygen that the body requires for aerobic respiration. Red blood cells also carry away some carbon dioxide wastes.

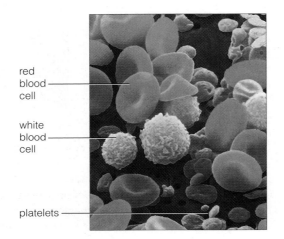

red blood cell

white blood cell

platelets

Figure 8.1
Components of blood. In the micrograph the dark red cells are red blood cells. Platelets are pink. The fuzzy gold balls are white blood cells.

Components	Relative Amounts	Functions
Plasma Portion (*50%–60% of total volume*):		
1. Water	91%–92% of plasma volume	Solvent
2. Plasma proteins (albumin, globulins, fibrinogen, etc.)	7%–8%	Defense, clotting, lipid transport, roles in extracellular fluid volume, etc.
3. Ions, sugars, lipids, amino acids, hormones, vitamins, dissolved gases	1%–2%	Roles in extracellular fluid volume, pH, etc.
Cellular Portion (*40%–50% of total volume*):		
1. White blood cells:		
Neutrophils	3,000–6,750	Phagocytosis during inflammation
Lymphocytes	1,000–2,700	Immune responses
Monocytes (macrophages)	150–720	Phagocytosis in all defense responses
Eosinophils	100–360	Defense against parasitic worms
Basophils	25–90	Secrete substances for inflammatory response and for fat removal from blood
2. Platelets	250,000–300,000	Roles in clotting
3. Red blood cells	4,800,000–5,400,000 per microliter	Oxygen, carbon dioxide transport

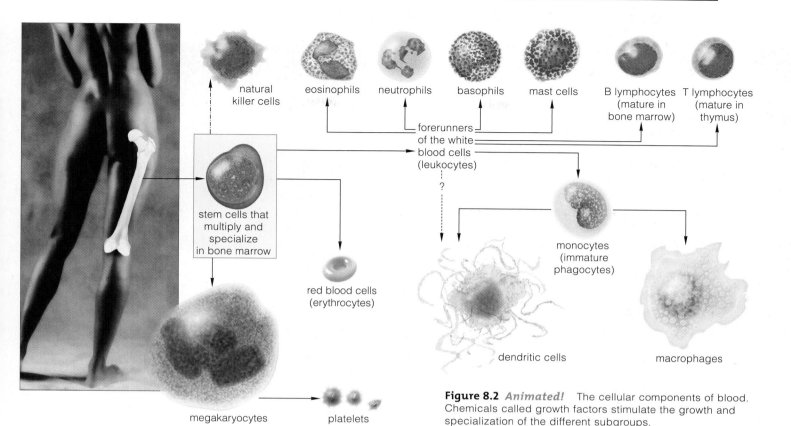

natural killer cells

eosinophils　neutrophils　basophils　mast cells　B lymphocytes (mature in bone marrow)　T lymphocytes (mature in thymus)

forerunners of the white blood cells (leukocytes)

?

stem cells that multiply and specialize in bone marrow

red blood cells (erythrocytes)

monocytes (immature phagocytes)

dendritic cells　　macrophages

megakaryocytes　　platelets

Figure 8.2 *Animated!*　The cellular components of blood. Chemicals called growth factors stimulate the growth and specialization of the different subgroups.

Red blood cells arise from stem cells in bone marrow. You may recall that a **stem cell** stays unspecialized and retains the ability to divide. Some of the daughter cells, however, do become specialized for particular functions, as you can see in Figure 8.2.

WHITE BLOOD CELLS PERFORM DEFENSE AND CLEANUP DUTIES

Leukocytes, or **white blood cells**, make up a tiny fraction of whole blood. (With platelets, they are the thin, pale, middle layer in your test tube.) Leukocytes function in housekeeping and defense. Some scavenge dead or worn-out cells, or material identified as foreign to the body. Others target or destroy disease agents such as bacteria or viruses. Most go to work after they squeeze out of blood vessels and enter tissues. The number of them in the body varies, depending on whether a person is sedentary or highly active, healthy or fighting an infection.

All white blood cells develop from stem cells in bone marrow. In the various kinds of cells, the nucleus varies in its size and shape, and there are other differences as well. **Granulocytes** include neutrophils, eosinophils, and basophils. When this type of cell is stained, various types of granules are visible in its cytoplasm. The majority of leukocytes are neutrophils. They and eosinophils,

basophils, and mast cells have roles in body defenses that you will read more about in Chapter 10.

The leukocytes called **agranulocytes** don't have visible granules in their cytoplasm. One type, called monocytes, develops into macrophages, "big eaters" that engulf and destroy invading microbes and debris. Another type, lymphocytes—B cells, T cells, and natural killer cells— operates in immune responses. Most types of white blood cells live for only a few days or, during a major infection, perhaps a few hours. Others may live for years.

PLATELETS HELP CLOT BLOOD

Some stem cells in bone marrow develop into "giant" cells called megakaryocytes (mega = large). These cells shed bits of cytoplasm that become enclosed in a plasma membrane. The fragments, known as **platelets**, last only about a week, but millions are always circulating in our blood. Platelets release substances that begin the process of blood clotting described in Section 8.7.

Blood consists of plasma, in which proteins and other substances are dissolved; red blood cells; white blood cells; and platelets.

8.2 How Blood Transports Oxygen

LINK TO
SECTION
2.12

A key function of blood is transporting oxygen, and the key to oxygen transport is the protein called hemoglobin.

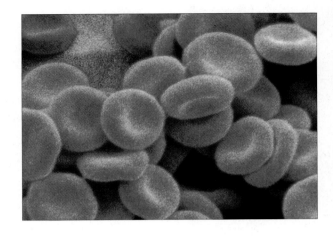

HEMOGLOBIN IS THE OXYGEN CARRIER

If you were to analyze a liter of blood drawn from an artery, you would find only a quarter teaspoon of oxygen dissolved in the plasma—just 3 milliliters. Yet, like all large, active, warm-bodied animals, humans require a lot of oxygen to maintain the metabolic activity of their cells. Hemoglobin (Hb) meets this need. In addition to the small amount of dissolved oxygen, a liter of arterial blood usually carries around 65 times more O_2 bound to the heme groups of hemoglobin molecules. This oxygen-bearing hemoglobin is called **oxyhemoglobin**.

WHAT DETERMINES HOW MUCH OXYGEN HEMOGLOBIN CAN CARRY?

As conditions change in different tissues and organs, so does the tendency of hemoglobin to bind with and hold on to oxygen. Several factors influence this process. The most important factor is how much oxygen is present relative to the amount of carbon dioxide. Other factors are the temperature and acidity of tissues. Hemoglobin is most likely to bind oxygen in places where blood plasma contains a relatively large amount of oxygen, where the temperature is relatively cool, and where the pH is roughly neutral. This is exactly the environment in our lungs, where the blood must take on oxygen. By contrast, metabolic activity in cells *uses* oxygen. It also increases both the temperature and the acidity (lowers the pH) of tissues. Under those conditions, the oxyhemoglobin of red blood cells arriving in tissue capillaries tends to release oxygen, which then can enter cells. We can summarize these events this way:

LUNGS   TISSUES

more O_2
cooler
less acidic
$$Hb + O_2 \Rightarrow HbO_2$$
$$HbO_2 \Rightarrow Hb + O_2$$
less O_2
warmer
more acidic

The protein portion of hemoglobin also carries some of the carbon dioxide wastes cells produce, along with hydrogen ions (H^+) that affect the pH of body fluids. You'll read more about hemoglobin in Chapter 11, where we consider the many interacting elements that enable the respiratory system to transport gases efficiently to and from body cells.

You can see the structure of a hemoglobin molecule in Figure 8.3. Notice that it has two parts: the protein globin, and heme groups that contain iron. Globin is built of four linked polypeptide chains, and each chain

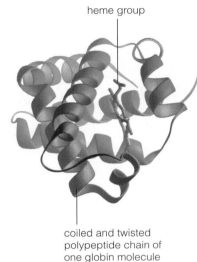

heme group

coiled and twisted
polypeptide chain of
one globin molecule

Figure 8.3 *Animated!* The structure of hemoglobin. Recall from Chapter 2 that hemoglobin is a globular protein consisting of four polypeptide chains and four iron-containing heme groups. Oxygen binds to the iron in heme groups, which is one reason why humans require iron as a mineral nutrient.

is associated with a heme group. It is the iron molecule at the center of each heme group that binds oxygen.

Oxygen in the lungs diffuses into the blood plasma and then into individual red blood cells. There it binds with the iron in hemoglobin. This oxyhemoglobin is deep red. Hemoglobin that is depleted of oxygen looks scarlet, especially when it is observed through skin and the walls of blood vessels.

Hemoglobin in red blood cells transports oxygen. The oxygen is bound to iron molecules in heme groups in each hemoglobin molecule.

The relative amounts of oxygen and carbon dioxide present in blood, and the temperature and acidity of tissues, affect how much oxygen hemoglobin binds—and therefore the amount of oxygen available to tissues.

8.3 Hormonal Control of Red Blood Cell Production

Red blood cells do not live long. In response to hormones stem cells in bone marrow constantly produce new ones.

Each second, about 3 million new red blood cells enter your bloodstream. They gradually lose their nucleus and other organelles, structures that are unnecessary because red blood cells do not divide or synthesize new proteins.

Red blood cells have enough enzymes and other proteins to function for about 120 days. As they near the end of their life, die, or become damaged or abnormal, phagocytes called macrophages ("big eaters") remove them from the blood. Much of this "cleanup" occurs in the spleen, which is located in the upper left abdomen. As a macrophage dismantles a hemoglobin molecule, amino acids from its proteins return to the bloodstream and the iron in its heme groups returns to red bone marrow, where it may be recycled in new red blood cells. The rest of the heme group is converted to the orangish pigment bilirubin. Liver cells take up this pigment, which is mixed with bile that is released into the small intestine during digestion.

Steady replacements from stem cells in bone marrow keep a person's red blood cell count fairly constant over time. A **cell count** is a tally of the number of cells in a microliter of blood. On average, an adult male's red blood cell count is around 5.4 million. In an adult female the count averages about 4.8 million red blood cells.

Having a stable red blood cell count is important for homeostasis, because body cells need a reliable supply of oxygen. Your kidneys make the hormone erythropoietin, and it stimulates the production of new red blood cells as needed.

The process relies on a negative feedback loop (Figure 8.4). In this loop, the kidneys monitor the level of oxygen in the blood. When it falls below a set point, kidney cells detect the change and in short order they release erythropoietin. It stimulates stem cells in bone marrow to produce more red blood cells. As new red blood cells enter your bloodstream, the blood's capacity for carrying oxygen increases. As the oxygen level rises in your blood and in tissues, this information feeds back to the kidneys. They then make less erythropoietin, and the production of red blood cells in bone marrow drops.

Cells in the kidneys monitor the oxygen-carrying capacity of blood. When more red blood cells are needed to carry oxygen, the kidneys release the hormone erythropoietin, which stimulates the production of new red blood cells by stem cells in bone marrow.

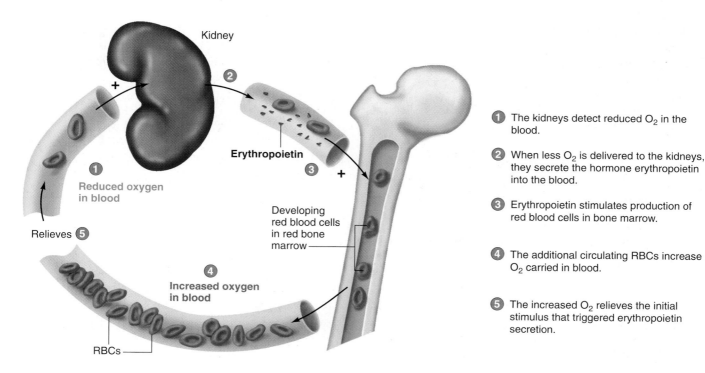

- Kidney
- ① Reduced oxygen in blood
- **Erythropoietin**
- Developing red blood cells in red bone marrow
- Relieves ⑤
- ④ Increased oxygen in blood
- RBCs

① The kidneys detect reduced O_2 in the blood.

② When less O_2 is delivered to the kidneys, they secrete the hormone erythropoietin into the blood.

③ Erythropoietin stimulates production of red blood cells in bone marrow.

④ The additional circulating RBCs increase O_2 carried in blood.

⑤ The increased O_2 relieves the initial stimulus that triggered erythropoietin secretion.

Figure 8.4 The feedback loop that helps maintain a normal red blood cell count.

8.4 Blood Types—Genetically Different Red Blood Cells

LINK TO
SECTION
3.2

You probably know that there are different human blood types. The differences are due to variations in the surface markers on red blood cells.

Each of your body cells has proteins on its surface that mark the cell as "self." Your genes have determined the chemical characteristics of these self markers, which vary from person to person. The variations are medically important because the markers on cells and substances that are *not* part of an individual's own body are antigens. An **antigen** is a chemical characteristic of a cell, particle, or substance that causes the immune system to mount an immune response. Defensive proteins called *antibodies* identify and attack antigens in a process that is a major topic of Chapter 10.

Our red blood cells bristle with self markers. To date biologists have identified at least 30 common ones, and many more rare ones. Because each kind of marker can have several forms, they are often called "blood groups." Two of them, the Rh blood group and the ABO blood group, are extremely important in situations where the blood of two people mixes. We will look at the Rh blood group in Section 8.5. For now, let's look more closely at the ABO blood group, which is a vital consideration in blood transfusions.

THE ABO GROUP OF BLOOD TYPES INCLUDES KEY SELF MARKERS ON RED BLOOD CELLS

One of our genes carries the instructions for building the ABO self markers on red blood cells. Different versions of this gene carry instructions for different markers, called type A and type B. A third version of the gene does not call for a marker, and red blood cells of someone who has this gene are dubbed type O. Collectively, these markers make up the ABO blood group.

In type A blood, red blood cells bear A markers. Type B blood has B markers, and type AB has both A and B. Type AB blood is quite rare, but a large percentage of people have type O red blood cells—they have neither A nor B markers. Depending on your ABO blood type, your blood plasm also will contain antibodies to other blood types, even if you have never been exposed to them. As you will read shortly, a severe immune response takes place when incompatible blood types are mixed. This is why donated blood must undergo a chemical analysis called **ABO blood typing** (Table 8.1).

MIXING INCOMPATIBLE BLOOD TYPES CAN CAUSE THE CLUMPING CALLED AGGLUTINATION

As you can see in Table 8.1, if you are type A, your body does not have antibodies against A markers but does have them against B markers. If you are type B, you don't have antibodies against B markers, but you do have antibodies against A markers. If you are type AB, you do not have antibodies against either form of the marker. If you are type O, however, you have antibodies against *both* forms of the marker, so you can only receive blood from another type O individual.

In theory, type O people are "universal donors," because they have neither A nor B antigens, and—again, only in theory—type AB people are "universal recipients." In fact, however, as already noted there are *many* markers

Blood Type	Antigens on Plasma Membranes of RBCs	Antibodies in Blood	Safe to Transfuse	
			To	From
A	A	Anti-B	A, AB	A, O
B	B	Anti-A	B, AB	B, O
AB	A + B	none	AB	A, B, AB, O
O	—	Anti-A Anti-B	A, B, AB, O	O

Table 8.1   Summary of ABO Blood Types

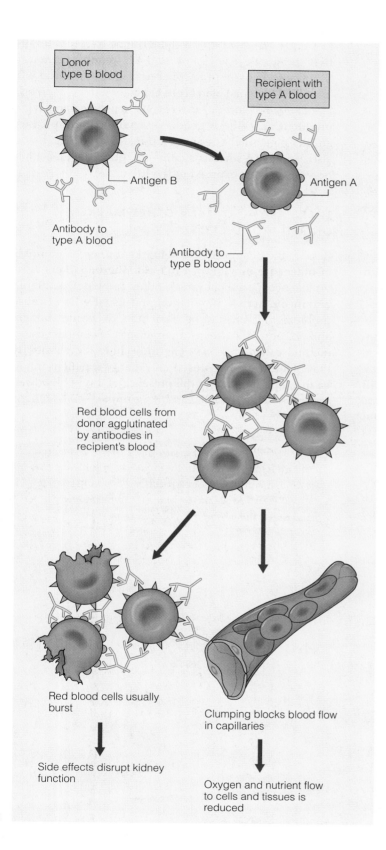

Donor type B blood

Recipient with type A blood

Antigen B

Antibody to type A blood

Antigen A

Antibody to type B blood

Red blood cells from donor agglutinated by antibodies in recipient's blood

Red blood cells usually burst

Clumping blocks blood flow in capillaries

Side effects disrupt kidney function

Oxygen and nutrient flow to cells and tissues is reduced

a

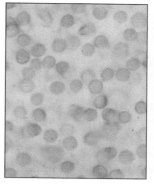
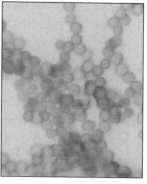

b

compatible blood cells

incompatible blood cells

Figure 8.5 *Animated!* Agglutination in red blood cells. (**a**) Example of an agglutination reaction. This diagram shows what happens when type B blood is transfused into a person who has type A blood. (**b**) What an agglutination reaction looks like. In the micrograph on the left, commingled red blood cells are compatible and have not clumped. The cells on the right are a mix of incompatible ABO types, and they have clumped together. Donated blood is typed in order to avoid an agglutination response when the blood is transfused into another person.

associated with our red blood cells, and any of them can trigger the defense response called **agglutination** (Figure 8.5). When the mixing of incompatible blood causes agglutination, antibodies act against the "foreign" cells and cause them to clump. The clumps can clog small blood vessels, severely damaging tissues throughout the body and sometimes even causing death.

We turn next to the Rh blood group. As you will now read, agglutination is also a danger when mismatched Rh blood types mix.

Like all cells, red blood cells bear genetically determined proteins on their surface. These proteins serve as "self" markers and determine a person's ABO (and Rh) blood type.

When incompatible blood types mix, an agglutination response occurs in which antibodies cause potentially fatal clumping of red blood cells.

8.5 Rh Blood Typing

Another surface marker on red blood cells that can cause agglutination is the "Rh factor," so named because it was first identified in the blood of Rhesus monkeys.

RH BLOOD TYPING LOOKS FOR AN RH MARKER

Rh blood typing determines the presence or absence of an Rh marker. If you are type Rh1, your blood cells bear this marker and you are Rh$^+$ (positive). If you are type Rh$^-$, they don't have the marker and you are Rh$^-$ (negative). When a person's blood type is determined, the ABO blood type and Rh type are usually combined. For instance, if your blood is type A and Rh negative, your blood type will be given as type A$^-$.

Most people don't have antibodies against the Rh marker. But someone who receives a transfusion of Rh1 blood will make antibodies against the marker, and these will continue circulating in the person's bloodstream.

If an Rh$^-$ woman becomes pregnant by an Rh$^+$ man, there is a chance the fetus will be Rh$^+$. During pregnancy or childbirth, some of the fetal red blood cells may leak into the mother's bloodstream. If they do, her body will produce antibodies against Rh (Figure 8.6). If she gets pregnant *again*, Rh antibodies will enter the bloodstream of this new fetus. If its blood is type Rh1, its mother's antibodies will cause its red blood cells to swell and burst. In extreme cases, called *hemolytic disease of the newborn*, so many red blood cells are destroyed that the fetus dies. If the condition is diagnosed before or during a live birth, the baby can survive by having its blood replaced with transfusions free of Rh antibodies.

Currently, a known Rh$^-$ woman can be treated after her first pregnancy with an anti-Rh gamma globulin (RhoGam) that will protect her next fetus. The drug will inactivate Rh1 fetal blood cells circulating in the mother's bloodstream before she can become sensitized and begin producing anti-Rh antibodies. In non-maternity cases, an Rh$^-$ person who receives a transfusion of Rh$^+$ blood also can have a severe negative reaction if he or she has previously been exposed to the Rh marker.

THERE ARE ALSO MANY OTHER MARKERS ON RED BLOOD CELLS

Besides the Rh and AB blood marker proteins, hundreds of others are now known to exist. These markers are a bit like needles in a haystack—they are widely scattered within the human population and usually don't cause problems in transfusions. Reactions do occur, though, and except in extreme emergencies, hospitals use a method called *cross-matching* to exclude the possibility that blood to be transfused and that of a patient might be incompatible due to the presence of a rare blood cell marker outside the ABO and Rh groups.

In some people, red blood cells are marked with an Rh protein. If this Rh$^+$ blood mixes with the Rh$^-$ blood of someone else, the Rh$^-$ individual will develop antibodies against it. The antibodies will trigger an immune response against Rh$^+$ red blood cells if the person is exposed to them again.

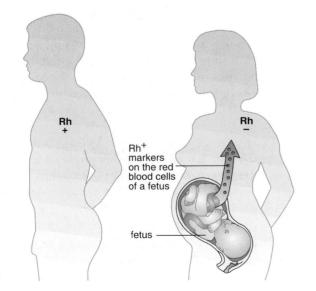

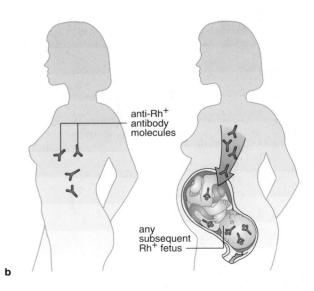

a

b

Figure 8.6 *Animated!* Development of antibodies in response to Rh$^+$ blood. (**a**) Blood cells from an Rh$^+$ fetus leak into the Rh$^-$ mother's bloodstream. (**b**) The mother now develops antibodies against a subsequent Rh$^+$ fetus.

BLOOD TYPES

8.6 New Frontiers of Blood Typing

Because blood types are genetically determined, they can be used to help establish a person's genetic heritage.

BLOOD + DNA: INVESTIGATING CRIMES AND IDENTIFYING MOM OR DAD

In addition to helping ensure that a blood transfusion will be safe or that a mother's antibodies will not harm her fetus, the markers on red blood cells have a variety of other uses. For example, investigations of rapes, murders, and sometimes other crimes often compare the blood groups of victims and any possible perpetrators.

Today, blood samples often are used for DNA testing, which provides the most definitive information about a person's genetic heritage. For instance, there is a lot of similarity in the blood types found in and among people of different ethnic backgrounds (Table 8.2; notice that AB is the rarest blood type).

At one time blood typing was also commonly used to help determine the identity of a child's father or mother in cases where parentage was disputed. This is another area in which DNA testing is now the norm.

FOR SAFETY'S SAKE, SOME PEOPLE BANK THEIR OWN BLOOD

A blood transfusion is inherently risky. There is the need for an accurately matched blood type, and the risk of being exposed to blood-borne pathogens such as hepatitis viruses and HIV, the human immunodeficiency virus that causes AIDS. Although in general hospital blood supplies are carefully screened, some people who are slated for elective surgery take the extra precaution of pre-donating blood for an *autologous transfusion* (Figure 8.7). This means they have some of their own blood

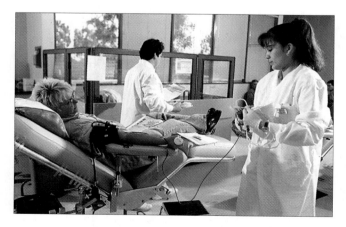

Figure 8.7 Donating blood.

Table 8.2	ABO Blood Groups in the U.S. Population (percentages)			
Blood Group	White	Black	Asian	Native American
AB	4	4	5	<1
B	11	20	27	4
A	40	27	28	16
O	45	49	40	79

removed and stored before the procedure so it can be used during the surgery if a transfusion is necessary.

BLOOD SUBSTITUTES MUST ALSO AVOID SPARKING AN IMMUNE RESPONSE

For years medical researchers have been trying to develop a safe, effective blood substitute that can be used in emergencies when matching a person's blood type isn't feasible, as in an ambulance or on a battlefield. A substitute might also be acceptable to people who refuse blood transfusions on religious grounds. As you've read, however, blood is extremely complex, and red blood cells, which are the crucial oxygen transporters, have many different self markers on their plasma membranes. Under these circumstances, it has been a tall order to find the right recipe for a blood substitute.

To date the most promising approach seems to be a substitute oxygen carrier that will not trigger an immune response. At this writing a product called Oxygent™, pictured at right, is in the final stage of being tested in clinical trials. If this milky-white fluid is approved for general use, it will have to be used with care, because tissues can be damaged if there is too much oxygen in the blood-stream. Inevitably, there will also be negative side effects in some people.

The more we explore options for blood substitutes, the more we understand just what a remarkable substance we have coursing through our arteries and veins!

The presence of self markers on red blood cells allows blood to be used to help identify individuals. The markers also make transfusions risky, so some patients opt for autologous transfusions.

The need to match blood groups also is a challenge in the development of blood substitutes.

8.7 Hemostasis and Blood Clotting

Small blood vessels can easily tear or be damaged by a cut or blow. To maintain homeostasis, it is extremely important that small tears are quickly repaired.

HEMOSTASIS PREVENTS BLOOD LOSS

Hemostasis is the name of a process that stops bleeding and so helps prevent the excessive loss of blood. In this process, an affected blood vessel constricts, platelets plug up the tear, and blood coagulates, or clots (Figure 8.8). Although hemostasis can only seal tears or punctures in relatively small blood vessels, most cuts and punctures fall into this category.

When a blood vessel ruptures, smooth muscle in the damaged vessel wall contracts in an automatic response called a spasm. The muscle contraction constricts the blood vessel, so blood flow through it slows or stops. This response can last for up to half an hour, and it is vital in stemming the immediate loss of blood. Then, while the flow of blood slows, platelets arrive and clump together, creating a temporary plug in the damaged wall.

They also release the hormone serotonin and other chemicals that help prolong the spasm and attract more platelets. Lastly, blood coagulates—that is, it converts to a gel—and forms a clot.

FACTORS IN BLOOD ARE ONE TRIGGER FOR BLOOD CLOTTING

Two different mechanisms can cause a blood clot to form. The first is called an "intrinsic" clotting mechanism because it involves substances that are in the blood itself. Figure 8.8 diagrams this process. It gets under way when a protein in the blood plasma, called "factor X," is activated. This triggers reactions that produce thrombin. This is an enzyme that acts on a rod-shaped protein called fibrinogen. The fibrinogen rods stick together, forming long threads of fibrin. The fibrin threads also stick to one another. The result is a net that entangles blood cells and platelets, as you can see in the micrograph in Figure 8.8. The entire mass is a blood clot. With time, the clot becomes more compact, drawing the torn walls of the vessel back together.

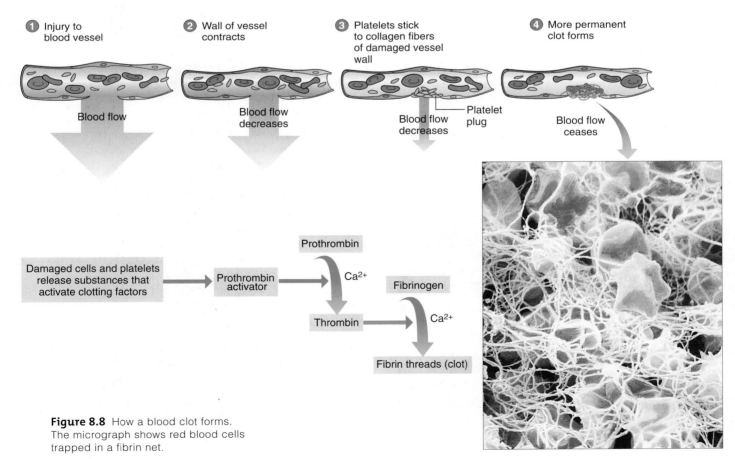

Figure 8.8 How a blood clot forms. The micrograph shows red blood cells trapped in a fibrin net.

FACTORS FROM DAMAGED TISSUE ALSO CAN CAUSE A CLOT TO FORM

Blood also can coagulate through an extrinsic clotting mechanism. "Extrinsic" means that the reactions leading to clotting are triggered by the release of enzymes and other substances *outside* the blood. These chemicals come from damaged blood vessels or from tissue around the damaged area. The substances lead to the formation of thrombin, and the remaining steps are like the steps of the intrinsic pathway.

Because aspirin reduces the aggregation of platelets, it is sometimes prescribed in small doses to help prevent blood clots. A clot that forms in an unbroken blood vessel can be a serious threat because it can block the flow of blood. A clot that stays where it forms is called a *thrombus*, and the condition is called a *thrombosis*.

Even scarier is an *embolus*, a clot that breaks free and circulates through the bloodstream. A person who suffers an *embolism* in the heart, lungs, brain, or some other organ may suddenly die when the roving clot shuts down the organ's blood supply. This is what happens when a person suffers a **stroke**. A blood clot blocks the flow of blood to some part of the brain and the affected brain tissue dies. Strokes can be mild to severe. In serious cases the person may be paralyzed on one side of the body and have trouble speaking. Physical therapy and speech therapy may help minimize the long-term effects.

The disease **hemophilia** is a genetic disorder in which the blood does not contain the usual clotting factors and so does not clot properly. You will read more about this disorder, and its central role in some historic events, in Chapter 21.

THE FORMATION OF A BLOOD CLOT IS A KEY STEP IN HEALING WOUNDED SKIN

When the skin is punctured or torn, blood clotting gets under way immediately to help seal the breach (Figure 8.9). With minor cuts, it usually takes less than 30 minutes for a clot to seal off injured vessels. In a few more hours, phagocytes are at work cleaning up debris and a scab has begun to form. This quick action is vital to minimize blood loss and the chances of infection.

> *Hemostasis refers to processes that slow or stop the flow of blood from a ruptured vessel.*
>
> *The mechanisms include spasms that constrict blood vessel walls, the formation of platelet plugs, and blood clotting.*
>
> *Blood clotting can be triggered by substances in the blood itself (such as thrombin), or by way of reactions involving substances in damaged tissue.*

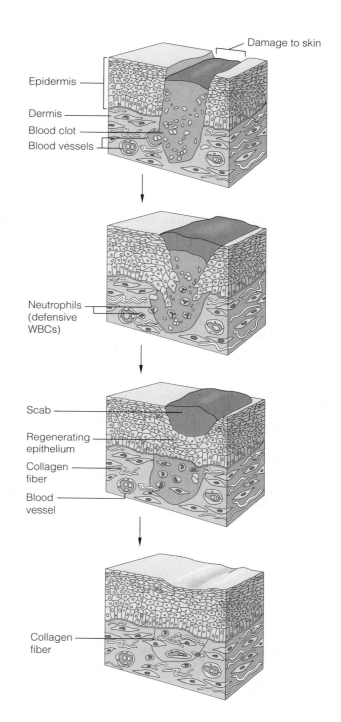

Figure 8.9 How blood clotting helps heal a wound in the skin.

8.8 Blood Disorders

LINK TO
SECTION
7.11

Various disorders can hamper the ability of blood cells to function normally.

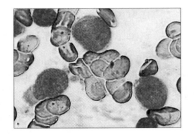

Figure 8.11 Blood from a person with chronic myelogenous leukemia. Abnormal white blood cells (purple) are starting to crowd out normal cells.

ANEMIAS ARE RED BLOOD CELL DISORDERS

At least half a dozen **anemias** (meaning "no blood") are signs that red blood cells are not delivering enough oxygen to meet body needs. All anemias result from other, underlying problems. To varying degrees they make a person feel tired and listless, among other symptoms.

Two common types of anemia result from nutrient deficiencies. For example, **iron-deficiency anemia** develops when the body's iron supply is too low to form enough hemoglobin (with its iron-containing heme groups). Folic acid and vitamin B_{12} both are needed for the production of red blood cells in bone marrow. A deficiency of either one can lead to **pernicious anemia**. A balanced diet usually provides both nutrients, but other conditions can prevent them from being absorbed.

The rare malady **aplastic anemia** arises when red bone marrow, including the stem cells that give rise to red and white blood cells and platelets, has been destroyed by radiation, drugs, or toxins.

"Hemolytic" means "blood breaking," and **hemolytic anemias** develop when red blood cells die or are destroyed before the end of their normal useful life. The root cause may be an inherited defect, as in sickle-cell anemia, in which red blood cells take a sickle shape (Figure 8.10*a* and *b*) and can burst. Chapter 20 looks more fully at the genetic trigger for these changes.

Worldwide, **malaria** is a major cause of hemolytic anemia. It is caused by a protozoan that is transmitted by mosquitoes. One life stage of this pathogen multiplies inside red blood cells, leading to disease symptoms such as fever, chills, and trembling. Eventually the red blood cells burst (Figure 8.10*c*). Chapter 18 provides more information about this global scourge.

Like people who have sickle-cell anemia, those with **thalassemia** produce abnormal hemoglobin. Too few red blood cells form, and those that do form are thin and extremely fragile.

CARBON MONOXIDE POISONING PREVENTS HEMOGLOBIN FROM BINDING OXYGEN

Carbon monoxide, or CO, is a colorless odorless gas. It is present in auto exhaust fumes and in smoke from burning wood, coal, charcoal, and tobacco. It binds to hemoglobin at least 200 times more tightly than oxygen does. As a result, breathing even tiny amounts of it can tie up half of the body's hemoglobin and prevent tissues from receiving the oxygen they need. CO poisoning is especially dangerous because an affected person may not realize that the symptoms—headache and feeling "woozy"—are signs of life-threatening distress.

MONONUCLEOSIS AND LEUKEMIAS AFFECT WHITE BLOOD CELLS

Our white blood cells also can be affected by disease. For example, **infectious mononucleosis** is caused by the Epstein-Barr virus, which causes overproduction of lymphocytes. The patient feels achy and tired and runs a low-grade fever for several weeks as the highly contagious disease runs its course.

Far more serious are **leukemias**, which all are the result of cancer in the bone marrow. The word "leukemia" means "white blood," and the hallmark of leukemias (like other cancers) is runaway multiplication of the abnormal cells and destruction of healthy bone marrow.

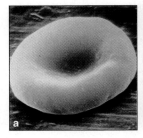
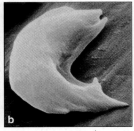
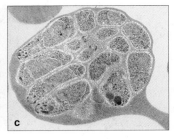

Figure 8.10 Some causes of hemolytic anemia. Scanning electron micrographs of normal (**a**) and sickled (**b**) red blood cells. (**c**) A life stage of the microorganism that causes malaria, about to rupture a red blood cell.

BLOOD TYPES

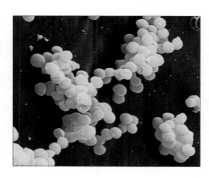

Figure 8.12
The bacterium *Staphylococcus aureus*.

In the most serious forms of leukemia, which tend to strike children, the marrow cavities in bones become choked with cancerous white blood cells. As other types of blood cells (and stem cells) are excluded, leukemia's symptoms develop—fever, weight loss, anemia, internal bleeding, pain, and susceptibility to infections. Modern treatments now save thousands of lives, and there is hope that experimental gene therapies will one day provide more help. Figure 8.11 shows cells of one type of leukemia, called **chronic myelogenous leukemia**.

Viral infections can also hamper or destroy white blood cells. The most notorious culprit is HIV, the human immunodeficiency virus, which causes AIDS. Its ability to kill lymphocytes of the immune system is a major topic in Chapter 18.

TOXINS CAN DESTROY BLOOD CELLS OR POISON THE BLOOD IN OTHER WAYS

A variety of bacteria can release toxins into the blood, a condition called **septicemia**. One of our most fearsome bacterial foes is *Staphylococcus aureus*, or simply "staph A" (Figure 8.12). This microbe produces enzymes that destroy red blood cells and prevent blood clotting. Unfortunately, some strains have become highly resistant to antibiotics, a growing problem that we will discuss again in Chapter 18.

Metabolic poisons in the body cause *toxemia*. For example, the kidneys remove many toxic wastes from the blood. In a person whose kidneys do not function well due to disease or some other cause, the buildup of certain wastes prevents the normal replacement of red blood cells. It also prevents platelets from functioning. Thus the person becomes anemic and blood does not clot properly. Chapter 11 discusses some other extremely serious effects of kidney disease.

Summary

Section 8.1   Blood is a fluid connective tissue that helps maintain homeostasis as it performs the following functions:

a. Transporting oxygen and other substances to and from the extracellular fluid bathing cells.

b. Transporting many proteins and ions. The proteins (such as albumin) help maintain the proper fluid volume of blood. Ions help stabilize the pH of extracellular fluid.

Blood consists of plasma, red and white blood cells, and cell fragments called platelets. Blood cells and platelets arise from stem cells in bone marrow.

Plasma, the liquid part of blood, transports blood cells and platelets. Plasma water is a solvent for proteins, simple sugars, amino acids, mineral ions, vitamins, hormones, and several gases.

Red blood cells carry oxygen from the lungs to body tissues. Major categories of white blood cells are granulocytes and agranulocytes. Granulocytes, such as neutrophils, operate in body defense. Agranulocytes include a type that develops into macrophages, which scavenge dead or worn-out cells and other debris and cleanse tissues of "non-self" material. Still other white blood cells (the lymphocytes) form armies that destroy specific microbes and other disease agents.

Platelets release substances that begin the process of blood clotting.

Section 8.2   Red blood cells contain hemoglobin, an iron-containing pigment molecule that binds reversibly with oxygen, forming oxyhemoglobin. Red blood cells also carry some carbon dioxide (also bound to hemoglobin) from extracellular fluid back to the lungs (to be exhaled).

Section 8.3   Red blood cells live for about 120 days. A cell count measures the number of them in a microliter of blood. Macrophages remove dead or damaged red blood cells while stem cells provide replacements.

Section 8.4   Blood type is determined by certain proteins on the surface of red blood cells. The four main human blood types are A, B, AB, and O. Agglutination is an immune response activated when a person's blood mingles with an incompatible type. Rh blood typing determines the presence or absence of Rh factors (+ or −) on red blood cells. If incompatible Rh types commingle, the immune system will attack and destroy the "foreign" cells.

 Thomson NOW!   *Learn about ABO and Rh blood types.*

Section 8.7

Processes of hemostasis slow or stop bleeding. They include spasms that constrict blood vessels, the formation of platelet plugs, and blood clotting.

Review Questions

1. What is blood plasma, and what is its function?

2. What are the cellular components of blood? Where do the various kinds come from?

3. Add the missing labels to Figure 8.13 at the right. Then, on a separate sheet of paper, list the factors that affect the tendency of hemoglobin to bind with oxygen.

4. Explain what an agglutination response is, and how it can be avoided when blood is transfused.

5. What is the function of hemostasis? What are the two ways a blood clot can form?

Self-Quiz

Answers in Appendix V

1. Which are *not* components of blood?
   a. plasma
   b. blood cells and platelets
   c. gases and other dissolved substances
   d. all of the above are components of blood

2. The _____ produces red blood cells, which transport _____ and some _____.
   a. liver; oxygen; mineral ions
   b. liver; oxygen; carbon dioxide
   c. bone marrow; oxygen; hormones
   d. bone marrow; oxygen; carbon dioxide

3. The _____ produces white blood cells, which function in _____ and _____.
   a. liver; oxygen transport; defense
   b. lymph glands; oxygen transport; stabilizing pH
   c. bone marrow; day-to-day housekeeping; defense
   d. bone marrow; stabilizing pH; defense

4. In the lungs, the main factor in boosting the tendency of hemoglobin to bind with and hold oxygen is _____.
   a. temperature
   b. the amount of O_2 relative to the amount of CO_2 in plasma
   c. acidity (pH)
   d. all are equally important

5. Match the blood terms with the best description.
   ___ red blood cell   a. plug leaks
   ___ platelets   b. blood markers
   ___ stem cell   c. blood cell source
   ___ plasma   d. erythrocyte
   ___ A, B, O   e. more than half of whole blood

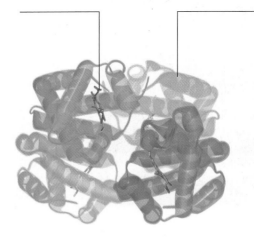

Figure 8.13 A hemoglobin molecule.

Critical Thinking

1. Thrombocytopenia (throm-bo-sye-tow-PEE-ne-ah) is a disorder that develops when certain drugs, bone marrow cancer, or radiation destroys red bone marrow, including stem cells that give rise to platelets. Predict a likely symptom of this disorder.

2. As the text described, when a person's red blood cell count drops, the kidneys receive less oxygen. In response they release erythropoietin, which prompts the bone marrow to make more red blood cells. As the rising number of red blood cells carry *more* oxygen to the kidneys, they stop releasing the hormone. What type of homeostatic control mechanism are we talking about here?

Explore on Your Own

What is your "Blood IQ"?

To find out how much you know about blood and public blood supplies, visit www.RedCross.org or www.givelife.org. Both are sponsored by the American Red Cross. At the GIVELIFE website, take the ten-question Blood IQ test and see how much you know about blood types and other issues. The websites offer information about blood, blood donation, and even current research on blood substitutes and other topics.

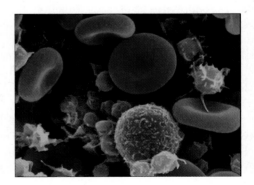

The Breath of Life

Each year in the U.S. 250,000 people have a sudden cardiac arrest, usually outside a hospital. The heart stops beating and blood stops flowing through the vessels. A problem with the electrical signals that stimulate cardiac muscle is the most common cause. The normal heartbeat abruptly shifts into an erratic pattern called ventricular fibrillation (VF).

It happened to Tammy Higgins. The 28-year-old mother collapsed as she was leaving church with her husband Chris and their daughter Lindsay. She had no pulse, and she had stopped breathing. Chris knew that getting oxygen-rich blood to his wife's brain was vital. He immediately began CPR—cardiopulmonary resuscitation. Using this technique, he and others kept Tammy alive until an ambulance arrived.

Emergency medical technicians used a heart-shocking device called a defibrillator to get Tammy's heart restarted. In the hospital, she was diagnosed with a heart rhythm disturbance. She also learned that she was pregnant.

Doctors implanted a tiny defibrillator that constantly monitors the rhythm of Tammy's heart and shocks it back into action if it stops. The device shocked her heart once during her pregnancy and once again in the three years after the

birth of her daughter Nicole. Without the device, either of these cardiac arrests could have been fatal.

Tammy was lucky—her husband and several bystanders knew how to do CPR. But while CPR can keep a person alive for a short while, it can't restore the heart's normal rhythm. That requires the use of a defibrillator. As with CPR, the sooner electrical stimulation begins, the better. For each minute without defibrillation, the odds of survival drop as much as 10 percent.

Automated external defibrillators (AEDs) in public places allow trained bystanders to provide the life-saving shocks before an ambulance arrives. An AED is about the size of a laptop computer. Its voice commands direct the user to perform the appropriate steps. AEDs are now available in many senior centers, shopping malls, hotels, and other public places.

What you learn in this chapter will help you to understand the biology that underlies CPR and the use of an AED. If you would like to learn how to save lives with these methods, the American Heart Association, the American Red Cross, and many community organizations provide training.

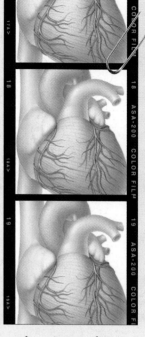

 How Would You Vote? *Some advocates think that CPR training should be a required mini-course in high schools. People who learn CPR also must be periodically recertified. Would you favor mandatory CPR training in high schools? Cast your vote online at www.thomsonedu.com/biology/starr/humanbio.*

Key Concepts

CIRCULATING BLOOD
The cardiovascular system transports oxygen, nutrients, hormones, and other substances swiftly to body cells and carries away wastes and cell products.

PUMPING BLOOD
The heart is a muscular pump. Its contractions provide the force that drives blood through the cardiovascular system's arteries and veins.

BLOOD VESSELS
Various types of blood vessels—arteries, arterioles, capillaries, venules, and veins—are specialized for different blood transport functions.

Links to Earlier Concepts

Building on what you learned about blood in Chapter 8, our focus now shifts to the blood-pumping cardiovascular system—the heart and blood vessels. This chapter looks more closely at cardiac muscle (4.3) and at the specialized cell junctions in this tissue (4.6). You will also see how the dynamic tubelike organs we call blood vessels are built from epithelium, connective tissue, and smooth muscle (4.1–4.3). We also consider links between cardiovascular health and lipoproteins and cholesterol (2.10 and 2.12).

9.1 The Cardiovascular System—Moving Blood through the Body

LINK TO SECTION 8.1

"Cardiovascular" comes from the Greek kardia (heart) and the Latin vasculum (vessel). The cardiovascular system—also called the circulatory system—is built to rapidly transport blood to every living cell in the body.

THE HEART AND BLOOD VESSELS MAKE UP THE CARDIOVASCULAR SYSTEM

As you can see in Figure 9.1 below, the **cardiovascular system** has two main elements:

- the **heart**, a muscular pump that generates the pressure required to move blood throughout the body

- blood vessels, which are tubes of different diameters that transport blood.

The heart pumps blood into large-diameter **arteries**. From there blood flows into smaller **arterioles**, which branch into even narrower **capillaries**. Blood flows from capillaries into small **venules**, then into large-diameter **veins** that return blood to the heart. Because the heart pumps constantly, the volume of flow through the entire system each minute is equal to the volume of blood returned to the heart each minute.

As you will read later on, the rate and volume of blood flow through the cardiovascular system can be adjusted to suit conditions in the body. For example, blood flows rapidly through arteries, but in capillaries it must flow slowly so that there is enough time for substances moving to and from cells to diffuse into and out of extracellular fluid. This slow flow occurs in *capillary beds*, where blood moves through vast numbers of slender capillaries. By

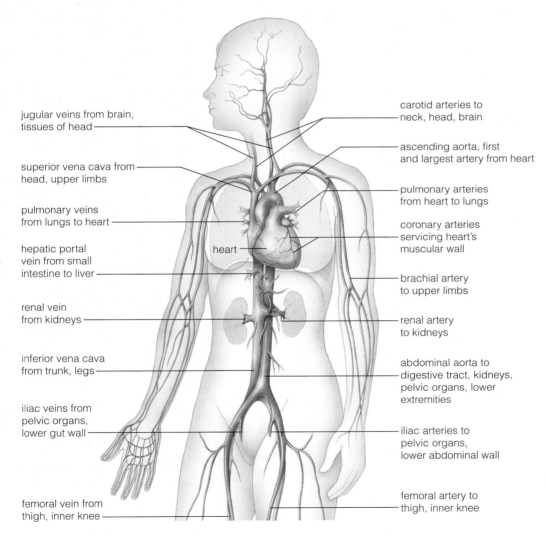

jugular veins from brain, tissues of head

superior vena cava from head, upper limbs

pulmonary veins from lungs to heart

hepatic portal vein from small intestine to liver

heart

renal vein from kidneys

inferior vena cava from trunk, legs

iliac veins from pelvic organs, lower gut wall

femoral vein from thigh, inner knee

carotid arteries to neck, head, brain

ascending aorta, first and largest artery from heart

pulmonary arteries from heart to lungs

coronary arteries servicing heart's muscular wall

brachial artery to upper limbs

renal artery to kidneys

abdominal aorta to digestive tract, kidneys, pelvic organs, lower extremities

iliac arteries to pelvic organs, lower abdominal wall

femoral artery to thigh, inner knee

Figure 9.1 *Animated!* The human cardiovascular system. Arteries, which carry oxygenated blood to tissues, are shaded red. Veins, which carry deoxygenated blood away from tissues, are shaded blue. Notice, however, that for the pulmonary arteries and veins the roles are reversed.

dividing up the blood flow, the capillaries handle the same total volume of flow as the large-diameter vessels, but at a slower pace.

CIRCULATING BLOOD IS VITAL TO MAINTAIN HOMEOSTASIS

Recall from Chapter 8 that blood is aptly called "the river of life." It brings cells such essentials as oxygen, nutrients from food, and secretions, such as hormones. It also takes away the wastes produced by our metabolism, along with excess heat. In fact, cells depend on circulating blood to make constant pickups and deliveries of an amazingly diverse range of substances, including those that move into or out of the digestive system and the respiratory and urinary systems (Figure 9.2).

Homeostasis is one of our constant themes in this book, so it's good to keep in mind that maintaining it would be impossible were it not for our circulating blood. Cells must exchange substances with blood because that is a key way they adjust to changes in the chemical makeup of the extracellular fluid around them—part of the "internal environment" in which they live.

THE CARDIOVASCULAR SYSTEM IS LINKED TO THE LYMPHATIC SYSTEM

The heart's pumping action puts pressure on blood flowing through the cardiovascular system. Partly because of this pressure, small amounts of water and some proteins dissolved in blood are forced out and become part of interstitial fluid (the fluid between cells). An elaborate network of drainage vessels picks up excess extracellular fluid and reclaimable solutes—such as water, proteins, and fatty acids—and returns them to the cardiovascular system. This network is part of the lymphatic system, which we consider in Chapter 10.

The cardiovascular system consists of the heart and the blood vessels. It transports substances to and from the interstitial fluid that bathes all living cells.

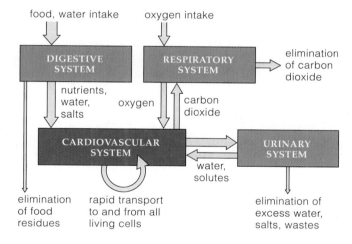

Figure 9.2 Together with the other systems shown here, the cardiovascular system helps maintain favorable operating conditions in the internal environment.

9.2 The Heart: A Double Pump

LINKS TO
SECTIONS
4.1 AND 4.2

In a lifetime of 70 years, the human heart beats some 2.5 billion times. This durable pump is the centerpiece of the cardiovascular system.

Roughly speaking, your heart is located in the center of your chest (Figure 9.3*a*). Its structure reflects its role as a long-lasting pump. The heart is mostly cardiac muscle tissue, the **myocardium** (Figure 9.3*b*). A tough, fibrous sac, the pericardium (*peri* = around), surrounds, protects, and lubricates it. The heart's chambers have a smooth lining (endocardium) composed of connective tissue and a layer of epithelial cells. The epithelial cell layer, known as endothelium, also lines the inside of blood vessels.

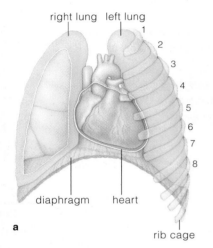

right lung left lung

1
2
3
4
5
6
7
8

diaphragm   heart

a

rib cage

THE HEART HAS TWO HALVES AND FOUR CHAMBERS

A thick wall, the **septum**, divides the heart into two halves, right and left. Each half has two chambers: an **atrium** (plural: atria) located above a **ventricle**. Flaps of membrane separate the two chambers and serve as a one-way **atrioventricular valve** (AV valve) between them. The AV valve in the right half of the heart is called a *tricuspid valve* because its three flaps come together in pointed cusps (Figure 9.3*c*). In the heart's left half the AV valve consists of just two flaps; it is called the *bicuspid valve* or *mitral valve*. Tough, collagen-reinforced strands (chordae tendineae, or "heartstrings") connect the AV valve flaps to cone-shaped muscles that extend out from the ventricle wall. When a blood-filled ventricle contracts, this arrangement prevents the flaps from opening backward into the atrium. Each half of the heart also has a half-moon–shaped **semilunar valve** between the ventricle and the arteries leading away from it. During a heartbeat, this valve opens and closes in ways that keep blood moving in one direction through the body.

The heart has its own "coronary circulation." Two **coronary arteries** lead into a capillary bed that services most of the cardiac muscle (Figure 9.4). They branch off the **aorta**, the major artery carrying oxygenated blood away from the heart.

IN A "HEARTBEAT," THE HEART'S CHAMBERS CONTRACT, THEN RELAX

Blood is pumped each time the heart beats. It takes less than a second for a "heartbeat"—one sequence of contraction and relaxation of the heart chambers. The sequence occurs almost simultaneously in both sides of the heart. The contraction phase is called **systole** (SISS-toe-lee), and the relaxation phase is called **diastole** (dye-ASS-toe-lee). This sequence is the **cardiac cycle** diagrammed in Figure 9.5.

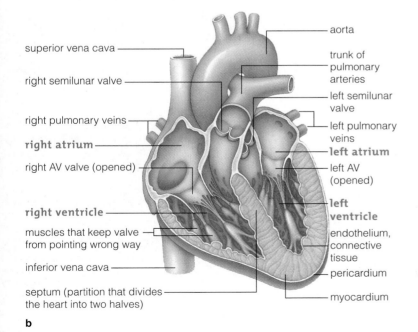

superior vena cava

right semilunar valve

right pulmonary veins

right atrium

right AV valve (opened)

right ventricle

muscles that keep valve from pointing wrong way

inferior vena cava

septum (partition that divides the heart into two halves)

aorta

trunk of pulmonary arteries

left semilunar valve

left pulmonary veins

left atrium

left AV (opened)

left ventricle

endothelium, connective tissue

pericardium

myocardium

b

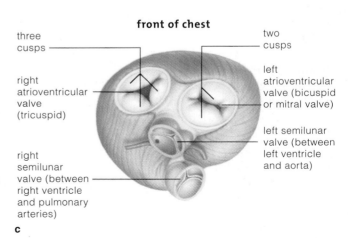

front of chest

three cusps

right atrioventricular valve (tricuspid)

right semilunar valve (between right ventricle and pulmonary arteries)

two cusps

left atrioventricular valve (bicuspid or mitral valve)

left semilunar valve (between left ventricle and aorta)

c

Figure 9.3 *Animated!* (**a**) Location of the heart. (**b**) Cutaway view showing the heart's internal organization, and (**c**) valves of the heart. In this drawing, you are looking down at the heart. The atria have been removed so that the atrioventricular (AV) and semilunar valves are visible.

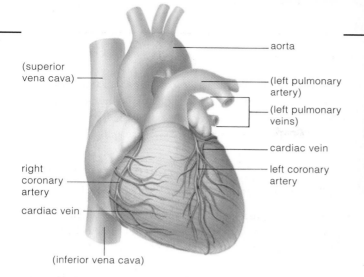

aorta

(superior vena cava)

(left pulmonary artery)

(left pulmonary veins)

cardiac vein

left coronary artery

right coronary artery

cardiac vein

(inferior vena cava)

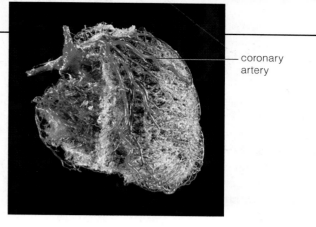

coronary artery

Figure 9.4 Coronary arteries and veins. The photograph shows a resin cast of the heart's arteries and veins.

During the cycle, the ventricles relax before the atria contract, and the ventricles contract when the atria relax. When the relaxed atria are filling with blood, the fluid pressure inside them rises and the AV valves open. Blood flows into the ventricles, which are 80 percent filled by the time the atria contract. As the filled ventricles begin to contract, fluid pressure inside *them* increases, forcing the AV valves shut. The rising pressure then forces the semilunar valves open—and blood flows out of the heart and into the aorta and pulmonary artery. Now the ventricles relax, and the semilunar valves close. For about half a second the atria and ventricles are all in diastole. Then the blood-filled atria contract, and the cycle repeats.

The amount of blood each ventricle pumps in a minute is called the **cardiac output**. On average, every sixty seconds the cardiac output from each ventricle is about 5 liters—nearly all the blood in the body. This means that in a year each half of your heart pumps at least 2.5 million liters of blood. That is more than 600,000 gallons!

The blood and heart movements during the cardiac cycle generate an audible "lub-dup" sound made by the forceful closing of the heart's one-way valves. At each "lub," the AV valves are closing as the two ventricles contract. At each "dup," the semilunar valves are closing as the ventricles relax.

Each half of the heart is divided into an atrium and a ventricle. Valves help control the direction of blood flow.

During a cardiac cycle, contraction of the atria helps fill the ventricles. Contraction of the ventricles provides the force that drives blood away from the heart.

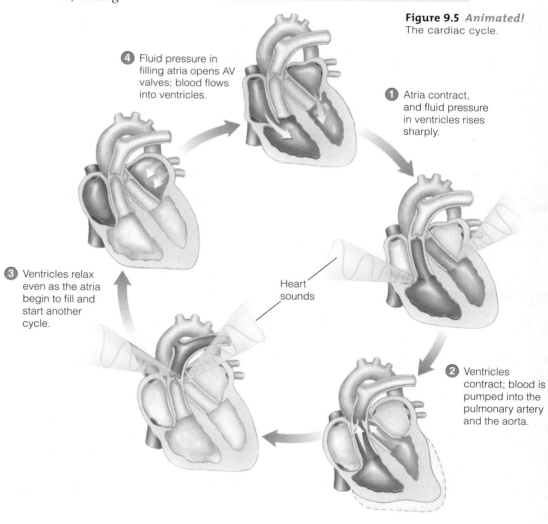

Figure 9.5 *Animated!* The cardiac cycle.

④ Fluid pressure in filling atria opens AV valves; blood flows into ventricles.

① Atria contract, and fluid pressure in ventricles rises sharply.

③ Ventricles relax even as the atria begin to fill and start another cycle.

Heart sounds

② Ventricles contract; blood is pumped into the pulmonary artery and the aorta.

9.3 The Two Circuits of Blood Flow

Each half of the heart pumps blood. The two side-by-side pumps are the basis of two cardiovascular circuits through the body, each with its own set of arteries, arterioles, capillaries, venules, and veins.

THE PULMONARY CIRCUIT: BLOOD PICKS UP OXYGEN IN THE LUNGS

The **pulmonary circuit** diagrammed in Figure 9.6a receives blood from tissues and circulates it through the lungs for gas exchange. The circuit begins as blood from tissues enters the right atrium, then moves through the AV valve into the right ventricle. As the ventricle fills, the atrium contracts. Blood arriving in the right ventricle is fairly low in oxygen and high in carbon dioxide. When the ventricle contracts, the blood moves through the right semilunar valve into the *main* pulmonary artery, then into the *right* and *left* pulmonary arteries. These arteries carry the blood to the two lungs, where (in capillaries) it picks up oxygen and gives up carbon dioxide that will be exhaled. The freshly oxygenated blood returns through two sets of pulmonary veins to the heart's left atrium, completing the circuit.

(a) pulmonary circuit for blood flow

right pulmonary artery

left pulmonary artery

capillary bed of right lung

capillary bed of left lung

pulmonary trunk

(to systemic circuit)

(from systemic circuit)

pulmonary veins

heart

(b) systemic circuit for blood flow

capillary beds of head and upper extremities

(to pulmonary circuit)

aorta

(from pulmonary circuit)

heart

capillary beds of other organs in thoracic cavity

diaphragm (muscular partition between thoracic and abdominal cavities)

capillary bed of liver

hepatic portal vein

capillary beds of intestines

capillary beds of other abdominal organs and lower extremities

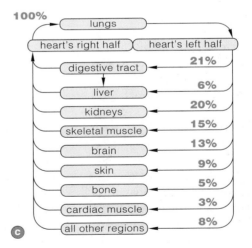

100%

lungs

heart's right half | heart's left half

digestive tract — 21%

liver — 6%

kidneys — 20%

skeletal muscle — 15%

brain — 13%

skin — 9%

bone — 5%

cardiac muscle — 3%

all other regions — 8%

(c)

Figure 9.6 *Animated!* The (**a**) pulmonary and (**b**) systemic circuits for blood flow in the cardiovascular system. (**c**) Distribution of the heart's output in people napping.

IN THE SYSTEMIC CIRCUIT, BLOOD TRAVELS TO AND FROM TISSUES

In the **systemic circuit** (Figure 9.6b), oxygenated blood pumped by the left half of the heart moves through the body and returns to the right atrium. This circuit begins when the left atrium receives blood from pulmonary veins, and this blood moves through an AV (bicuspid) valve to the left ventricle. This chamber contracts with great force, sending blood coursing through a semilunar valve into the aorta.

As the aorta descends into the torso (see Figure 9.1), major arteries branch off it, funneling blood to organs and tissues where O_2 is used and CO_2 is produced. For example, in a resting person, each minute a fifth of the blood pumped into the systemic circulation enters the kidneys (Figure 9.6c) via *renal arteries*. Deoxygenated blood returns to the right half of the heart, where it enters the pulmonary circuit. Notice that in both the pulmonary and the systemic circuits, blood travels through arteries, arterioles, capillaries, and venules, finally returning to the heart in veins. Blood from the head, arms, and chest arrives through the *superior vena cava*. The *inferior vena cava* collects blood from the lower part of the body.

BLOOD FROM THE DIGESTIVE TRACT IS SHUNTED THROUGH THE LIVER FOR PROCESSING

As you can see near the bottom of Figure 9.6, blood passing through capillary beds in the GI tract travels to another capillary bed in the liver. This is the route described in Section 7.5 by which nutrient-laden blood is sent to the liver through the *hepatic portal vein* after a meal. As blood seeps through this second bed, the liver can remove impurities and process absorbed substances. Part of this processing synthesizes cholesterol. The Impacts/Issues box at right explains how, in people who have too much cholesterol in their blood, drugs called statins can reduce the liver's cholesterol output.

Blood leaving the liver's capillary bed enters the general circulation through a *hepatic vein*. The liver receives oxygenated blood via the *hepatic artery*.

A short pulmonary circuit carries blood through the lungs for gas exchange. A long systemic circuit transports blood to and from tissues.

After meals, the blood in capillary beds in the GI tract is diverted to the liver for processing before reentering the general circulation.

9.4 How Cardiac Muscle Contracts

LINK TO
SECTION
4.3

Unlike skeletal muscle, which contracts only when orders arrive from the nervous system, cardiac muscle contracts— and the heart beats—spontaneously.

ELECTRICAL SIGNALS FROM "PACEMAKER" CELLS DRIVE THE HEART'S CONTRACTIONS

Cardiac muscle cells branch, then link to one another at their endings. Junctions called *intercalated discs* span both plasma membranes of neighboring cells (Figure 9.7). With each heartbeat, signals calling for contraction spread so rapidly across the junctions that cardiac muscle cells contract together, almost as if they were a single unit.

Where do the contraction signals come from? About 1 percent of cardiac muscle cells do not contract, but instead function as the **cardiac conduction system**. Some of these cells are self-exciting "pacemaker" cells—that is, they spontaneously generate and conduct electrical impulses. Those impulses are the signals that stimulate contractions in the heart's contractile cells. Because the cardiac conduction system is independent of the nervous system, the heart will keep right on beating even if all nerves leading to the heart are severed!

Excitation begins with a cluster of cells in the upper wall of the right atrium (Figure 9.8). About 70 times a minute, this **sinoatrial (SA) node** generates waves of excitation. Each wave spreads swiftly over both atria and causes them to contract. It then reaches the **atrioventricular (AV) node** in the septum dividing the two atria.

When a stimulus reaches the AV node, it slows a little, then quickly continues along bundles of conducting fibers

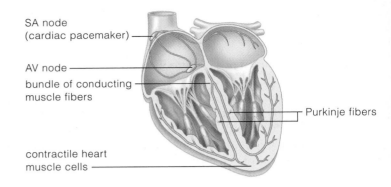

SA node (cardiac pacemaker)

AV node

bundle of conducting muscle fibers

Purkinje fibers

contractile heart muscle cells

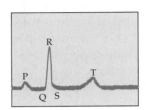

Figure 9.8 *Animated!* The cardiac conduction system. (*left*) Recording of a heartbeat. Letters indicate three waves of electrical activity that were caused by the spread of nerve impulses across cardiac muscle.

that extend to each ventricle. At intervals along each bundle, conducting cells called *Purkinje fibers* pass the signal on to contractile muscle cells in each ventricle. The slow conduction in the AV node is an important part of this sequence. It gives the atria time to finish contracting before the wave of excitation spreads to the ventricles.

Of all cells of the cardiac conduction system, the SA node fires off impulses at the highest frequency and is the first region to respond in each cardiac cycle. It is called the **cardiac pacemaker** because its rhythmic firing is the basis for the normal rate of heartbeat. People whose SA node chronically malfunctions may have an artificial pacemaker implanted to provide a regular stimulus for their heart contractions.

THE NERVOUS SYSTEM ADJUSTS HEART ACTIVITY

The nervous system initiates the contraction of skeletal muscle, but it can only *adjust* the rate and strength of cardiac muscle contraction. Stimulation by one set of nerves increases the force and rate of heart contractions, while stimulation by another set of nerves can slow heart activity. The centers for neural control of heart functions are in the spinal cord and parts of the brain. They are discussed more fully in Chapter 13.

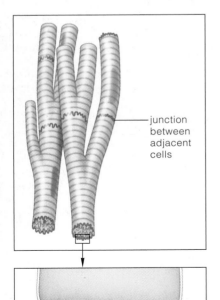

junction between adjacent cells

intercalated disc

Figure 9.7 Intercalated discs. The discs contain communication junctions at the ends of abutting cardiac muscle cells. Signals travel rapidly across the junctions and cause cells to contract nearly in unison.

The SA node is the cardiac pacemaker—it establishes a regular heartbeat. Its spontaneous, repeated excitation signals spread along a system of muscle cells that stimulate a rhythmic cycle of contraction in the heart's atria, then the ventricles.

9.5 Blood Pressure

Heart contractions generate blood pressure, which changes as blood moves through the cardiovascular system.

BLOOD EXERTS PRESSURE AGAINST THE WALLS OF BLOOD VESSELS

Blood pressure is the fluid pressure that blood exerts against vessel walls. Blood pressure is highest in the aorta; then it drops along the systemic circuit. The pressure typically is measured when a person is at rest (Figure 9.9). For an adult, the National Heart, Lung, and Blood Institute has established blood pressure values under 120/80 as the healthiest (Table 9.1). The first number, *systolic pressure*, is the peak of pressure in the aorta while the left ventricle contracts and pushes blood into the aorta. The second number, *diastolic pressure*, measures the lowest blood pressure in the aorta, when blood is flowing out of it and the heart is relaxed.

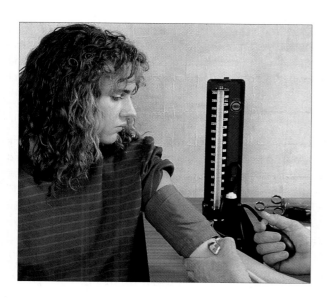

Figure 9.9 *Animated!* Measuring blood pressure. A hollow cuff attached to a pressure gauge is wrapped around the upper arm. The cuff is inflated to a pressure above the highest pressure of the cardiac cycle—at systole, when ventricles contract. Above this pressure, you can't hear sounds through a stethoscope positioned below the cuff and above the brachial artery, because no blood is flowing through the vessel. As air in the cuff is slowly released, some blood flows into the artery. The turbulent flow causes soft tapping sounds. When the tapping starts, the gauge's value is the systolic pressure, measured in millimeters of mercury (Hg). This value measures how far the pressure would force mercury to move upward in a narrow glass column.

More air is released from the cuff. Just after the sounds grow dull and muffled, blood is flowing steadily, so the turbulence and tapping end. The silence corresponds to diastolic pressure at the end of a cardiac cycle, before the heart pumps out blood. A desirable reading is under 80 mm Hg.

Table 9.1	Blood Pressure Values (mm of Hg)	
	Systolic	Diastolic
Normal	100–119	60–79
Hypotension	Less than 100	Less than 60
Prehypertension	120–139	80–139
Hypertension	140 and up	90 and up

Values for systolic and diastolic pressure provide important health information. Chronically elevated blood pressure, or **hypertension**, can be associated with a variety of ills, such as atherosclerosis (Section 9.8). The chart in Figure 9.10 lists some of the major causes and risk factors. Hypertension is a "silent killer" that can lead to a stroke or heart attack. Each year it kills about 180,000 Americans, many of whom may not have had any outward symptoms. Roughly 40 million people in the U.S. are unaware that they have hypertension.

Hypotension is abnormally *low* blood pressure. This condition can develop when for some reason there is not enough water in blood plasma—for instance, if there are not enough proteins in the blood to "pull" water in by osmosis. A large blood loss also can cause blood pressure to plummet. Such a drastic decrease is one sign of a dangerous condition called *circulatory shock.*

Heart contractions generate blood pressure. Systolic pressure is the peak of pressure in the aorta while blood pumped by the left ventricle is flowing into it. Diastolic pressure measures the lowest blood pressure in the aorta, when blood is flowing out of it.

Risk Factors for Hypertension

1. Smoking
2. Obesity
3. Sedentary lifestyle
4. Chronic stress
5. A diet low in fruits, vegetables, dairy foods, and other sources of potassium and calcium
6. Excessive salt intake (in some individuals)
7. Poor salt management by the kidneys, usually due to disease

Figure 9.10 Some major factors associated with hypertension.

9.6 Structure and Functions of Blood Vessels

LINKS TO
SECTIONS
4.1 AND 4.2

As with all body parts, structure is key to the functions of blood vessels. All our vessels transport blood, but there are important differences in how different kinds "manage" blood flow and blood pressure.

ARTERIES ARE LARGE BLOOD PIPELINES

The wall of an artery has several tissue layers (Figure 9.11*a*). The outer layer is mainly collagen, which anchors the vessel to the tissue it runs through. A thick middle layer of smooth muscle is sandwiched between thinner layers containing elastin. The innermost layer is a thin sheet of endothelium. Together these layers form a thick, muscular, and elastic wall. In a large artery the wall bulges slightly under the pressure surge caused when a ventricle contracts. In arteries near the body surface, as in the wrist, you can feel the surges as your **pulse**.

The bulging of artery walls helps keep blood flowing on through the system. How? For a moment, some of the blood pumped during the systole phase of each cardiac cycle is stored in the "bulge"; the elastic recoil of the artery then forces that stored blood onward during diastole, when heart chambers are relaxed. In addition to stretchable walls, arteries also have large diameters. For this reason, they present little resistance to blood flow, so blood pressure does not drop much in the large arteries of the systemic and pulmonary circuits (Figure 9.12).

ARTERIOLES ARE CONTROL POINTS FOR BLOOD FLOW

Arteries branch into narrower arterioles, which have a wall built of rings of smooth muscle over a single layer of elastic fibers (Figure 9.11*b*). Because they are built this way, arterioles can dilate (enlarge in diameter) when the smooth muscle relaxes or constrict (shrink in diameter) when the smooth muscle contracts. Arterioles offer more resistance to blood flow than other vessels do. As the blood flow slows, it can be controlled in ways that adjust how much of the total volume goes to different body regions. For example, you become drowsy after a large meal in part because control signals divert blood away from your brain in favor of your digestive system.

CAPILLARIES ARE SPECIALIZED FOR DIFFUSION

Your body has about 2 miles of arteries and veins but a whopping 62,000 miles of capillaries. Each capillary bed is where substances can diffuse between blood and tissue fluid. This is truly where "the rubber meets the road" when it comes to exchanges of gases (oxygen and carbon dioxide), nutrients, and wastes. As befits its function in diffusion, a capillary has the thinnest wall of any blood vessel—a single layer of flat endothelium (Figure 9.11*c*).

a Artery
connective tissue coat — smooth muscle — endothelium — elastic tissue — elastic tissue

b Arteriole
smooth muscle rings over elastic tissue — endothelium

c Capillary
endothelium

d Venule
connective tissue coat — smooth muscle — endothelium

e Vein
connective tissue coat — smooth muscle, elastic fibers — endothelium — valve

Figure 9.11 *Animated!* Structure of blood vessels.

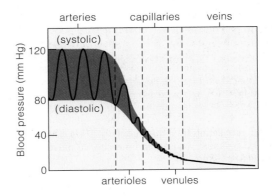

Figure 9.12 Changes in blood pressure in different parts of the cardiovascular system.

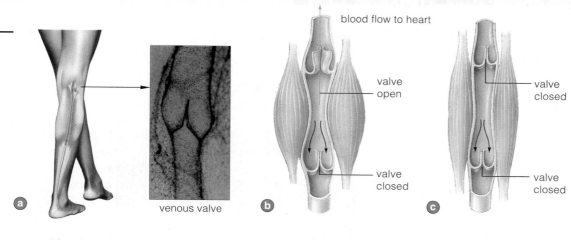

blood flow to heart

valve open

valve closed

valve closed

valve closed

Figure 9.13 *Animated!* How contracting skeletal muscles can increase fluid pressure in a vein. (**a**) Valves in medium-sized veins prevent backflow of blood. (**b**) Skeletal muscles next to the vein contract, helping blood flow forward. (**c**) Skeletal muscles relax and valves in the vein shut—preventing backflow.

venous valve

Blood can't move very fast in capillaries. However, because they are so extensive, capillary beds present less total resistance to flow than do the arterioles leading into them, so overall blood pressure drops more slowly in them. We'll look more closely at how capillaries function in the next section.

VENULES AND VEINS RETURN BLOOD TO THE HEART

Capillaries merge into venules, or "little veins," which in turn merge into large-diameter veins. Venules function a little like capillaries, in that some solutes diffuse across their relatively thin walls (Figure 9.11*d*).

Veins are large-diameter, low-resistance transport tubes to the heart (Figure 9.11*e*). Their valves prevent backflow. When blood starts moving backward due to gravity, it pushes the valves closed. The vein wall can bulge greatly under pressure, more so than an arterial wall. Thus veins are reservoirs for variable volumes of blood. Together, the veins of an adult can hold up to 50 to 60 percent of the total blood volume.

When blood must circulate faster (as during exercise), the smooth muscle in veins contracts. The wall stiffens, the vein bulges less, and venous pressure rises—so more blood flows to the heart (Figure 9.13). Venous pressure also rises when contracting skeletal muscle—especially in the legs and abdomen—bulges against adjacent veins. This muscle activity helps return blood through the venous system.

Obesity, pregnancy, and other factors can weaken venous valves. The walls of a *varicose vein* have become overstretched because, over time, weak valves have allowed blood to pool there.

VESSELS HELP CONTROL BLOOD PRESSURE

Some arteries, all arterioles, and even veins have roles in homeostatic mechanisms that help maintain adequate blood pressure over time. Centers in the brain's medulla monitor resting blood pressure. When blood pressure rises abnormally, they order the heart to contract less often and less forcefully. They also order smooth muscle in arterioles to relax. The result is **vasodilation**—an enlargement (dilation) of the vessel diameter. On the other hand, when the centers detect an abnormal *decrease* in blood pressure, they command the heart to beat faster and contract more forcefully. Neural signals also cause the smooth muscle of arterioles to contract. The result is **vasoconstriction**, a narrowing of the vessel diameter. In some parts of the body arterioles have receptors for hormones that trigger vasoconstriction or vasodilation, thus helping to maintain blood pressure.

Recall that the nervous and endocrine systems also control how blood is allocated to different body regions at different times. In addition, conditions in a particular part of the body can alter blood flow there. For instance, when you run, the amount of oxygen in your skeletal muscle tissue falls, while levels of carbon dioxide, H^+, potassium ions, and other substances rise. These chemical changes cause the smooth muscle in arterioles to relax. The vasodilation results in more blood flowing past the active muscles. At the same time, arterioles in your digestive tract and kidneys constrict.

A **baroreceptor reflex** helps provide short-term control over blood pressure. Baroreceptors are pressure receptors in the **carotid arteries** in the neck, in the arch of the aorta, and elsewhere. They monitor changes in mean arterial pressure ("mean" = the midpoint) and send signals to centers in the brain. As described in Chapter 13, this information is used to coordinate the rate and strength of heartbeats with changes in the diameter of arterioles and veins. The baroreceptor reflex helps keep blood pressure within normal limits in the face of sudden changes—such as when you leap up from a chair.

Arteries are the main pipelines for oxygenated blood. Because arterioles can dilate and constrict, they are control points for blood flow (and pressure). Capillary beds are diffusion zones. Blood moves back to the heart through venules and veins. Valves in veins prevent the backflow of blood due to gravity.

9.7 Capillaries: Where Blood Exchanges Substances with Tissues

LINK TO SECTION 3.9

Blood enters the systemic circulation moving swiftly in the aorta, but this speed has to slow in order for substances to move into and out of the bloodstream.

A VAST NETWORK OF CAPILLARIES WEAVES CLOSE TO NEARLY ALL LIVING BODY CELLS

Your body comes equipped with one aorta, a few hundred branching arteries and veins, more than half a million arterioles and venules—and as many as 40 billion capillaries! They are so thin that it would take 100 of them to equal the thickness of a human hair. And at least one of these tiny vessels is next to living cells in nearly all body tissues.

In addition to forming a vast network of vessels (Figure 9.14a), this branching system also affects the speed at which blood flows through it. The flow is fastest in the aorta, quickly "loses steam" in the more numerous arterioles, and slows to a relative crawl in the narrow capillaries. The flow of blood speeds up again as blood moves into veins for the return trip to the heart.

MANY SUBSTANCES ENTER AND LEAVE CAPILLARIES BY DIFFUSION

Why do we have such an extensive system of capillaries in which blood slows to a snail's pace? Remember from Section 9.6 that capillaries are where all the substances that enter and leave cells are exchanged with the blood, many of them by diffusion. But diffusion is a slow process that is not efficient over long distances. In a large, multicellular organism such as a human, having billions of narrow capillaries solves both these problems. There is a capillary very close to nearly every cell, and in each one the blood is barely moving. As blood "creeps" along in capillaries, there is time for the necessary exchanges of fluid and solutes to take place. In fact, most solutes, including molecules of oxygen and carbon dioxide, diffuse across the capillary wall.

SOME SUBSTANCES PASS THROUGH "PORES" IN CAPILLARY WALLS

Some substances enter and leave capillaries by way of slitlike areas between the cells of capillary walls (Figure 9.14c). These "pores" are filled with water. They are passages for substances that cannot diffuse through the lipid bilayer of the cells that make up the capillary wall, but that *can* dissolve in water.

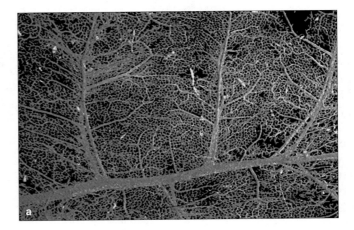

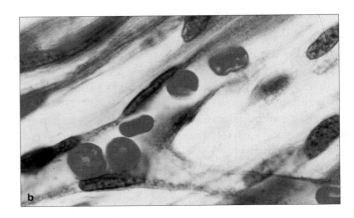

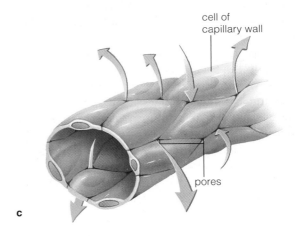

Figure 9.14 Capillaries. (**a**) A resin cast showing a dense network of capillaries. (**b**) Red blood cells moving single file in capillaries. (**c**) How substances pass through slitlike pores in the wall of a capillary.

When the blood pressure inside a capillary is greater than pressure from the extracellular fluid outside, water and solutes may be forced out of the vessel—a type of fluid movement called "bulk flow" (Figure 9.15). Various factors affect this process, but on balance, a little more water leaves capillaries than enters them. The lymphatic system, which consists of lymph vessels, lymph nodes, and some other organs, returns the fluid to the blood. This system also plays a major role in body defense, and you will learn more about it in Chapter 10.

Overall, the movements of fluid and solutes into and out of capillaries help maintain blood pressure by adding water to, or subtracting it from, blood plasma. The fluid traffic also helps maintain the proper fluid balance between blood and surrounding tissues.

BLOOD IN CAPILLARIES FLOWS ONWARD TO VENULES

Capillary beds are the "turnaround points" for blood in the cardiovascular system. They receive blood from arterioles, and after the blood flows through the bed it enters channels that converge into venules—the beginning of its return trip to the heart (Figure 9.16).

At the point where a capillary branches into the capillary bed, a wispy ring of smooth muscle wraps around it. This structure, a **precapillary sphincter**, regulates the flow of blood into the capillary. The smooth muscle is sensitive to chemical changes in the capillary bed. It can contract and prevent blood from entering the capillary, or it can relax and let blood flow in.

For example, if you sit quietly and listen to music, only about one-tenth of the capillaries in your skeletal muscles are open. But if you decide to get up and boogie, precapillary sphincters will sense the demand for more blood flow to your muscles to deliver oxygen and carry away carbon dioxide. Many more of the sphincters will relax, allowing a rush of blood into the muscle tissue. The same mechanism brings blood to the surface of your skin when you blush or become flushed with heat.

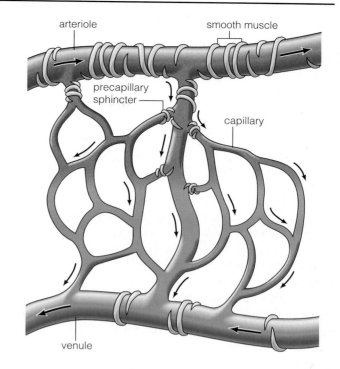

Figure 9.16 The general direction of blood flow through a capillary bed. A precapillary sphincter wraps around the base of each capillary.

The cardiovascular system's extensive network of narrow capillaries ensures that every living cell is only a short distance from a capillary.

In capillary beds, substances move between the blood and extracellular fluid by diffusion, through capillary pores, or by bulk flow. Movements of water and other substances help maintain blood pressure and the proper fluid balance between blood and tissues.

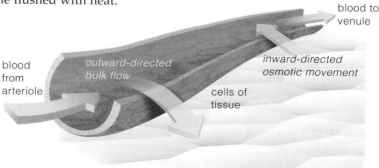

Figure 9.15 *Animated!* The "bulk flow" of fluid into and out of a capillary bed.

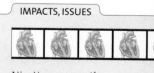

Cardiovascular Disorders

LINKS TO
SECTIONS
7.10 AND 8.5

More than 50 million Americans have cardiovascular disorders, which are the leading cause of death in the United States.

What are your chances of developing a cardiovascular disorder? Some major risk factors include a family history of heart trouble, high levels of blood lipids such as cholesterol and trans fats, hypertension, obesity, smoking, lack of exercise, and simply getting older. Interestingly, however, more than half of people who suffer heart attacks do not have any of these risk factors. What is going on? As Chapter 10 describes, inflammation has powerful, sometimes damaging effects on tissues. Recent studies have implicated this as a trigger for the formation of artery-blocking plaques, which you will read about shortly. Infections by certain viruses and bacteria can trigger inflammation in coronary arteries. Inflamed tissue also leads to the production of *C-reactive protein* (by the liver); this link is why infection-related inflammation and C-reactive protein are listed in Table 9.2.

Another suspect is homocysteine, an amino acid that is released as certain proteins are broken down. Too much of it in the blood also may cause damage that is a first step in a major cardiovascular disorder, atherosclerosis.

Table 9.2	Major Risk Factors for Cardiovascular Disease
1.	Inherited predisposition
2.	Elevated blood lipids (cholesterol, trans fats)
3.	Hypertension
4.	Obesity
5.	Smoking
6.	Lack of exercise
7.	Age 50+
8.	Inflammation due to infections by viruses, bacteria
9.	High levels of C-reactive protein in blood
10.	Elevated blood levels of the amino acid homocysteine

ARTERIES CAN BE CLOGGED OR WEAKENED

In *arteriosclerosis*, or "hardening of the arteries," arteries become thicker and stiffer. In **atherosclerosis**, this condition gets worse as cholesterol and other lipids build up in the artery wall. When this *atherosclerotic plaque* grows large enough to protrude into the artery, there is less room for blood (Figure 9.17).

Coronary arteries and their branches are narrow and vulnerable to clogging by plaques. When the artery is narrowed further to one-quarter of its starting diameter, symptoms can range from mild chest pain, called *angina pectoris*, to a full-scale heart attack.

Having too many lipids in the blood—often, due to a diet high in cholesterol and trans fat—is a major risk factor for atherosclerosis. In the blood, proteins called **LDLs** (*low-density lipoproteins*) bind cholesterol and other fats and carry them to body cells. Proteins called **HDLs** (*high-density lipoproteins*) pick up cholesterol in the blood and carry it back to the liver, where it is mixed into bile and eventually excreted in feces. Because HDLs help remove excess cholesterol from the body, they are called "good cholesterol."

If there are more LDLs in the blood than cells can remove, the surplus increases the risk of atherosclerosis. This is why LDLs are called "bad cholesterol." As LDLs infiltrate artery walls, cholesterol accumulates there. Other changes occur also, and eventually a fibrous net forms over the mass—an atherosclerotic plaque. Blood tests measure the relative amounts of HDLs and LDLs in a person's blood (in milligrams). A total of 200 mg or less per milliliter of blood is considered acceptable (for most people), but experts agree that LDLs should make up only about one-third of this total, or about 70 to 80 mg.

Surgery may be the only answer for a severely blocked coronary artery. In a *coronary bypass*, a section of a large vessel taken from the chest is stitched to the aorta and to

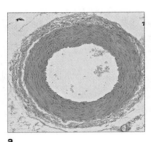

a

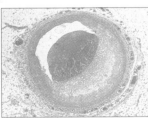

b

Figure 9.17 Sections from (**a**) a normal artery, and (**b**) one with its lumen narrowed by a plaque. (**c**) Coronary bypasses (green).

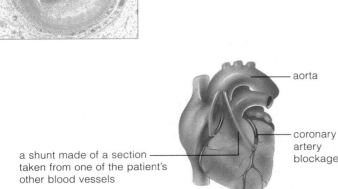

aorta

coronary artery blockage

a shunt made of a section taken from one of the patient's other blood vessels

c

the coronary artery below the affected region (Figure 9.17c). In *laser angioplasty*, laser beams vaporize the plaques. In *balloon angioplasty*, a small balloon is inflated inside a blocked artery to flatten a plaque so there is more room in the artery. A small wire cylinder called a stent may then be inserted to help keep the artery open. "Plaque-busting" drugs called statins, which reduce cholesterol in the blood, can help prevent new plaques from forming.

Disease, an injury, or an inborn defect can weaken an artery so that part of its wall balloons outward. This pouchlike weak spot is called an **aneurysm**. Aneurysms can develop in various parts of the cardiovascular system, including vessels in the brain, abdomen, and the aorta. If an aneurysm bursts, it can cause serious and even fatal blood loss. A minor aneurysm may not present any immediate worry, but in the brain, especially, an aneurysm is potentially so dangerous that it requires immediate medical treatment.

HEART DAMAGE CAN LEAD TO HEART ATTACK AND HEART FAILURE

A **heart attack** is damage to or death of heart muscle. Warning signs of a heart attack include sensations of pain or squeezing behind the breastbone, pain or numbness radiating down the left arm, sweating, and nausea. Women more often experience neck and back pain, fatigue, a sense of indigestion, a fast heartbeat, shortness of breath, and low blood pressure. Risk factors include hypertension, a circulating blood clot (an embolus, described in Section 8.6), and atherosclerosis.

In **heart failure** (HF), the heart is weakened and so does not pump blood as well as it should. Even a basic exertion such as walking can become difficult. Because patients may require repeated hospitalization, HF has become the nation's most costly health problem.

ARRHYTHMIAS ARE ABNORMAL HEART RHYTHMS

An electrocardiogram, or ECG, is a recording of the electrical activity of the cardiac cycle (Figure 9.18a). ECGs reveal **arrhythmias**, or irregular heart rhythms. Some arrhythmias are abnormal, others are not. For example, endurance athletes may have a below-average resting cardiac rate, or *bradycardia*, which is an adaptation to regular strenuous exercise. A cardiac rate above 100 beats per minute, called *tachycardia*, occurs normally during exercise or stressful situations. Serious tachycardia can be triggered by drugs (including caffeine, nicotine, alcohol, and cocaine), excessive thyroid hormones, and other factors.

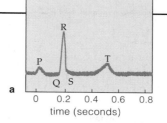

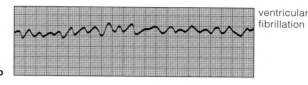

Figure 9.18 *Animated!* (**a**) ECG of a normal heartbeat. The P wave is generated by electrical signals from the SA node that stimulate contraction of the atria. As the stimulus moves over the ventricles, it is recorded as the QRS wave complex. After the ventricles contract, they rest briefly. The T wave marks electrical activity during this period. (There is also an atrial recovery period "hidden" in the QRS complex.) (**b**) A recording of ventricular fibrillation.

Ventricular fibrillation is the most dangerous arrythmia. In parts of the ventricles, the cardiac muscle contracts haphazardly, so blood isn't pumped normally. This is what happens in sudden cardiac arrest, as described in the chapter introduction. Ventricular fibrillation is a medical emergency, but with luck, a strong electrical shock to the patient's heart or the use of defibrillating drugs can restore a normal rhythm before the damage is too serious.

A HEART-HEALTHY LIFESTYLE

Everybody ages, and none of us can control the genes we inherit. But as Table 9.2 makes clear, there are some things each of us can do to improve our chances of living free of serious cardiovascular disease. Watching our intake of foods rich in cholesterol and trans fats, getting regular exercise, and not smoking are three strategies, and they provide multiple benefits. A diet that's moderate in fats may also help keep weight under control. Exercise helps with weight control, too. It also relieves stress and helps keep muscles and bones fit and strong. Smoking is bad for just about every body system; you'll get a closer look at the devastating damage it can do to the respiratory system in Chapter 11.

Summary

Section 9.1 The cardiovascular system consists of the heart and blood vessels including arteries, arterioles, capillaries, venules, and veins. The system helps maintain homeostasis by providing rapid internal transport of substances to and from cells.

 Explore the human cardiovascular system.

Section 9.2 The heart muscle is called the myocardium. A partition, the septum, divides the heart into two halves, each with two chambers, an atrium and a ventricle. Valves in each half help control the direction of blood flow. These include a semilunar valve and an atrioventricular valve. Coronary arteries provide much of the heart's blood supply. They branch off the aorta, which carries oxygenated blood away from the heart.

Blood is pumped each time the heart beats, in a cardiac cycle of contraction and relaxation. Systole, the contraction phase, alternates with the relaxation phase, called diastole.

 Learn about the structure and function of the heart.

Section 9.3 The partition between the heart's two halves separates the blood flow into two circuits, one pulmonary and the other systemic.

a. In the pulmonary circuit, deoxygenated blood in the heart's right half is pumped to capillary beds in the lungs. The blood picks up oxygen, then flows to the heart's left atrium.

b. In the systemic circuit, the left half of the heart pumps oxygenated blood to body tissues. There, cells take up oxygen and release carbon dioxide. The blood, now deoxygenated, flows to the heart's right atrium.

Section 9.4 Electrical impulses stimulate heart contractions by way of the heart's cardiac conduction system. In the right atrium, a sinoatrial node—the cardiac pacemaker—generates the impulses and establishes a regular heartbeat. Signals from the SA node pass to the atrioventricular node, a way station for stimulation that triggers contraction of the ventricles. The nervous and endocrine systems can adjust the rate and strength of heart contractions.

Section 9.5 Blood pressure is the fluid pressure blood exerts against vessel walls. It is highest in the aorta, which receives blood pumped by the left ventricle, and drops along the systemic circuit.

 See how blood pressure is measured.

Section 9.6

a. Arteries are strong, elastic pressure reservoirs. They smooth out pressure changes resulting from heartbeats and so smooth out blood flow. When a ventricle contracts, it causes a pressure surge, or pulse, in large arteries.

b. Arterioles are control points for distributing different volumes of blood to different regions.

c. Capillary beds are diffusion zones where blood and extracellular fluid exchange substances.

d. Venules overlap capillaries and veins somewhat in function. Some solutes diffuse across their walls.

e. Veins are blood reservoirs that can be tapped to adjust the volume of flow back to the heart. Valves in some veins, such as those in the limbs, prevent blood that must return to the heart (and lungs) from flowing backward due to gravity.

Blood vessels, especially arterioles, help control blood pressure. Arterioles dilate when monitoring centers in the brain detect an abnormal rise in blood pressure. If blood pressure falls below a set point, the centers trigger vasoconstriction of arterioles. A baroreceptor reflex relies on baroreceptors in carotid arteries. It provides short-term blood pressure control by way of signals that adjust the pressure when sudden changes occur.

Section 9.7 Capillaries are where fluids and solutes move between the bloodstream and body cells. These substances move by diffusion, through pores between cells, and by bulk flow of fluid. The movements help maintain the proper fluid balance between the blood and surrounding tissues, and also help maintain proper blood volume.

Section 9.8 Cardiovascular disorders collectively are the number one cause of death in the U.S. In atherosclerosis, a buildup of cholesterol and other material develops into plaques that narrow the interior space in arteries and reduce blood flow to the heart or other tissues and organs. HDLs (high-density lipoproteins) help transport excess blood cholesterol to the liver for disposal. High levels of LDLs (low-density lipoproteins) and trans fats, smoking, obesity, and inflammation in coronary arteries are some of the major risk factors associated with atherosclerosis.

Disease, injury, or an inborn defect can weaken an artery so that part of its wall balloons outward and forms an aneurysm.

Other serious cardiovascular disorders are heart attack (damage to or death of heart muscle) and heart failure (a weakened heart that cannot pump blood efficiently). An arrhythmia—irregular heart rhythm—can be a sign of heart problems. The most serious arrhythmia is ventricular fibrillation, haphazard contractions of the ventricles that greatly reduce blood pumping.

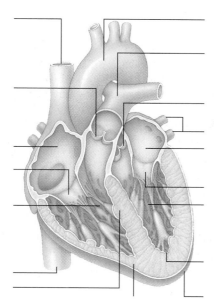

4. In the systemic circuit, the heart's _____ half pumps _____ blood to all body regions; then _____ blood flows to the heart.
a. left; deoxygenated; oxygenated
b. right; deoxygenated; oxygenated
c. left; oxygenated; deoxygenated
d. right; oxygenated; deoxygenated

5. After you eat, blood passing through the GI tract travels through the _____ to a capillary bed in the _____.
a. aorta; liver
b. hepatic portal vein; liver
c. hepatic vein; spleen
d. renal arteries; kidneys

6. The cardiac pacemaker _____.
a. sets the normal rate of heartbeat
b. is the same as the AV node
c. establishes resting blood pressure
d. all of these are correct

7. Blood pressure is highest in _____ and lowest in _____.
a. arteries; veins   c. arteries; ventricles
b. arteries; relaxed atria d. arterioles; veins

8. _____ contraction drives blood through the systemic and pulmonary circuits; outside the heart, blood pressure is highest in the _____.
a. Atrial; ventricles   c. Ventricular; arteries
b. Atrial; atria   d. Ventricular; aorta

9. Match the type of blood vessel with its major function.
_____ arteries   a. diffusion
_____ arterioles   b. control of blood distribution
_____ capillaries   c. transport, blood volume
_____ veins   reservoirs
                    d. blood transport and pressure
                       regulators

10. Match these three circulation components with their descriptions.
_____ capillary beds   a. two atria, two ventricles
_____ heart chambers   b. driving force for blood
_____ heart contractions c. zones of diffusion

Review Questions

1. List the functions of the cardiovascular system.

2. Define a "heartbeat," giving the sequence of events that make it up.

3. Distinguish between the systemic and pulmonary circuits.

4. Explain the function of (*a*) the sinoatrial node, (*b*) the atrioventricular node, and (*c*) the cardiac pacemaker.

5. State the main function of blood capillaries. Name the main ways substances cross the walls of capillaries.

6. In the diagram above, label the heart's components.

7. State the main functions of venules and veins. What forces work together in returning venous blood to the heart?

Self-Quiz   *Answers in Appendix V*

1. Cells obtain nutrients from and deposit waste into _____.
a. blood   c. each other
b. lymph vessels   d. both a and b

2. The contraction phase of the heartbeat is _____; the relaxation phase is _____.

3. In the pulmonary circuit, the heart's _____ half pumps _____ blood to capillary beds inside the lungs; then _____ blood flows to the heart.
a. left; deoxygenated; oxygenated
b. right; deoxygenated; oxygenated
c. left; oxygenated; deoxygenated
d. right; oxygenated; deoxygenated

Critical Thinking

1. A patient suffering from hypertension may receive drugs that decrease the heart's output, dilate arterioles, or increase urine production. In each case, how would the drug treatment help relieve hypertension?

2. Heavy smokers often develop abnormally high blood pressure. The nicotine in tobacco is a potent vasoconstrictor. Explain the connection between these two facts, including what kind of blood vessels are likely affected.

3. Before antibiotics were available, it wasn't uncommon for people in the United States (and elsewhere) to develop *rheumatic fever*. This disease develops after the patient is infected by *Streptococcus pyrogenes*, a hemolytic (red blood cell–destroying) bacterium. The infection can trigger an inflammation that ultimately damages valves in the heart. How must this disease affect the heart's functioning? What kinds of symptoms would arise as a consequence?

4. The highly publicized deaths of several airline travelers led to warnings about "economy-class syndrome." The idea is that economy-class passengers don't have as much leg room as passengers in more costly seating, so they are more likely to sit essentially motionless for long periods on flights—conditions that may allow blood to pool and clots to form in the legs. This condition is called deep-vein thrombosis, or DVT. In addition, low oxygen levels in airplane cabins may increase clotting. If a clot gets large enough to block blood flow or breaks free and is carried to the lungs or brain, it can lethally block an artery.

There could be a time lag between when a clot forms and health problems, so an air traveler who later develops DVT might easily overlook the possible connection with a flight. Studies are now under way to determine whether economy-class travel represents a significant risk of DVT. Given what you know about blood flow in the veins, explain why periodically getting up and moving around in the plane's cabin during a long flight may lower the risk that a clot will form.

Explore on Your Own

As described in Section 9.6, a pulse is the pressure wave created during each cardiac cycle as the body's elastic arteries expand and then recoil. Common pulse points—places where an artery lies close to the body surface—include the inside of the wrist, where the radial artery travels, and the carotid artery at the front of the neck. Monitoring your pulse is an easy way to observe how a change in your posture or activity affects your heart rate.

To take your pulse, simply press your fingers on a pulse point and count the number of "beats" during one minute. For this exercise, take your first measurement after you've been lying down for a few minutes. If you are a healthy adult, it's likely that your resting pulse will be between 65 and 70 beats per minute. Now sit up, and take your pulse again. Did the change in posture correlate with a change in your pulse? Now run in place for 30 seconds and take your pulse rate once again. In a short paragraph, describe what changes in your heart's activity led to the pulse differences.

10 IMMUNITY

The Face of AIDS

The photograph below is a snapshot of Chedo Gowero when she was thirteen years old. With both parents dead from AIDS, she left school to support herself, her ten-year-old brother, and her grandmother. She started spending her days gathering firewood and working in the homes and fields of neighbors. To keep her younger brother in school, she proudly assumed adult responsibilities.

Chedo and her brother are among the estimated 12 million African children orphaned because of AIDS. Worldwide, at least 40 million are now infected with HIV, the virus that causes it. Even after twenty years of high-priority research all over the world, we still do not have an effective vaccine against AIDS.

There are reasons for hope, however. For example, in some African countries, the rates of infection are declining as a result of educational and prevention programs. And most Africans—including Chedo and her brother—are not infected.

HIV disables the immune system, leaving the body vulnerable to all manner of infections and some otherwise rare cancers. And while the ongoing search for a preventive vaccine has been both frustrating and challenging, it is increasing our knowledge of how the body defends itself against threats, the subject of this chapter. We now know a lot about the body's responses to tissue damage, disease-causing agents, and cancer cells. Even so, as AIDS reminds us with every passing day, we still have a great deal to learn.

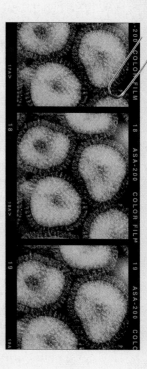

 How Would You Vote? *The cost of drugs that extend the life of AIDS patients puts them out of reach of people in most developing countries. Should the federal government offer incentives to companies to discount the drugs for developing countries? What about AIDS patients at home? Who should pay for their drugs? Cast your vote online at www.thomsonedu.com/ biology/starr/humanbio.*

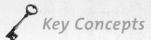 ## Key Concepts

THE BODY'S DEFENSES
The human body has a variety of physical, chemical, and cellular defenses against bacteria, viruses, and other disease threats, including cancer. Some of these are innate (inborn), others are acquired as we encounter pathogens.

ACQUIRED IMMUNITY
In acquired immunity white blood cells mount a specific immune response against anything that is chemically recognized as not being a normal part of the body.

IMMUNE SYSTEM DISORDERS
Allergies, autoimmune disorders, and immune deficiencies are the result of faulty or failed immune mechanisms.

Links to Earlier Concepts

In this chapter you will see how several body systems and cells, including the skin (4.8) and white blood cells (8.1), work to fight infection. You will be using what you have learned about proteins (2.11) and processes of endocytosis and phagocytosis (3.10). Finally you will see how circulating blood (9.2) serves as a highway for many defensive cells and how it interacts with the lymphatic system—the body-wide network of vessels and organs where key defensive white blood cells acquire their ability to recognize threats.

10.1 Overview of Body Defenses

LINKS TO
SECTIONS
4.8, 8.1, AND 8.4

Without knowing it, every day we encounter a vast number of health threats. Our defenses include physical barriers and two interacting sets of cells and proteins.

WE ARE BORN WITH SOME GENERAL DEFENSES AND ACQUIRE OTHER, SPECIFIC ONES

Pathogen is the general term for viruses, bacteria, fungi, protozoa, and parasitic worms that cause disease. No matter what we do, we can't really avoid pathogens. They are in the air we breathe, the food we eat, and on everything we touch. This means that our survival depends on having effective defenses against them.

You may remember from Section 8.4 that an **antigen** is something that the body identifies as nonself and that triggers an immune response. Virus particles, foreign cells, toxins, and cancer cells all have antigens on their surface. Most antigens are proteins, lipids, or the large sugar molecules called oligosaccharides.

Immunity is the body's overall ability to resist and combat something that is nonself. The responses involved in immunity all are governed by genes, and they fall into two categories. Each of us is born with some preset responses, which provide **innate immunity**. These responses are launched quickly when tissue is damaged or when the body detects general chemical signals that microbes have invaded. Innate immune responses are carried out by certain white blood cells and proteins in blood plasma.

By contrast, other immune responses develop only after the body detects antigens of specific pathogens, toxins, or abnormal body cells. These responses provide **adaptive immunity**, in which armies of specialized lymphocytes and proteins mount a counterattack against invasion. They take longer to develop, but as you will read in a later section, every adaptive immune response leaves behind cells that "remember" a pathogen and protect

against it for a long time, perhaps even for life. Also, some versatile genetic mechanisms underlie adaptive immune responses. They can produce lymphocytes sensitive to billions of different antigens. As a result, adaptive responses can combat billions of potential threats. Table 10.1 summarizes the features of adaptive and innate immunity.

THREE LINES OF DEFENSE PROTECT THE BODY

Biologists often portray the protections of immunity as three "lines of defense." This approach can make it easier to remember what each "line" does, even though in fact all our defenses function as parts of a whole.

The first barrier to invasion is physical. Intact skin and the linings of body cavities and tubes effectively bar most pathogens from entering the body. We'll take a closer look at these barriers in Section 10.3.

The innate immune system is the second line of defense. It swings into action as soon as an antigen has been detected internally. The responses are general; they don't target specific intruders. Still, innate responses can wipe out many pathogens before an infection becomes established. Section 10.4 describes these countermeasures, which include inflammation. When an innate immune response gets under way, it also unleashes the third line of defense, the adaptive immune system.

WHITE BLOOD CELLS AND THEIR CHEMICALS ARE THE DEFENDERS IN IMMUNE RESPONSES

You probably recall from Section 8.1 that stem cells in bone marrow give rise to white blood cells (WBCs). White blood cells, the core of the **immune system**, have crucial roles in both the innate and adaptive immune responses.

Several types of white blood cells are phagocytes, and all of them release chemical signals that help muster or strengthen defense responses. These chemicals include several types of **cytokines**, "cell movers" that promote and regulate many aspects of immunity (Table 10.2). Examples are *interleukins*, which cause inflammation and fever and also stimulate the activity of various kinds of white blood cells. *Interferons* help defend against viruses and activate certain lymphocytes. *Tumor necrosis factor* ("necrosis" means death) triggers inflammation and kills tumor cells. Some white blood cells also secrete enzymes and toxins that kill microbes.

Another chemical weapon is a set of proteins called **complement**. There are about 30 complement proteins. They are carried in the blood and can kill microbes or flag them for phagocytes such as macrophages, which then engulf and destroy the invader.

Table 10.1	Adaptive and Innate Immunity	
	Innate Immunity	Adaptive Immunity
Response time:	Immediate	Slower
How antigen is detected:	About 1,000 preset receptors	Billions of different receptors
Triggers:	Damage to tissues; proteins on microbes	Pathogens, toxins, altered body cells
Memory:	None	Long-term

THE BODY'S DEFENSES

Table 10.2	Chemical Weapons of Immunity
Complement	Directly kills cells; stimulates lymphocytes
Cytokines	Cell–cell and cell–tissue communication:
Interleukins	Cause inflammation and fever, cause T cells and B cells to divide and specialize; stimulate bone marrow stem cells, attract phagocytes, activate NK cells
Interferons	Confer resistance to viruses; activate NK cells
Tumor Necrosis Factor	Causes inflammation; kills tumor cells, causes T cells to accumulate in lymph nodes during infection
Other Chemicals	Various antimicrobial and defensive effects
	Enzymes and peptides; clotting factors; protease inhibitors; toxins; hormones

Many white blood cells also circulate in the blood, as well as in lymph, a pale fluid that circulates in vessels of the lymphatic system. As you will read in the following section, this system works with the cardiovascular system in moving many substances throughout the body and it has major roles in defense.

Figure 10.1 gives a visual summary of white blood cells. About two-thirds of our WBCs are **neutrophils**, which follow chemical trails to infected, inflamed, or damaged tissues. **Basophils** that circulate in blood and **mast cells** in tissues release enzymes and chemicals called histamines when they detect an antigen. **Macrophages** are phagocytes that patrol the bloodstream; each of these "big eaters" can engulf as many as one hundred bacteria. **Eosinophils** target worms, fungi, and other pathogens that are too big for phagocytosis. **Dendritic cells** alert the adaptive immune system when an antigen is present in tissue fluid in the skin and body linings. The **B** and **T lymphocytes**—which we call B and T cells—have the most important roles in adaptive immunity. They are the only defensive cells that are equipped with receptors for specific antigens. **Natural killer cells** (NK cells) also are lymphocytes. They have a role in adaptive immunity, but they act mostly in innate responses that destroy cancer cells and cells that have been infected by a virus.

The body's three lines of defense are physical barriers, innate immunity, and adaptive immunity.

Immune responses are executed by white blood cells and the chemicals they release.

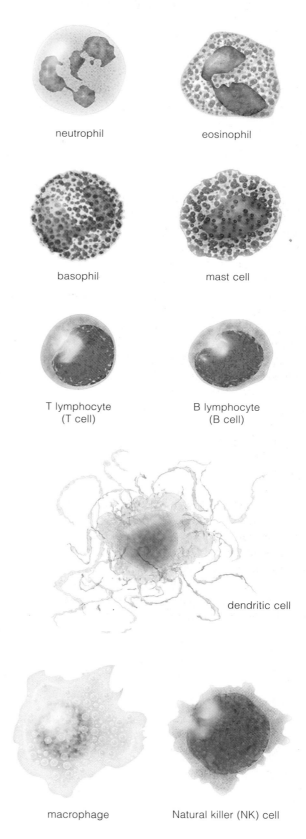

neutrophil

eosinophil

basophil

mast cell

T lymphocyte (T cell)

B lymphocyte (B cell)

dendritic cell

macrophage

Natural killer (NK) cell

Figure 10.1 *Animated!* White blood cells, including lymphocytes, that carry out immune responses.

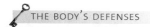

10.2 The Lymphatic System

LINKS TO
SECTIONS
7.5, 9.1,
AND 9.11

As you've just read, the **lymphatic system** does several things in the body. It works with the cardiovascular system by picking up fluid that is lost from capillaries and returning it to the bloodstream. The lymphatic system's other key task is defense. As sketched in Figure 10.2, the system consists of drainage vessels, "lymphoid" organs such as the spleen and lymph nodes, and lymphoid tissues. The tissue fluid that has moved into lymph vessels is aptly called **lymph**.

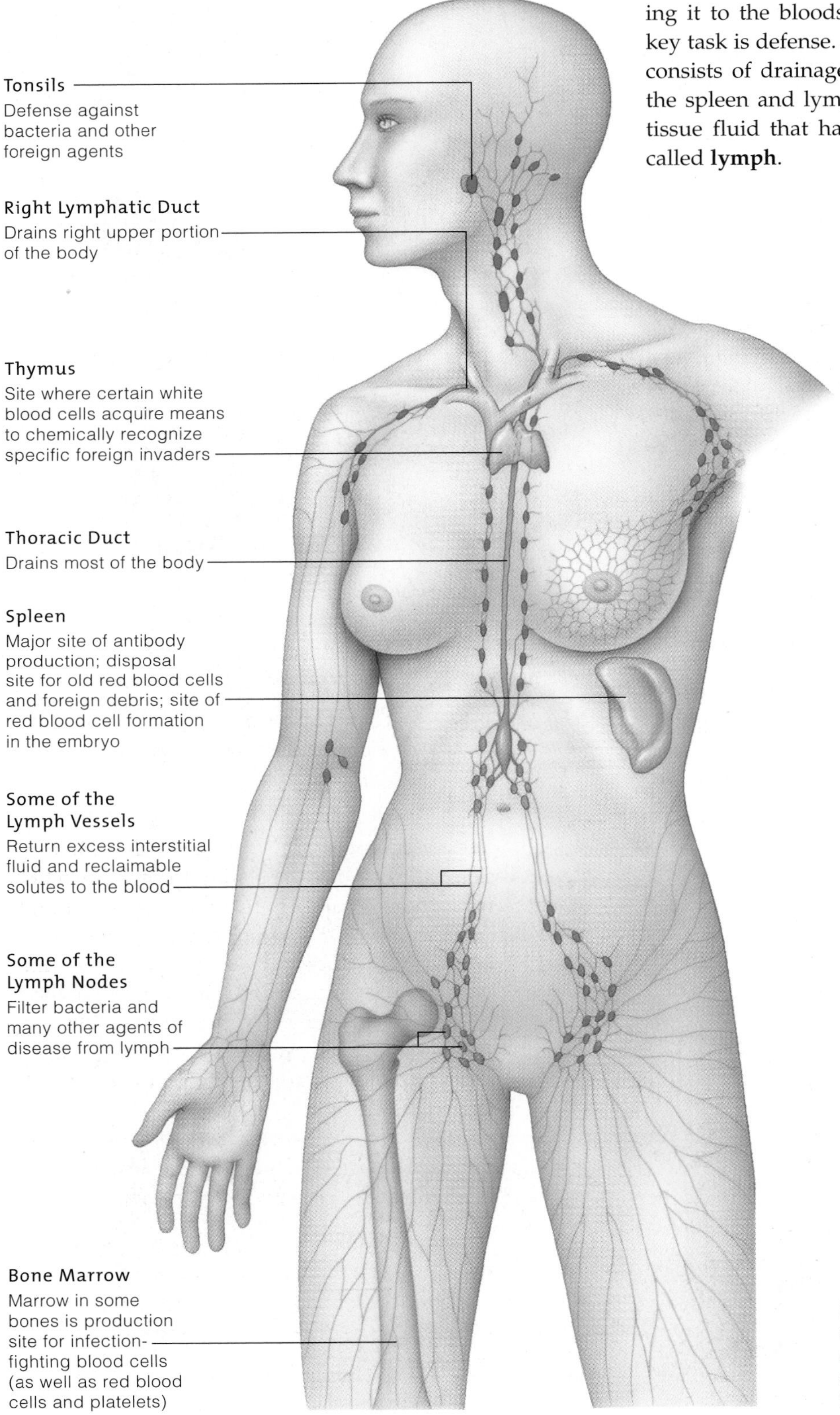

Tonsils
Defense against bacteria and other foreign agents

Right Lymphatic Duct
Drains right upper portion of the body

Thymus
Site where certain white blood cells acquire means to chemically recognize specific foreign invaders

Thoracic Duct
Drains most of the body

Spleen
Major site of antibody production; disposal site for old red blood cells and foreign debris; site of red blood cell formation in the embryo

Some of the Lymph Vessels
Return excess interstitial fluid and reclaimable solutes to the blood

Some of the Lymph Nodes
Filter bacteria and many other agents of disease from lymph

Bone Marrow
Marrow in some bones is production site for infection-fighting blood cells (as well as red blood cells and platelets)

Figure 10.2 *Animated!* The lymphatic system. The small green ovals show some of the major lymph nodes. The system also includes patches of lymphoid tissue in the small intestine and in the appendix.

ACQUIRED IMMUNITY

THE LYMPH VASCULAR SYSTEM FUNCTIONS IN DRAINAGE, DELIVERY, AND DISPOSAL

The **lymph vascular system** consists of lymph capillaries and other vessels that collect water and dissolved substances from tissue fluid and transport them to ducts of the cardiovascular system. The lymph vascular system has three functions, which we could call the "three Ds"—drainage, delivery, and disposal.

To begin with, the system's vessels are drainage channels. They collect water and solutes that have leaked out of the blood in capillary beds (due to fluid pressure there) and return those substances to the bloodstream. The system also picks up fats that the body has absorbed from the small intestine and delivers them to the bloodstream, in the way described in Section 7.5. And finally, lymphatic vessels transport foreign material and cellular debris from body tissues to the lymph vascular system's disposal centers, the lymph nodes.

The lymph vascular system starts at capillary beds (Figure 10.3a), where fluid enters the lymph capillaries. These capillaries don't have an obvious entrance. Instead, water and solutes move into their tips at flaplike "valves." These are areas where endothelial cells overlap (see Figure 9.11c).

Lymph capillaries merge into larger lymph vessels. Like veins, these vessels have smooth muscle in their wall and valves that prevent backflow. They converge into collecting ducts that drain into veins in the lower neck. This is how the lymph fluid is returned to circulating blood. Movements of skeletal muscles and of the rib cage (during breathing) help move fluid through our lymph vessels, just as they do for veins.

LYMPHOID ORGANS AND TISSUES ARE SPECIALIZED FOR BODY DEFENSE

Several elements of the lymphatic system operate in the body's defenses. These parts are the lymph nodes, the spleen, and the thymus, as well as the tonsils and patches of tissue in the small intestine, in the appendix, and in airways leading to the lungs.

The **lymph nodes** are strategically located at intervals along lymph vessels (Figures 10.2 and 10.3b). Before lymph enters the bloodstream, it trickles through at least one of these nodes. A lymph node has several chambers where white blood cells accumulate after they have been produced in bone marrow. During an infection, lymph nodes become battlegrounds where armies of lymphocytes form and where foreign agents are destroyed. Macrophages in the nodes help clear the lymph of bacteria and other unwanted substances.

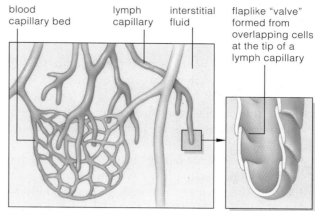

a Lymph capillaries

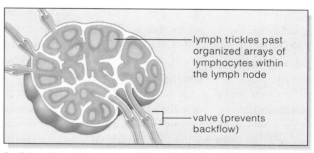

b A lymph node, cross section

Figure 10.3 *Animated!* (**a**) Some of the lymph capillaries at the start of the drainage network called the lymph vascular system. (**b**) Cutaway diagram of a lymph node. Its inner chambers are packed with highly organized arrays of infection-fighting white blood cells.

The largest lymphoid organ, the **spleen**, is a filtering station for blood and a holding station for lymphocytes. The spleen has inner chambers filled with soft red and white tissue called "pulp." The red pulp is a reservoir of red blood cells and macrophages. (In a developing embryo, the spleen produces red blood cells.) In the white pulp, masses of lymphocytes are arrayed close to blood vessels. If an invader reaches the spleen during an infection, the lymphocytes are mobilized to destroy it, just as in lymph nodes.

The **thymus** is where T cells multiply and become specialized to combat specific foreign antigens. You will soon be learning more about how it functions.

The lymphatic system includes lymph vessels that carry tissue fluid to the blood, transport fats, and carry debris and foreign material to lymph nodes. Lymph nodes, the spleen, and the thymus all function in defense.

10.3 Surface Barriers

LINK TO SECTION 4.8

Pathogens usually can't get past our skin or the linings of other body surfaces such as the GI tract.

If you showered today, there are probably thousands of microorganisms on every square inch of your skin. They usually are harmless as long as they stay outside the body, and some types grow so densely that they help prevent more harmful species from gaining a foothold (Figure 10.4).

Similarly, normally "friendly" bacteria in the mucosal lining of the GI tract help protect you. In females, lactate produced by *Lactobacillus* bacteria in the vaginal mucosa helps maintain a low vaginal pH that most bacteria and fungi cannot tolerate. Anything that changes the conditions in which these organisms grow can cause an infection. For example, some antibiotics used to cure bacterial infections can trigger a vaginal yeast infection because the drug also kills *Lactobacillus*. If the skin between your toes is chronically moist and warm, these conditions favor the growth of fungi that cause *athlete's foot*.

The inner walls of the branching, tubular respiratory airways leading to your lungs are coated with a sticky mucus. That mucus contains protective substances such as **lysozyme**, an enzyme that chemically attacks and helps destroy many bacteria. Broomlike cilia in the airways sweep out the pathogens.

Lysozyme and some other chemicals in tears, saliva, and gastric fluid offer more protection. Urine's low pH and flushing action help bar pathogens from the urinary tract. In adults, mild diarrhea can rid the lower GI tract of irritating pathogens; blocking it can prolong infection. (In children, however, diarrhea must be controlled to prevent dangerous dehydration.)

Intact skin, mucous membranes, lysozyme, and other physical barriers all help prevent pathogens from entering the internal environment of the body.

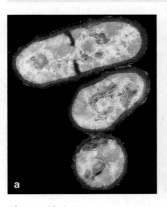
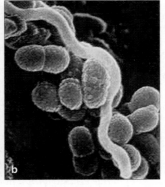

Figure 10.4 Some microbes on body surfaces. (**a**) Overgrowth of this bacterium, *Propionibacterium acnes*, causes acne. (**b**) A variety of *Streptococcus mutans*, which causes dental plaque.

10.4 Innate Immunity

Phagocytosis, inflammation, and fever are the body's "off-the-shelf" mechanisms that act at once to counter threats in general and prevent infection.

Once a pathogen has managed to enter the body, macrophages in tissue fluid are usually the first defenders on the scene. They engulf and destroy virtually anything other than undamaged body cells (Figure 10.5). If they detect an antigen, they release cytokines that, among other effects, attract dendritic cells, neutrophils, and more macrophages.

Complement is also an important aspect of innate immunity. As they circulate in blood and tissue fluid, complement proteins chemically detect the presence of pathogens. The encounter "activates" a complement protein, which in turn activates more complement molecules, which then activate more, and so on. The cascade of reactions quickly floods a damaged area with complement molecules.

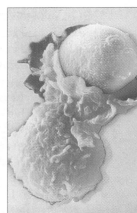

Figure 10.5 A macrophage about to engulf a yeast cell

Activated complement molecules attract phagocytes, such as macrophages and neutrophils, to damaged tissues. They also attach themselves to invaders. Phagocytes, in turn, have receptors that bind to the complement proteins. An invader that is coated with complement molecules sticks to the phagocyte, which ingests and kills it. Some complement proteins form *membrane attack complexes* (Figure 10.6). When an attack complex is inserted into the plasma membrane of a pathogen, it forms a pore—that is, a hole—in the membrane and the punctured cell quickly disintegrates.

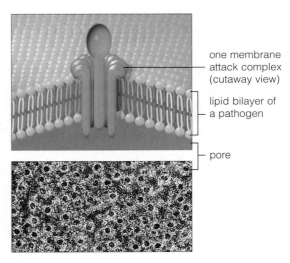

one membrane attack complex (cutaway view)

lipid bilayer of a pathogen

pore

Figure 10.6 *Animated!* Pores formed in the plasma membrane of a bacterium by membrane attack complexes.

ACQUIRED IMMUNITY

Activated complement and cytokines secreted by macrophages both trigger acute (sudden) **inflammation**, a fast, local, general response to tissue invasion (Figure 10.7). Symptoms of inflammation are redness, swelling, warmth, and pain, and they are caused by a series of internal events.

First, mast cells in tissues respond to complement proteins or to an antigen by releasing histamines and cytokines into tissue fluid. Histamines make arterioles in the tissue dilate. As a result, more blood flows through them and the tissue reddens and warms with blood-borne metabolic heat.

Histamine also makes capillaries leaky. The narrow gaps between the cells of the capillary wall become a bit wider, so plasma proteins and phagocytes slip out through them (Figure 10.8). Water flows out as well. As a result of these and other changes, the tissue balloons with fluid. This swelling is called *edema*. The pain that comes with inflammation is due to edema and the effects of inflammatory chemicals.

The plasma proteins leaking into tissue fluid include factors that cause blood to clot. Clots can wall off inflamed areas and delay the spread of microbes into nearby tissues.

A **fever** is a core body temperature above the normal 37°C (98.6°F). Fever develops when cytokines released by macrophages stimulate the brain to release prostaglandins—signaling molecules that can up the set

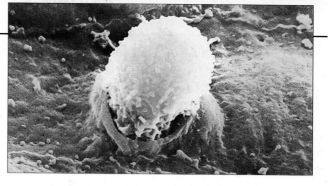

Figure 10.8 A white blood cell squeezing through the wall of a capillary.

Fevers are not usually harmful. A fever of about 39°C (100°F) is actually helpful. Among other benefits, it increases body temperature to a level that is too hot for many pathogens to function normally.

Phagocytosis, inflammation, and fever rid the body of most pathogens before they do major harm. If an infection does take hold, the adaptive immune system takes over. Three defenders we have been discussing—dendritic cells, macrophages, and complement proteins—also take part in adaptive immunity, the topic we turn to next.

Phagocytes such as macrophages, inflammation, and fever are the body's "first strike" weapons against infection. They are the tools of innate immunity, which is a general response to health challenges by pathogens.

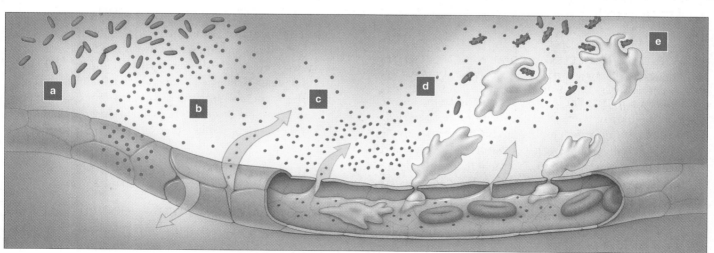

a Bacteria invade a tissue and directly kill cells or release metabolic products that damage tissue.

b Mast cells in tissue release histamine, which then triggers arteriolar vasodilation (hence redness and warmth) as well as increased capillary permeability.

c Fluid and plasma proteins leak out of capillaries; localized edema (tissue swelling) and pain result.

d Plasma proteins attack bacteria. Clotting factors wall off inflamed area.

e Neutrophils, macrophages, and other phagocytes engulf invaders and debris. Activated complement attracts phagocytes and directly kills invaders.

Figure 10.7 *Animated!* Acute inflammation in response to invading bacteria. In addition to combating the attack, the process helps prepare the damaged tissue for repair.

ACQUIRED IMMUNITY

LINK TO
SECTION
8.4

When physical barriers and inflammation don't deter an invader, the adaptive immune system is mobilized.

ADAPTIVE IMMUNITY HAS THREE KEY FEATURES

Adaptive immunity is the body's third line of defense. It mobilizes B and T cells, which attack cells and substances they recognize as antigens—that is, as foreign intruders. The three defining feaures of adaptive immunity are:

1. The adaptive immune system is *specific*: Each B or T cell makes receptors for only one kind of antigen.

2. A hallmark of adaptive immunity is its *diversity*: B and T cells collectively may have receptors for at least a billion specific threats.

3. The adaptive immune response has *memory*: Some of the B and T cells formed during a first response to an invader are held in reserve for future battles with it.

When a B cell or T cell recognizes an antigen, the meeting stimulates round after round of cell division. In the end, a huge number of identical T cells or B cells form. Each one of them can now counterattack the pathogen.

All the new cells produced by dividing B or T cells are sensitive to the same antigen. Some become **effector cells** that can immediately begin destroying the enemy, while others become **memory cells**. Instead of joining the first battle, memory cells enter a resting phase. If the threat appears again, they will mount a larger, faster response to it. Memory cells are what make you "immune" to a given cold or flu virus once you have recovered from the first infection.

B CELLS AND T CELLS BECOME SPECIALIZED TO ATTACK ANTIGENS IN DIFFERENT WAYS

Chapter 8 noted that lymphocytes arise from stem cells in bone marrow. Cells that are destined to specialize as B cells continue developing in the bone marrow, but cells that will specialize as T cells travel via the blood to the thymus gland. As they complete their development, they split into two groups—helper T cells and effector cells called cytotoxic ("killer") T cells.

When B and T cells are mature, most move into lymph nodes, the spleen, and other lymphoid tissues. Some B and T cells are said to be "naive" until they are activated. Like a defensive "light bulb" blinking on, this activation happens when the cell recognizes an antigen.

When B cells and T cells identify intruders, they attack in different ways. B cells don't directly engage a

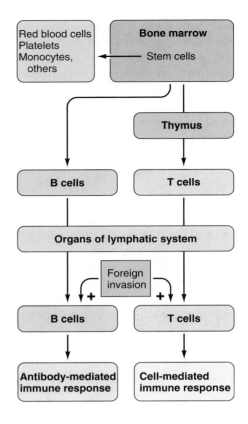

Figure 10.9 A "life history" of B cells and T cells.

pathogen. Instead they produce the defensive proteins called **antibodies**. For this reason their response is called **antibody-mediated immunity**. By contrast, cytotoxic T cells do attack invaders directly, so the T cell response is called **cell-mediated immunity** (Figures 10.9 and 10.10). Helper T cells help launch both responses, and we consider them both in more detail later. For the moment we will complete this overview with a closer look at how T and B cells "learn" they have encountered an antigen.

PROTEINS CALLED MHC MARKERS LABEL BODY CELLS AS SELF

Chapter 8 described the APO self markers on red blood cells. All body cells also have **MHC markers**. These self markers are named after the genes that code for them (*Major Histocompatibility Complex* genes). They are some of the proteins that stick out above the plasma membrane of body cells. T cells have receptors called TCRs (meaning *T Cell Receptor*) that recognize MHC

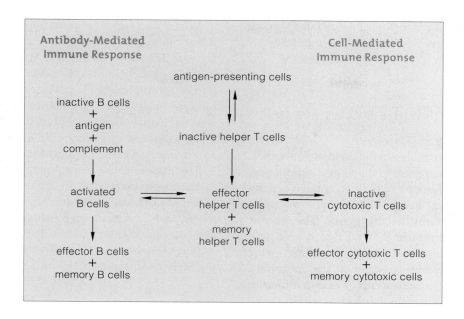

Antibody-Mediated Immune Response

Cell-Mediated Immune Response

antigen-presenting cells

inactive B cells
+
antigen
+
complement

inactive helper T cells

activated
B cells

effector
helper T cells
+
memory
helper T cells

inactive
cytotoxic T cells

effector B cells
+
memory B cells

effector cytotoxic T cells
+
memory cytotoxic cells

Figure 10.10 *Animated!* Overview of the links between antibody-mediated and cell-mediated immune responses—the two arms of adaptive immunity.

markers and other self tags on body cells. Part of the receptor also can recognize a particular antigen, so the antigen can be linked up with an MHC marker. As it turns out, this is a key step in starting specific immune responses, as you will read in Section 10.6.

ANTIGEN-PRESENTING CELLS INTRODUCE ANTIGENS TO T CELLS AND B CELLS

T cells and B cells can't detect an enemy by themselves. They must meet the threat after it has been "processed" by an **antigen-presenting cell**, an APC. The adaptive immune system allows plenty of opportunities for this to happen, for macrophages, dendritic cells, and B cells all can present antigens. To begin the process, the APC engulfs something bearing an antigen. Then enzymes (made by the APC's lysosomes) break the antigen into pieces. Some of the ·fragments are joined with MHC markers inside the cell. These *antigen–MHC complexes* move to the plasma membrane and are displayed like "come and get me" flags at the cell's surface.

When a helper T cell binds to an antigen–MHC complex, it releases cytokines. These chemicals are the signals that trigger the repeated rounds of division that produce

huge armies of activated B or T cells. They also stimulate the specialization of activated B and T cells into subgroups of effector and memory cells.

Effector B cells are called **plasma cells**. As you will now read, when called into action they can flood the bloodstream with antibodies at dizzying speed.

Adaptive immune responses are carried out mainly by T and B cells. The responses are specific, they allow for amazing diversity, and they produce memory cells that can mount a faster, stronger response if the same antigen appears in the body again.

Macrophages, dendritic cells, and B cells all can serve as antigen-presenting cells that expose T and B cells to processed antigens—a form that inactive T and B cells can recognize.

Helper T cells release cytokines that stimulate the repeated rounds of cell division by activated T and B cells.

Armies of T and B cells are produced in adaptive immune responses. Their counterattacks are carried out by helper T cells, cytotoxic T cells, and antibodies from plasma (B) cells.

10.6 Antibody-Mediated Immunity: Defending against Threats Outside Cells

LINK TO
SECTION
3.6

Antibodies are crucial for proper functioning of the immune system. This section looks more closely at how antibodies help defend the body and what roles different kinds of antibodies play.

ANTIBODIES DEVELOP WHILE B CELLS ARE IN BONE MARROW

While a B cell is in bone marrow, it develops antibodies. Figure 10.11 shows the typical Y-shape of a simple one. The place where an antibody can bind an antigen usually is near the tip of the two "arms," and its shape and other characteristics are determined by genes. The genetic mechanisms involved ensure that no two B cells will make antibodies that are alike. This is the source of the diversity and specificity of antibody-mediated immunity.

As a B cell matures, it makes copies of its antibodies and they become embedded in its plasma membrane so that the two arms stick out. Before long the B cell bristles with antibodies, each one with receptor sites for one kind of antigen.

ANTIBODIES TARGET PATHOGENS THAT ARE OUTSIDE CELLS

Antibodies can't enter cells and bind to enemies hidden there. Instead, antibodies target pathogens and toxins that are circulating in tissues or body fluids.

To get a more complete picture of how an antibody-mediated response unfolds, let's follow a B cell that has made its antibodies but that has not yet been activated. In this state, a B cell can function as an antigen-presenting cell. When an antigen binds with some of the B cell's antibodies, it links them together. This linking triggers endocytosis, which moves the antigen into the cell. There, antigen–MHC complexes form and are displayed at the B cell surface.

When TCRs of a responding helper T cell bind to the antigen–MHC complex, the T and B cells exchange signals. Then they disengage. This step activates the B cell. Now when the B cell meets an antigen that is *not* part of a complex, the B cell's antibodies bind to it. The binding helps spur the B cell to divide; a boost comes from cytokines secreted from nearby helper T cells. The B cell's descendants become specialized as plasma cells and memory B cells (Figure 10.12).

The plasma cells release huge numbers of antibodies in the bloodstream—up to 2,000 of them each minute. When any of these antibodies binds to an antigen, it flags the invader for destruction by phagocytes and complement proteins. The memory B cells do not engage in battle but are available to respond rapidly to the antigen if it attacks the body another time (Section 10.8).

THERE ARE FIVE CLASSES OF ANTIBODIES, EACH WITH A PARTICULAR FUNCTION

B cells produce five classes of antibodies. Collectively they are called **immunoglobulins**, or Igs. They are the proteins that result from the gene shuffling that takes place while B cells mature (Section 10.5) and while an immune response is under way. We abbreviate them as IgM, IgD, IgG, IgA, and IgE. Each type has antigen-binding sites and other sites with special roles. When B cells secrete them they have roughly these shapes:

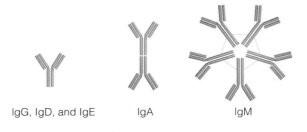

IgG, IgD, and IgE   IgA   IgM

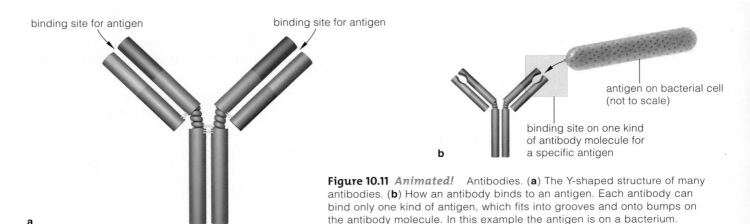

binding site for antigen   binding site for antigen

antigen on bacterial cell (not to scale)

binding site on one kind of antibody molecule for a specific antigen

b

a

Figure 10.11 *Animated!*   Antibodies. (**a**) The Y-shaped structure of many antibodies. (**b**) How an antibody binds to an antigen. Each antibody can bind only one kind of antigen, which fits into grooves and onto bumps on the antibody molecule. In this example the antigen is on a bacterium.

a A dendritic cell engulfs and digests a bacterium in interstitial fluid, and then migrates to a lymph node. There, it presents antigen–MHC complexes. Binding to this antigen-presenting cell causes inactive "naive" helper T cells to multiply, producing effector (active) helper T cells and memory helper T cells.

b Each inactive B cell has more than 100,000 receptors, all specific for the same antigen. This B cell binds to its antigen on the surface of a bacterium in a lymph node. After also binding complement, the bacterium enters the B cell and is digested. Its fragments bind to MHC molecules, and the complexes are displayed at the B cell's surface.

c TCRs of an activated helper T cell bind to the antigen–MHC complexes on the B cell. Binding makes the helper T cell secrete cytokines. These signals cause the B cell to divide, producing a huge population of B cells with identical antigen receptors. The cells specialize into effector B cells and memory B cells.

d Effector B cells begin making huge numbers of IgA, IgG, or IgE antibodies, all of which recognize the same antigen as the original B cell receptor. The new antibodies circulate throughout the body and bind to any remaining bacteria.

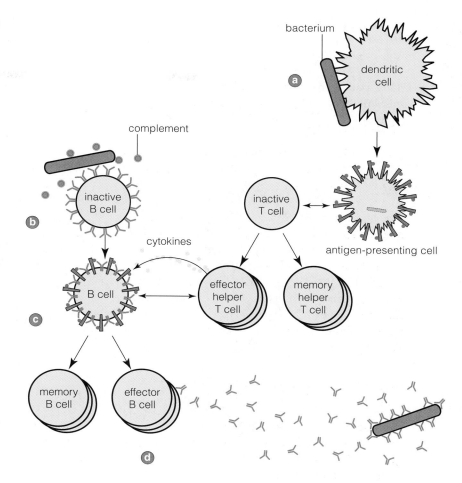

Figure 10.12 *Animated!* Antibody-mediated immune response. This example is a response to a bacterial invasion.

IgM is the first antibody secreted during immune responses and the first one produced by newborns. IgM molecules cluster into a structure with ten antigen-binding sites. This makes it more efficient at binding clumped targets, such as agglutinating red blood cells (Section 8.4) and clumps of virus particles.

Along with IgM, *IgD* is the most common antibody bound to inactive B cells. It may help activate helper T cells.

IgG makes up about 80 percent of the antibodies in blood. It's the most efficient one at turning on complement proteins, and it neutralizes many toxins. This long-lasting antibody easily crosses the placenta. It helps protect the developing fetus with the mother's acquired immunities. IgG secreted into early milk is also absorbed into a suckling newborn's bloodstream.

IgA is the main immunoglobulin in the secretions of exocrine glands, such as tears, saliva, and breast milk. It also is in mucus that coats the respiratory, digestive, and reproductive tracts, areas that are vulnerable to infection. Like IgM, it can form large structures that can bind larger antigens. Bacteria and viruses can't bind to the cells of mucous membranes when IgA is bound to them, and IgA is effective in fighting the pathogens that cause salmonella, cholera, gonorrhea, influenza, and polio.

The *IgE* antibody is involved in allergic reactions, including asthma, hay fever, and hives. IgE also triggers inflammation after attacks by parasitic worms and other pathogens. The tails of IgE antibodies lock onto basophils and mast cells, with their antigen receptors facing outward. When the receptors bind to an antigen, basophils and mast cells release histamine, which promotes inflammation.

B cells secrete five classes of antibodies (immunoglobulins). All help protect the body against diverse threats. They bind to antigens of pathogens or toxins that are outside cells and flag them for destruction by other defenders.

10.7 Cell-Mediated Responses—Defending against Threats Inside Cells

Antibody-mediated responses can't reach threats inside cells. So when cells become infected or altered in harmful ways, other "warrior" cells must come to the defense.

Many pathogens evade antibodies. They hide in body cells, kill them, and often reproduce inside them. They are exposed only briefly after they slip out of one cell and before they infect others. Viruses, bacteria, and some fungi and protozoans all can enter cells. Cell-mediated immune responses are the body's weapons against these dangers as well as abnormal body cells such as cancer cells.

Figure 10.13 gives you an overview of how a cell-mediated immune response takes place. Like an antibody-mediated response, it gets under way when an APC such as a dendritic cell presents an antigen to T cells. The response also leaves cadres of memory cells.

Some of the warriors in cell-mediated immunity are helper T cells and cytotoxic T cells, which respond to

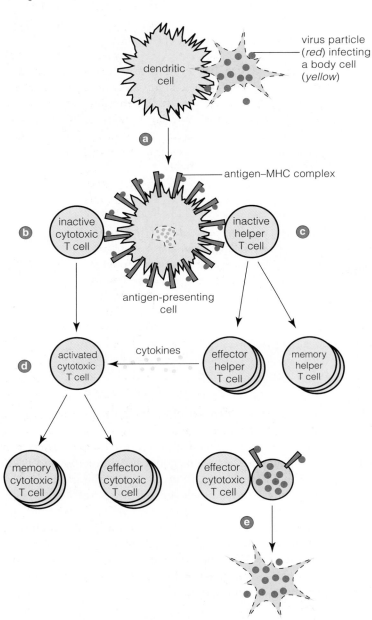

a A dendritic cell patrolling tissues meets and engulfs the remains of a virus-infected cell. The digested antigen fragments bind to MHC molecules, and the complexes are displayed at the cell's surface. The dendritic cell migrates to a lymph node or to the spleen.

b In the lymph node or spleen, TCR receptors on an inactive cytotoxic T cell bind to the complexes on the surface of the antigen-presenting dendritic cell. The interaction activates the cytotoxic T cell.

c In the lymph node, receptors of an inactive helper T cell bind to antigen–MHC complexes on the dendritic cell. The helper T cell is activated and begins dividing. The daughter cells differentiate into effector and memory helper T cells.

d Cytokines released by effector helper T cells stimulate the activated cytotoxic T cell to divide as it returns to circulating blood. Its descendants specialize into effector and memory cytotoxic T cells.

e One of the new circulating cytotoxic T cells encounters antigen–MHC complexes on the surface of a cell infected with the same virus. It touch-kills the cell by injecting it with perforin and enzymes that cause apoptosis.

Figure 10.13 *Animated!* Diagram of a T cell–mediated immune response.

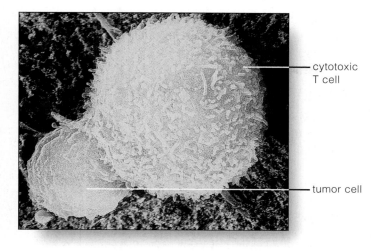

Figure 10.14 A cytotoxic T cell caught in the act of touch-killing a tumor cell.

particular antigens. Others, including NK cells and macrophages, make more general responses.

Helper T cell cytokines stimulate NK cells. These killer cells don't need to have an antigen presented to them. Instead, they simply attack any body cell that has too few or altered MHC markers, or that antibodies have tagged for destruction. They also kill body cells flagged with chemical "stress markers" that develop when a cell is infected or has become cancerous.

Cytotoxic T cells are so sensitive to antigen–MHC complexes and altered body cells that they don't need further signals to start multiplying. They release molecules that can "touch-kill" infected and abnormal body cells (Figure 10.14). Cytotoxic cells also secrete chemicals that cause the genetically programmed death of a target cell. This programmed cell death is called **apoptosis** (a-poh-TOE-sys). The term comes from a Greek word meaning to fall apart, and that's what happens to the cell. Its cytoplasm dribbles out and its DNA and organelles are broken up. After a cytotoxic T cell makes its lethal hit, it disengages from the doomed cell and moves on.

CYTOTOXIC T CELLS CAUSE THE BODY TO REJECT TRANSPLANTED TISSUE

Cytotoxic T cells cause the rejection of tissue and organ transplants. This is partly because features of the MHC markers on donor cells differ enough from the recipient's to be recognized as antigens.

To help prevent rejection, before an organ is transplanted the MHC markers of a potential donor are analyzed to determine how closely they match those of the patient. Because such tissue grafts generally succeed only when the donor and recipient share at least 75 percent of their MHC markers, the best donor is a close relative of the recipient, such as a parent or sibling, who is likely to have a similar genetic makeup.

More commonly, however, the donated organ comes from a fresh cadaver. In addition to having well-matched MHC markers, the donor and recipient also must have compatible blood types (Section 8.4).

After surgery, the organ recipient receives drugs that suppress the immune system. The treatment also may include other therapies designed to fend off an attack by B and T cells. Suppression of the immune system means that the patient must take large doses of antibiotics to control infections. In spite of the difficulties, many organ recipients survive for years beyond the surgery.

Interestingly, not all transplanted tissues provoke a recipient's immune defenses. Two examples are tissues of the eye and the testicles. In simple terms, the plasma membrane of cells of these organs apparently bears receptors that can detect activated lymphocytes in the surroundings. Before such a defender can launch an attack, the protein signals the soon-to-be-besieged cell to secrete a chemical that triggers apoptosis in the approaching lymphocytes—so the attack is averted. Our ability to readily transplant the cornea—the outermost layer of the eye that is vital to clear vision—depends on this mechanism.

Cell-mediated immune responses are mounted against infected or altered body cells. Helper T cells and cytotoxic T cells target antigens. NK cells, macrophages, and various other white blood cells make nonspecific responses.

10.8 Immunological Memory

Memory cells produced during an adaptive immune response can provide decades of immunity against pathogens.

Memory cells that form during a primary (first) immune response circulate in the blood for years, even decades. Compared to the B and T cells that initiate a primary response, these patrolling battalions have many more cell "soldiers," so they intercept antigens far sooner. Plasma cells and effector T cells form sooner, in greater numbers, so the infection is ended before the host—you—gets sick (Figure 10.15). Even more memory T and plasma cells form during a secondary adaptive response.

Over time, the kinds of memory T and plasma cells in the body are determined by the antigens you are exposed to. That is why you likely will not have immunity to a bacterium or virus that is not in your usual surroundings.

> Memory cells enable the adaptive immune system to make a faster, more powerful secondary response to another encounter with a pathogen.

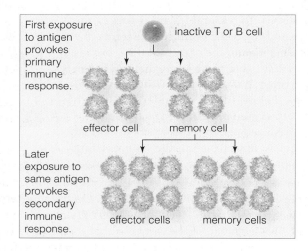

a

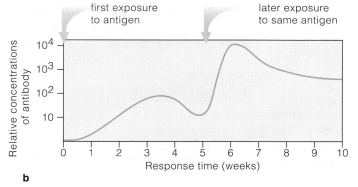

b

Figure 10.15 *Animated!* Immunological memory. (**a**) In immune responses, some plasma cells and T cells are set aside as memory cells. (**b**) Comparison of a primary and secondary immune response.

10.9 Applications of Immunology

Modern science has developed powerful weapons that can enhance the immune system's functioning or harness it in new ways to treat disease.

IMMUNIZATION GIVES "BORROWED" IMMUNITY

Immunization is a way to increase immunity against specific diseases. In *active immunization*, a **vaccine** is injected into the body or taken orally, sometimes according to a schedule (Figure 10.16). A vaccine is a prepared substance that contains an antigen. The first injection elicits a primary immune response. A "booster shot" given later elicits a secondary response, in which more effector cells and memory cells form and can provide long-lasting disease protection.

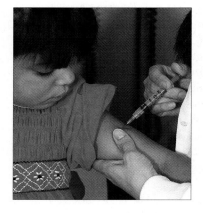

Figure 10.16 From the Centers for Disease Control and Prevention, the 2005 immunization guidelines for children in the United States. Low-cost or free vaccinations are available at many community clinics and health departments.

Recommended Vaccines	Recommended Ages
Hepatitis B	Birth–2 months
Hepatitis B booster 1	1–4 months
Hepatitis B booster 2	6–18 months
DTP Diphtheria, tetanus, and pertussis (whooping cough)	2, 4, and 6 months
DTP booster 1	15–18 months
DTP booster 2	4–6 years
DT	11–12 years
HiB (*Haemophilus influenzae*)	2, 4, and 6 months
HiB booster	12–15 months
Polio	2 and 4 months
Polio booster 1	6–18 months
Polio booster 2	4–6 years
MMR (Measles, Mumps, Rubella)	12–15 months
MMR booster	4–6 years
Pneumococcal	2, 4, and 6 months
Pneumococcal booster 1	12–15 months
Pneumococcal booster 2	2–18 years
Varicella	12–18 months
Hepatitis A series (in some areas)	2–12 years
Influenza	Yearly, 1–18 years

Many vaccines are made from killed or extremely weakened pathogens. For example, weakened poliovirus particles are used for the Sabin polio vaccine. Other vaccines are based on inactivated forms of natural toxins, such as the bacterial toxin that causes tetanus. Today many vaccines are made with harmless genetically engineered viruses (Chapter 22). These "transgenic" viruses incorporate genes from three or more different viruses in their genetic material. After a person is vaccinated with an engineered virus, body cells use the new genes to produce antigens, and immunity is established.

Passive immunization often helps people who are already infected with pathogens, such as those that cause tetanus, measles, hepatitis B, and rabies. A person receives injections of antibodies that have been purified from another source, preferably someone who already has produced a large amount of the antibody. The effects don't last long because the recipient's own B cells are not producing antibodies. However, the injected antibodies may counter the immediate attack.

Vaccines are powerful weapons, but they can fail or have adverse effects. In rare cases, a vaccine can damage the nervous system or result in chronic immunological problems. A physician can explain the risks and benefits.

MONOCLONAL ANTIBODIES ARE USED IN RESEARCH AND MEDICINE

Commercially prepared **monoclonal antibodies** harness antibodies for medical and research uses (Figure 10.17). The term "monoclonal antibody" refers to the fact that the antibodies are made by cells cloned from just a single antibody-producing B cell.

At one time laboratory mice were the "factories" for making monoclonal antibodies. Today most monoclonal antibodies are produced using genetically altered bacteria. Genetically engineered plants such as corn also are being used to make antibodies that may be both cost-effective and safe (few plant pathogens can infect people). The first "plantibody" to be used on human volunteers prevented infection by a bacterium that causes tooth decay.

Monoclonal antibodies have become useful tools in diagnosing health conditions. Because they can recognize and bind to specific antigens, they can detect substances in the body—a bacterial cell, another antibody, or a chemical—even if only a tiny amount is present. Uses include home pregnancy tests and screening for prostate cancer and some sexually transmitted diseases. As you'll read next, monoclonal antibodies also have potential uses as "magic bullets" to deliver drugs used to treat certain forms of cancer.

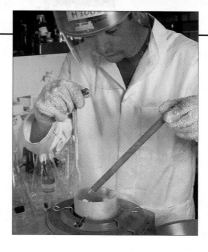

Figure 10.17
Monoclonal antibody-producing cells stored in liquid nitrogen.

IMMUNOTHERAPIES REINFORCE DEFENSES

Immunotherapy bolsters defenses against infections and cancer cells by manipulating the body's own immune mechanisms. Cytokines that activate B and T cells are being used to treat some cancers. Monoclonal antibodies are another weapon. For example, some aggressive breast cancers have excess HER2 proteins at their surface. The drug Herceptin is a monoclonal antibody that binds to the proteins and draws a response from NK cells. The drug can be a double-edged sword, however, because some healthy body cells also have HER2 proteins, and they are attacked as well.

Monoclonal antibodies also can be bound to poisons to make *immunotoxins*. When these substances bind to an antigen on a cancer cell, they enter it and block processes that allow it to survive and multiply. Some experimental immunotoxins are being tested against HIV, the virus that causes AIDS.

Various body cells, including ones infected by a virus, can make and secrete interferons. When these cytokines reach an uninfected cell, they trigger a chemical attack that prevents the virus from multiplying. *Gamma* interferon, which is made by T cells, has other functions, too. It calls NK cells into action and also boosts the activity of macrophages. Genetically engineered gamma interferon is used to treat hepatitis C, a chronic, potentially lethal viral disease. Some kinds of cells (not lymphocytes) produce *beta* interferon. This protein has recently been approved for the treatment of a type of **multiple sclerosis**, a disease in which the immune system mounts an attack on parts of the nervous system.

Immunization can enhance immunity to specific diseases by stimulating the production of both effector and memory lymphocytes.

Monoclonal antibodies and cytokines such as interferons are important tools in medical research, testing, and the treatment of disease.

10.10 Disorders of the Immune System

Sometimes immune responses are misguided, weakened, or even nonexistent. This section surveys some of the most common immune system difficulties and disorders.

IN ALLERGIES, HARMLESS SUBSTANCES PROVOKE AN IMMUNE ATTACK

Most allergies won't kill you, but they sure can make you miserable. In at least 15 percent of the people in the United States, normally harmless substances can provoke immune responses. These substances are *allergens*, and the response to them is an **allergy**. Common allergens are pollen (Figure 10.18*a*), a variety of foods and drugs, dust mites, fungal spores, insect venom, and ingredients in cosmetics. Some responses start within minutes; others are delayed. Either way, the allergens trigger mild to severe inflammation of mucous membranes and in some cases other tissues as well.

Some people are genetically predisposed to develop allergies. Infections, emotional stress, or changes in air temperature also may cause reactions that otherwise might not occur. When an allergic person first is exposed to certain antigens, IgE antibodies are secreted and bind to mast cells (Figure 10.18*b*). When the IgE binds an allergen, mast cells secrete prostaglandins, histamine, and other substances that fan inflammation. They also cause an affected person's airways to constrict. In **hay fever**, the allergic response is miserably evident in stuffed sinuses, a drippy nose, and sneezing.

Like other allergies, food allergies are skewed responses of the immune system in which a particular food is interpreted as an "invader." The most common culprits are shellfish, eggs, and wheat. Depending on the person and the food involved, symptoms typically include diarrhea, vomiting, and sometimes swelling or tingling of mucous membranes. Some food allergies can be lethal. For example, in people who are allergic to peanuts even a tiny amount can trigger **anaphylactic shock**—a whole-body allergic response in which the person's blood pressure plummets, among other frightening symptoms.

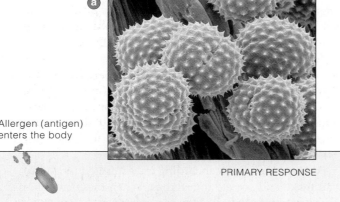

Allergen (antigen) enters the body

PRIMARY RESPONSE

SECONDARY RESPONSE (allergy)

IgE antibodies

histamine granules

histamine molecules

mast cell

mitochondrion   nucleus

Allergen binds B cell receptors; the sensitized B cell now processes the antigen and, with the help of T cells (not shown), proceeds through the steps leading to cell proliferation

Effector B cells (plasma cells) produce and secrete IgE antibodies to the allergen

IgE antibodies attach to mast cells in tissues, which have granules containing histamine molecules

After the first exposure, when the allergen enters the body it binds with IgE antibodies on mast cells; binding stimulates the mast cell to release histamine and other substances

Figure 10.18 (**a**) Micrograph of ragweed pollen. (**b**) The basic steps leading to an allergic response.

IMMUNE SYSTEM DISORDERS

Anaphylactic shock is also a concern for people who are allergic to wasp or bee venom, for they can die within minutes of a single sting. Air passages to the lungs rapidly constrict, closing almost completely. Fluid gushes from dilated, permeable (and hence extremely leaky) blood vessels all over the body. Blood pressure plummets, which can lead to the complete collapse of the person's cardiovascular system.

The emergency treatment for anaphylactic shock is an injection of the hormone epinephrine. People who know they are at risk (usually because they've already had a bad reaction to an allergen) can carry the necessary medication with them, just in case.

Antihistamines are anti-inflammatory drugs that are often used to relieve short-term allergy symptoms. In some cases a person may opt to undergo a desensitization program. First, skin tests are used to identify offending allergens. Inflammatory responses to some of them can be blocked if the patient's body can be stimulated to make IgG instead of IgE. Gradually, larger and larger doses of specific allergens are administered. Each time, the person's body produces more circulating IgG molecules and IgG memory cells. The IgG will bind with an allergen and block its attachment to IgE. As a result, inflammation is blocked, too.

AUTOIMMUNE DISORDERS ATTACK "SELF"

In an **autoimmune response**, the immune system's powerful weapons are unleashed against normal body cells or proteins. An example is **rheumatoid arthritis**. People with this disorder are genetically predisposed to it. Their macrophages and T and B cells become activated by antigens associated with the joints. Immune responses are mounted against their body's collagen molecules and also apparently against antibodies that have bound to an (as yet unknown) antigen. Tissues in the joints are damaged even more by the inflammation and the complement

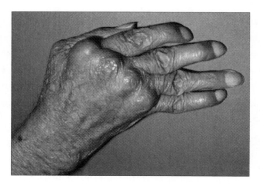

Figure 10.19 Hand of a person affected by rheumatoid arthritis.

system (Figure 10.19). Abnormal repair mechanisms compound the problem. Eventually the affected joints fill with synovial membrane cells and become immobile.

Another common autoimmune disease is **type 1 diabetes**. This is a type of *diabetes mellitus*, in which the pancreas does not secrete enough of the hormone insulin for proper absorption of glucose from the blood. For reasons that are still being investigated, the immune system attacks and destroys the insulin-secreting cells. A viral infection may trigger the response. Chapter 15 looks at the various forms of diabetes in more detail.

Systemic lupus erythematosus (SLE) primarily affects younger women, but males may also develop it. A characteristic symptom is a rash on the face that extends from cheek to cheek, roughly in the shape of a butterfly. The rash is one sign that the affected person has developed antibodies to her or his own DNA and other "self" components. Antigen–antibody complexes accumulate in joints, blood vessel walls, the skin, and the kidneys. In addition to the "butterfly" rash, symptoms include fatigue, painful arthritis, and in some cases a near-total breakdown of kidney function. Therapeutic drugs can help relieve many SLE symptoms, but there is no cure.

Immune responses tend to be stronger in women than in men. And autoimmunity is far more frequent in women. We know that the receptor for estrogen is involved in certain genetic controls. Is the receptor also implicated in autoimmune responses? It's a question that researchers are exploring.

IMMUNE RESPONSES CAN BE DEFICIENT

The term **immunodeficiency** applies when a person's immune system is weakened or lacking altogether. When the body has too few properly functioning lymphocytes, its immune responses are not effective. Both T and B cells are in short supply in **severe combined immune deficiency** (SCID). This disorder usually is inherited, and infants born with it may die early in life. Lacking adequate immune responses, they are extremely vulnerable to infections that are not life-threatening to other people. One type of SCID is now being treated by gene therapy (Chapter 22).

Infection by the human immunodeficiency virus (HIV) causes **AIDS** (acquired immunodeficiency syndrome). HIV is transmitted when body fluids of an infected person enter another person's tissues. The virus cripples the immune system by attacking macrophages and helper T cells. This leaves the body dangerously susceptible to infections and to some otherwise rare forms of cancer. We return to this topic in Chapter 18, which considers the growing global threat of infectious diseases.

Summary

Section 10.1 The body protects itself from pathogens with general and specific responses of white blood cells and chemicals they release. Preset, inborn responses provide innate immunity. Responses that develop after the body detects antigens of specific pathogens provide adaptive immunity (Table 10.3). An antigen is a protein or other type of molecule that triggers an immune response against itself.

The chemical signals that help organize or strengthen immune responses are called cytokines. They include interleukins, interferons, and complement proteins.

Section 10.2 The lymphatic system has a key role in defense. T and B lymphocytes are stationed in lymph nodes, the spleen, the tonsils, and other parts of the system. Lymph vessels also recover water and dissolved substances that have escaped from blood capillaries and return them to the general circulation.

 Learn more about how the lymphatic system functions.

Section 10.3 Physical barriers to infection, such as intact skin and mucous membranes lining body surfaces, are the first line of defense against pathogens. Lysozyme in mucus attacks many bacteria. Other chemical barriers include tears, saliva, and gastric juice. Urine and diarrhea can help flush pathogens from the urinary tract and GI tract.

Table 10.3 The Human Body's Three Lines of Defense against Pathogens
BARRIERS AT BODY SURFACES (*nonspecific* targets)
Intact skin; mucous membranes at other body surfaces
Infection-fighting chemicals in tears, saliva, gastric fluid
Normally harmless bacteria on body surfaces, which outcompete pathogens
Flushing effect of tears, saliva, urination, diarrhea, sneezing, and coughing
INNATE IMMUNE RESPONSES (*nonspecific* targets)
Inflammation
1. Fast-acting white blood cells (neutrophils, eosinophils, and basophils)
2. Macrophages (also take part in immune responses)
3. Complement proteins, blood-clotting proteins, and other infection-fighting cytokines
Organs with pathogen-killing functions (such as lymph nodes)
Some cytotoxic cells (e.g., NK cells) with a range of targets
ADAPTIVE IMMUNE RESPONSES (*specific* targets only)
1. White blood cells (T cells, B cells, and macrophages that interact with them)
2. Communication signals (e.g., interleukins) and chemical weapons (e.g., antibodies, perforins)

Section 10.4 Innate immune responses counter threats in a general way that does not require the detection of specific antigens. They often can prevent an infection from becoming established.

Macrophages are "first responders" that engulf and digest foreign agents and clean up damaged tissue. Complement proteins bind to pathogens and lethally puncture them by inserting membrane attack complexes into the invader's plasma membrane. They also attract phagocytes.

Activated complement and cytokines from macrophages trigger inflammation, a fast, local response to tissue damage. In this response, mast cells in the tissue release histamine, which dilates arterioles. As more blood flows through the arterioles, the tissue reddens and becomes warmer. Fluid leaking from permeable blood capillaries leads to edema, causing swelling and pain. Blood-clotting proteins help repair damaged blood vessels.

Chemical signals triggered by an infection can lead to an increase in the body temperature set point. The result is a fever.

Section 10.5 Adaptive defenses are specific, can combat a great diversity of antigens, and generate memory T and B cells that provide extended immunity to conquered pathogens. B cells and T cells are activated when they recognize an antigen. They then multiply and form large populations of identical cells.

Activated B cells produce antibodies. These are receptors for specific antigens that bind antigens and flag them to be destroyed by phagocytes or other defender cells. Effector B cells, called plasma cells, can release floods of antibodies.

The response by T cells provides cell-mediated immunity. T cells recognize combinations of antigen fragments and MHC self markers. These complexes are produced by antigen-presenting cells (dendritic cells, macrophages, B cells). Cytotoxic T cells are the effectors that attack intruders directly. Helper T cells release cytokines that mobilize and strengthen defense responses.

Section 10.6 Antibodies target pathogens that are outside body cells. In the antibody-mediated response, plasma cells secrete large numbers of antibodies that circulate in the bloodstream. Antibodies are proteins, often Y-shaped, and each has binding sites for one kind of antigen. The five classes of antibodies—IgG, IgD, IgE, IgA, and IgM—are immunoglobulins.

 See how antibodies combat pathogens in the blood and lymphatic system.

Section 10.7 Cell-mediated responses destroy infected cells, tumor cells, and cells of tissue or organ transplants. Cytotoxic T cells secrete chemicals that

can trigger apoptosis, or programmed cell death, in an invading cell.

 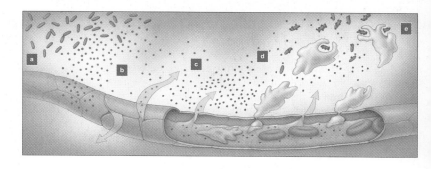

See how a cell-mediated immune response unfolds.

Section 10.8 Memory cells that form during a primary adaptive response circulate in the blood for years. They can mount a stronger, more rapid secondary response to a pathogen if it invades the body again.

Section 10.9 In active immunization, a vaccine provokes an immune response, including the production of memory cells. In passive immunization, injections of purified antibodies help patients combat an infection. Monoclonal antibodies are tools in medical research, testing, and the treatment of various diseases.

Section 10.10 An allergy is an immune response to a generally harmless substance. An autoimmune response is an attack by lymphocytes on normal body cells. Immunodeficiency is a weakened or nonexistent capacity to mount an immune response. A prime example is AIDS, caused by the HIV virus.

Review Questions

1. While you're jogging in the surf, your toes land on a jellyfish. Soon the bottoms of your toes are swollen, red, and warm to the touch. Using the diagram at the upper right as a guide, describe how these signs of inflammation came about.

2. Distinguish between:
   a. neutrophil and macrophage
   b. cytotoxic T cell and natural killer cell
   c. effector cell and memory cell
   d. antigen and antibody

3. What is the difference between innate immunity and adaptive immunity?

4. How does a macrophage or a dendritic cell become an antigen-presenting cell?

5. What is the difference between an allergy and an autoimmune response?

Self-Quiz
Answers in Appendix V

1. _____ are barriers to pathogens at body surfaces.
   a. Intact skin and mucous membranes
   b. Tears, saliva, and gastric fluid
   c. Resident bacteria
   d. all are correct

2. Complement proteins function in defense by _____.
   a. neutralizing toxins
   b. enhancing resident bacteria
   c. promoting inflammation
   d. forming pores that cause pathogens to disintegrate
   e. both a and b are correct
   f. both c and d are correct

3. _____ are molecules that lymphocytes recognize as foreign and that elicit an immune response.
   a. Interleukins   d. Antigens
   b. Antibodies   e. Histamines
   c. Immunoglobulins

4. Another term for antibodies is _____; there are _____ classes of these molecules.
   a. B cells; three
   b. immunoglobulins; three
   c. B cells; five
   d. immunoglobulins; five

5. Antibody-mediated responses work best against _____.
   a. pathogens inside cells   d. both b and c
   b. pathogens outside cells   e. all are correct
   c. toxins

6. The most common antigens are _____.
   a. nucleotides   c. steroids
   b. triglycerides   d. proteins

7. The ability to develop a secondary immune response is based on _____.
   a. memory cells   d. effector cytotoxic T cells
   b. circulating antibodies e. mast cells
   c. plasma cells

8. Tears are part of the body's defensive arsenal. What defense category do they fall into, and why?

9. Match the immunity concepts:
   ____ inflammation   a. neutrophil
   ____ antibody secretion   b. plasma cell
   ____ phagocyte   c. nonspecific response
   ____ immunological memory d. purposely causing
   ____ vaccination   memory cell
   ____ allergy   production
                              e. basis of secondary
                                 immune response
                              f. nonprotective immune
                                 response

Critical Thinking

1. New research suggests a link between some microbes that normally live in the body and seemingly unrelated major illnesses. The gum disease called periodontitis itself is not life-threatening, for instance, but it is a fairly good predictor for heart attacks. Bacteria that cause gum disease can trigger inflammation. Thinking back to your reading in Chapter 9, how do you suppose that this response also may be harmful to the heart?

2. Given what you now know about how foreign invaders trigger immune responses, explain why mutated forms of viruses, which have altered surface proteins, pose a monitoring problem for a person's memory cells.

3. Researchers have been trying to develop a way to get the immune system to accept foreign tissue as "self." Can you think of some clinical applications for such a development?

4. Elena developed chicken pox when she was in kindergarten. Later in life, when her children developed chicken pox, she remained healthy even though she was exposed to countless virus particles each day. Explain why.

5. Quickly review Section 4.9 on homeostasis. Then write a short essay on how the immune response contributes to stability in the internal environment.

6. In 1796 the English physician Edward Jenner (below) injected a young boy with material from cowpox scabs. Cowpox is a mild, smallpox-like disease that is not nearly so dangerous as smallpox. Jenner had noticed that people who got cowpox never later got smallpox, which was a major killer at the time. He suspected—rightly as it turned out—that having cowpox somehow made a person immune to smallpox. The boy was his test subject for this hypothesis. After the boy's bout of cowpox was over, Jenner injected him with pus from a smallpox sore. The boy stayed healthy, and the episode led to the discovery of vaccination—a term that literally means "encowment." What do you think would happen if a physician tried this experiment today?

Explore on Your Own

The photograph in Figure 10.20 below shows a reaction to a skin test for tuberculosis. For this test, a health care worker scratches a bit of TB antigen into a small patch of a patient's skin. In people who have a positive reaction to the test, a red swelling develops at the scratch site, usually within a day or two. Even in a person with no medical history of the disease, this response is visible evidence of immunological memory. It shows that there has been an immune response against the tuberculosis bacterium, which the person's immune system must have encountered at some time in the past. Tests for allergies work the same way.

In many communities, a TB test is required for people who are applying for jobs that involve public contact, such as teaching in the public schools. To learn more about this public health measure, find out if the test is required in your community, where it is available, and why public health authorities believe it is important.

Figure 10.20 A positive reaction to a tuberculosis skin test.

Down in Smoke

Each day, about 3,000 teenagers—most younger than 15—join the ranks of smokers in the United States. The first time someone lights up, they typically cough and choke on the irritants in smoke, and they may feel dizzy and nauseated.

So why do smoking "recruits" ignore the threat signals their body is sending and keep on lighting up? Research tells us that teens take up the habit in order to fit in socially. At the time, the threat that tobacco use poses to their health and survival seems remote. And of course, the nicotine in cigarette smoke is extremely addictive.

Tobacco smoke is really bad news for the respiratory system, our topic in this chapter. Cilia that line the airways to the lungs normally sweep away airborne pollutants and microbes. Unfortunately, smoke from a single cigarette immobilizes them for hours. Smoke also kills white blood cells that patrol and defend the respiratory tract. Microbes may start living there, leading to more colds, bronchitis, even asthma attacks.

You're probably aware that smoking also is a major risk factor for lung cancer. It also is linked with other cancers. For example, females who start smoking in their teens are about 70 percent more likely to develop breast cancer than those who don't smoke. Other "bad-efits" of smoking include increased blood pressure, higher levels of "bad" cholesterol (LDL), and lower levels of "good" cholesterol (HDL).

The respiratory system has one basic job—to help maintain homeostasis by bringing in oxygen for body cells and to carry away cells' carbon dioxide wastes. Structures such as lungs and functions such as breathing allow the respiratory system to perform this vital gas exchange.

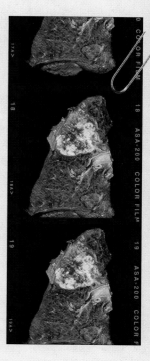

 How Would You Vote? Tobacco is both a worldwide threat to health and a profitable product for American companies. As tobacco use by its citizens declines, should the United States encourage international efforts to reduce tobacco use? Cast your vote online at www.thomsonedu.com/biology/starr/humanbio.

Key Concepts

THE RESPIRATORY SYSTEM
Respiration provides the body with oxygen for aerobic respiration in cells and removes carbon dioxide. These gases enter and leave the body by way of the respiratory system.

GAS EXCHANGE
Oxygen and carbon dioxide are exchanged across the thin walls of alveoli, tiny sacs in the lungs. The cardiovascular system carries gases to and from the lungs.

BREATHING CONTROLS
Various controls regulate respiration. The nervous system controls the rate, depth, and rhythmic pattern of breathing.

Links to Earlier Concepts

In this chapter you will once again use your knowledge of concentration gradients and diffusion (3.9) to help you understand the mechanisms that move oxygen into and carbon dioxode out of the body. You will see how the respiratory system works together with the cardiovascular system (9.1) to supply oxygen and remove carbon dioxide, and you will learn exactly how hemoglobin and red blood cells function in gas exchange (8.1, 9.3, 9.6).

11.1 The Respiratory System—Built for Gas Exchange

Getting oxygen from air and releasing carbon dioxide wastes are the vital functions of the respiratory system.

AIRWAYS ARE PATHWAYS FOR OXYGEN AND CARBON DIOXIDE

Our body cells require oxygen for aerobic respiration and must get rid of carbon dioxide. The **respiratory system** handles these key tasks (Figure 11.1).

When a person breathes quietly, air typically enters and leaves the respiratory system by way of the nose. Hairs at the entrance to the nasal cavity and in its ciliated epithelial lining filter out large particles, such as dust, from incoming air. The air also is warmed in the nose and picks up moisture from mucus. A septum (wall) of bone and cartilage separates the nasal cavity's two chambers. Channels link the cavity with paranasal sinuses above and behind it (which is why nasal sprays for colds or allergies can relieve mucus-clogged sinuses). Tear glands produce moisture that drains into the nasal cavity. Crying increases the flow, which is why your nose "runs" when you cry.

From the nasal cavity, air moves into the **pharynx**. This is the entrance to both the **larynx** (an airway) and

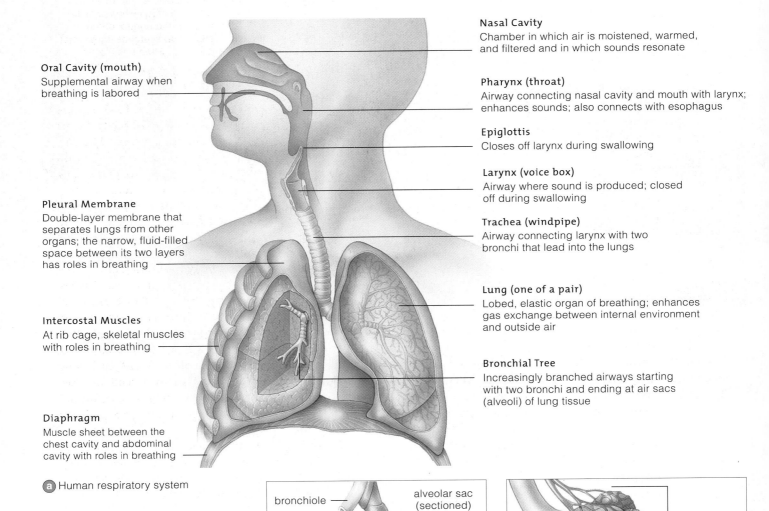

Oral Cavity (mouth)
Supplemental airway when breathing is labored

Pleural Membrane
Double-layer membrane that separates lungs from other organs; the narrow, fluid-filled space between its two layers has roles in breathing

Intercostal Muscles
At rib cage, skeletal muscles with roles in breathing

Diaphragm
Muscle sheet between the chest cavity and abdominal cavity with roles in breathing

Nasal Cavity
Chamber in which air is moistened, warmed, and filtered and in which sounds resonate

Pharynx (throat)
Airway connecting nasal cavity and mouth with larynx; enhances sounds; also connects with esophagus

Epiglottis
Closes off larynx during swallowing

Larynx (voice box)
Airway where sound is produced; closed off during swallowing

Trachea (windpipe)
Airway connecting larynx with two bronchi that lead into the lungs

Lung (one of a pair)
Lobed, elastic organ of breathing; enhances gas exchange between internal environment and outside air

Bronchial Tree
Increasingly branched airways starting with two bronchi and ending at air sacs (alveoli) of lung tissue

a Human respiratory system

Figure 11.1 *Animated!*
Components of the human respiratory system and their functions. Also shown are the diaphragm and other structures with secondary roles in respiration.

b
bronchiole
alveolar duct
alveoli
alveolar sac (sectioned)

c
alveolar sac
pulmonary capillary

Figure 11.2 Color-enhanced scanning electron micrograph of cilia and mucus-secreting cells (orange) in the respiratory tract.

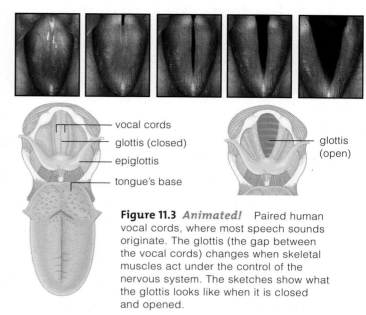

Figure 11.3 *Animated!* Paired human vocal cords, where most speech sounds originate. The glottis (the gap between the vocal cords) changes when skeletal muscles act under the control of the nervous system. The sketches show what the glottis looks like when it is closed and opened.

the esophagus (which leads to the stomach). Nine pieces of cartilage form the larynx. One of these, the thyroid cartilage, is the "Adam's apple."

Luckily, our airways are nearly always open. The flaplike *epiglottis*, attached to the larynx, points up during breathing. However, recall from Chapter 7 that when you swallow, the larynx moves up so that the epiglottis partly covers the opening of the larynx. This helps prevent food from entering the respiratory tract and causing choking.

From the larynx, air moves into the **trachea** (TRAY-key-uh), or windpipe. Press gently at the lower front of your neck, and you can feel some of the bands of cartilage that ring the tube, adding strength and helping to keep it open. The trachea branches into two airways, one leading to each lung. Each airway is a **bronchus** (BRAWN-kus; plural: bronchi). The epithelial lining of bronchi includes mucus-secreting cells and cilia (Figure 11.2). Bacteria and airborne particles stick in the mucus; then the upward-beating cilia sweep the debris-laden mucus toward the mouth.

Near the entrance to the larynx, part of a mucous membrane forms horizontal folds that are the **vocal cords** (Figure 11.3). When you exhale, air is forced through the *glottis*, a gap between the vocal cords that is the opening to the larynx. Air moving through it makes the cords vibrate. By controlling the vibrations we can make sounds. Using our lips, teeth, tongue, and the soft roof over the tongue (the soft palate), we can modify these sounds into speech, song, and other vocalizations.

LUNGS ARE ELASTIC AND PROVIDE A LARGE SURFACE AREA FOR GAS EXCHANGE

Your **lungs** are elastic cone-shaped organs separated from each other by the heart. The left lung has two lobes, the right lung three. The lungs are located inside the rib cage above the **diaphragm**, a sheet of muscle between the thoracic (chest) and abdominal cavities. The lungs are soft and spongy, and they don't attach directly to the chest cavity wall. Instead, each lung is enclosed by a pair of thin membranes called **pleurae** (singular: pleura). You can visualize this arrangement if you think of pushing your closed fist into a fluid-filled balloon. A lung occupies the same kind of position as your fist, and the pleural membrane folds back on itself (as the balloon does) to form a closed *pleural sac*. An extremely narrow *intrapleural space* (*intra-* means between) separates the membrane's two facing surfaces. A thin film of lubricating *intrapleural fluid* in the space reduces chafing between the membranes. Inside each lung, the bronchi narrow as they branch and form "bronchial trees." These narrowing airways are **bronchioles** and their endings are called **respiratory bronchioles**. Tiny air sacs bulge out from their walls. Each sac is an **alveolus** (plural: alveoli), and each lung has about 150 million of them. Usually alveoli are clustered as an alveolar sac. Alveoli are where gases diffuse between the lungs and lung capillaries (Figure 11.1*b* and 11.1*c*).

Collectively the alveoli provide a huge surface area for the diffusion of gases. If they were stretched out as a single layer, they would cover the body several times over—or the floor of a racquetball court!

Taking in oxygen and removing carbon dioxide are the major functions of the respiratory system.

In alveoli inside the lungs, oxygen enters lung capillaries and carbon dioxide leaves them to be exhaled.

LINKS TO
SECTIONS
3.7 AND 3.11

11.2 Respiration = Gas Exchange

All living cells in the body rely on respiration to supply them with oxygen and dispose of carbon dioxide.

Chapter 3 discussed how aerobic respiration inside cells uses oxygen and produces carbon dioxide wastes that must be removed from the body. **Respiration**, in contrast, is the overall exchange of oxygen inhaled from the air for waste carbon dioxide, which is exhaled:

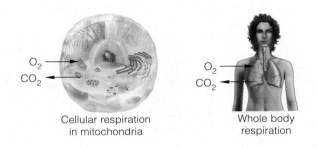

Cellular respiration
in mitochondria

Whole body
respiration

As you just read in Section 11.1, gas exchange takes place in alveoli in the lungs. The alveoli are where the respiratory system's role in respiration ends. From there, the cardiovascular system takes over the task of moving gases (Figure 11.4), which it transports along with other substances arriving from the digestive system and moving into and out of the urinary system.

> *Respiration is the exchange of gases—oxygen and carbon dioxide—with the outside world. The respiratory system brings in oxygen from air and expels carbon dioxide.*
>
> *The cardiovascular system transports O_2 and CO_2 between the lungs and tissues.*

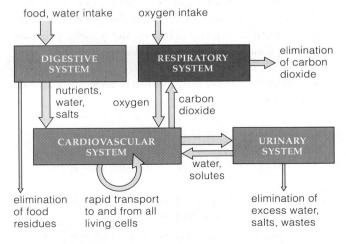

Figure 11.4 Links between the respiratory system, the cardiovascular system, and other organ systems.

11.3 The "Rules" of Gas Exchange

Gas exchange depends on the diffusion of oxygen and carbon dioxide down a concentration gradient.

Gas exchange in the body relies on the tendency of oxygen and carbon dioxide to diffuse down their respective concentration gradients—or, as we say for gases, their *pressure gradients*. When molecules of either gas are more concentrated outside the body, they tend to move into the body, and vice versa.

At sea level the air is about 78 percent nitrogen, 21 percent oxygen, 0.04 percent carbon dioxide, and 0.96 percent other gases. Atmospheric pressure at sea level is about 760 mm Hg, as measured by a mercury barometer (Figure 11.5). Each gas accounts for only *part* of the total pressure exerted by the whole mix of gases. Oxygen's partial pressure is 21 percent of 760, about 160 mm Hg. Carbon dioxide's partial pressure is about 0.3 mm Hg.

Gas exchange must be efficient in order to meet the metabolic needs of a large, active animal such as a human. Various factors influence the process. To begin with, gases enter and leave the body by crossing a thin **respiratory surface** of epithelium. The respiratory surface must be moist, because gases can't diffuse across it unless they are dissolved in fluid. Two factors affect how many gas molecules can move across the respiratory surface in a given period of time. The first is surface area, and the second is the partial pressure gradient across it. The larger the surface area and the steeper the partial pressure gradient, the faster diffusion takes place. The millions of thin-walled alveoli in your lungs provide a huge surface area for gas exchange.

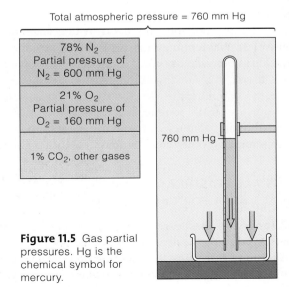

Figure 11.5 Gas partial pressures. Hg is the chemical symbol for mercury.

Figure 11.6 Breathing challenges. (**a**) A climber approaches the summit of Chomolungma (Mt. Everest), where the air contains only a small amount of oxygen. (**b**) The human body is unable to extract oxygen dissolved in water.

WHEN HEMOGLOBIN BINDS OXYGEN, IT HELPS MAINTAIN THE PRESSURE GRADIENT

Gas exchange also gets a boost from the hemoglobin in red blood cells. Each hemoglobin molecule binds with as many as four oxygen molecules in the lungs, where the oxygen concentration is high. When blood carries red blood cells into tissues where the oxygen concentration is low, hemoglobin *releases* oxygen. Thus, by carrying oxygen away from the respiratory surface, hemoglobin helps maintain the pressure gradient that helps draw oxygen into the lungs—and into the blood in lung capillaries. Later in this chapter you will learn more about the way oxygen binds to and is released from hemoglobin.

GAS EXCHANGE "RULES" CHANGE WHEN OXYGEN IS SCARCE

In environments where there is less oxygen than normal, the rules of gas exchange change. For instance, the partial pressure of oxygen falls the higher you go (Figure 11.6a). A person who isn't acclimatized to the thinner air at high altitude can become *hypoxic*—meaning that tissues are chronically short of oxygen. Above 2,400 meters (about 8,000 feet), the brain's respiratory centers trigger the response known as *hyperventilation*—faster, deeper breathing—to compensate for the oxygen deficiency.

When you swim or dive, there may be ample oxygen dissolved in the water but the body has no way to extract it. (Gills do this for a fish.) Humans trained to dive without oxygen tanks can stay submerged only for about three minutes (Figure 11.6b).

Deep divers risk "raptures of the deep" or nitrogen narcosis. This condition develops because water pressure increases the deeper you go, and at about 45 meters (150 feet) dangerous levels of nitrogen gas (N_2) start to become dissolved in tissue fluid and move into cells. In brain cells the nitrogen interferes with nerve impulses, and the diver becomes euphoric and drowsy. If a diver ascends from depth too quickly, the falling pressure causes N_2 to enter the blood faster than it can be exhaled, so nitrogen bubbles may form in blood and tissues. The resulting pain (especially in joints) is called *decompression sickness*, or "the bends."

> Gas exchange depends on steep partial pressure gradients between the outside and inside of the body. The larger the respiratory surface and the larger the partial pressure gradient, the faster gases diffuse.
>
> When hemoglobin in red blood cells binds oxygen, it helps maintain the pressure gradient that draws air into the lungs.

GAS EXCHANGE

11.4 Breathing—Air In, Air Out

LINK TO SECTION 2.6

You will take about 500 million breaths by age 75—even more if you consider that young children breathe faster than adults do. But what does "taking a breath" mean?

WHEN YOU BREATHE, AIR PRESSURE GRADIENTS REVERSE IN A CYCLE

Breathing ventilates the lungs in a continuous, in/out pattern called a **respiratory cycle**. Ventilation has two phases. First, **inspiration**—or inhalation—draws a breath of air into the airways. Then, in the phase of **expiration** or exhalation, a breath moves out.

In each respiratory cycle, the volume of the chest cavity increases, then decreases (Figure 11.7). At the same time, pressure gradients between the lungs and the air outside the body are *reversed*. To understand how this shift affects breathing, it helps to remember that air in your airways (oxygen, carbon dioxide, and the other atmospheric gases) is at the same pressure as the outside atmosphere.

Before you inhale, the pressure inside all your alveoli (called *intrapulmonary pressure*) is also the same as that of outside air.

THE BASIC RESPIRATORY CYCLE As you start to inhale, the diaphragm contracts and flattens, and external intercostal muscle movements lift the rib cage up and out (Figure 11.7a). As the chest cavity expands, the lungs expand too. At that time, the air pressure in alveolar sacs is lower than the atmospheric pressure. Fresh air follows this gradient and flows down the airways, then into the alveoli. If you take a deep breath, the volume of the chest cavity increases even more because contracting neck muscles raise the sternum and the first two ribs.

During normal, quiet breathing, expiration is passive. The muscles that contracted to bring about inspiration simply relax and the lungs recoil, like a stretched rubber band. As the lung volume shrinks, the air in the alveoli is compressed. Because pressure in the sacs now is greater than the atmospheric pressure, air follows the gradient, out of the lungs (Figure 11.7b).

If your lungs must rapidly expel more air—for instance, when you huff and puff while working out—expiration becomes active. Muscles in the wall of the abdomen contract, pushing your diaphragm upward, and other muscle movements reduce the volume of the chest cavity even more. Add to these changes the natural recoil of the lungs, and a great deal of air in the lungs is pushed outward.

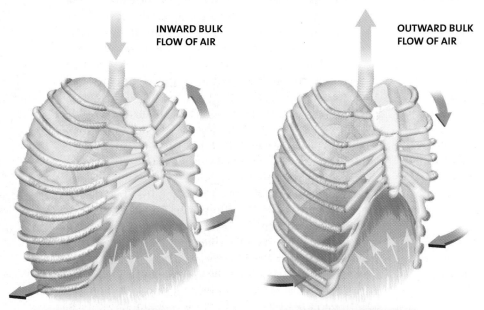

INWARD BULK FLOW OF AIR

OUTWARD BULK FLOW OF AIR

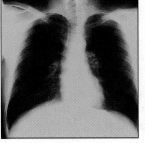

ⓐ Inhalation. Diaphragm contracts and moves down. The external intercostal muscles contract and lift the rib cage upward and outward. The lung volume expands.

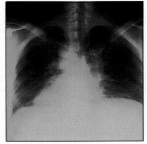

ⓑ Exhalation. Diaphragm and external intercostal muscles return to the resting positions. Rib cage moves down. Lungs recoil passively.

Figure 11.7 *Animated!* Changes in the size of the chest (thoracic) cavity during a respiratory cycle. The X-ray image in (**a**) shows how taking a deep breath changes the volume of the thoracic cavity. Part (**b**) shows how the volume shrinks after exhalation.

ANOTHER PRESSURE GRADIENT AIDS THE PROCESS

A negative pressure gradient *outside* the lungs contributes to the respiratory cycle. Atmospheric pressure is a bit higher than the pressure in the pleural sac that encloses the lungs. The pressure difference is enough to make the lungs stretch and fill the expanded chest cavity. It keeps the lungs snug against the chest wall even when air is being exhaled, when the lung volume is much smaller than the space inside the chest cavity. As a result, when the chest cavity expands with the next breath, so do the lungs.

You may recall from Chapter 2 that the hydrogen bonds between water molecules prevent them from being easily pulled apart. This cohesiveness of water molecules in the fluid in the pleural sac also helps your lungs hug the chest wall, in much the same way that two wet panes of glass resist being pulled apart.

A "collapsed lung"—medically, called *pneumothorax*—is caused by an injury or illness that allows air to enter the pleural cavity. The lungs can't expand normally and breathing becomes difficult and painful.

HOW MUCH AIR IS IN A "BREATH"?

About 500 milliliters (two cupfuls) of air enters or leaves your lungs in a normal breath. This volume of air is called **tidal volume**. You can increase the amount of air you inhale or exhale, however. In addition to air taken in as part of the tidal volume, a person can forcibly inhale roughly 3,100 milliliters of air, called the *inspiratory reserve volume*. By forcibly exhaling, you can expel an additional

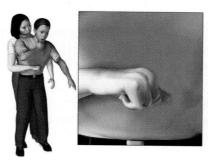
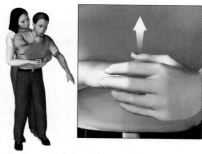
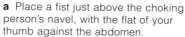

a Place a fist just above the choking person's navel, with the flat of your thumb against the abdomen.

b Cover the fist with your other hand. Thrust both fists up and in with enough force to lift the person off his or her feet.

Figure 11.9 *Animated!* The Heimlich maneuver.

expiratory reserve volume of about 1,200 milliliters of air. **Vital capacity** is the maximum volume of air that can move out of the lungs after you inhale as deeply as possible. It is about 4,800 milliliters for a healthy young man and about 3,800 milliliters for a healthy young woman. As a practical matter, people rarely take in more than half their vital capacity, even when they breathe deeply during strenuous exercise. At the end of your deepest exhalation, your lungs still are not completely emptied of air; another roughly 1,200 milliliters of *residual volume* remains (Figure 11.8).

How much of the 500 milliliters of inspired air is actually available for gas exchange? Between breaths, about 150 milliliters of exhaled "dead" air remains in the airways and never reaches the alveoli. Thus only about 350 (500 − 150) milliliters of fresh air reaches the alveoli each time you inhale. An adult typically breathes at least twelve times per minute. This rate of ventilation supplies the alveoli with 4,200 (350 × 12) milliliters of fresh air every 60 seconds. This is about the volume of soda pop in four 1-liter bottles.

When food "goes down the wrong way" and enters the trachea (instead of the esophagus), air can't be inhaled or exhaled normally. A choking person can suffocate in just a few minutes. The emergency procedure called the Heimlich maneuver can dislodge food from the trachea by elevating the diaphragm muscle. This reduces the chest volume, forcing air up the trachea. Figure 11.9 shows how to perform the maneuver. With luck, the air will rush out with enough force to eject the obstruction.

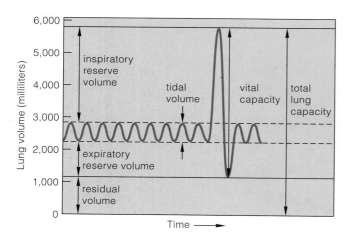

Figure 11.8 *Animated!* Lung volume during quiet breathing and during forced inspiration and expiration ("spikes" above and below the normal tidal volume).

> In the respiratory cycle, the air movements of breathing occur as the volume of the chest cavity expands and shrinks. These changes alter the pressure gradients between the lungs and outside air.

11.5 How Gases Are Exchanged and Transported

LINKS TO SECTIONS 2.6, 2.7, 3.9, 3.11, 8.1, AND 8.2

Ventilation moves gases into and out of the lungs. But it is respiration that provides body cells with oxygen for cellular respiration and picks up their carbon dioxide wastes.

Physiologists divide respiration into "external" and "internal" phases. *External* respiration moves oxygen from alveoli into the blood, and moves carbon dioxide in the opposite direction. During *internal* respiration, oxygen moves from the blood into tissues, and carbon dioxide moves from tissues into the blood.

ALVEOLI ARE MASTERS OF GAS EXCHANGE

The alveoli in your lungs are ideally constructed for their function of gas exchange. The wall of each alveolus is a single layer of epithelial cells, supported by a gossamer-thin basement membrane. Hugging the alveoli are lung capillaries (Figure 11.10a). They, too, have an extremely thin basement membrane around their wall. In between the two basement membranes is a film of fluid. It may seem like a lot of layers, but the **respiratory membrane** they form is far narrower than even a fine baby hair. This is why oxygen and carbon dioxide can diffuse rapidly across it—oxygen moving in and carbon dioxide moving out (Figure 11.10b,c).

Some cells in the epithelium of alveoli secrete *pulmonary surfactant*. This substance reduces the surface tension of the watery film between alveoli. Without it, the force of surface tension can collapse the delicate alveoli. This can happen to premature babies whose underdeveloped lungs do not yet have working surfactant-secreting cells. The result is the dangerous disorder called **infant respiratory distress syndrome**.

HEMOGLOBIN IS THE OXYGEN CARRIER

Blood plasma can carry only so much dissolved oxygen and carbon dioxide. To meet the body's requirements, the gas transport must be improved. The hemoglobin in red blood cells binds and transports both O_2 and CO_2. This pigment enables blood to carry some 70 times more oxygen than it otherwise would and to transport 17 times more carbon dioxide away from tissues.

Air inhaled into your alveoli contains plenty of oxygen and relatively little carbon dioxide. Just the opposite is true of blood arriving from tissues—which, remember, enters lung capillaries at the "end" of the pulmonary circuit (Section 9.3). Thus, in the lungs, oxygen diffuses down its pressure gradient into the blood plasma and then into red blood cells, where up to four oxygen molecules rapidly form a weak, reversible bond with each molecule of hemoglobin. Hemoglobin with oxygen bound to it is called **oxyhemoglobin**, or HbO_2.

The amount of HbO_2 that forms depends on several factors. One is the partial pressure of oxygen—that is, the relative amount of oxygen in blood plasma. In general, the higher its partial pressure, the more oxygen will be picked up by hemoglobin, until oxygen is attached to all hemoglobin binding sites. HbO_2 will give up its oxygen in tissues where the partial pressure of oxygen is lower than in the blood. Figure 11.11 will give you an idea of the pressure gradients in different areas of the body.

In tissues with high metabolic activity—and therefore a greater demand for oxygen—the chemical conditions loosen hemoglobin's "grip" on oxygen. For example, the binding of oxygen weakens as temperature rises or as acidity increases and pH falls. Several events contribute to a falling pH. The reaction that forms HbO_2 releases

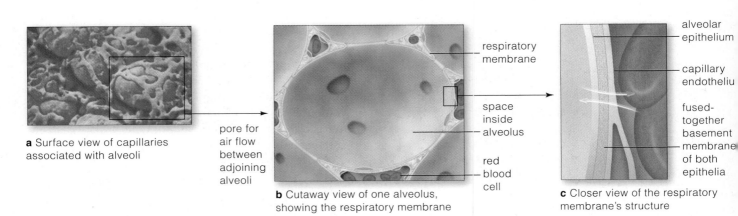

a Surface view of capillaries associated with alveoli

pore for air flow between adjoining alveoli

respiratory membrane

space inside alveolus

red blood cell

b Cutaway view of one alveolus, showing the respiratory membrane

alveolar epithelium

capillary endotheliu

fused-together basement membrane of both epithelia

c Closer view of the respiratory membrane's structure

Figure 11.10 *Animated!* Gas exchange between blood in pulmonary capillaries and air in alveoli.

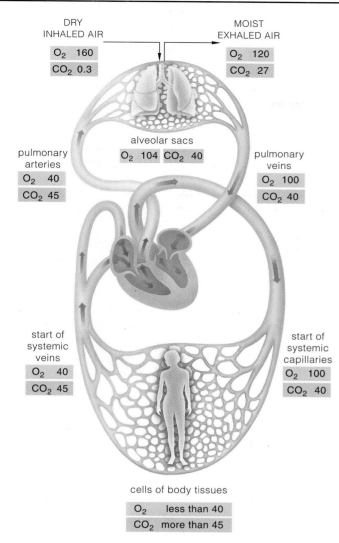

DRY INHALED AIR

| O_2 | 160 |
| CO_2 | 0.3 |

MOIST EXHALED AIR

| O_2 | 120 |
| CO_2 | 27 |

alveolar sacs

| O_2 | 104 | CO_2 | 40 |

pulmonary arteries

| O_2 | 40 |
| CO_2 | 45 |

pulmonary veins

| O_2 | 100 |
| CO_2 | 40 |

start of systemic veins

| O_2 | 40 |
| CO_2 | 45 |

start of systemic capillaries

| O_2 | 100 |
| CO_2 | 40 |

cells of body tissues

| O_2 | less than 40 |
| CO_2 | more than 45 |

Figure 11.11 *Animated!* Partial pressure gradients for oxygen and carbon dioxide through the respiratory tract. Remember that *each gas moves from regions of higher to lower partial pressure.*

hydrogen ions (H^+), making the blood more acidic. Blood pH also falls as the level of carbon dioxide given off by active cells increases.

When tissues chronically receive too little oxygen, red blood cells increase their production of a compound called 2,3-diphosphoglycerate, DPG for short. DPG reversibly binds hemoglobin. The more of it that is bound to hemoglobin, the *more loosely* hemoglobin binds oxygen—and thus the more oxygen is available to tissues.

HEMOGLOBIN AND BLOOD PLASMA CARRY CARBON DIOXIDE

As you know, aerobic respiration in cells produces carbon dioxide as a waste. For this reason, there is more carbon dioxide in metabolically active tissues than in the blood in the nearby capillaries. So, following its pressure gradient, carbon dioxide diffuses into these capillaries. It will be carried toward the lungs in three ways. About 7 percent stays dissolved in plasma. About another 23 percent binds with hemoglobin in red blood cells, forming the compound *carbaminohemoglobin* ($HbCO_2$). Most of the carbon dioxide, about 70 percent, combines with water to form bicarbonate (HCO_3^-). The reaction has two steps. First carbonic acid (H_2CO_3) forms; then it dissociates (separates) into bicarbonate ions and hydrogen ions:

$$CO_2 + H_2O \rightleftharpoons \underset{\text{carbonic acid}}{H_2CO_3} \rightleftharpoons \underset{\text{bicarbonate}}{HCO_3^-} + H^+$$

This reaction takes place in the blood plasma and in red blood cells. However, it is faster in red blood cells, which contain the enzyme carbonic anhydrase. This enzyme increases the reaction rate by at least 250 times. Newly formed bicarbonate in red blood cells diffuses into the plasma, which will carry it to the lungs. The reactions rapidly reduce the amount of carbon dioxide in the blood. This "sopping up" of CO_2 in turn helps maintain the gradient that keeps carbon dioxide diffusing from tissue fluid into the bloodstream.

The reactions that make bicarbonate are reversed in alveoli, where the partial pressure of carbon dioxide is *lower* than it is in surrounding capillaries. The CO_2 that forms as the reactions go in reverse diffuses into the alveoli and is exhaled.

If you look again at the chemical reactions outlined in the pink shaded area above, you can see that the steps that form bicarbonate also produce some H^+, which makes blood more acid. What happens to these hydrogen ions? Hemoglobin binds some of them and thus acts as a buffer (Chapter 2). Certain proteins in blood plasma also bind H^+. These buffering mechanisms are extremely important in homeostasis, because they help prevent an abnormal decline in blood pH.

Driven by its partial pressure gradient, oxygen diffuses from alveoli, through tissue fluid, and into lung capillaries. Carbon dioxide diffuses in the opposite direction, driven by its partial pressure gradient.

Hemoglobin in red blood cells greatly enhances the oxygen-carrying capacity of the blood.

Hemoglobin and blood plasma also carry carbon dioxide.

In plasma, most carbon dioxide is carried in the form of bicarbonate. Buffers help prevent the blood from becoming too acid due to H^+ that is released when bicarbonate forms.

GAS EXCHANGE

11.6 Homeostasis Depends on Controls over Breathing

LINK TO
SECTION
9.4

Your nervous system controls the muscle movements that lead to the normal rhythm of inspiration and expiration. It also controls how often and how deeply you breathe.

A RESPIRATORY PACEMAKER CONTROLS THE RHYTHM OF BREATHING

You normally take about 12 to 15 breaths a minute. If you had to remember to inhale and exhale each time, could you do it, even when you sleep? Fortunately, none of us has to take on that responsibility, because automatic mechanisms ensure that a regular cycle of ventilation moves air into and out of the lungs. Clustered nerve cells in the medulla in the brain stem provide this service. Like the SA node in the heart, these neurons fire impulses spontaneously. They are the pacemaker for respiration.

The diaphragm muscle and the muscles that move the rib cage are under the control of neurons in a system of nerve cells (neurons) running through the brain stem, at the lower rear of the brain. For the moment, we are concerned with two small clusters of cells in the brain stem. One cluster coordinates signals that call for inspiration, "telling" you to take a breath. The other coordinates the signals calling for expiration. The resulting rhythmic contractions of the breathing muscles are fine-tuned by centers in a nearby part of the brain stem (the pons).

As Figure 11.12 suggests, when you inhale, signals from the brain stem travel nerve pathways to the diaphragm and chest. These signals stimulate the rib muscles and diaphragm to contract. As you read in Section 11.4, this causes the rib cage to expand, and air moves into the lungs. When the diaphragm and chest muscles relax, elastic recoil returns the rib cage to its unexpanded state, and air in the lungs moves out. When you breathe rapidly or deeply, stretch receptors in airways send signals to the brain control centers, which then inhibit contraction of the diaphragm and rib cage muscles—so you exhale.

CO₂ IS THE TRIGGER FOR CONTROLS OVER THE RATE AND DEPTH OF BREATHING

You might suppose that body controls over breathing mainly involve monitoring the level of oxygen in blood. However, the nervous system is *more* sensitive to changes in the level of carbon dioxide. Both gases are monitored in blood flowing through arteries. When the conditions warrant, nervous system signals adjust contractions of the diaphragm and muscles in the chest wall and so adjust the rate and depth of your breathing.

Sensory receptors in the medulla of the brain (another part of the brain stem) can detect rising carbon dioxide levels. How? The mechanism is indirect, but (luckily!) extremely sensitive. The receptors detect hydrogen ions that are produced when dissolved CO_2 leaves the bloodstream and enters fluid—called *cerebrospinal fluid*—that bathes the medulla. In cerebrospinal fluid, the drop in

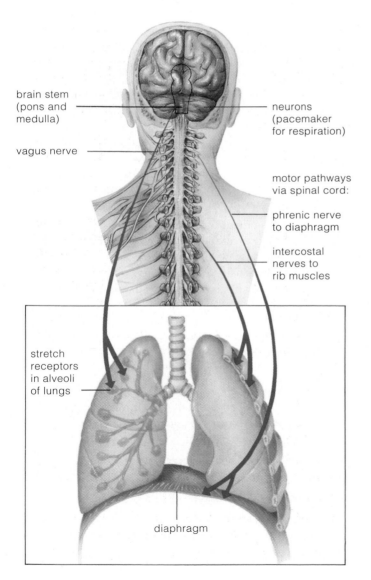

brain stem (pons and medulla)

vagus nerve

neurons (pacemaker for respiration)

motor pathways via spinal cord:

phrenic nerve to diaphragm

intercostal nerves to rib muscles

stretch receptors in alveoli of lungs

diaphragm

Figure 11.12 Controls over breathing. In quiet breathing, centers in the brain stem coordinate signals to the diaphragm and muscles that move the rib cage, triggering inhalation. When a person breathes deeply or rapidly, another center receives signals from stretch receptors in the lungs and coordinates signals for exhalation.

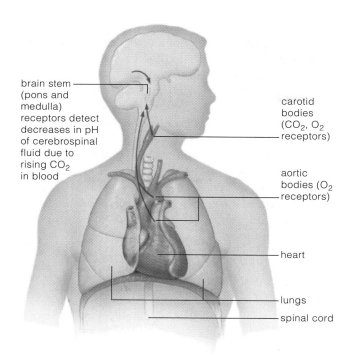

Figure 11.13 Sensory receptors that detect changes in the concentrations of carbon dioxide and oxygen in the blood.

brain stem (pons and medulla) receptors detect decreases in pH of cerebrospinal fluid due to rising CO_2 in blood

carotid bodies (CO_2, O_2 receptors)

aortic bodies (O_2 receptors)

heart

lungs

spinal cord

pH that goes along with increasing H^+ stimulates receptors that signal the change to the brain's respiratory centers (Figure 11.13). In response, breathing becomes more rapid and deeper, and soon the blood level of CO_2 falls. Notice that this is another example of a negative feedback loop helping to maintain homeostasis.

Our brain also receives input from other sensory receptors, including **carotid bodies**, where the carotid arteries branch to the brain, and **aortic bodies** in artery walls near the heart. Both types of receptors detect changes in levels of CO_2 and of oxygen in the blood. They also detect changes in blood pH. The brain responds by increasing the ventilation rate, so more oxygen can be delivered to tissues.

CHEMICAL CONTROLS IN ALVEOLI HELP MATCH AIR FLOW TO BLOOD FLOW

Chemical controls over air flow operate in the lungs, in the millions of alveoli. For example, if you go for a job interview and get nervous, your heart may start pumping hard and fast but your lungs may not be ventilating at a corresponding pace. Then, the flow of blood in alveolar capillaries outpaces the movement of CO_2-laden air out of the lungs. The rising blood level of carbon dioxide affects smooth muscle in the walls of bronchioles. The bronchioles then dilate, so more air flows through them.

On the other hand, a *decrease* in carbon dioxide levels causes the bronchiole walls to constrict, so less air flows through them.

Similar local controls also work on lung capillaries. When too much air is flowing into the lungs relative to the amount of blood traveling through capillaries, the oxygen level rises in parts of the lungs. As with carbon dioxide, this increase in oxygen also affects the smooth muscle in blood vessel walls. The vessels dilate, so more blood flows through them. Conversely, if there is too little air entering the lungs with respect to the volume of blood flowing in the capillaries, the vessels constrict and less blood moves through them.

APNEA IS A CONDITION IN WHICH BREATHING CONTROLS MALFUNCTION

You can voluntarily hold your breath, but not for long. As CO_2 builds up in your blood, "orders" from the nervous system force you to take a breath. The mechanisms by which the nervous system regulates the respiratory cycle normally operate under involuntary control, as you've just read. In some situations, however, a person can fail to breathe when the arterial CO_2 level falls below a set point. Breathing that stops briefly and then resumes spontaneously is called *apnea*. During certain times in the normal sleep cycle (see Section 13.10), breathing may stop for one or two seconds or even minutes—in extreme cases, as often as 500 times a night. Apnea may be a contributing factor in heavy snoring.

Aging also takes its toll on the respiratory system. **Sleep apnea** is a common problem in the elderly, because the mechanisms for sensing a change in oxygen and carbon dioxide levels gradually become less effective over the years. Also, as we age, our lungs lose some of their elasticity. This along with other changes reduces the efficiency of ventilation. Even so, staying physically fit, and maintaining a "lung-healthy" lifestyle in other ways, can go a long way toward keeping the respiratory system functioning well throughout life.

Respiratory centers in the brain stem control the rhythmic pattern of breathing.

Brain centers that adjust the rate and depth of breathing receive information mainly from sensors that monitor blood levels of carbon dioxide.

These controls contribute to homeostasis by helping to maintain proper levels of carbon dioxide, oxygen, and hydrogen ions in arterial blood.

11.7 Disorders of the Respiratory System

A variety of infections and other disorders can prevent the respiratory system from functioning properly. Some of these problems develop when we inadvertantly inhale a pathogen or noxious substances, while others we bring on ourselves.

TOBACCO IS A MAJOR THREAT

People who start smoking tobacco begin wreaking havoc on their lungs. Smoke from a single cigarette can prevent cilia in bronchioles from beating for hours. Toxic particles smoke contains can stimulate mucus secretion and kill the infection-fighting phagocytes that normally patrol the respiratory epithelium.

Today we know that cigarette smoke, including "secondhand smoke" inhaled by a nonsmoker, causes **lung cancer** and contributes to other ills. In the body, some compounds in coal tar and cigarette smoke are converted to carcinogens (cancer-causing substances); they trigger genetic damage leading to lung cancer. Susceptibility to lung cancer is related to the number of cigarettes smoked per day and how often and how deeply the smoke is inhaled. In all, cigarette smoking causes at least 80 percent of all lung cancer deaths. Figure 11.14 lists the known health risks associated with tobacco smoking, as well as the benefits of quitting.

A VARIETY OF PATHOGENS CAN INFECT THE RESPIRATORY SYSTEM

Inhaling viruses, bacteria, fungi, or even toxic fumes can cause some common respiratory disorders. A dry cough, chest pain, and shortness of breath all are symptoms of **pneumonia**. The infection causes inflammation in lung tissue, and then fluid (from edema) builds up in the lungs and makes breathing difficult. Bacterial pneumonia can be treated with antibiotics. Sometimes the trigger for pneumonia is **influenza**, in which an infection that began in the nose or throat spreads to the lungs.

RISKS ASSOCIATED WITH SMOKING	REDUCTION IN RISKS BY QUITTING
SHORTENED LIFE EXPECTANCY: Nonsmokers live 8.3 years longer on average than those who smoke two packs daily from the mid-twenties on.	Cumulative risk reduction; after 10 to 15 years, life expectancy of ex-smokers approaches that of nonsmokers.
CHRONIC BRONCHITIS, EMPHYSEMA: Smokers have 4–25 times more risk of dying from these diseases than do nonsmokers.	Greater chance of improving lung function and slowing down rate of deterioration.
LUNG CANCER: Cigarette smoking is a major contributing factor.	After 10 to 15 years, risk approaches that of nonsmokers.
CANCER OF MOUTH: 3–10 times greater risk among smokers.	After 10 to 15 years, risk is reduced to that of nonsmokers.
CANCER OF LARYNX: 2.9–17.7 times more frequent among smokers.	After 10 years, risk is reduced to that of nonsmokers.
CANCER OF ESOPHAGUS: 2–9 times greater risk of dying from this.	Risk proportional to amount smoked; quitting should reduce it.
CANCER OF PANCREAS: 2–5 times greater risk of dying from this.	Risk proportional to amount smoked; quitting should reduce it.
CANCER OF BLADDER: 7–10 times greater risk for smokers.	Risk decreases gradually over 7 years to that of nonsmokers.
CORONARY HEART DISEASE: Cigarette smoking is a major contributing factor.	Risk drops sharply after a year; after 10 years, risk reduced to that of nonsmokers.
EFFECTS ON OFFSPRING: Women who smoke during pregnancy have more stillbirths, and weight of liveborns averages less (hence, babies are more vulnerable to disease, death).	When smoking stops before fourth month of pregnancy, risk of stillbirth and lower birthweight eliminated.
IMPAIRED IMMUNE SYSTEM FUNCTION: Increase in allergic responses, destruction of defensive cells (macrophages) in respiratory tract.	Avoidable by not smoking.
BONE HEALING: Evidence suggests that surgically cut or broken bones require up to 30 percent longer to heal in smokers, possibly because smoking depletes the body of vitamin C and reduces the amount of oxygen reaching the tissues. Reduced vitamin C and reduced oxygen interfere with production of collagen fibers, a key component of bone. Research in this area is continuing.	Avoidable by not smoking.

Figure 11.14 From the American Cancer Society, a list of the risks incurred by smoking and the benefits of quitting. The photograph shows swirls of cigarette smoke at the entrance to the two bronchi that lead into the lungs.

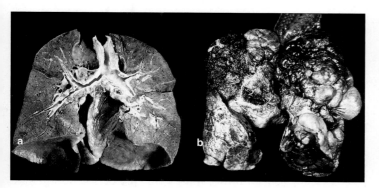

Figure 11.15 (**a**) Normal human lungs (this lung tissue looks darker than normal because it has been chemically preserved). (**b**) Lungs from a person with emphysema.

Tuberculosis (TB) is a serious lung infection caused by the bacterium *Mycobacterium tuberculosis*. It starts with flulike symptoms but eventually can destroy patches of lung tissue and can spread to other parts of the body. Although TB is curable with antibiotics, newer drug-resistant strains of *M. tuberculosis* have made treatment more challenging. Untreated it can be fatal.

A microscopic fungus causes **histoplasmosis**. The symptoms include cough, fever, and inflammation in the lungs and airways. Antifungal drugs can cure "histo," but the infection may spread to the retina of the eye, leading to permanently impaired vision or blindness.

IRRITANTS CAUSE OTHER DISORDERS

In cities, in certain occupations, and anywhere near a smoker, airborne particles and irritating gases put extra workloads on the lungs.

Bronchitis can be brought on when air pollution increases mucus secretions and interferes with ciliary action in the lungs. Ciliated epithelium in the bronchioles is especially sensitive to cigarette smoke. Mucus and the particles it traps—including bacteria—accumulate in airways, coughing starts, and the bronchial walls become inflamed. Bacteria or chemical agents start destroying the wall tissue. Cilia in the lining die, and mucus-secreting cells multiply as the body attempts to get rid of the accumulating debris. Eventually scar tissue forms and can block parts of the respiratory tract.

In an otherwise healthy person, even acute bronchitis is easily treated with antibiotics. When inflammation continues, however, scar tissue builds up and the bronchi become chronically clogged with mucus. Also, the walls of some alveoli break down and become surrounded by stiffer fibrous tissue. The result is **emphysema**, in which the lungs are so distended and inelastic that gases cannot be exchanged efficiently (Figure 11.15). Running, walking,

Figure 11.16 An asthma sufferer using an aerosol inhaler.

even exhaling can be difficult. About 1.3 million people in the United States have emphysema.

Smoking, frequent colds, and other respiratory ailments sometimes make a person susceptible to emphysema. Many emphysema sufferers lack a normal gene coding for a protein that inhibits tissue-destroying enzymes made by bacteria. Emphysema can develop over 20 or 30 years. Unfortunately, by the time the disease is detected, the lungs are permanently damaged.

Millions of people suffer from **asthma**, a disorder in which the bronchioles suddenly narrow when the smooth muscle in their walls contracts in strong spasms. At the same time, mucus gushes from the bronchial epithelium, clogging the constricted passages even more. Breathing can become extremely difficult so quickly that the victim may feel in imminent danger of suffocating. The triggers include allergens such as pollen, dairy products, shellfish, pet hairs, flavorings, or even the dung of tiny mites in house dust. In susceptible people, attacks also can be triggered by noxious fumes, stress, strenuous exercise, or a respiratory infection. While the reasons aren't fully understood, the incidence of asthma in the United States has grown rapidly in the last several decades. Some researchers believe that increased air pollution is at least partly to blame.

Many asthma sufferers rely on aerosol inhalers, which squirt a fine mist into the airways (Figure 11.16). A drug in the mist dilates bronchial passages and helps restore free breathing. Some devices contain powerful steroids that can harm the immune system, so inhalers should be used only with medical supervision.

Summary

Section 11.1 The respiratory system brings air, which contains oxygen, into the body and disposes of carbon dioxide.

Airways include the nasal cavity, pharynx, larynx, trachea, bronchi, and bronchioles. Gas exchange occurs in millions of saclike alveoli located at the end of the terminal respiratory bronchioles. The vocal cords are located near the entrance to the larynx.

Airways lead to the lungs, which are elastic organs located in the rib cage above the diaphragm. Membranes called pleurae enclose the lungs.

 Explore the respiratory system's parts and their functions.

Section 11.2 Respiration is the process of bringing oxygen from air into the blood and removing carbon dioxide from blood. Both these processes occur in the lungs. The cardiovascular system partners with the respiratory system as it circulates blood throughout the body. Aerobic cellular respiration is the process in cells (in mitochondria) that uses oxygen to make ATP and produces carbon dioxide.

Section 11.3 Air is a mixture of oxygen, carbon dioxide, and other gases. Each gas exerts a partial pressure, and each tends to move (diffuse) from areas of higher to lower partial pressure. Following pressure gradients, oxygen tends to diffuse into deoxygenated blood in the lungs, and carbon dioxide tends to diffuse out of the blood and into the lungs to be exhaled.

In respiration, oxygen and carbon dioxide diffuse across a respiratory surface—a moist, thin layer of epithelium in the alveoli of the lungs. Airways carry gases to and from one side of the respiratory surface, and blood vessels carry gases to and away from the other side.

 Investigate the effects of partial pressure gradients in the body.

Section 11.4 Breathing ventilates the lungs in a respiratory cycle. During inspiration (inhalation), the chest cavity expands, pressure in the lungs falls below atmospheric pressure, and air flows into the lungs. During normal expiration (exhalation), these steps are reversed.

The volume of air in a normal breath, called the tidal volume, is about 500 milliliters. Vital capacity is the maximum volume of air that can move out of the lungs after you inhale as deeply as possible.

 Learn more about the respiratory cycle.

Section 11.5 Driven by its partial pressure gradient, oxygen in the lungs diffuses from alveoli into pulmonary capillaries. Then it diffuses into red blood cells and binds with hemoglobin, forming oxyhemoglobin. In tissues where cells are metabolically active, hemoglobin gives up oxygen, which diffuses out of the capillaries, across tissue fluid, and into cells.

Hemoglobin binds with or releases oxygen in response to shifts in oxygen levels, carbon dioxide levels, pH, and temperature.

Driven by its partial pressure gradient, carbon dioxide diffuses from cells across tissue fluid and into the bloodstream. Most CO_2 reacts with water to form bicarbonate; the reactions are speeded by the enzyme carbonic anhydrase. They are reversed in the lungs, where carbon dioxide diffuses from lung capillaries into the air spaces of the alveoli, then is exhaled.

Section 11.6 Gas exchange is regulated by the nervous system and by chemical controls in the lungs. A respiratory pacemaker in the medulla (part of the brain stem) sets the normal, automatic rhythm of breathing in and out (ventilation).

The nervous system monitors the levels of oxygen and carbon dioxide in arterial blood by way of sensory receptors. These include carotid bodies (at branches of carotid arteries leading to the brain), aortic bodies (in an arterial wall near the heart), and receptors in the medulla of the brain. Blood levels of carbon dioxide are most important in triggering nervous system commands that adjust the rate and depth of breathing.

Section 11.7 Infections, toxins in tobacco smoke and polluted air, and accumulated damage from inflammation cause respiratory disorders including cancer, bronchitis, emphysema, pneumonia, tuberculosis, and asthma.

Review Questions

1. In the diagram on page 209, label the components of the respiratory system and the structures that enclose some of its parts.

2. What is the difference between respiration and aerobic cellular respiration?

3. Explain what a partial pressure gradient is and how such gradients figure in gas exchange.

4. What is oxyhemoglobin? Where does it form?

5. What drives oxygen from the air spaces in alveoli, through tissue fluid, and across capillary epithelium? What drives carbon dioxide in the opposite direction?

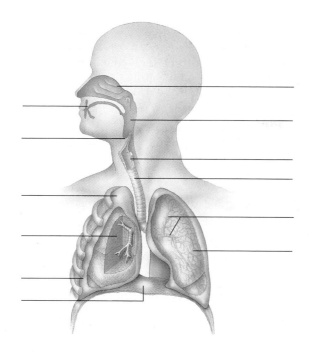

6. How does hemoglobin help maintain the oxygen partial pressure gradient during gas transport in the body?

7. What reactions enhance the transport of carbon dioxide throughout the body? How is carbon dioxide moved out of the body?

8. How do nerve impulses from the brain regulate ventilation of the lungs? How are the rate and depth of breathing controlled?

9. Why does your breathing rate increase when you exercise? What happens to your heart rate at the same time—and why?

Self-Quiz
Answers in Appendix V

1. A partial pressure gradient of oxygen exists between ———.
   a. air and lungs
   b. lungs and metabolically active tissues
   c. air at sea level and air at high altitudes
   d. all of the above

2. The ——— is an airway that connects the nose and mouth with the ———.
   a. oral cavity; larynx
   b. pharynx; trachea
   c. trachea; pharynx
   d. pharynx; larynx

3. Oxygen in air must diffuse across ——— to enter the blood.
   a. pleural sacs   c. a moist respiratory surface
   b. alveolar sacs   d. both b and c

4. Each lung encloses a ———.
   a. diaphragm   c. pleural sac
   b. bronchial tree   d. both b and c

5. Gas exchange occurs at the ———.
   a. two bronchi   c. alveoli
   b. pleural sacs   d. both b and c

6. Breathing ———.
   a. ventilates the lungs
   b. draws air into airways
   c. expels air from airways
   d. causes reversals in pressure gradients
   e. all of the above

7. After oxygen diffuses into lung capillaries it also diffuses into ——— and binds with ———.
   a. tissue fluid; red blood cells
   b. tissue fluid; carbon dioxide
   c. red blood cells; hemoglobin
   d. red blood cells; carbon dioxide

8. Due to its partial pressure gradient, carbon dioxide diffuses from cells into interstitial fluid and into the ———; in the lungs, carbon dioxide diffuses into the ———.
   a. alveoli; bronchioles
   b. bloodstream; bronchioles
   c. alveoli; bloodstream
   d. bloodstream; alveoli

9. Hemoglobin performs which of the following respiratory functions?
   a. transports oxygen
   b. transports some carbon dioxide
   c. acts as a buffer to help maintain blood pH
   d. all of the above

10. Most carbon dioxide in the blood is in the form of ———.
    a. carbon dioxide   c. carbonic acid
    b. carbon monoxide   d. bicarbonate

Critical Thinking

1. People occasionally poison themselves with carbon monoxide by building a charcoal fire in an enclosed area. Assuming help arrives in time, what would be the *most* effective treatment: placing the victim outdoors in fresh air, or administering pure oxygen? Explain your answer.

2. Skin divers and swimmers sometimes purposely hyperventilate. Doing so doesn't increase the oxygen available to tissues. It does increase blood pH (making it more alkaline), and it decreases the blood level of carbon dioxide. Based on your reading in this chapter, what effect is hyperventilation likely to have on the neural controls over breathing?

3. Underwater, we humans can't compete with whales and other air-breathing marine mammals, which can stay submerged for extended periods. At the beach one day

you meet a surfer who tells you that special training could allow her to swim underwater without breathing for an entire hour. From what you know of respiratory physiology, explain why she is mistaken.

4. When you sneeze or cough, abdominal muscles contract suddenly, pushing your diaphragm upward. After reviewing the discussion of the respiratory cycle in Section 11.4, explain why this change forcefully expels air out your nose and mouth.

5. Physiologists have discovered that the nicotine in tobacco is as addictive as heroin. The cigarette-smoking child in Figure 11.17 probably is already addicted, and for sure has already begun to endanger her health. Based on the discussion in Section 11.7, what negative health effects might beset her in the coming years?

Figure 11.17 A child in Mexico City who is already adept at smoking cigarettes—a behavior that, if continued, will one day endanger her capacity to breathe.

Explore on Your Own

Air pollution is a serious problem in many parts of the world. Even if you don't live near a large urban area, you may be breathing the kinds of air pollutants shown in the chart in Figure 11.18. The ultrafine particulates can stay in the air for weeks or months before they settle to earth or are washed down by rain, and all of them are known to cause respiratory problems, especially in people who have asthma or emphysema.

Explore this health issue by finding out if your community monitors its air quality. If so, what do authorities consider to be the greatest threats to the health of you and your fellow citizens? Where do these pollutants come from?

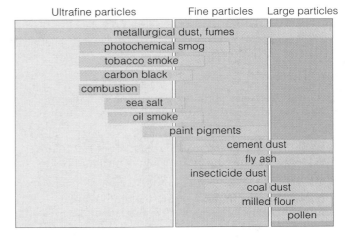

Figure 11.18 Examples of the kinds of particles that may be present in the air you breathe.

12 THE URINARY SYSTEM

Truth in a Test Tube

Light or dark? Clear or cloudy? A lot or a little? Today physicians routinely check the chemical composition of our urine. Acidic urine can signal metabolic problems. Alkaline urine can signal a bacterial infection. Too much protein dissolved in urine might mean the kidneys are not functioning properly. Specialized urine tests can detect chemicals produced by cancers of the kidney, bladder, and prostate gland.

Do-it-yourself urine tests have now become popular for monitoring a woman's fertile period or early signs she may be pregnant. A test for older women may reveal declining hormone levels that signal the onset of menopause.

Not everyone is anxious to have their urine tested. Olympic athletes can be stripped of their medals when mandatory urine tests reveal they use prohibited drugs. Major League Baseball players agreed to urine tests only after repeated allegations that some star players had taken prohibited steroids. Each year the National Collegiate Athletic Association (NCAA) tests urine samples from about 3,300 student athletes for performance-enhancing substances and also for street drugs.

If you use marijuana, cocaine, Ecstasy, or other kinds of illegal drugs, urine tells the tale. For example, after the active ingredient of marijuana enters the blood, the liver converts it to another compound. The kidneys filter the blood and they add this telltale compound to the newly forming urine. It can take up to ten days for all of it to be metabolized and removed from the body. Until then, urine tests can detect it.

That urine is such a remarkable indicator of health, hormonal status, and drug use is a tribute to the urinary system. Each day, your two kidneys filter all of the blood in your body not once but thirty times. When all goes well, the kidneys eliminate excess water and excess or harmful solutes, including many metabolic by-products, toxins, hormones, and drugs.

In the last several chapters you have considered organ systems that work to keep cells supplied with oxygen, nutrients, water, and other substances. Now we turn to the urinary system, which helps maintain the proper chemical composition and volume of body fluids— the internal environment.

How Would You Vote? *Many companies use urine testing to screen prospective employees for drug and alcohol use. Some people say this is an invasion of privacy. Do you think employers should be allowed to require a person to undergo urine testing before being hired? Cast your vote online at www.thomsonedu.com/biology/starr/humanbio.*

 ## Key Concepts

MAINTAINING THE EXTRACELLULAR FLUID
The body must eliminate chemical wastes from extracellular fluid and manage the levels of water and solutes in it. The urinary system partners with other organ systems in this task.

THE URINARY SYSTEM
The urinary system consists of the kidneys, ureters, bladder, and urethra. In the kidneys, structures called nephrons filter water and solutes from the blood, returning needed substances to it and eliminating the rest in urine.

WHAT THE KIDNEYS DO
The kidneys form urine in steps called filtration, reabsorption, and secretion. Hormones and a thirst mechanism adjust the chemical makeup of urine.

 ## Links to Earlier Concepts

This chapter explores how operations of the urinary system help maintain homeostasis in the extracellular fluid—that is, blood and tissue fluid. As you study these processes, you will tap your understanding of pH and buffer systems (2.7) and of osmosis and transport mechanisms (3.9, 3.10). You will also use what you have learned about the functions of blood, blood circulation by the cardiovascular system, and the movement of substances into and out of blood capillaries (8.1, 9.1, 9.7).

12.1 The Challenge: Shifts in Extracellular Fluid

LINKS TO SECTIONS 2.11, 3.12, 7.5, 7.6, 7.7, 8.1, 9.6, 9.7, AND 11.5

If you are an adult female in good health, by weight your body is about 50 percent fluid. If you are an adult male, the ratio is about 60 percent. The chemical makeup of this fluid changes constantly as water and solutes enter and leave it.

Fluid is vital both in our anatomy (body structures) and in our physiology (body functions). This fluid occurs both outside our cells and inside them. Recall that tissue fluid fills the spaces between cells and other components of our body tissues. Blood—which is mostly watery plasma—circulates in blood vessels. Together, tissue fluid, blood plasma, and the relatively small amounts of other fluids (such as lymph) outside cells are the body's **extracellular fluid**, or ECF.

The fluid *inside* our cells is **intracellular fluid**. From previous chapters you know that a variety of gases and other substances move constantly between intracellular and extracellular fluid. Those exchanges are crucial for keeping cells functioning smoothly. They cannot occur properly unless the volume and composition of the ECF are stable.

Yet the ECF is always changing, because gases, cell secretions, ions, and other materials enter or leave it. To maintain stable conditions in the ECF, especially the concentrations of water and vital ions such as sodium (Na^+) and potassium (K^+), there must be mechanisms that remove substances as they enter the extracellular fluid or add needed ones as they leave it. This task is the job of the **urinary system**. Before examining the parts of this system, however, we will look more closely at the traffic of substances into and out of extracellular fluid.

THE BODY GAINS WATER FROM FOOD AND METABOLIC PROCESSES

Ordinarily, each day you take in about as much water as your body loses (Table 12.1). Some of the water is absorbed from foods and liquids you consume. The rest is a by-product of metabolic reactions, including cellular respiration and condensation reactions, that produce water.

Thirst influences how much water we take in. When there is a water deficit in body tissues, our brain "urges" us to seek out water—for example, from a water fountain or a cold drink from the refrigerator. We will be looking at the thirst mechanism later in the chapter.

THE BODY LOSES WATER IN URINE, SWEAT, FECES, AND BY EVAPORATION

Water leaves the body by four routes: Excretion in urine, evaporation from the lungs and skin, sweating, and in feces. Of these four routes of water loss, **urinary excretion** is the one over which the body can exert the most control. Urinary excretion eliminates excess water, as well as excess or harmful solutes, in the form of **urine**. Some water also evaporates from our skin and from the respiratory surfaces of the lungs. These are sometimes called "insensible" water losses, because a person is not always aware they are taking place. As noted in Chapter 7, normally very little water that enters the GI tract is lost; most is absorbed and only a little is eliminated in feces.

Table 12.1	Normal Daily Balance between Water Gain and Water Loss in Adult Humans		
Water Gain (milliliters)		**Water Loss (milliliters)**	
Ingested in solids:	850	Urine:	1,500
Ingested as liquids:	1,400	Feces:	200
Metabolically derived:	350	Evaporation:	900
	2,600		2,600

SOLUTES ENTER EXTRACELLULAR FLUID FROM FOOD, METABOLISM, AND OTHER WAYS

Solutes enter the body's extracellular fluid mainly by four routes. When we eat, a variety of nutrients (including glucose) and mineral ions (such as potassium and sodium ions) are absorbed from the GI tract. So are drugs and food additives. Living cells also continually secrete substances into tissue fluid and circulating blood. The respiratory system brings oxygen into the blood, and respiring cells add carbon dioxide to it (Figure 12.1).

SOLUTES LEAVE THE ECF BY URINARY EXCRETION, IN SWEAT, AND DURING BREATHING

Solutes including mineral ions and metabolic wastes leave extracellular fluid in several ways. Carbon dioxide is the most abundant metabolic waste. We get rid of it by exhaling it from our lungs. All other major wastes—and metabolism produces more than 200 of them—leave in urine. One, uric acid, is formed when cells break down nucleic acids. If it builds up in the ECF, it can crystallize and collect in the joints, causing the painful condition called *gout*.

Other major metabolic wastes include by-products of processes that break down proteins. One of these wastes, ammonia, is formed in "deamination" reactions, which remove the nitrogen-containing amino groups from amino acids. Ammonia is highly toxic if it accumulates in the body. Reactions in the liver combine ammonia with carbon dioxide, producing the much less toxic **urea**. Accordingly, urea is the main waste product when cells break down proteins. About half of the urea filtered from blood in the kidneys is reabsorbed. The rest is excreted. Protein breakdown also produces creatine, phosphoric acid, sulfuric acid, and small amounts of other, nitrogen-containing compounds, some of which are toxic. These also are excreted.

Although sweat carries away a small percentage of urea and uric acid, by far the most nitrogen-containing wastes are removed by our kidneys while they filter other substances from the blood. In addition to removing wastes and excess water, the kidneys also help maintain the balance of important ions such as sodium, potassium, and calcium. These ions are sometimes called **electrolytes** because a solution in which they are dissolved will carry an electric current. Chapter 13 describes the extremely important roles electrolytes have in the functioning of the nervous system.

Normally only a little of the water and solutes that enter the kidneys leaves as urine. In fact, except when you drink lots of fluid (without exercise), all but about 1

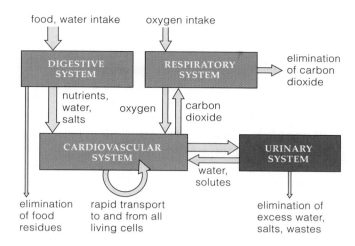

Figure 12.1 How activities of the urinary system coordinate with those of some other organ systems.

percent of the water is returned to the blood. However, the chemical composition of the fluid that is returned has been adjusted in vital ways. Just how this happens will be our focus as we turn our attention to the urinary system.

The kidneys adjust the volume and chemical composition of the blood. In this way they help maintain homeostasis in the extracellular fluid.

Each day the body gains water consumed in liquids and solid foods and from metabolism. It loses an approximately equal amount of water through urinary excretion, evaporation, sweating, and elimination in feces.

The body gains solutes from digested food, secretion by cells, metabolism, and respiration. Solutes are removed by urinary excretion, respiration, and sweating.

12.2 The Urinary System—Built for Filtering and Waste Disposal

LINKS TO
SECTIONS
3.11, 8.3, AND 9.7

The urinary system consists of filtering organs—the kidneys—and structures that carry and store urine.

Each **kidney** is a bean-shaped organ about the size of a rolled-up pair of socks (Figure 12.2). It has several internal lobes. In each lobe, an outer *cortex* wraps around a central region, the *medulla*, as you can see sketched in Figure 12.2c. The whole kidney is wrapped in a tough coat of connective tissue, the *renal capsule* (from the Latin *renes*, meaning kidneys). The kidney's central cavity is called the *renal pelvis*.

Our kidneys have several functions. They produce the hormone erythropoietin, which stimulates the production of red blood cells (Section 8.3). They also convert vitamin D to a form that stimulates the small intestine to absorb calcium in food. In addition, kidneys make the enzyme renin, which helps regulate blood pressure, as you will read later in this chapter. The main function of kidneys, however, is to remove metabolic wastes from the blood and adjust fluid balance in the body.

In addition to the two kidneys, the urinary system includes "plumbing" that transports or stores urine. Once urine has formed in a kidney, it flows into a tubelike **ureter**, then on into the **urinary bladder**, where it is stored until you urinate. It leaves the bladder through the **urethra**, a muscular tube that opens at the body surface.

NEPHRONS ARE THE KIDNEY FILTERS

Each kidney lobe contains blood vessels and more than a million slender tubes called **nephrons**. Nephrons are the structures that filter water and solutes from blood.

A nephron is shaped a little like the piping under a sink (Figure 12.3a). Its wall is a single layer of epithelial cells, but the cells and junctions between them vary in different parts of the tube. Water and solutes pass easily through some parts, but other parts completely block solutes unless they are moved across by active transport (Section 3.11).

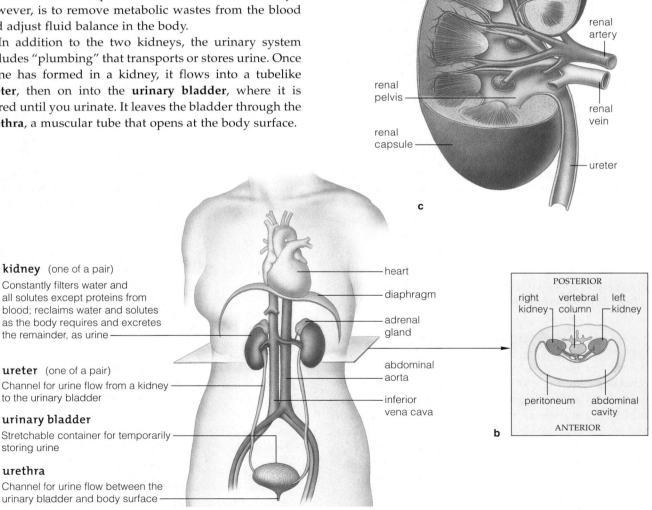

kidney (one of a pair)
Constantly filters water and all solutes except proteins from blood; reclaims water and solutes as the body requires and excretes the remainder, as urine

ureter (one of a pair)
Channel for urine flow from a kidney to the urinary bladder

urinary bladder
Stretchable container for temporarily storing urine

urethra
Channel for urine flow between the urinary bladder and body surface

Figure 12.2 *Animated!* (**a**) The urinary system and its functions. (**b**) The two kidneys, ureters, and urinary bladder are located between the abdominal cavity's wall and its lining, the peritoneum. (**c**) Internal structure of a kidney.

THE URINARY SYSTEM

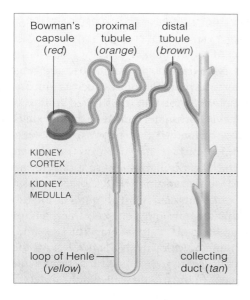

Bowman's capsule (*red*)   proximal tubule (*orange*)   distal tubule (*brown*)

KIDNEY CORTEX

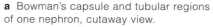

KIDNEY MEDULLA

loop of Henle (*yellow*)   collecting duct (*tan*)

a Bowman's capsule and tubular regions of one nephron, cutaway view.

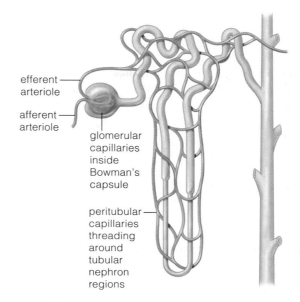

efferent arteriole

afferent arteriole

glomerular capillaries inside Bowman's capsule

peritubular capillaries threading around tubular nephron regions

b Blood vessels associated with the nephron.

Figure 12.3 *Animated!* (**a**) Diagram of a nephron. Interacting with two sets of capillaries, nephrons are a kidney's blood-filtering units. (**b**) The arterioles and capillaries associated with a nephron.

As sketched in Figure 12.3*b*, the nephron wall balloons around a tiny cluster of blood capillaries called the **glomerulus** (plural: glomeruli). The cuplike wall region, called the **Bowman's** (glomerular) **capsule**, receives the substances that are filtered from blood. The rest of the nephron is a winding tubule ("little tube"). Filtrate flows from the cup into the **proximal tubule** (proximal means "next to"), then through a hairpin-shaped **loop of Henle** and into the **distal tubule** ("most distant" from the glomerular capsule). This part of the nephron tubule empties into a collecting duct.

SPECIAL VESSELS TRANSPORT BLOOD TO, IN, AND AWAY FROM NEPHRONS

Each hour, about 75 gallons of blood course through your kidneys, delivered by the renal artery. An **afferent arteriole** brings blood to each nephron (afferent means "carrying toward"). The blood flows into the glomerular capillaries inside Bowman's capsule. These capillaries are not like capillaries in other parts of the body, however. Slitlike pores between the cells of their walls make them much more permeable than other capillaries. Thus it is much easier for water and solutes to move across the wall.

The glomerular capillaries also do not channel blood to venules, as other capillaries do (Section 9.7). Instead,

the glomerular capillaries merge to form an **efferent** ("carrying away from") **arteriole**. This arteriole branches into yet another set of capillaries, called **peritubular** ("around the tubule") **capillaries**. As you can see in Figure 12.3*b*, the peritubular capillaries weave around a nephron's tubules. They merge into venules, which carry filtered blood out of the kidneys.

As we see next, the elaborate network of capillaries that feed and drain blood from nephrons is a key factor in the kidneys' ability to fine-tune the chemical makeup of the blood.

The urinary system consists of two kidneys, two ureters, the urinary bladder, and the urethra.

Kidney nephrons filter water and solutes from blood. A tiny cluster of capillaries called a glomerulus is the nephron's blood-filtering unit.

The capillaries in a glomerulus have pores in their walls that make the vessels much more permeable than usual.

Afferent arterioles deliver blood to nephrons and efferent arterioles carry it away. Peritubular capillaries weave around nephron tubules and deliver filtered blood back to the general circulation.

12.3 How Urine Forms: Filtration, Reabsorption, and Secretion

LINKS TO
SECTIONS
3.10, 3.11, AND 9.5

The processes that form urine normally ensure that only nonessential substances are excreted from the body.

The fluid we call urine forms in a sequence of three steps called filtration, reabsorption, and secretion. Figure 12.4 gives you an overview of these steps.

FILTRATION REMOVES A LARGE AMOUNT OF FLUID AND SOLUTES FROM THE BLOOD

Blood pressure generated by the heart's contractions is the driving force for **filtration**, the first step in forming urine. Efferent arterioles have small diameters, so they deliver blood to the glomerulus under high pressure. This pressure forces about 20 percent of the blood plasma into Bowman's capsule. Blood cells, platelets, proteins, and other large solutes remain in the blood. Everything else—water and some small solutes such as glucose, amino acids, vitamins, sodium, and urea—can filter out of the glomerular capillaries and into Bowman's capsule. From there the filtrate flows into the proximal tubule (Figure 12.5a), where reabsorption can begin.

NEXT, REABSORPTION RETURNS USEFUL SUBSTANCES TO THE BLOOD

The body cannot afford to lose the huge amounts of water and valuable solutes such as glucose, amino acids, and electrolytes that are filtered from the blood by the kidneys. Fortunately, most of the filtrate is recovered by **reabsorption**. In this process, substances leak or are pumped out of the nephron tubule and then enter peritubular capillaries and so return to the bloodstream.

Most reabsorption takes place across the walls of proximal tubules. As in all parts of the tubule, the walls in this area are only one cell thick. Figure 12.5b shows what happens with water, glucose, and salt (ions of sodium and chloride, Na^+ and Cl^-). All these substances can diffuse from the filtrate in a tubule into and through the cells of the tubule wall. On the outer side of the cells, active transport (through proteins in the cells' plasma membranes) moves glucose and Na^+ into the tissue fluid. Sodium ions (Na^+) are positively charged, and negatively charged ions, including chloride (Cl^-), follow the sodium.

As the concentration of solutes rises in the fluid, water moves out of the tubule cells by osmosis. In a final step, solutes are actively transported into peritubular capillaries and water again follows by osmosis. These substances now have been reabsorbed. The solutes and water that remain in the tubule become part of urine.

Reabsorption usually returns almost 99 percent of the filtrate's water, all of the glucose and most amino acids, all but about 0.5 percent of the salt (sodium and chloride ions), and 50 percent of the urea to the blood (Table 12.2).

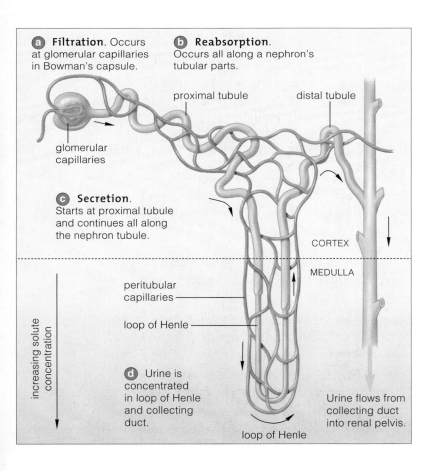

(a) **Filtration.** Occurs at glomerular capillaries in Bowman's capsule.

(b) **Reabsorption.** Occurs all along a nephron's tubular parts.

proximal tubule

distal tubule

glomerular capillaries

(c) **Secretion.** Starts at proximal tubule and continues all along the nephron tubule.

CORTEX

MEDULLA

peritubular capillaries

loop of Henle

increasing solute concentration

(d) Urine is concentrated in loop of Henle and collecting duct.

Urine flows from collecting duct into renal pelvis.

loop of Henle

Figure 12.4 *Animated!* Overview of the steps that form urine.

Table 12.2	Average Daily Reabsorption Values for a Few Substances		
	Amount Filtered	Percentage Excreted	Percentage Reabsorbed
Water	180 liters	1	99
Glucose	180 grams	0	100
Amino acids	2 grams	5	95
Sodium ions	630 grams	0.5	99.5
Urea	54 grams	50	50

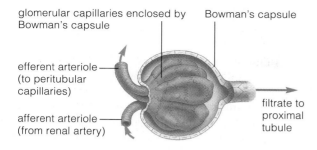

a **Filtration**. Water and solutes forced out across the glomerular capillary wall collect in Bowman's capsule, which drains into the proximal tubule.

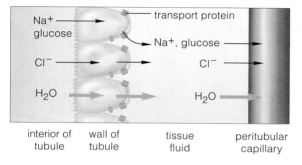

b **Reabsorption**. As filtrate flows through the proximal tubule, ions and some nutrients are actively and passively transported outward, into tissue fluid. Water follows, by osmosis. Cells of peritubular capillaries transport them into blood. Water again follows by osmosis.

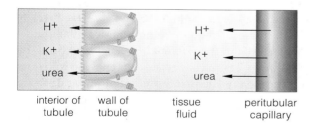

c **Secretion**. Transport proteins move H+, K+, urea, and wastes out of peritubular capillaries. Transporters in the nephron tubule move them into the filtrate.

Figure 12.5 *Animated!* Filtration, reabsorption, and secretion in a nephron.

SECRETION RIDS THE BODY OF EXCESS HYDROGEN IONS AND SOME OTHER SUBSTANCES

Secretion takes up unwanted substances that have been transported out of peritubular capillaries and adds them to the urine that is forming in nephron tubules (Figure 12.5c). Among other functions, this highly controlled process rids the body of urea and of excess hydrogen ions (H+) and potassium ions (K+).

Secretion is crucial to maintaining the body's acid–base balance, which you will read about in a later section. It also helps ensure that some wastes (such as uric acid and some breakdown products of hemoglobin) and foreign substances (such as antibiotics and some pesticides) do not build up in the blood. The drug testing noted in the chapter introduction relies on the use of urinalysis to detect drug residues that have been secreted into urine.

Homeostasis requires that the total volume of fluid in the blood and tissues stay fairly stable. Blood and tissue fluid are mostly water, and while your kidneys are removing impurities from your blood they are also adjusting the amount of water that is excreted in urine or returned to the bloodstream.

URINATION IS A CONTROLLABLE REFLEX

Urination is urine flow from the body. It is a reflex response. As the bladder fills, tension increases in the smooth muscle of its strong walls. Where the bladder joins the urethra, an *internal urethral sphincter* built of smooth muscle helps prevent urine from flowing into the urethra. As tension in the bladder wall increases, though, the sphincter relaxes; at the same time, the bladder walls contract and force urine through the urethra.

Skeletal muscle forms an *external urethral sphincter* closer to the urethral opening. Learning to control it is the basis of urinary "toilet training" in young children.

Urine consists of water and solutes not needed to maintain the chemical balance of extracellular fluid, as well as water-soluble wastes.

Urine forms through the sequence of steps called filtration, reabsorption, and secretion.

In filtration, water and other small molecules are filtered from the blood and into the nephron.

Reabsorption recaptures needed water and solutes.

Secretion adds unwanted substances into urine, including hydrogen ions and foreign substances such as antibiotics.

12.4 How Kidneys Help Manage Fluid Balance and Blood Pressure

LINKS TO
SECTIONS
2.3 AND 9.5

In addition to removing wastes from blood, the kidneys concentrate urine by way of mechanisms that also help regulate blood volume and blood pressure.

Overall, the total volume of your body fluids, including blood plasma, doesn't vary much. This is because during reabsorption, the kidneys adjust how much water and salt (sodium + chloride ions) the body conserves or excretes in urine. As you know, blood and tissue fluid are mostly water. In general, when the volume of blood increases or decreases, so does blood pressure. The kidneys help ensure that the volume of extracellular fluid, and blood in particular, stays within a normal range.

WATER FOLLOWS SALT AS URINE FORMS

Although about two-thirds of filtered salt and water is reabsorbed in the proximal tubule, the filtrate usually still contains more of both than the body can afford to lose in urine. This situation is addressed as the filtrate enters the loop of Henle, which descends into the kidney medulla (Figure 12.6). There the loop is surrounded by extremely salty tissue fluid. Water can pass through the thin wall of the loop's descending limb, so more water moves out by osmosis and is reabsorbed. As the water leaves, the salt concentration in the fluid still inside the descending limb increases until it matches that in the fluid outside.

Now the filtrate "rounds the turn" of the loop and enters the ascending limb. The wall of this part of the nephron tubule does not allow water to pass through. This is an important variation in the tubule's structure, because here sodium is actively transported out of the ascending limb—but water cannot move with it.

The filtrate now moves into the distal tubule. Its cells continue to remove salt, but also do not let water escape. Hence, a dilute urine moves on into the collecting duct.

Naturally, as salt leaves the filtrate moving through a nephron tubule, the concentration of solutes rises outside the tubule and falls inside it. This steep gradient helps drive the reabsorption of valuable solutes, which move into peritubular capillaries. It also draws water out of the descending limb by osmosis.

Urea boosts the gradient. As water is reabsorbed, the urea left behind in the filtrate becomes concentrated. Some of it will be excreted in urine, but when filtrate enters the final portion of the collecting duct, some urea also will diffuse out—so the concentration of solutes in the inner medulla rises even more.

Drink a large glass of water and the next time you "go" your urine may be pale and dilute. If you sleep eight hours without a break, your urine will be concentrated and darker yellow. As described next, hormonal controls allow the kidneys to vary the amount of water in urine. These controls also adjust blood pressure.

HORMONES CONTROL WHETHER KIDNEYS MAKE URINE THAT IS CONCENTRATED OR DILUTE

When you do not take in as much water as your body loses, the salt concentration in your blood rises. In the brain, receptors sense this change and trigger the release of antidiuretic hormone, or **ADH**. This communication molecule acts on the cells in distal tubules and collecting ducts so that more water moves out of them and is reabsorbed (Figure 12.7). As a result, the urine becomes more concentrated. Gradually the increased water in blood reduces the salt concentration there. It also increases the blood volume and blood pressure, and less ADH is released. Figure 12.8 shows this negative feedback loop.

A decrease in the volume of extracellular fluid also activates cells in the efferent arterioles that bring blood to nephrons. These cells release an enzyme called renin. They are part of the **juxtaglomerular apparatus** (Figure 12.9a). *Juxta-* means "next to," and this "apparatus" is an area where arterioles of the glomerulus come into contact with a nephron's distal tubule.

Renin triggers reactions that produce a protein called angiotensin I and then convert it to angiotensin II. Among other effects, angiotensin II stimulates cells of the adrenal cortex, the outer portion of a gland perched on top of each kidney, to secrete the hormone **aldosterone** (Figures 12.7 and 12.9b). Aldosterone causes cells of the distal tubules and collecting ducts to reabsorb sodium faster, so less sodium and less water is excreted in urine.

What must the kidneys do to make dilute urine? Not much. Urine is automatically dilute as long as ADH levels are low, so little of the hormone acts on the distal tubules and collecting ducts.

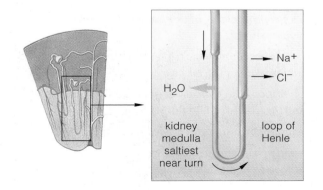

Figure 12.6 Reabsorption of water and salt in the loop of Henle.

H_2O

Na^+

Cl^-

kidney medulla saltiest near turn

loop of Henle

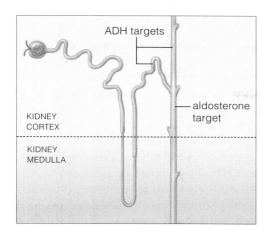

Figure 12.7 Where ADH and aldosterone act in kidney nephrons.

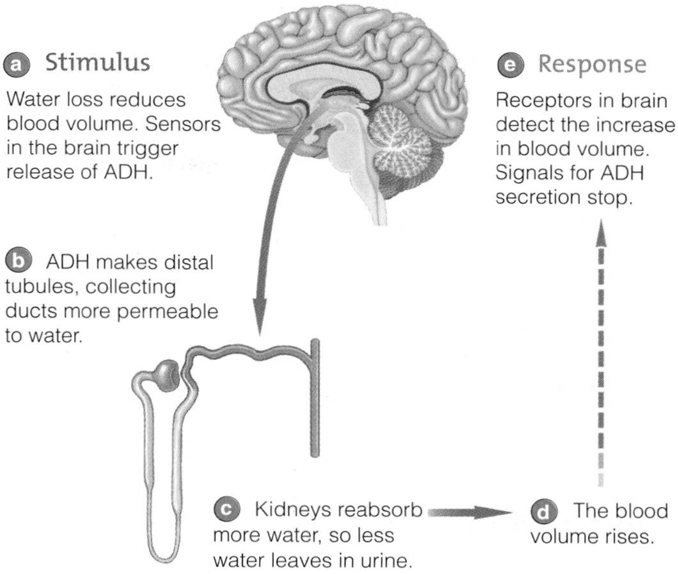

A *diuretic* is any substance that promotes the loss of water in urine. For example, caffeine reduces the reabsorption of sodium along nephron tubules, so more water is excreted.

A THIRST CENTER MONITORS SODIUM

When you don't drink enough, after a while you realize you're thirsty. Why? The concentration of salt in your blood has risen, and this change reduces the amount of saliva your salivary glands produce. A drier mouth stimulates nerve endings that signal a **thirst center** in the brain. The center also receives signals from the same sensors that stimulate the release of ADH. In this case the signals are relayed to a part of the brain that "tells" you to find and drink fluid.

ⓐ Stimulus
Water loss reduces blood volume. Sensors in the brain trigger release of ADH.

ⓔ Response
Receptors in brain detect the increase in blood volume. Signals for ADH secretion stop.

ⓑ ADH makes distal tubules, collecting ducts more permeable to water.

ⓒ Kidneys reabsorb more water, so less water leaves in urine.

ⓓ The blood volume rises.

Figure 12.8 A negative feedback loop from the kidneys to the brain that helps adjust the fluid volume of the blood.

In a nephron tubule, water and salt can be reabsorbed or excreted as required to maintain the volume of the extracellular fluid, including blood.

ADH stimulates the kidneys to conserve water. It acts on distal tubules and collecting ducts. Aldosterone promotes the reabsorption of sodium, which indirectly increases the amount of water the body retains.

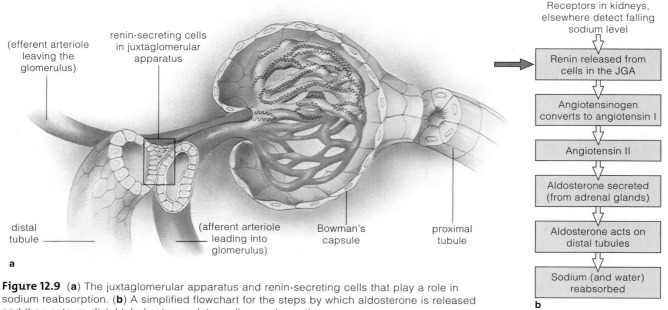

Figure 12.9 (**a**) The juxtaglomerular apparatus and renin-secreting cells that play a role in sodium reabsorption. (**b**) A simplified flowchart for the steps by which aldosterone is released and then acts on distal tubules to regulate sodium reabsorption.

12.5 Removing Excess Acids and Other Substances in Urine

LINKS TO
SECTIONS
2.7, 7.6,
AND 11.5

As the kidneys form urine, nephrons make adjustments that also help keep the extracellular fluid from becoming too acidic or too basic.

You may recall from Chapter 2 that normal pH in the blood and other body fluids is between 7.37 and 7.43. Because acids lower pH and bases raise it, pH reflects the body's **acid–base balance**—the relative amounts of acidic and basic substances in extracellular fluid. Remember also that a buffer system involves substances that reversibly bind and release H^+ and OH^- ions. Buffers minimize pH changes as acidic or basic molecules enter or leave body fluids.

Chapter 11 described how bicarbonate (HCO_3^-) serves as a buffer in the lungs. It forms when carbon dioxide combines with water. The bicarbonate then reacts with H^+ to form carbonic acid, and enzyme action converts carbonic acid into water and carbon dioxide. The CO_2 is exhaled, while the hydrogen ions are now a part of water molecules. H^+ is not eliminated permanently, however. Only the kidneys can do that. They also restore the buffer bicarbonate.

Depending on changes in the acid–base balance of the blood that enters nephrons, the kidneys can either excrete bicarbonate or form new bicarbonate and add it to the blood. The necessary chemical reactions go on in the cells of nephron tubule walls. For example, when the blood is too acid (a too high concentration of H^+), water and carbon dioxide combine with the help of an enzyme. They form carbonic acid that then can be broken into bicarbonate and H^+. Figure 12.10 summarizes these steps.

As you can see, bicarbonate produced in the reactions moves into peritubular capillaries. It ends up circulating in the blood, where it buffers excess H^+. When the blood is too basic (alkaline), chemical adjustments in the kidneys normally ensure that less bicarbonate is reabsorbed into the bloodstream.

The H^+ that is formed in the tubule cells is secreted into the filtrate in the tubule. There the excess H^+ may combine with phosphate ions, ammonia (NH_3), or even bicarbonate. In this way the excess H^+ is excreted.

When the kidneys have finished processing fluid and solutes from the blood, the result is urine that contains a wide variety of substances. In addition to revealing traces of drugs, urinalysis provides a chemical snapshot of many physiological processes in the body, and it can be extremely helpful in diagnosing illness or disease. For example, glucose in urine may be a sign of diabetes. White blood cells (pus) frequently indicate a urinary tract infection. Red blood cells in urine can reveal bleeding due to infection, cancer, or an injury. Abnormally high levels of albumin or other proteins in urine may indicate kidney disease, severe hypertension, or other disorders. Bile pigments enter the urine when liver functions are impaired by cirrhosis and hepatitis.

It's relatively easy to keep your urinary tract healthy. Drink plenty of water and practice careful hygiene to minimize the chances for bacteria to invade the urethra. People who are susceptible to bladder infections may also want to limit their intake of alcohol, caffeine, and spicy foods, all of which can irritate the bladder.

Along with buffering systems and the respiratory system, the kidneys help keep the extracellular fluid from becoming to acidic or too basic.

The urinary system eliminates excess hydrogen ions and also replenishes bicarbonate used in buffering reactions.

Figure 12.10 How the kidneys remove H^+ from the body, preventing the blood from becoming too acidic.

12.6 Kidney Disorders

From the preceding sections, you can sense that good health depends on normal kidney function. Disorders or injuries that interfere with it can be mild to severe.

For example, **kidney stones** are deposits of uric acid, calcium salts, and other substances that have settled out of urine and collected in the renal pelvis. Smaller kidney stones usually are eliminated naturally during urination. Larger ones can become lodged in the renal pelvis or ureter or even in the bladder or urethra. The blockage can partially dam urine flow and cause intense pain and kidney damage. Large kidney stones must be removed medically or surgically. A procedure called *lithotripsy* uses high-energy sound waves to blast the stone to fragments that are small enough to pass out in the urine.

Urinary tract infections routinely plague millions of people. Women especially are susceptible to bladder infections because of their urinary anatomy: The female urethra is short, just a little over an inch long. (An adult male's urethra is about 9 inches long.) The outer opening of a female's urethra also is close to the anus, so it is fairly easy for bacteria from outside the body to make their way to a female's bladder and trigger an inflammation called **cystitis**—or even all the way to the kidneys to cause **pyelonephritis**. In both sexes, urinary tract infections sometimes result from sexually transmitted microbes, including the microorganisms that cause *chlamydia*. Chapter 16 provides more information on this topic.

Polycystic kidney disease is an inherited disorder in which cysts (semisolid masses) form in the kidneys and in many cases gradually destroy normal kidney tissue. Frequent urinary tract infections are a common early symptom; in severe cases, kidney dialysis (Figure 12.11 and described below) or a kidney transplant is the only real option for treatment.

Nephritis is an inflammation of the kidneys. It can be caused by various factors, including bacterial infections. As you may remember from Chapter 10, inflamed tissue tends to swell as fluid accumulates in it. However, because a kidney is "trapped" inside the tough renal capsule, it can't increase in size. As a result, hydrostatic pressure builds up in or around glomerular capillaries, blocking them and hampering or preventing the passage of blood. Then, of course, blood filtering becomes difficult or impossible.

Glomerulonephritis is an umbrella term for several disorders (often involving faulty immune responses) that can severely damage the kidneys. Hypertension and diabetes can disrupt blood circulation to and within the kidneys, sometimes virtually blocking the flow of blood through the glomeruli. In roughly 13 million people in the United States kidney nephrons have become so

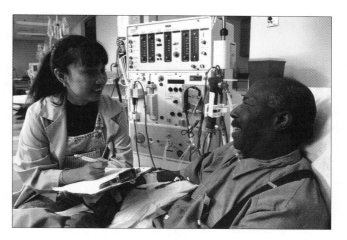

Figure 12.11 *Animated!* Patient undergoing hemodialysis.

impaired that the filtering of blood and formation of urine are woefully inefficient. Control of the volume and composition of the extracellular fluid is disturbed, and toxic by-products of protein breakdown can accumulate in the bloodstream. Patients can suffer nausea, fatigue, and memory loss. In advanced cases, death may result. A kidney dialysis machine can restore the proper solute balances. Like the kidneys, the machine helps maintain extracellular fluid by selectively removing and adding solutes to the patient's bloodstream.

"Dialysis" refers to the exchange of substances across a membrane between chemically different solutions. In *hemodialysis*, the dialysis machine is connected to an artery or a vein, and then blood is pumped through tubes made of a material similar to cellophane. The tubes are submerged in a warm-water bath. The precise mix of salts, glucose, and other substances in the bath sets up the correct gradients with the blood. Dialyzed blood is returned to the body.

Hemodialysis generally must be performed three times a week. It is a temporary measure for patients with reversible kidney disorders. In chronic cases, the procedure must be used for the rest of the patient's life or until a healthy kidney can be transplanted.

Although chronic kidney disease can impose some inconveniences, with proper treatment and a controlled diet, many people are able to pursue a surprisingly active, close-to-normal lifestyle.

Summary

Section 12.1   The fluid inside cells is intracellular fluid. By contrast, body cells are bathed by extracellular fluid (ECF)—various types and amounts of substances dissolved in water. The ECF fills tissue spaces and (in the form of blood plasma) fills blood vessels. Its volume and composition are maintained only when the daily intake of water and solutes is in balance. The following processes maintain the balance:

   a. The body takes in water by absorbing it from the GI tract and by metabolism. Water is lost by urinary excretion, evaporation from the lungs and skin, sweating, and elimination in feces.

   b. Solutes are gained by absorption from the GI tract, secretion, respiration, and metabolism. They are lost by excretion, respiration, and sweating. The solutes include important electrolytes such as ions of sodium, potassium, and calcium.

   c. Losses of water and solutes are controlled mainly by adjusting the volume and composition of urine.

Section 12.2   The urinary system consists of two kidneys, two ureters, a urinary bladder, and a urethra. In the kidneys, blood is filtered and urine forms in nephrons.

   a. A nephron starts as a cup-shaped capsule that is followed by three tubelike regions: the proximal tubule, loop of Henle, and distal tubule, which empties into a collecting duct.

   b. The Bowman's (glomerular) capsule surrounds a set of highly permeable capillaries. Together, they are a blood-filtering unit, the glomerulus.

 Explore the anatomy of the urinary system and kidneys.

Section 12.3   Urine forms through a sequence of steps: filtration, reabsorption, and secretion.

   a. Filtration of blood at the glomerulus of a nephron, which puts water and small solutes into the nephron.

   b. Reabsorption. Water and solutes to be retained leave the nephron's tubular parts and enter the peritubular capillaries that thread around them. Many solutes are reabsorbed passively, following their concentration gradients back into the bloodstream. In other instances, active transport is required. Sodium is reabsorbed by active transport. The reabsorption of water is always passive, by osmosis occurring along water's concentration gradient. A small amount of water and solutes remains in the nephron.

   c. Secretion. Some ions and a few other substances leave the peritubular capillaries and enter the nephron, for disposal in urine.

 Learn more about the processes that form urine.

Section 12.4   During reabsorption in kidney nephrons, water and salt are reabsorbed or excreted as required to conserve or eliminate water. The mechanisms that concentrate urine also help regulate blood volume and blood pressure.

   Urine becomes more or less concentrated by the action of two hormones, ADH and aldosterone, on cells of distal tubules and collecting ducts as follows:

   a. ADH is secreted when the body must conserve water; it enhances reabsorption from the distal nephron tubule and collecting ducts. Inhibition of ADH allows more water to be excreted.

   b. Aldosterone conserves sodium by enhancing its reabsorption in the distal tubule. It is secreted when cells in the juxtaglomerular apparatus (next to the distal tubule) secrete renin, an enzyme that triggers reactions that lead to aldosterone secretion. By contrast, inhibition of aldosterone allows more sodium to be excreted. Because "water follows salt," aldosterone indirectly influences water reabsorption.

Section 12.5   Together with the respiratory system and other mechanisms, the kidneys also help maintain the body's overall acid–base balance. They help regulate pH by eliminating excess hydrogen ions and replenishing the supply of bicarbonate, which acts as a buffer elsewhere in the body.

Section 12.6   Urinary tract infections can develop when bacteria enter through the urethra. Disorders and diseases that damage kidney tissues can interfere seriously with the excretion of wastes in urine and with the kidneys' ability to help regulate blood volume and pressure.

Review Questions

1. Label the parts of this kidney and nephron:

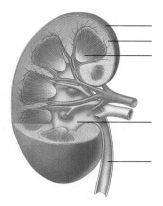 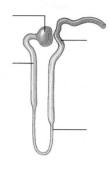

2. How does the formation of urine help maintain the body's internal environment?

3. Explain what is meant when we talk about filtration, reabsorption, and secretion in the kidneys.

4. Which hormone or hormones promote (*a*) water conservation, (*b*) sodium conservation, and (*c*) thirst behavior?

5. Explain how the kidneys help to maintain the balance of acids and bases in extracellular fluid.

Self-Quiz

Answers in Appendix V

1. The body gains water by _____.
   a. absorption in the gut
   b. metabolism
   c. responding to thirst
   d. all of the above

2. The body loses water by way of the _____.
   a. skin
   b. lungs
   c. digestive system
   d. urinary system
   e. c and d
   f. a through d

3. Water and small solutes enter nephrons during _____.
   a. filtration
   b. reabsorption
   c. secretion
   d. both a and b

4. Kidneys return water and small solutes to blood by _____.
   a. filtration
   b. reabsorption
   c. secretion
   d. both a and c

5. Some substances move out of the peritubular capillaries and are moved into the nephron during _____.
   a. filtration
   b. reabsorption
   c. secretion
   d. both a and c

6. Reabsorption depends on _____.
   a. osmosis across the nephron wall
   b. active transport of sodium across the nephron wall
   c. a steep solute concentration gradient
   d. all of the above

7. _____ directly promotes water conservation.
   a. ADH
   b. Renin
   c. Aldosterone
   d. both b and c

8. _____ enhances sodium reabsorption.
   a. ADH
   b. Renin
   c. Aldosterone
   d. both b and c

9. Match the following salt–water balance concepts:
   _____ aldosterone
   _____ nephron
   _____ thirst mechanism
   _____ reabsorption
   _____ glomerulus
   a. blood filter of a nephron
   b. controls sodium reabsorption
   c. occurs at nephron tubules
   d. site of urine formation
   e. controls water gain

Critical Thinking

1. A urinalysis reveals that the patient's urine contains glucose, hemoglobin, and white blood cells (pus). Are any of these substances abnormal in urine? Explain.

2. As a person ages, nephron tubules lose some of their ability to concentrate urine. What is the effect of this change?

3. Fatty tissue holds the kidneys in place. Extremely rapid weight loss may cause this tissue to shrink so that the kidneys slip from their normal position. On rare occasions, the slippage can put a kink in one or both ureters and block urine flow. Suggest what might then happen to the kidneys.

4. Licorice is used as a remedy in Chinese traditional medicine and also is a flavoring for candy. When licorice is eaten, one of its components triggers the formation of a compound that mimics aldosterone and binds to receptors for it. Based on this information, explain why people who have high blood pressure are advised to avoid eating much licorice.

5. Drinking too much water can be a bad thing. If someone sweats heavily and drinks lots of water, their sodium levels drop. The resulting "water intoxication" can be fatal. Why is the sodium balance so important?

6. As the text noted, two-thirds of the water and solutes that the body reclaims by reabsorption in nephrons occurs in the proximal tubule. Proximal tubule cells have large numbers of mitochondria and demand a great deal of oxygen. Explain why.

Explore on Your Own

The rider and horse shown at the left are living examples of the mammalian body's ability to cool itself by producing sweat. Since sweat is mostly water, how is heavy sweating likely to affect the concentration of urine, especially if the athlete— in this case, a polo player— doesn't remember to drink fluid during the match? (You may well have observed this effect in your own body after exercise.)

Drink one quart of water in one hour. What changes might you expect (and can you observe) in your kidney function and the nature of your urine?

13 THE NERVOUS SYSTEM

In Pursuit of Ecstasy

"Ecstasy" is an illegal but popular drug that relieves anxiety and sharpens the senses. Users say they feel socially accepted and get a mild high. Ecstasy also can leave you dying in a hospital, foaming at the mouth, and bleeding from every orifice as your temperature skyrockets. When Lorna Spinks was nineteen years old, her life ended that way.

Her anguished parents released the photograph at right, taken just minutes after her death. They wanted others to know what Lorna did not: Ecstasy can kill.

Ecstasy's active ingredient, MDMA, is related to amphetamine, or "speed." It interferes with the function of serotonin, a signaling molecule that works in the brain. MDMA causes neurons to release too much serotonin. Instead of being cleared away, as normally happens, serotonin molecules simply saturate receptors on the target cells, which can't be released from overstimulation.

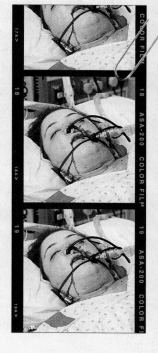

An overdose killed Lorna. Waves of panic and seizures set in. Her heart pounded, her blood pressure soared, and her temperature rose so high that organ systems shut down one by one.

An MDMA overdose does not often end in death, but other problems are common. For example, neurons can't rebound quickly when the brain's serotonin stores are depleted. Below-normal levels of serotonin can contribute to loss of concentration, depression, and memory problems. As studies of Ecstasy users reveal, the more often you use it, the worse memory loss becomes. If you stop using the drug, it can be many months before your brain function returns to normal.

How we function as individuals depends largely on our nervous system—and whether we nurture or abuse it. In this chapter we start by looking at the structure and function of neurons. Then we'll examine how neurons interact in the nervous system and how the brain serves as the body's master control center.

 How Would You Vote? *Would you support legislation that forces nonviolent drug offenders to enter drug rehab programs as an alternative to jail? Cast your vote online at www.thomsonedu.com/biology/starr/humanbio.*

 ## Key Concepts

HOW NEURONS WORK
Messages that travel through the nervous system are based on electrical charges across the plasma membrane of neurons and on signals sent to the next cell in line.

THE NERVOUS SYSTEM
Different parts of the nervous system detect information about conditions inside and outside the body, process it, and then select or control muscles and glands that carry out responses.

THE BRAIN
The brain receives, integrates, stores, and retrieves sensory information. It also orders and coordinates responses by adjusting body activities.

Links to Earlier Concepts

In this chapter you will draw on your knowledge of the structure of cell plasma membranes (3.3), concentration gradients and diffusion (3.9), and mechanisms of active and passive transport (3.10). You will also gain a deeper understanding of neuromuscular junctions and how nervous system signals lead to muscle contractions (6.4).

Above all, you will learn a great deal more about neurons and glial cells that make up the body's nervous tissue (4.4).

13.1 Neurons—The Communication Specialists

Sensing and responding to sounds, sights, hunger, fear—it all begins with cells of the nervous system.

What does your **nervous system** do? Its role is to detect and integrate information about external and internal conditions, then select or control muscles and glands that carry out responses. The system's communication cells are **neurons**, and there are three basic kinds:

Sensory neurons collect and relay information about stimuli to the spinal cord and brain. A stimulus is a form of energy, such as light, detected by a specific receptor.

Interneurons in the spinal cord and brain receive and process sensory input, and send signals to other neurons.

Motor neurons relay signals from interneurons to the body's effectors—muscles and glands—that carry out the specified responses.

NEURONS HAVE SEVERAL FUNCTIONAL ZONES

Every neuron has a cell body, where its nucleus and organelles are. The cell body and slender extensions called **dendrites** are *input zones* for information. Nearby is a **trigger zone**. In motor neurons and interneurons the trigger zone is called the *axon hillock* ("little hill"). At this patch of the neuron's plasma membrane, information travels along a slender and often long extension called an **axon**, the neuron's *conducting zone*. As you can see in the diagram of a motor neuron in Figure 13.1, dendrites tend to be shorter than axons and their number and length vary, depending on the type of neuron. The axon's endings are *output zones* where messages are sent to other cells.

Only about 10 percent of your nervous system consists of neurons. The other 90 percent consists of **neuroglia**, or simply "glia." There are various types of glia, including the star-shaped astroglia shown in Figure 13.2. They help maintain proper concentrations of vital ions in the fluid around neurons, among other tasks. Some glia physically support and protect neurons, as you will read later, and some provide insulation that allows signals to move rapidly along sensory and motor neurons. Others do "clean-up" duty in the central nervous system.

Neurons function so well in communication in part because they are *excitable*—that is, a neuron can respond to certain stimuli by producing an electrical signal. Let's look at the factors that make this possible.

PROPERTIES OF A NEURON'S PLASMA MEMBRANE ALLOW IT TO CARRY SIGNALS

Chapter 3 noted that the plasma membrane's lipid bilayer prevents charged substances—such as ions of potassium (K^+) and sodium (Na^+)—from freely crossing it. Even so, ions can move through the interior of channel proteins that span the bilayer (Figure 13.3). Some channels are

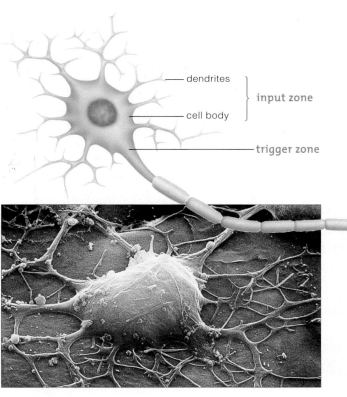

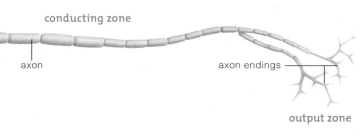

— dendrites

input zone

— cell body

— trigger zone

conducting zone

axon

axon endings

output zone

Figure 13.1 *Animated!* The functional zones of a motor neuron. The micrograph shows a motor neuron with its plump cell body and branching dendrites.

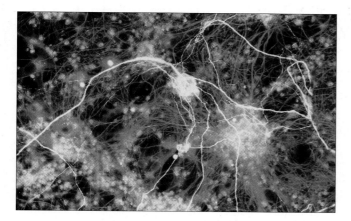

Figure 13.2 In this light micrograph of brain tissue, astrocytes appear orange and a neuron is yellow.

Because the ion concentrations on either side of a neuron's plasma membrane differ, the cytoplasm next to the membrane is negatively charged, compared to the fluid just outside the membrane. Electrical charges may be measured in millivolts, and for many neurons, the steady charge difference across the plasma membrane is about -70 millivolts (indicating that the cytoplasm side of the membrane is more negative). This difference is called the **resting membrane potential**. The name means that the charge difference has the potential to do physiological work in the body.

Various kinds of signals occur in the nervous system, but not all of them spark nerve impulses. Only a signal that is strong enough when it arrives at a resting neuron's input zone may spread to a trigger zone. When a strong enough signal does arrive, however, it can cause the voltage difference across the plasma membrane to reverse, just for an instant. As we see next, these reversals launch nervous system signals.

always open, so that ions can steadily "leak" (diffuse) in or out. Other channels have "gates" that open only under certain circumstances. These controls over ion movements mean that the concentrations of different ions can be different on either side of the plasma membrane.

For example, in a resting neuron, the gated sodium channels are closed. The cell's plasma membrane also does not allow much sodium to leak inward but is more permeable to K^+. As a result, each ion has a concentration gradient across the membrane (Figure 13.3*a*). Following the rules of diffusion, sodium tends to move in and potassium tends to move out.

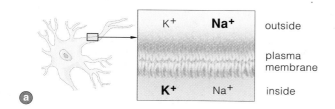

Sensory neurons, interneurons, and motor neurons make up the communication lines of the nervous system.

In a resting neuron, differences in the concentrations of Na$^+$ and K$^+$ across the plasma membrane produce a resting membrane potential—a difference in electrical charge across the plasma membrane. The difference has the potential to do physiological work.

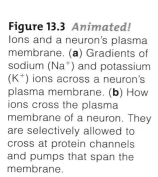

Figure 13.3 *Animated!*
Ions and a neuron's plasma membrane. (**a**) Gradients of sodium (Na$^+$) and potassium (K$^+$) ions across a neuron's plasma membrane. (**b**) How ions cross the plasma membrane of a neuron. They are selectively allowed to cross at protein channels and pumps that span the membrane.

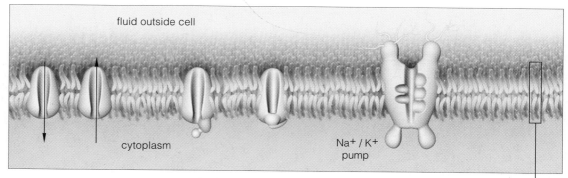

fluid outside cell

cytoplasm

Na$^+$ / K$^+$ pump

lipid bilayer of neuron membrane

Passive transporters with open channels let ions steadily leak across the membrane.

Other passive transporters have voltage-sensitive gated channels that open and shut. They assist diffusion of Na$^+$ and K$^+$ across the membrane as the ions follow concentration gradients.

Active transporters pump Na$^+$ and K$^+$ across the membrane, against their concentration gradients. They counter ion leaks and restore resting membrane conditions.

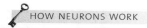

13.2 Action Potentials = Nerve Impulses

LINK TO
SECTION
3.9

It is easy to understand how a nerve impulse develops if you remember that ions can only cross cell membranes through "tunnels" in transport proteins.

As you've just read, when a strong enough signal arrives at a resting neuron's input zone, it can trigger the reversal of the voltage difference across the plasma membrane. The signal has this effect when it causes sodium gates in the membrane to open, so that Na⁺ rushes into the neuron.

As the positively charged sodium flows inward, the cytoplasm next to the plasma membrane becomes less negative (Figure 13.4 *a,b*). Then, more gates open, more sodium enters, and so on (note that this is an example of positive feedback). When the voltage difference across the neuron's plasma membrane shifts by a certain minimum amount—the **threshold** level of stimulation—the result is an **action potential**, the "nerve impulse" that is a neuron's communication signal.

The threshold for an action potential can be reached at any patch of plasma membrane where there are voltage-sensitive gated channels for sodium ions. Because of the positive feedback, when the threshold level is reached, the opening of more sodium gates doesn't depend any longer on the strength of the stimulus. The gates open on their own.

It's important to remember that an action potential occurs only if the stimulus to a neuron is strong enough. A weak stimulus—say, mechanical pressure from a tiny insect walking on your skin—that arrives at an input zone may not upset the ion balance enough to cause an action potential. This is because input zones don't have gated sodium channels, so sodium can't flood in there. On the other hand, a neuron's trigger zone is riddled with sodium channels. If a stimulus at an input zone is strong enough to spread to the trigger zone, an action potential may "fire."

ACTION POTENTIALS SPREAD BY THEMSELVES

To transmit messages throughout the body, action potentials must spread to other neurons or to cells in muscles or glands. Each action potential propagates itself—it moves away from its starting point. This self-propagation is possible in part because the changes in membrane potential leading up to an action potential don't lose strength. When the change spreads from one patch of a neuron's plasma membrane to another patch, approximately the same number of gated channels open (Figure 13.4 *c,d*). Action potentials never spread back into the trigger zone. They always propagate *away* from it, for reasons described next.

A NEURON CAN'T "FIRE" AGAIN UNTIL ION PUMPS RESTORE ITS RESTING POTENTIAL

When an incoming signal causes an action potential in a neuron's trigger zone, that area of the cell's plasma membrane can't receive another signal until its resting membrane potential is restored.

To understand how this happens, remember that a neuron's resting membrane potential is due in part to the differing concentrations of Na⁺ and K⁺ across the plasma membrane. There also is an *electric* gradient across the membrane. The inside of the cell is a little more negative than the outside, partly because there are many negatively charged proteins in the cytoplasm. In addition, K⁺ can diffuse out of the neuron, moving down its concentration gradient. Together, these factors mean that in a resting motor neuron, some Na⁺ is always leaking *into* the cell, down its electrochemical gradient, and K⁺ is leaking *out* down *its* concentration gradient.

Figure 13.4 *Animated!* (**a**,**b**) Steps leading to an action potential. (**c**,**d**) How an action potential propagates.

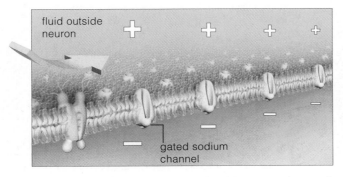

a In a membrane at rest, the inside of the neuron is negative relative to the outside. An electrical disturbance (yellow arrow) spreads from an input zone to an adjacent trigger zone of the membrane, which has a large number of gated sodium channels.

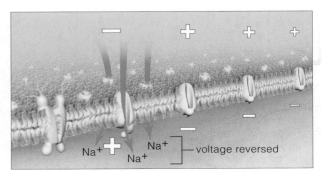

b A strong disturbance initiates an action potential. Sodium gates open. Sodium flows in, reducing the negativity inside the neuron. The change causes more gates to open, and so on until threshold is reached and the voltage difference across the membrane reverses.

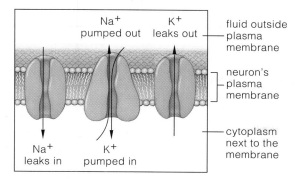

Figure 13.5 Pumping and leaking processes that maintain the distribution of sodium and potassium ions across a resting neuron's plasma membrane. The inward and outward movements of each kind of ion are balanced.

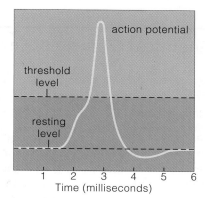

Figure 13.6 *Animated!* A recording of an action potential. You can see clearly how the membrane potential spikes once threshold is reached.

A neuron can't respond to an incoming signal unless the concentration and electric gradients across its plasma membrane are in place. Yet the Na$^+$ and K$^+$ leaks never stop. You might expect that the net amount of K$^+$ in the cell would continue to fall while the amount of Na$^+$ would slowly, surely increase. This imbalance doesn't develop, however, because a resting neuron expends energy on an active transport mechanism that maintains the gradients. This mechanism takes the form of carrier proteins called **sodium–potassium pumps** that span the membrane (Figure 13.5). With energy from ATP, they actively transport potassium *in* and sodium *out*.

ACTION POTENTIALS ARE "ALL-OR-NOTHING"

There is no such thing as a "small" or "large" action potential. Every action potential in a neuron spikes to the same level above threshold as an all-or-nothing event. That is, once the positive-feedback cycle of opening sodium gates starts, nothing will stop the full spiking. If threshold is not reached, the disturbance to the plasma membrane will fade away as soon as the stimulus is removed. Figure 13.6 shows a recording of the voltage difference

across a neuron's plasma membrane before, during, and after an action potential.

Each spike lasts for about a millisecond. At the place on the membrane where the charge reversed, the gated sodium channels close and the influx of sodium stops. About halfway through the action potential, potassium channels open, so potassium ions flow out and restore the original voltage difference across the membrane. And sodium–potassium pumps restore ion gradients, as you've read. Later, after the resting membrane potential has been restored, most potassium gates are closed and sodium gates are in their initial state, ready to be opened again when a suitable stimulus arrives.

An action potential occurs when a neuron's resting membrane potential briefly reverses. Action potentials self-propagate and always move away from the trigger zone.

After an action potential, sodium–potassium pumps restore the neuron's resting potential.

An action potential is an all-or-nothing event. Once the spiking starts, nothing can stop it.

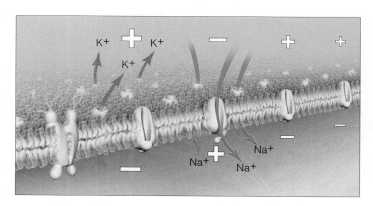

c At the next patch of membrane, another group of gated sodium channels open. In the previous patch, some K$^+$ moves out through other gated channels. That region becomes negative again.

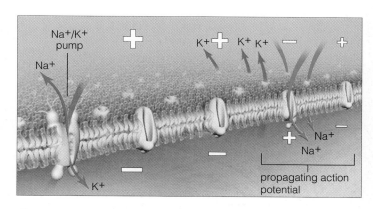

d After each action potential, the sodium and potassium concentration gradients in a patch of membrane are not yet fully restored. Active transport at sodium–potassium pumps restores them.

13.3 Chemical Synapses: Communication Junctions

LINK TO
SECTION
6.6

When action potentials reach a neuron's output zone, they usually stop there. But they may prompt the neuron to release signaling molecules that diffuse to a receiving cell. This is one way that information flows from cell to cell.

Action potentials can trigger the release of one or more **neurotransmitters**. These are signaling molecules that diffuse across a **chemical synapse**, a narrow gap between a neuron's output zone and the input zone of a neighboring cell (Figure 13.7). Some chemical synapses occur between neurons, others between a neuron and a muscle cell or gland cell.

At a chemical synapse, one of the two cells stores neurotransmitter molecules in synaptic vesicles in its cytoplasm. This is the *pre*synaptic cell. Gated channels for calcium ions span the cell's plasma membrane, and they open when an action potential arrives. There are more calcium ions outside the cell, and when they flow in (down their gradient), synaptic vesicles fuse with the plasma membrane. Neurotransmitter molecules in the vesicles now pour into the synapse, diffuse across it, and bind with receptor proteins on the plasma membrane of the *post*synaptic, or receiving, cell. Binding changes the shape of these proteins, so that a channel opens up through them. Ions then diffuse through the channels and enter the receiving cell (Figure 13.7*b*).

NEUROTRANSMITTERS CAN EXCITE OR INHIBIT A RECEIVING CELL

How a receiving cell responds to a neurotransmitter depends on several factors—the type and amount of neurotransmitter, the kinds of receptors the cell has, and the types of channels at its input zone. *Excitatory* signals help drive the membrane toward an action potential. *Inhibitory* signals have the opposite effect.

One neurotransmitter, **acetylcholine (ACh)**, can excite *or* inhibit different target cells in the brain, spinal cord, glands, and muscles. Figure 13.8 shows a chemical synapse between a motor neuron and a muscle cell. ACh released from the neuron diffuses across the gap and binds to receptors on the muscle cell membrane. It excites this kind of cell, triggering action potentials that cause muscle contraction.

Serotonin is a neurotransmitter that acts on brain cells that govern sleeping, sensory perception, regulation of body temperature, and emotional states. Some neurons secrete *nitric oxide* (NO), a gas that controls blood vessel dilation. It is not stored in synaptic vesicles but instead is manufactured as needed. As an example, a sexually aroused male has an erection when NO calls on blood vessels in his penis to dilate, allowing blood to rush in. Section 13.10 looks at the role of some neurotransmitters in disorders of the nervous system.

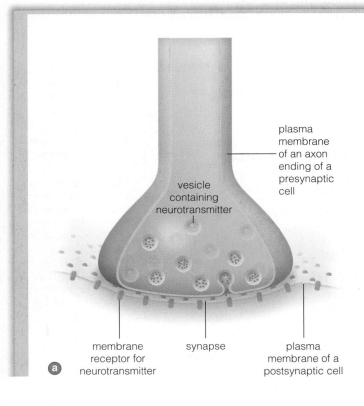

a   membrane receptor for neurotransmitter   synapse   plasma membrane of a postsynaptic cell

vesicle containing neurotransmitter

plasma membrane of an axon ending of a presynaptic cell

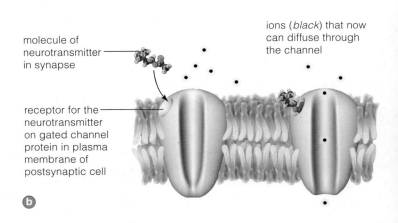

molecule of neurotransmitter in synapse

ions (*black*) that now can diffuse through the channel

receptor for the neurotransmitter on gated channel protein in plasma membrane of postsynaptic cell

b

Figure 13.7 *Animated!* Example of a chemical synapse. (**a**) Only a narrow gap separates a presynaptic cell from a postsynaptic one. (**b**) A neurotransmitter carries signals from the presynaptic neuron to the receiving cell.

HOW NEURONS WORK

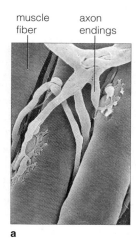

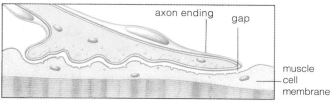

muscle fiber
axon endings

axon ending
gap

muscle cell membrane

Motor end plate (troughs in muscle cell membrane)

b

a

Figure 13.8 One kind of chemical synapse—a neuromuscular junction. (**a**) Micrograph of a neuromuscular junction. It forms between axon endings of motor neurons and muscle cells. (**b**) The axon's myelin sheath stops at the neuromuscular junction, so the membranes of the two cells are exposed. There are troughs in the muscle cell membrane where the axon endings are positioned.

Neuromodulators can magnify or impede the effects of a neurotransmitter. These substances include natural painkillers called *endorphins*. Endorphins inhibit nerves from releasing substance P, which conveys information about pain. In athletes who push themselves beyond normal fatigue, endorphins can produce a euphoric "high." Endorphins also may have roles in functions such as memory, learning, and sexual behavior.

COMPETING SIGNALS ARE "SUMMED UP"

Between 1,000 and 10,000 communication lines form synapses with a typical neuron in your brain. And your brain contains at least *100 billion* neurons, humming with messages about doing what it takes to be a human.

At any moment, many signals are washing over the input zones of a receiving neuron. All of them are graded potentials (their magnitude can be large or small), and they compete for control of the membrane potential at the trigger zone. The ones called EPSPs (for excitatory postsynaptic potentials) *depolarize* the membrane—they bring it closer to threshold. On the other hand, IPSPs (inhibitory postsynaptic potentials) may *hyperpolarize* the membrane (drive it away from threshold) or help keep the membrane at its resting level.

Synaptic integration tallies up the competing signals that reach an input zone of a neuron at the same time—a little like adding up the pros and cons of a certain course of action. This process, called *summation*, is how signals arriving at a neuron are suppressed, reinforced, or sent onward to other cells in the body.

Integration occurs when neurotransmitter molecules from more than one presynaptic cell reach a neuron's input zone at the same time. Signals also are integrated after a neurotransmitter is released repeatedly, over a short time period, from a neuron that is responding to a rapid series of action potentials.

NEUROTRANSMITTER MOLECULES MUST BE REMOVED FROM THE SYNAPSE

The flow of signals through the nervous system depends on the rapid, controlled removal of neurotransmitter molecules from synapses. Some of the neurotransmitter molecules diffuse out of the gap. Enzymes cleave others in the synapse, as when acetylcholinesterase breaks down ACh. Also, membrane transport proteins actively pump the neurotransmitter molecules back into presynaptic cells or into neighboring neuroglia.

Some drugs can block the reuptake of certain neurotransmitters. For example, some antidepressant drugs (such as Prozac) alter a person's mood by blocking the reuptake of serotonin.

Neurotransmitters are signaling molecules that bridge the synapse (a narrow gap) between two neurons or between a neuron and a muscle cell or gland cell. They may excite or inhibit the activity of different kinds of target cells.

In synaptic integration, incoming signals that excite or inhibit the same postsynaptic cell are summed. In this way messages traveling through the nervous system can be reinforced or downplayed, sent onward or suppressed.

13.4 Information Pathways

Once a message is "sent" in the nervous system, what determines where it will go? That depends on how neurons are organized in the body.

NERVES ARE LONG-DISTANCE LINES

Nerves are communication lines between the brain or spinal cord and the rest of the body. A **nerve** consists of nerve fibers, which are the long axons of sensory neurons, motor neurons, or both. Connective tissue encloses most of the axons like electrical cords inside a tube (Table 13.1 and Figure 13.9a). In the central nervous system (the brain and spinal cord) nerves are called **nerve tracts**.

Each axon has an insulating **myelin sheath**, which allows action potentials to propagate faster than they would otherwise. The sheath consists of glia called **Schwann cells**, which wrap around the long axons like jelly rolls. As you can see in Figure 13.9b, an exposed node, or gap, separates each cell from the next one. There, voltage-sensitive, gated sodium channels pepper the plasma membrane. In a manner of speaking, action potentials jump from node to node (a phenomenon also called saltatory conduction, after a Latin word meaning

Table 13.1	Basic Components of the Nervous System
Neuron	Nervous system cell specialized for communication
Nerve fiber	Long axon of one neuron
Nerves	Long axons of several neurons enclosed by connective tissue

"to jump"). The sheathed areas between nodes hamper the movement of ions across the plasma membrane, so stimulation tends to travel along the membrane until the next node in line. At each node, however, the flow of ions can produce a new action potential. In large sheathed axons, action potentials propagate at a remarkable 120 meters (nearly 400 feet) per second!

There are no Schwann cells in the central nervous system. There, glia called oligodendrocytes sheath all myelinated axons.

REFLEX ARCS ARE THE SIMPLEST NERVE PATHWAYS

Sensory and motor neurons of certain nerves take part in automatic responses called reflexes. A **reflex** is a simple, stereotyped movement (it is always the same) in response to a stimulus. In the simplest **reflex arcs**, sensory neurons synapse directly on motor neurons.

The *stretch reflex* contracts a muscle after gravity or some other load has stretched the muscle. Suppose you hold out a bowl and keep it stationary as someone loads peaches into it, adding weight to the bowl. When your hand starts to drop, a muscle in your arm (the biceps) is stretched.

In the muscle, stretching activates receptor endings that are a part of muscle spindles. These are sensory organs in which specialized cells are enclosed in a sheath that runs parallel with the muscle. The receptor endings are the input zones of sensory neurons whose axons synapse with motor neurons in the spinal cord (Figure 13.10). Axons of the motor neurons lead back to the stretched muscle. Action potentials that reach the axon endings trigger the release of ACh, which triggers contraction. As long as receptors continue to send messages, the motor neurons are excited. This allows them to maintain your hand's position.

In most reflex pathways, the sensory neurons also interact with several interneurons. These excite or inhibit motor neurons as needed for a coordinated response.

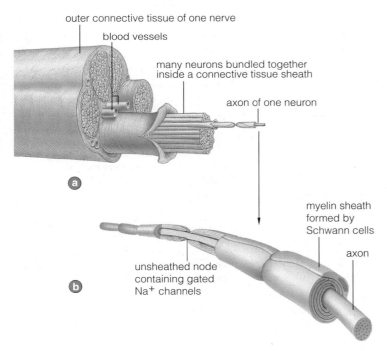

Figure 13.9 *Animated!* (**a**) Structure of a nerve. (**b**) Structure of a sheathed axon. A myelin sheath (a series of Schwann cells wrapped like a jelly roll around the axon) blocks the flow of ions except at nodes between Schwann cells.

outer connective tissue of one nerve

blood vessels

many neurons bundled together inside a connective tissue sheath

axon of one neuron

myelin sheath formed by Schwann cells

axon

unsheathed node containing gated Na+ channels

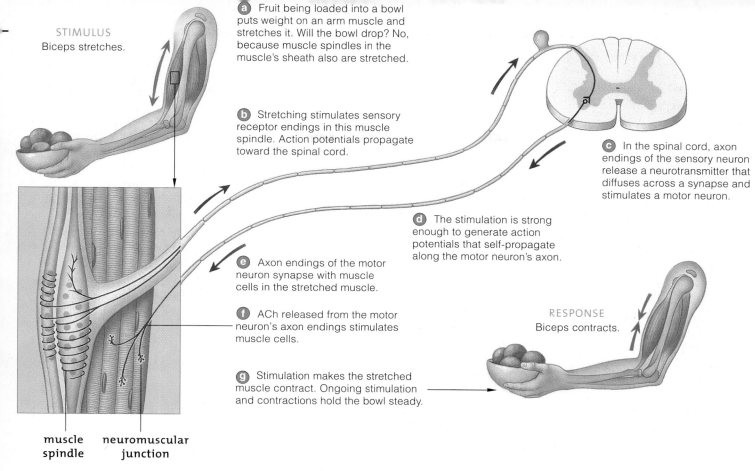

a Fruit being loaded into a bowl puts weight on an arm muscle and stretches it. Will the bowl drop? No, because muscle spindles in the muscle's sheath also are stretched.

STIMULUS
Biceps stretches.

b Stretching stimulates sensory receptor endings in this muscle spindle. Action potentials propagate toward the spinal cord.

c In the spinal cord, axon endings of the sensory neuron release a neurotransmitter that diffuses across a synapse and stimulates a motor neuron.

d The stimulation is strong enough to generate action potentials that self-propagate along the motor neuron's axon.

e Axon endings of the motor neuron synapse with muscle cells in the stretched muscle.

f ACh released from the motor neuron's axon endings stimulates muscle cells.

RESPONSE
Biceps contracts.

g Stimulation makes the stretched muscle contract. Ongoing stimulation and contractions hold the bowl steady.

muscle spindle   neuromuscular junction

Figure 13.10 *Animated!* How nerves are organized in a reflex arc that deals with muscle stretching. In a skeletal muscle, stretch-sensitive receptors of a sensory neuron are located in muscle spindles. The stretching generates action potentials, which reach axon endings in the spinal cord. These synapse with a motor neuron that carries signals to contract from the spinal cord back to the stretching muscle.

IN THE BRAIN AND SPINAL CORD, NEURONS INTERACT IN CIRCUITS

The diagram below shows the overall direction of the flow of information in your nervous system. Sensory nerves relay information into the spinal cord, where they form chemical synapses with interneurons. The spinal cord and brain contain only interneurons, which integrate the signals. Many interneurons synapse with motor neurons, which carry signals away from the spinal cord and brain.

In the brain and spinal cord, interneurons are grouped into blocks of hundreds or thousands. The blocks in turn are parts of circuits. Each block receives signals—some that excite, others that inhibit—and then integrates the messages and responds with new ones. For example, in some brain regions the circuits diverge—the processes of

neurons in one block fan out to form connections with other blocks. Elsewhere signals from many neurons are funneled to just a few. And in still other places in the brain, neurons synapse back on themselves, repeating signals among themselves. These "reverberating" circuits include the ones that make your eye muscles twitch rhythmically as you sleep.

Nerves containing the long axons of sensory neurons, motor neurons, or both, connect the brain and spinal cord with the rest of the body.

In a reflex arc, sensory neurons synapse directly on motor neurons. This is the simplest path of information flow.

Interneurons in the brain and spinal cord are organized in information-processing blocks.

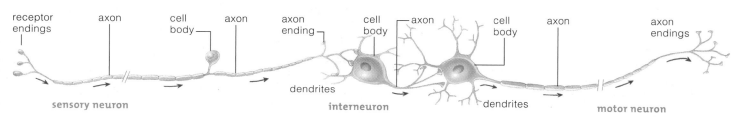

receptor endings   axon   cell body   axon   axon ending   cell body   axon   cell body   axon   axon endings

dendrites   dendrites

sensory neuron   interneuron   motor neuron

13.5 Overview of the Nervous System

Up to this point we have focused on the signals that travel through the nervous system. This section gives an overview of how the system as a whole is organized.

Humans have the most intricately wired nervous system in the animal world (Figure 13.11). We can simplify its complexity by dividing it according to function into two main regions. The brain and spinal cord make up the **central nervous system** (CNS). All of the nervous system's interneurons are in this system. The **peripheral nervous system** (PNS) consists mainly of nerves that thread through the rest of the body and carry signals into and out of the central nervous system.

Nerves that carry sensory input to the central nervous system sometimes are called *afferent* ("bringing to") nerves. Nerves that carry motor messages away from the central nervous system to muscles and glands may be termed *efferent* ("carrying outward") nerves.

As Figure 13.12 shows, the peripheral nervous system is organized into *somatic* and *autonomic* subdivisions, and the autonomic nerves are subdivided yet again. We'll consider the roles of those nerves in Section 13.6.

The peripheral nervous system consists of thirty-one pairs of spinal nerves that carry signals to and from the spinal cord and twelve pairs of cranial nerves that carry signals to and from the brain (Figure 13.13). At some places in the PNS, cell bodies of several neurons occur in

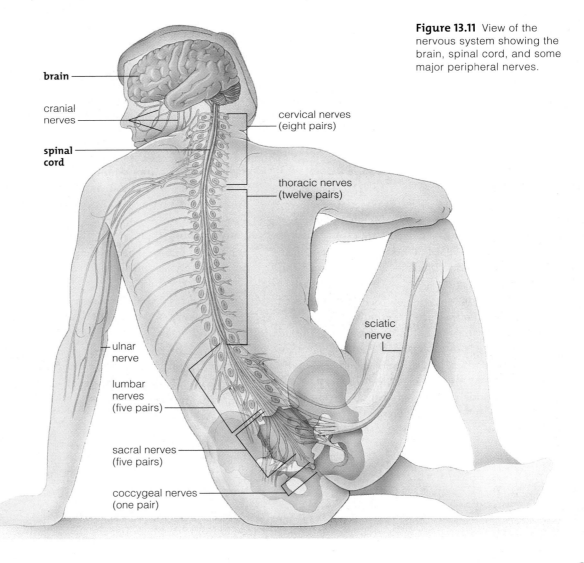

brain

cranial nerves

spinal cord

cervical nerves (eight pairs)

thoracic nerves (twelve pairs)

sciatic nerve

ulnar nerve

lumbar nerves (five pairs)

sacral nerves (five pairs)

coccygeal nerves (one pair)

Figure 13.11 View of the nervous system showing the brain, spinal cord, and some major peripheral nerves.

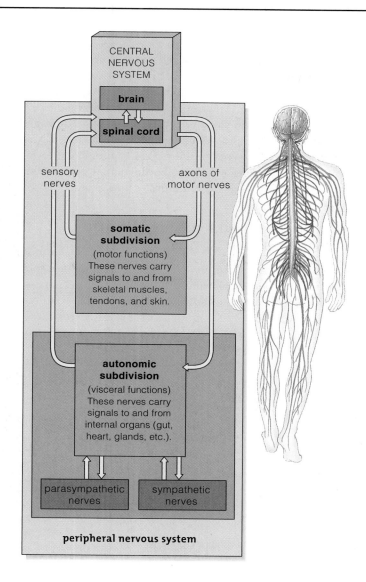

Figure 13.12 *Animated!* Divisions of the nervous system. The central nervous system is color-coded blue, somatic nerves are green, and autonomic nerves are red.

Inside the CNS box:

CENTRAL NERVOUS SYSTEM

brain

spinal cord

sensory nerves

axons of motor nerves

somatic subdivision

(motor functions) These nerves carry signals to and from skeletal muscles, tendons, and skin.

autonomic subdivision

(visceral functions) These nerves carry signals to and from internal organs (gut, heart, glands, etc.).

parasympathetic nerves

sympathetic nerves

peripheral nervous system

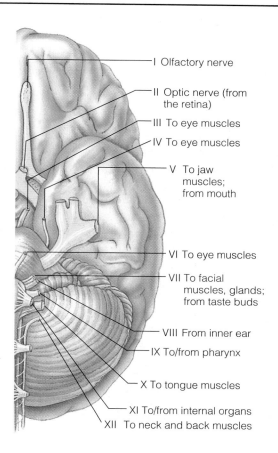

I Olfactory nerve

II Optic nerve (from the retina)

III To eye muscles

IV To eye muscles

V To jaw muscles; from mouth

VI To eye muscles

VII To facial muscles, glands; from taste buds

VIII From inner ear

IX To/from pharynx

X To tongue muscles

XI To/from internal organs

XII To neck and back muscles

Figure 13.13 Cranial nerves. Twelve pairs of cranial nerves extend from different regions of the brain stem. By tradition, Roman numerals are used to designate cranial nerves.

clusters called **ganglia** (singular: ganglion). The central and peripheral nervous systems both also have glia, such as the oligodendrocytes (CNS) and Schwann cells (PNS) described in Sections 13.1 and 13.4.

Throughout our lives, our remarkable nervous system integrates the array of body functions in ways that help maintain homeostasis. Operations of the CNS also give us much of our "humanness," as you will read shortly.

The nervous system is divided into the central nervous system (CNS) and the peripheral nervous system (PNS). The CNS consists of the brain and spinal cord. The PNS consists of nerves that carry signals to and from the CNS.

13.6 Major Expressways: Peripheral Nerves and the Spinal Cord

Peripheral nerves and the spinal cord interconnect as the major expressways for information flow through the body.

THE PERIPHERAL NERVOUS SYSTEM CONSISTS OF SOMATIC AND AUTONOMIC NERVES

Nerves of the PNS are grouped by function. To begin with, cranial and spinal nerves are subdivided into two groups. **Somatic nerves** carry signals related to movements of the head, trunk, and limbs. **Autonomic nerves** carry signals beween internal organs and other structures.

In somatic nerves, sensory axons carry information from receptors in skin, skeletal muscles, and tendons to the central nervous system. Their motor axons deliver commands from the brain and spinal cord to skeletal muscles. In the autonomic category, motor axons of spinal and cranial nerves carry messages to smooth muscle, cardiac (heart) muscle, and glands (Figure 13.14).

Unlike somatic neurons, single autonomic neurons do not extend the entire distance between muscles or glands and the central nervous system. Instead, preganglionic ("before a ganglion") neurons have cell bodies inside the spinal cord or brain stem, but their axons travel through nerves to autonomic system ganglia *outside* the CNS. There, the axons synapse with postganglionic ("after a ganglion") neurons, which make the actual connection with "effectors"—the body's muscles and glands.

AUTONOMIC NERVES ARE DIVIDED INTO PARASYMPATHETIC AND SYMPATHETIC GROUPS

Autonomic nerves are divided into *parasympathetic* and *sympathetic* nerves. Normally these two sets of nerves work antagonistically—the signals from one oppose those of the other. However, both these groups of nerves carry excitatory and inhibitory signals to internal organs. Often

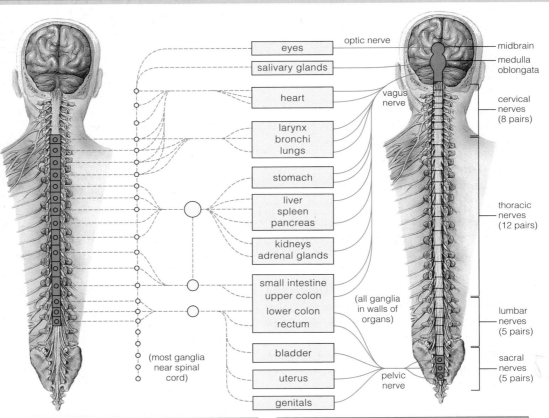

Figure 13.14 *Animated!* The autonomic nervous system. This is a diagram of the major sympathetic and parasympathetic nerves leading out from the central nervous system to some major organs. Remember, there are *pairs* of both kinds of nerves, servicing the right and left halves of the body. The ganglia are simply clusters of cell bodies of the neurons that are bundled together in nerves.

eyes
optic nerve
salivary glands
heart
vagus nerve
larynx
bronchi
lungs
stomach
liver
spleen
pancreas
kidneys
adrenal glands
small intestine
upper colon
lower colon
rectum
(all ganglia in walls of organs)
bladder
uterus
pelvic nerve
genitals

(most ganglia near spinal cord)

midbrain
medulla oblongata
cervical nerves (8 pairs)
thoracic nerves (12 pairs)
lumbar nerves (5 pairs)
sacral nerves (5 pairs)

a sympathetic outflow from the spinal cord

b parasympathetic outflow from the spinal cord and brain

Examples of Responses
Heart rate increases
Pupils of eyes dilate (widen, let in more light)
Glandular secretions decrease in airways to lungs
Salivary gland secretions thicken
Stomach and intestinal movements slow down
Sphincters (rings of muscle) contract

Examples of Responses
Heart rate decreases
Pupils of eyes constrict (keep more light out)
Glandular secretions increase in airways to lungs
Salivary gland secretions become dilute
Stomach and intestinal movements increase
Sphincters (rings of muscle) relax

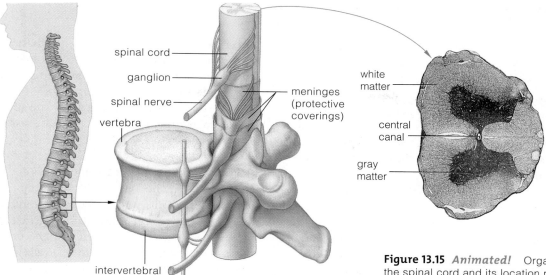

spinal cord

ganglion

spinal nerve

vertebra

meninges (protective coverings)

white matter

central canal

gray matter

intervertebral disk

Figure 13.15 *Animated!* Organization of the spinal cord and its location relative to the vertebral column.

their signals arrive at the same time at muscle or gland cells and compete for control. When that happens, synaptic integration leads to minor adjustments in an organ's activity.

Parasympathetic nerves dominate when the body is not receiving much outside stimulation. They tend to slow down the body overall and divert energy to basic "housekeeping" tasks, such as digestion.

Sympathetic nerves dominate during heightened awareness, excitement, or danger. They tend to shift activity away from housekeeping tasks. For example, as you read this, sympathetic nerves are prompting your heart to beat a bit faster, and parasympathetic nerves are commanding it to beat a little slower. Integration of these opposing signals influences your heart rate. If something scares or excites you, parasympathetic input to your heart drops. At the same time, sympathetic nerves release norepinephrine, a neurotransmitter that makes your heart beat faster and makes you breathe faster and sweat. In this **fight–flight response**, you are primed to fight (or play) hard or to get away fast.

When the stimulus for the fight–flight response stops, sympathetic activity may fall and parasympathetic activity may rise. This "rebound effect" can occur after someone has been mobilized, say, to rush onto a street to save a child from an oncoming car. The person may well collapse as soon as the child has been swept out of danger.

THE SPINAL CORD IS THE PATHWAY BETWEEN THE PNS AND THE BRAIN

The **spinal cord** is a vital expressway for signals between the peripheral nervous system and the brain. It threads through a canal made of bones of the vertebral column (Figure 13.15). Most of the cord consists of nerve tracts

(bundles of myelinated axons). Because the myelin sheaths of these axons are white, the tracts are called *white matter*. The cord also contains dendrites, cell bodies of neurons, interneurons, and neuroglial cells. These form its *gray matter*. In cross section, the cord's gray matter looks a little bit like a butterfly. The cord lies inside a closed channel formed by the bones of the vertebral column. Those bones, and ligaments attached to them, protect the soft nervous tissue of the cord. So do three coverings of connective tissue called *meninges* layered around the spinal cord and brain. They are discussed in Section 13.7.

In addition to carrying signals between the peripheral nervous system and the brain, the spinal cord is a control center for reflexes. Sensory and motor neurons involved in many reflex movements of skeletal muscle make direct connections in the cord; such *spinal reflexes* do not require the brain's input. When you jerk your hand away from a hot stove burner, you are experiencing a spinal reflex in action. Information about the sensory stimulus also reaches higher brain centers and so you become aware of "hot burner!" even as your hand is moving away from it. In addition to all of the above, the spinal cord contributes to some *autonomic reflexes*, which deal with internal organ functions such as bladder emptying.

The peripheral nervous system consists of the nerves to and from the brain and spinal cord.

Its somatic nerves deal with skeletal muscle movements. Its autonomic nerves govern functions of internal organs, such as the heart and glands. Autonomic nerves are divided into parasympathetic nerves (for housekeeping functions) and sympathetic nerves (for aroused states).

The spinal cord carries signals between peripheral nerves and the brain. It also is a control center for certain reflexes.

13.7 The Brain—Command Central

The brain is divided into three main regions, each one containing centers that manage specific biological tasks.

The spinal cord merges with the **brain**. Like the cord, the brain is protected by bones (of the cranium) and by the three **meninges** (meh-NIN-jeez). These are membranes of connective tissue layered between the skull and the brain (Figure 13.16). Meninges cover and protect the fragile CNS neurons and blood vessels that service the tissue. The leathery, outer membrane, the *dura mater,* is folded double around the brain. Its upper surface attaches to the skull. The lower surface is the outer covering of the brain and separates its right and left hemispheres. A thinner middle layer is called the *arachnoid,* and the even more delicate *pia mater* wraps the brain and spinal cord. The meninges also enclose fluid-filled spaces that cushion and nourish the brain.

THE BRAIN IS DIVIDED INTO A HINDBRAIN, MIDBRAIN, AND FOREBRAIN

The brain's three divisions are the *hindbrain, midbrain,* and *forebrain* (Figure 13.17). In the hindbrain and midbrain are centers that control many simple, basic reflexes; this tissue is the **brain stem**. As the ancestors of humans evolved, expanded layers of gray matter developed over the brain stem. These changes in brain structure have been correlated with our species' increasing reliance on three major sensory organs: the nose, ears, and eyes. They are topics in Chapter 14.

HINDBRAIN The medulla oblongata, cerebellum, and pons are all components of the hindbrain. The **medulla oblongata** contains reflex centers for a number of vital tasks, such as respiration and blood circulation. It also coordinates motor responses with certain complex reflexes, such as coughing. In addition, the medulla influences brain centers that help you sleep or wake up.

The **cerebellum** integrates sensory signals from the eyes, inner ears, and muscles with motor signals from the forebrain to coordinate movement and balance. It helps control dexterity. Some of its activities may also be crucial in language and other forms of mental "agility."

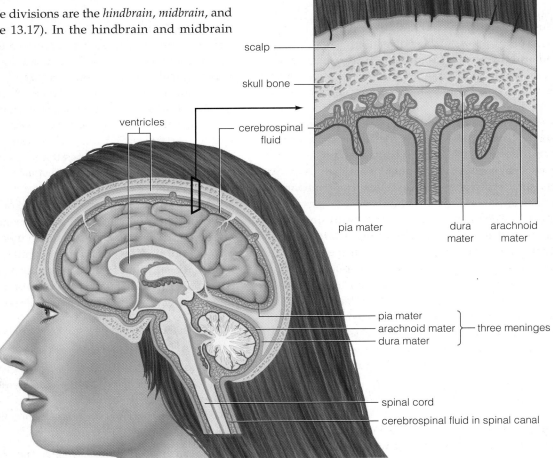

Figure 13.16 Location of the three meninges in relation to the brain. Cerebrospinal fluid fills the space between the arachnoid and the pia mater.

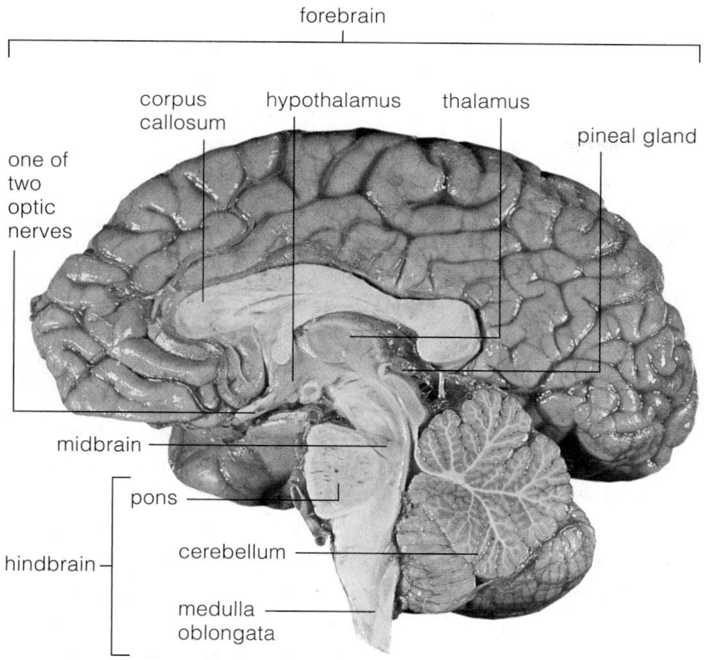

forebrain

corpus callosum · hypothalamus · thalamus

pineal gland

one of two optic nerves

midbrain

pons

hindbrain

cerebellum

medulla oblongata

Figure 13.17 *Animated!* The brain's right hemisphere. Each hemisphere has a cerebral cortex, a layer of gray matter about 2–4 millimeters (1/8 inch) thick. Interneuron cell bodies and dendrites, unmyelinated axons, glia, and blood vessels make up the gray matter.

Bands of many axons extend from the cerebellum into the **pons** ("bridge") in the brain stem. The pons directs the signal traffic between the cerebellum and the higher integrating centers of the forebrain.

MIDBRAIN The midbrain coordinates reflex responses to sights and sounds. It has a roof of gray matter, the *tectum* (Latin for "roof"), where visual and auditory sensory input converges before being sent on to higher brain centers.

FOREBRAIN The forebrain is the most highly developed brain region. It includes the cerebrum, olfactory bulbs, and the thalamus and hypothalamus. In the **cerebrum**, information is processed and sensory input and motor responses are integrated. A pair of *olfactory bulbs* deal with sensory information about smell. The **thalamus** is mainly a sensory relay switchboard. In it, incoming signals in sensory nerve tracts are relayed to clusters of neuron cell bodies (called *nuclei*), then relayed onward. The nuclei also process some outgoing motor information. As you will read in Section 13.10, Parkinson's disease results when functioning of *basal nuclei* in the thalamus is disrupted.

Located below the thalamus, the **hypothalamus** has evolved into the body's "supercenter" for controlling homeostatic adjustments in the activities of internal organs. As noted in previous chapters, for example, it helps govern states such as thirst and hunger. The hypothalamus also

has roles in sexual behavior and emotional expression, such as when fear causes a person to break into a sweat.

CEREBROSPINAL FLUID FILLS CAVITIES AND CANALS IN THE BRAIN

Our brain and spinal cord would both be highly vulnerable to damage if they were not protected by bones and meninges. In addition, as you can see in Figure 13.16, both of them are surrounded by **cerebrospinal fluid**, or CSF. This transparent fluid forms from blood plasma and is chemically similar to it. It is secreted from specialized capillaries inside a system of fluid-filled cavities and canals in the brain. The cavities in the brain are called ventricles. They connect with each other and with the central canal of the spinal cord and are filled with cerebrospinal fluid. The fluid also fills the space between the innermost layer of the meninges and the brain itself. Because the enclosed cerebrospinal fluid can't be compressed, it helps cushion the brain and spinal cord from jarring movements. Some diseases, such as **meningitis** (inflammation of the meninges), can be diagnosed by analyzing a sample of the CSF.

Maintaining homeostasis in the fluid that bathes your brain's neurons is vital. Yet as you know, the chemical makeup of extracellular fluid, including levels of ions and other substances, is constantly changing. In the brain this problem is solved by the unusual structure of brain capillaries. Their walls are much less permeable than the walls of capillaries elsewhere in the body, so substances must pass *through* the wall cells, rather than between them, to reach the brain. This **blood–brain barrier** helps control which blood-borne substances are allowed to reach the brain's neurons.

Transport proteins embedded in the plasma membrane of the cells in brain capillary walls allow glucose and other water-soluble substances to cross the barrier. However, lipid-soluble substances are another matter. They quickly diffuse through the lipid bilayer of the plasma membrane. This "lipid loophole" in the blood–brain barrier is one reason why lipid-soluble chemicals such as caffeine, nicotine, alcohol, barbiturates, heroin, and anesthetics can rapidly affect brain function.

The brain's main divisions are the hindbrain, midbrain, and forebrain. Their functions range from reflex controls over basic survival functions (as in the brain stem in the hindbrain) to the complex integration of sensory information and motor responses.

In the brain and spinal cord, cerebrospinal fluid fills a system of cavities and canals. This fluid provides a cushion against jarring movement.

THE BRAIN

13.8 A Closer Look at the Cerebrum

If you are an average-sized adult, your brain weighs about 1,300 grams (three pounds) and contains at least 100 billion neurons! Its cerebrum is where much of "the action" is.

THERE ARE TWO CEREBRAL HEMISPHERES

The human cerebrum looks somewhat like a much-folded walnut, and a deep fissure divides it into left and right **cerebral hemispheres** (Figure 13.18). Each hemisphere has a thin outer layer of gray matter, the **cerebral cortex**. (The cerebral cortex weighs about a pound. If stretched flat, it would cover a surface area of two and a half square feet.) Below the cortex are the white matter (axons) and the basal nuclei—patches of gray matter in the thalamus.

Each cerebral hemisphere receives, processes, and coordinates responses to sensory input mainly from the opposite side of the body. (For instance, "cold" signals from an ice cube in your left hand travel to your right cerebral hemisphere.) The left hemisphere deals mainly with speech, analytical skills, and mathematics. In most people it dominates the right hemisphere, which deals more with visual–spatial relationships, music, and other creative activities. A band of nerve tracts, the corpus callosum, carries signals back and forth between the hemispheres and coordinates their operations.

Each hemisphere is divided into frontal, occipital, temporal, and parietal lobes, which process different signals (Figure 13.19*a*). EEGs and PET scans (Figure 13.19*b*) can reveal activity in each lobe. EEG, short for

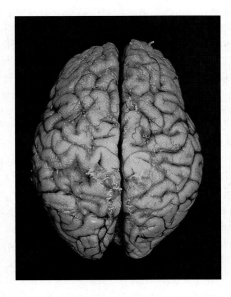

Figure 13.18 A top-down view of the brain's two cerebral hemispheres.

electroencephalogram, is a recording of summed electrical activity in some part of the brain.

THE CEREBRAL CORTEX CONTROLS THOUGHT AND OTHER CONSCIOUS BEHAVIOR

Everything you comprehend, communicate, remember, and voluntarily act upon arises in the cerebral cortex; it governs conscious behavior. Functionally, the cortex is divided into *motor* areas (control of voluntary motor activity), *sensory* areas (perception of the meaning of sensations), and *association* areas (the integration of information that precedes a conscious action). None of these areas functions alone; consciousness arises by way of interactions throughout the cortex.

MOTOR AREAS In the frontal lobe of each hemisphere, the whole body is spatially mapped out in the primary motor cortex. This area controls coordinated movements of skeletal muscles. Thumb, finger, and tongue muscles get much of the area's attention, indicating how much control is required for voluntary hand movements and verbal expression (Figure 13.20).

Also in the frontal lobe are the premotor cortex, Broca's area, and the frontal eye field. The premotor cortex deals with learned patterns or motor skills. Repetitive motor actions, such as bouncing a ball, are evidence that your motor cortex is coordinating the movements of several muscle groups. Broca's area (usually in the left hemisphere) and a corresponding area in the right hemisphere control the tongue, throat, and lip muscles used in speech. It kicks in when we are about to speak and even when we plan voluntary motor activities other than speaking (so you can talk on the phone and write down a message at the same time). Above Broca's area is the frontal eye field. It controls voluntary eye movements.

SENSORY AREAS Sensory areas occur in different parts of the cortex. In the parietal lobe, the body is spatially mapped out in the primary somatosensory cortex. This area is the main receiving center for sensory input from the skin and joints. The parietal lobe also has a primary cortical area dealing with perception of taste. At the back of the occipital lobe is the primary visual cortex, which receives sensory inputs from your eyes. Perception of sounds and of odors arises in primary cortical areas in each temporal lobe.

ASSOCIATION AREAS Association areas occupy all parts of the cortex except the primary motor and sensory regions. Each integrates, analyzes, and responds to many inputs. For instance, the visual association area surrounds

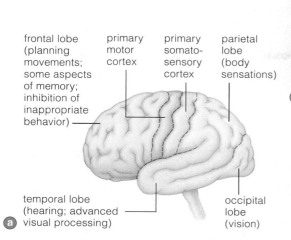

frontal lobe (planning movements; some aspects of memory; inhibition of inappropriate behavior)

primary motor cortex

primary somato-sensory cortex

parietal lobe (body sensations)

temporal lobe (hearing; advanced visual processing)

occipital lobe (vision)

a

b Motor cortex activity when speaking

Prefrontal cortex activity when generating words

Visual cortex activity when observing words

Figure 13.19 *Animated!* (**a**) Primary receiving and integrating centers for the human cerebral cortex. Primary cortical areas receive signals from receptors on the body's periphery. Association areas coordinate and process sensory input from different receptors. The PET scans (**b**) show which brain regions were active when a person performed three specific tasks: speaking, generating words, and observing words.

the primary visual cortex. It helps us recognize something we see by comparing it with visual memories. Neural activity in the most complex association area—the prefrontal cortex—is the basis for complex learning, intellect, and personality. Without it, we would be incapable of abstract thought, judgment, planning, and concern for others.

THE LIMBIC SYSTEM: EMOTIONS AND MORE

The prefrontal cortex interacts intimately with the **limbic system**, which is located inside the cerebral hemispheres. It governs our emotions and has roles in memory (Figure 13.21). The limbic system includes parts of the thalamus along with the hypothalamus, the amygdala, and the

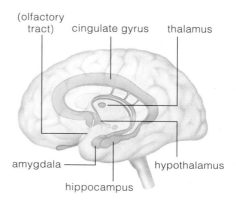

(olfactory tract) cingulate gyrus thalamus

amygdala

hippocampus

hypothalamus

Figure 13.21 Key structures in the limbic system, which encircles the upper brain stem. The amygdala and the cingulate gyrus are especially important in emotions. The hypothalamus is a clearinghouse for emotions and visceral activity. Both the hippocampus and the amygdala help convert stimuli into long-term memory (Section 13.9).

hippocampus. It is called our "emotional–visceral brain" because its operations produce "gut" reactions such as rage. The system's links with other brain centers also allow it to correlate self-gratifying behavior, such as eating and sex, with the activities of associated organs. Responses of the limbic system also are part of the reason you may feel "warm and fuzzy" when you recall the cologne of a special person who wore it.

Each cerebral hemisphere receives, processes, and coordinates responses to sensory input mainly from the opposite side of the body. The corpus callosum carries signals between them.

The left hemisphere deals mainly with speech, analytical skills, and mathematics. It usually dominates the right hemisphere, which deals more with creative activity, such as visual–spatial relationships and music.

The cerebral cortex, the outermost layer of gray matter of each hemisphere, contains motor, sensory, and association areas. Communication among these areas governs conscious behavior. The cerebral cortex also interacts with the limbic system, which governs emotions and memory.

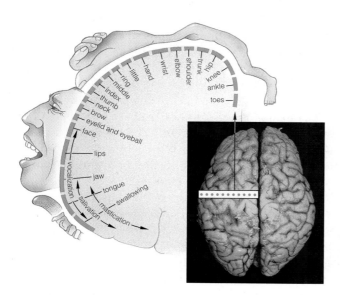

little
ring
middle
index
thumb
neck
brow
eyelid and eyeball
face
lips
vocalization
jaw
tongue
swallowing
salivation
mastication
hand
wrist
elbow
shoulder
trunk
hip
knee
ankle
toes

Figure 13.20 *Animated!* Diagram of a slice through the primary motor cortex of the left cerebral hemisphere. The distortions to the human body draped over the diagram indicate which body parts receive the most precise control.

13.9 Memory and Consciousness

Even before you were born, your brain began to build your memory—to store and retrieve information about your unique experiences.

MEMORY IS HOW THE BRAIN STORES AND RETRIEVES INFORMATION

Learning and adaptive modifications of our behavior would be impossible without **memory**. Information is stored in stages. *Short-term* storage is a stage of neural excitation that lasts a few seconds to a few hours. It is limited to bits of sensory information—numbers, words of a sentence, and so on. In *long-term* storage, seemingly unlimited amounts of information get tucked away more or less permanently, as shown in Figure 13.22.

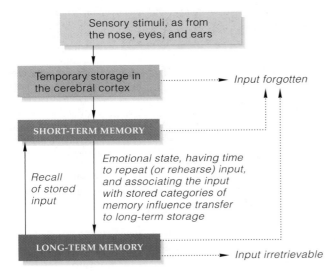

Figure 13.22 Stages of memory processing, starting with the temporary storage of sensory inputs in the cerebral cortex.

Not all of the sensory input bombarding the cerebral cortex ends up in memory storage. Only some is selected for transfer to brain structures involved in short-term memory. Information in these holding bins is processed for relevance, so to speak. If irrelevant, it is forgotten; otherwise it is consolidated with the banks of information in long-term storage structures.

The human brain processes facts separately from skills. Dates, names, faces, words, odors, and other bits of explicit information are *facts*, soon forgotten or filed away in long-term storage, along with the circumstance in which they were learned. Hence you might associate the smell of bread baking, say, with your grandmother's kitchen. By contrast, *skills* are gained by practicing specific motor activities. A skill such as maneuvering a snowboard or playing a piano concerto is best recalled by actually

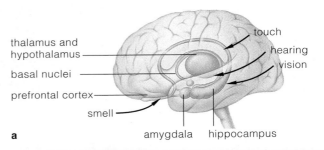

b

Figure 13.23 *Animated!* (**a**) Possible circuits involved in fact memory. (**b**) A dramatic demonstration of skill memory.

performing it, rather than by recalling the circumstances in which the skill was first learned.

Separate memory circuits handle different kinds of input. A circuit leading to fact memory (Figure 13.23*a*) starts with inputs at the sensory cortex that flow to the amygdala and hippocampus in the limbic system. The amygdala is the gatekeeper, connecting the sensory cortex with parts of the thalamus and with parts of the hippocampus that govern emotional states. Information flows on to the prefrontal cortex, where multiple banks of fact memories are retrieved and used to stimulate or inhibit other parts of the brain. The new input also flows to basal nuclei, which send it back to the cortex in a feedback loop that reinforces the input until it can be consolidated in long-term storage.

Skill memory also starts at the sensory cortex, but this circuit routes sensory input to a region deeper in the brain that promotes motor responses (Figure 13.23*b*). Motor skills entail muscle conditioning. As you might suspect, the circuit extends to the cerebellum, the brain region that coordinates motor activity.

Amnesia is a loss of fact memory. How severe the loss is depends on whether the hippocampus, amygdala, or both are damaged, as by a head blow. Amnesia does not affect a person's capacity to learn new skills.

STATES OF CONSCIOUSNESS INCLUDE ALERTNESS AND SLEEPING

The spectrum of consciousness ranges from being wide awake and fully alert to drowsiness, sleep, and coma. When you are awake and alert, the neural chattering in your brain shows up as wavelike patterns in an EEG. As mentioned earlier, EEGs are recordings of the summed electrical activity of the brain's neurons. PET scans like the ones in Figure 13.19b (Section 13.8) can show the exact location of brain activity as it takes place.

A network of neurons in the brain called the **reticular formation** (Figure 13.24a) helps govern muscle activity associated with maintaining balance, posture, and muscle tone. It also promotes chemical changes that influence whether you stay awake or fall asleep. Serotonin is a neurotransmitter released from one of the network's sleep centers. It inhibits neurons that arouse the brain and maintain wakefulness. High serotonin levels trigger drowsiness and sleep. When substances released from another brain center inhibit its effects, you wake up.

EEGs from electrodes placed on the scalp show up as wave forms. Figure 13.24b shows the patterns for full alertness and for the two major sleep stages: slow-wave, "normal" sleep and REM (*rapid eye movement*) sleep.

Most of the time you spend sleeping is slow-wave sleep. During this stage, your heart rate, breathing, and muscle tone change very little and you can be easily roused. About every 90 minutes, however, you normally enter a period of REM sleep, in which the eyelids flicker and the eyeballs move rapidly back and forth. Dreaming occurs during REM sleep, and it is much harder to wake up during this time. The heart rate and breathing become more erratic, and muscle tone decreases dramatically.

You probably know from personal experience that people who are deprived of sleep feel tired and cranky and have difficulty concentrating. In fact, researchers still do not know exactly why sleep is so important for us. Although neural activity changes during sleep, the brain clearly is not resting. One hypothesis is that sleep is the time when the brain does essential "housekeeping," such as consolidating memories and solidifying connections involved in learning.

Circuits between the cerebral cortex and parts of the limbic system, thalamus, and hypothalamus produce memories as sensory messages are processed through short-term and long-term storage.

The spectrum of consciousness, which includes sleeping and states of arousal, is influenced by the reticular formation.

Sleep has two stages, slow-wave sleep and REM sleep, in which the brain's activity is altered. Sleep may be important in memory and learning.

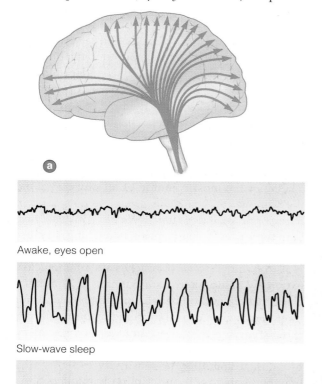

(a)

Awake, eyes open

Slow-wave sleep

(b) REM sleep

Figure 13.24 States of consciousness. (**a**) The communication pathways of the reticular formation. (**b**) EEG patterns for alertness, slow-wave sleep, and REM (rapid eye movement) sleep. The brain waves of the student pictured below would resemble the pattern in (**a**).

13.10 Disorders of the Nervous System

Injuries, viruses, bacteria, even skewed immune responses can seriously damage the nervous system.

In 1817, physician James Parkinson observed troubling symptoms in certain people navigating the streets of London. They walked slowly, taking short, shuffling steps. And their limbs trembled, sometimes violently. Today we know that the culprit is a degenerative brain disorder that now is called **Parkinson's disease**, or PD (Figure 13.25*a*). In PD, neurons in the basal nuclei of the thalamus (Section 13.7) begin to die. Those neurons make neurotransmitters (dopamine and norepinephrine) that are needed for normal muscle function, so PD symptoms include muscle tremors and balance problems, among others. Treatments include drugs that help replace absent neurotransmitters. Surgical treatments are available for advanced cases, but none is a cure.

Like PD, **Alzheimer's disease** involves the progressive degeneration of brain neurons. At the same time, there is an abnormal buildup of amyloid protein, leading to the loss of memory and intellectual functions. Alzheimer's is associated with aging and is considered in more detail in Chapter 17.

Figure 13.25
(**a**) Muhammad Ali during his prime as a champion athlete. After being diagnosed with Parkinson's disease, he established the Muhammad Ali Parkinson's Research Center in Phoenix, Arizona. (**b**) San Francisco 49ers star quarterback Steve Young retired after suffering a series of concussions.

Meningitis is an often fatal disease caused by a bacterial or viral infection. Symptoms include headache, a stiff neck, and vomiting. They develop when the meninges covering the brain and/or spinal cord become inflamed. **Encephalitis** is inflammation of the brain. It is usually caused by a viral infection, such as by HIV or a herpes virus. Like meningitis it can be extremely dangerous; the early symptoms include fever, confusion, and seizures.

In young adults, the most common acquired disease of the nervous system is **multiple sclerosis** (MS). An autoimmune disease that may be triggered by a viral infection in susceptible people, MS involves progressive destruction of myelin sheaths of neurons in the central nervous system. The symptoms, which develop over time, include muscle weakness or stiffness, fatigue, and slurred speech.

A blow to the head or neck can cause a **concussion**. Blurred vision and a brief loss of consciousness result when the blow temporarily upsets the electrical activity of brain neurons (Figure 13.25*b*).

Damage to the spinal cord can lead to lost sensation and muscle weakness or **paralysis** below the site of the injury. Immediate treatment is crucial to limit swelling. Although cord injuries usually have severe consequences, intensive therapy during the first year after an injury can improve the patient's long-term prognosis. Harnessing nerve growth factors or stem cells to repair spinal cord injuries is a major area of medical research.

Brain injury, birth trauma, or other assaults can cause various forms of *epilepsy*, or **seizure disorders**. In some cases the trigger may be an inherited predisposition. Each seizure results when the brain's normal electrical activity suddenly becomes chaotic. Worldwide, many thousands of people develop recurrent seizures either as children or later in life. All but the most intractable cases usually respond well to modern anticonvulsant drugs.

One of the most common of all physical ailments is the pain we call **headache**. There are no sensory nerves in the brain, so it does not "feel pain." Instead, headache pain typically is due to tension (stretching) in muscles or blood vessels of the face, neck, and scalp.

Throbbing *migraine* headaches are infamous for being extremely painful and lasting for up to 72 hours. In the U.S. alone, 28 million people, mainly female, suffer from migraines, which can be triggered by hormonal changes, fluorescent lights, and certain foods (such as chocolate), among other causes. Often, a migraine is accompanied by nausea, vomiting, or sensitivity to light. Migraines may be treated with prescription painkillers and drugs that act as neuromodulators (Section 13.3) to reduce the sensitivity of affected brain neurons to stimuli that trigger the headache in the first place.

13.11 The Brain on Drugs

Psychoactive drugs bind to CNS neuron receptors that normally bind to neurotransmitters. As a result, neurons send or receive altered messages.

DRUGS CAN ALTER MIND AND BODY FUNCTIONS

Psychoactive drugs affect parts of the brain that govern consciousness and behavior. Some also alter heart rate, respiration, sensory processing, and muscle coordination. Many affect a pleasure center in the hypothalamus and artificially fan the sense of pleasure we associate with eating, sex, or other activities.

Stimulants include caffeine, nicotine, cocaine, and amphetamines—including Ecstasy (MDMA). They increase alertness and physical activity at first, then depress you. Nicotine mimics ACh, directly stimulating various sensory receptors. It also increases the heart rate and blood pressure. At first amphetamines cause a flood of the neurotransmitters norepinephrine and dopamine, which stimulate the brain's pleasure center. Over time, however, the brain slows its production of dopamine and norepinephrine and depends more on the amphetamine. Chronic users may become psychotic, depressed, and malnourished. They may also develop heart problems.

Cocaine stimulates the pleasure center by *blocking* the reabsorption of dopamine and other neurotransmitters. It also weakens the cardiovascular and immune systems.

Alcohol alters cell functions. It produces a high at first, then *depresses* brain activity. Drinking only an ounce or two diminishes judgment and can produce disorientation and uncoordinated movements. *Blood alcohol concentration* (BAC) measures the percentage of alcohol in the blood. In most states, someone with a BAC of 0.08 per milliliter is considered legally drunk. When the BAC reaches 0.15 to 0.4, a drinker is visibly intoxicated and can't function normally. A BAC greater than 0.4 can kill.

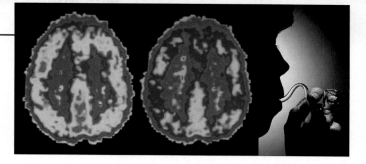

Figure 13.26 Effects of crack cocaine. (**a**) A PET scan of normal brain activity. (**b**) A PET scan showing cocaine's long-term effect. Red areas are most active; yellow, green, and blue indicate the least activity.

Morphine, an *analgesic* (painkiller), is derived from the seed pods of the opium poppy. Like its cousin heroin, it blocks pain signals by binding with certain receptors on neurons in the central nervous system. Both morphine and the synthetic version OxyContin produce euphoria. Thousands of people who obtained OxyContin illegally or by subterfuge have overdosed and died.

Marijuana is a *hallucinogen*. In low doses it is like a depressant. It slows but doesn't impair motor activity, and it elicits a mild euphoria. It can also cause disorientation, anxiety, and hallucinations. Like alcohol, it skews the performance of complex tasks, such as driving a car.

DRUG USE CAN LEAD TO ADDICTION

The body may develop *tolerance* to a drug, meaning that it takes larger or more frequent doses to produce the same effect. Tolerance reflects physical drug dependence. The liver produces enzymes that detoxify drugs in the blood. Tolerance develops when the level of detoxifying liver enzymes increases in response to the ongoing presence of the drug in the bloodstream. In effect, a drug user must increase his or her intake to stay ahead of the liver's growing ability (up to a point) to break down the drug.

In psychological drug dependence, or *habituation*, a user begins to crave the feelings associated with a particular drug. Without a steady supply of it the person can't "feel good" or function normally (Figure 13.26). Table 13.2 lists warning signs of potentially serious drug dependence. Habituation and tolerance both are evidence of addiction.

When different psychoactive drugs are used together, they can interact dangerously. For example, alcohol and barbiturates (such as Seconal and Nembutal) both depress the central nervous system. Used at the same time, they can lethally depress respiratory centers in the brain.

Table 13.2   Warning Signs of Drug Addiction*
1. Tolerance—it takes increasing amounts of the drug to produce the same effect.
2. Habituation—it takes continued drug use over time to maintain self-perception of functioning normally.
3. Inability to stop or curtail use of the drug, even if there is persistent desire to do so.
4. Concealment—not wanting others to know of the drug use.
5. Extreme or dangerous behavior to get and use a drug, as by stealing, asking more than one doctor for prescriptions, or jeopardizing employment by drug use at work.
6. Deteriorating professional and personal relationships.
7. Anger and defensive behavior when someone suggests there may be a problem.
8. Preferring drug use over previously customary activities.

*Having three or more of these signs may be cause for concern.

Psychoactive drugs alter consciousness and behavior. Some also affect physiological events, such as heart rate, respiration, sensory processing, and muscle coordination in harmful, even dangerous, ways.

Summary

Section 13.1 The nervous system detects, interprets, and responds directly to sensory stimuli. Sensory neurons collect information when they respond to external or internal stimuli. Interneurons receive sensory signals, integrate them with other input, and then send signals that influence other neurons. Motor neurons relay messages away from the brain and spinal cord to muscles or glands. Neuroglia provide various kinds of support for neurons.

Extensions of a neuron's cytoplasm form axons and dendrites. Axons carry outgoing signals, and dendrites receive them.

An unstimulated neuron shows a steady voltage difference across its plasma membrane. This difference is called the resting membrane potential. A resting neuron maintains concentration gradients of potassium ions, sodium ions, and other ions across the membrane.

Thomson NOW! *Review the structure and properties of neurons.*

Section 13.2 When the voltage difference across the membrane exceeds a threshold level, gated sodium channels in the membrane open and close rapidly and suddenly reverse the voltage difference. This reversal is a nerve impulse, or action potential. A sodium–potassium pump restores ion gradients after an action potential. Action potentials self-propagate away from the point of stimulation.

Thomson NOW! *View an action potential step by step.*

Section 13.3 Action potentials self-propagate along the neuron membrane until they reach a chemical synapse with another neuron or with a muscle or gland cell. The presynaptic cell releases a neurotransmitter into the synapse. The neurotransmitter excites or inhibits the receiving (postsynaptic) cell. Synaptic integration sums up the various signals acting on a neuron. Neuromodulators boost or reduce the effects of neurotransmitters.

Thomson NOW! *See what happens at a synapse between a motor neuron and a muscle cell.*

Section 13.4 Nerves consist of the long axons of motor neurons, sensory neurons, or both. A myelin sheath formed by Schwann cells insulates each axon, so that action potentials propagate along it much more rapidly. Nerve pathways extend from neurons in one body region to neurons or effectors in different regions.

A reflex is a simple, stereotyped movement. Reflex arcs, in which sensory neurons directly signal motor neurons that act on muscle cells, are the simplest nerve pathways. In more complex reflexes, interneurons coordinate and refine the responses.

Thomson NOW! *Observe what happens during a stretch reflex.*

Section 13.5 The central nervous system consists of the brain and spinal cord. The peripheral nervous system consists of nerves and ganglia in other body regions.

Section 13.6 The peripheral nervous system's somatic nerves deal with skeletal muscles involved in voluntary body movements and sensations arising from skin, muscles, and joints. Its autonomic nerves deal with the functions of internal organs.

Table 13.3 Summary of the Central Nervous System*

FOREBRAIN	Cerebrum	Localizes, processes sensory inputs; initiates, controls skeletal muscle activity. Governs memory, emotions, abstract thought
	Olfactory lobe	Relays sensory input from nose to olfactory centers of cerebrum
	Thalamus	Has relay stations for conducting sensory signals to and from cerebral cortex; has role in memory
	Hypothalamus	With pituitary gland, a homeostatic control center; adjusts volume, composition, temperature of internal environment. Governs organ-related behaviors (e.g., sex, thirst, hunger) and expression of emotions
	Limbic system	Governs emotions; has roles in memory
	Pituitary gland	With hypothalamus, provides endocrine control of metabolism, growth, development
	Pineal gland	Helps control some circadian rhythms; also has role in reproductive physiology
MIDBRAIN	Roof of midbrain (tectum)	In humans and other mammals, its reflex centers relay sensory input to the forebrain
HINDBRAIN	Pons	Tracts bridge cerebrum and cerebellum; other tracts connect spinal cord with forebrain. With the medulla oblongata, controls rate and depth of respiration
	Cerebellum	Coordinates motor activity for moving limbs and maintaining posture, and for spatial orientation
	Medulla oblongata	Its tracts relay signals between spinal cord and pons; its reflex centers help control heart rate, adjustments in blood vessel diameter, respiratory rate, vomiting, coughing, other vital functions
SPINAL CORD		Makes reflex connections for limb movements. Its tracts connect brain, peripheral nervous system

*The reticular formation extends from the spinal cord to the cerebral cortex.

Autonomic nerves are subdivided into sympathetic and parasympathetic groups. Parasympathetic nerves govern basic tasks such as digestion and tend to slow the pace of other body functions. In situations that demand increased awareness (excitement, danger), sympathetic nerves dominate. Their signals produce the fight–flight response, a state of intense arousal.

Spinal cord nerve tracts carry signals between the brain and the PNS. The cord also is a center for many reflexes.

 Explore the structure of the spinal cord and compare sympathetic and parasympathetic responses.

Section 13.7   The brain is divided into two cerebral hemispheres and has three main divisions (Table 13.3). It and the spinal cord are protected by bones (skull and vertebrae) and by the three meninges. Both are cushioned by cerebrospinal fluid. Specialized capillaries create a blood–brain barrier that prevents some blood-borne substances from reaching brain neurons.

The hindbrain includes the medulla oblongata, pons, and cerebellum. It contains reflex centers for vital functions and muscle coordination.

Midbrain centers coordinate and relay visual and auditory information. The midbrain, medulla oblongata, and pons make up the brain stem.

In the forebrain the thalamus relays sensory information and helps coordinate motor responses. The hypothalamus monitors internal organs and influences behaviors related to their functions (such as thirst). The limbic system has roles in learning, memory, and emotional behavior.

Section 13.8   The cerebral cortex is devoted to receiving and integrating information from sense organs and coordinating motor responses in muscles and glands.

 Review the structure and function of the brain.

Section 13.9   Memory occurs in short-term and long-term stages. Long-term storage depends on chemical or structural changes in the brain. States of consciousness vary between total alertness and deep coma. The levels are governed by the brain's reticular activating system.

Section 13.11   Psychoactive drugs cause brain neurons to send or receive altered signals and can change mental and physical functioning. Drug use can lead to physical tolerance and/or psychological dependence—both of which are elements of addiction.

Review Questions

1. Define sensory neuron, interneuron, and motor neuron.
2. What are the functional zones of a motor neuron?
3. Define an action potential.
4. What is a synapse? Explain the difference between an excitatory and an inhibitory synapse.
5. Explain what happens during synaptic integration.
6. What is a reflex? Describe the events of a stretch reflex.
7. Distinguish between the following:
   a. neurons and nerves
   b. somatic system and autonomic system
   c. parasympathetic and sympathetic nerves

Self-Quiz

Answers in Appendix V

1. The nervous system senses, interprets, and issues commands for responses to _____.
2. A neuron responds to adequate stimulation with _____, a type of self-propagating signal.
3. When action potentials arrive at a synapse between a neuron and another cell, they stimulate the release of molecules of a _____ that diffuse over to that cell.
4. In the simplest kind of reflex, _____ directly signal _____, which act on muscle cells.
   a. sensory neurons; interneurons
   b. interneurons; motor neurons
   c. sensory neurons; motor neurons
   d. motor neurons; sensory neurons
5. The accelerating flow of _____ ions through gated channels across the membrane triggers an action potential.
   a. potassium
   b. sodium
   c. hydrogen
   d. a and b are correct
6. _____ nerves slow down the body overall and divert energy to housekeeping tasks; _____ nerves slow down housekeeping tasks and increase overall activity during times of heightened awareness, excitement, or danger.
   a. Autonomic; somatic
   b. Sympathetic; parasympathetic
   c. Parasympathetic; sympathetic
7. Match each of the following central nervous system regions with some of its functions.
   ____ spinal cord
   ____ medulla oblongata
   ____ hypothalamus
   ____ limbic system
   ____ cerebral cortex

   a. receives sensory input, integrates it with stored information, coordinates motor responses
   b. monitors internal organs and related behavior (e.g., hunger)
   c. governs emotions
   d. coordinates reflexes
   e. makes reflex connections for limb movements, internal organ activity

Critical Thinking

1. In some cases of ADD (attention deficit disorder) the impulsive, erratic behavior can be normalized with drugs that *stimulate* the central nervous system. Explain this finding in terms of neurotransmitter activity in the brain.

2. Meningitis is an inflammation of the membranes that cover the brain and spinal cord. Diagnosis involves making a "spinal tap" (lumbar puncture) and analyzing a sample of cerebrospinal fluid for signs of infection. Why analyze this fluid and not blood?

3. In newborns and premature babies, the blood–brain barrier is not fully developed. Explain why this might be reason enough to pay careful attention to their diet.

4. At one time people deeply feared contracting the disease called *tetanus* (caused by the bacterium *Clostridium tetani*) because it usually meant an agonizing death. The bacterial toxin blocks the release of neurotransmitters that help control motor neurons. The result is continuous contraction of skeletal muscles and, eventually, the heart muscle also. Victims are aware of their plight, for the brain is not affected. What neurons does the toxin affect?

5. Research now demonstrates that new neurons can form in the adult brain, although slowly. Based on your reading in this chapter, name some diseases for which the ability to grow new brain neurons might be helpful.

Explore on Your Own

The "knee jerk" patellar reflex diagrammed in Figure 13.27 is a familiar example of a reflex arc. A doctor will often use a small rubber-tipped instrument to test for this reflex, but you can easily trigger it yourself just by tapping the base of one of your kneecaps (the patella) with a knuckle. The reflex occurs when stretch receptors in a tendon attached to the patella are activated, leading to a contraction of the quadriceps femoris, the extensor muscle of the knee.

Try tapping the base of one of your kneecaps (not too forcefully) and see if you can elicit the patellar reflex. Then write a short paragraph describing the path of the reflex arc, including the location and kind of neurons that integrated the sensory information and ordered a muscle response.

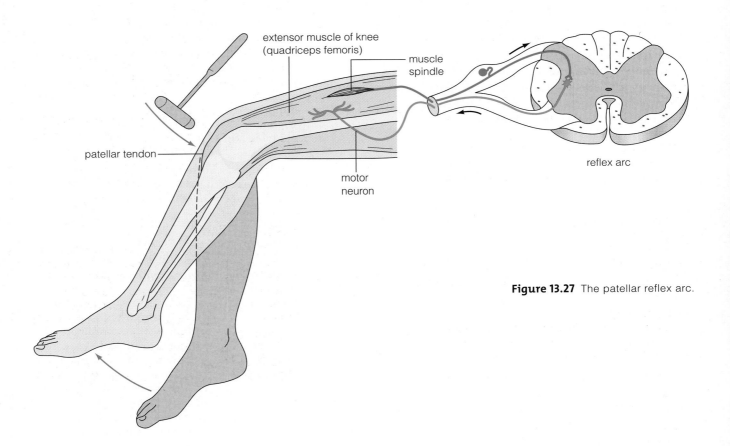

Figure 13.27 The patellar reflex arc.

IMPACTS, ISSUES

Private Eyes

Terrorist threats. Identity theft. Today the promise of "foolproof" security seems too good to be true. Yet something close to it is already in place at some airports, high-security chemical plants and office buildings, and even hospitals. You may have heard of this security breakthrough. It's iris scanning.

Iris scanning technology relies on the unique, spokelike arrangement of smooth muscle fibers in the iris of the eye, the surface region of the eyes colored brown or blue or some other hue. Like fingerprints, each person's iris pattern is different from that of every other human on Earth.

For iris scanning to be a reliable identity check, each person's iris pattern must first be recorded digitally and entered into an electronic database. A person who later wants to gain entry to a secure location—or maybe just withdraw money from an ATM—looks into a scanning device that can instantly compare their eyes' iris pattern with the patterns in the stored database. Advocates and manufacturers of iris scanners say that the technology is 99 percent foolproof.

All over the world, millions of people regularly pass through airports and

immigration checkpoints. They withdraw money from ATMs, visit offices, and check into and out of hospitals. Where would the "iris databases" come from? There are lots of possibilities. Travelers might be required to provide an "iris print" when applying for a passport or visa, or even when buying a ticket for travel. Your bank could conceivably iris-print you when you open an account. Employers could require potential employees to allow an iris print as part of the job application process. Already, a few hospitals in Europe make iris prints of newborns to prevent "baby switches" when new parents take infants home.

Our eyes are part of the powerful sensory system we call vision. In this chapter we consider vision and other sensory means by which the brain receives signals from the external and internal world. The signals are decoded in ways that give rise to awareness of sounds, sights, odors, and other sensations—including those that enable us to feel physical pain and to maintain our balance.

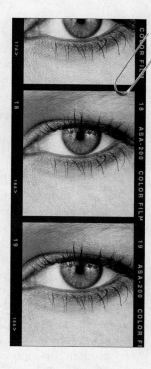

 How Would You Vote? *Do you favor laws that allow employers and others to collect the information required for iris scanning—and to be protected from liability if the scans were misused? Cast your vote online at www.thomsonedu.com/biology/starr/humanbio.*

 ## Key Concepts

SENSORY RECEPTORS
There are six main categories of sensory receptors, each based on the type of stimulus—such as light, sound, chemicals, or pressure—that the receptor detects.

SENSORY SYSTEMS
Sensory systems receive information about the external and internal world and convey it to the central nervous system. Processing in the CNS leads to vision, hearing, taste, smell, and other senses.

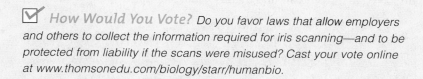 ## Links to Earlier Concepts

Senses sometimes are called "outposts of the brain" because they are the brain's sources of information about events going on inside and outside the body. Accordingly, this chapter builds directly on the discussion of the nervous system in Chapter 13. You will draw on what you have learned about action potentials, neurotransmitters, synapses between neurons and other cells, and nerves (13.2, 13.3, 13.4). You will also learn more about how the brain processes sensory input of all kinds (13.8).

14.1 Sensory Receptors and Pathways

LINKS TO
SECTIONS
13.2, 13.4,
AND 13.8

Sensory systems are the front doors of the nervous system. They notify the brain and spinal cord of specific changes inside and outside the body.

In a **sensory system**, energy from a stimulus activates receptors, which transduce it—that is, convert it—to a form that travels to the brain and may trigger a sensation or perception:

| stimulus energy received | → | stimulus energy converted to action potential | → | brain response (sensation or perception) |

A **stimulus** (plural: stimuli) is a form of energy that activates receptor endings of a sensory neuron. That energy is converted to the electrochemical energy of action potentials—the nerve impulses by which the brain receives information and sends out commands in response. The brain's responses are *sensations*—conscious awareness of a stimulus. By contrast, a *perception* is an understanding of what the sensation means.

Table 14.1 lists the six major categories of sensory receptors, based on the type of stimulus energy that each kind of receptor detects. **Mechanoreceptors** detect forms of mechanical energy: changes in pressure, position, or acceleration. **Thermoreceptors** are sensitive to heat or cold. **Nociceptors** (pain receptors) detect damage to tissues. **Chemoreceptors** detect chemical energy of substances dissolved in the fluid around them. **Osmoreceptors** detect

a

changes in water volume (solute concentration) in some body fluid. **Photoreceptors** detect visible light.

Regardless of their differences, all sensory receptors convert the stimulus energy to action potentials.

Action potentials that move along sensory neurons are all the same. So how does the brain determine the nature of a given stimulus? It assesses *which* nerves are carrying action potentials, the *frequency* of the action potentials on each axon in the nerve, and the *number* of axons that responded.

First, specific sensory areas of the brain can interpret action potentials only in certain ways. That is why you

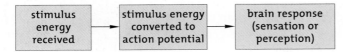

Table 14.1   Major Categories of Sensory Receptors

Category	Examples	Stimulus
MECHANORECEPTORS		
Touch, pressure	Certain free nerve endings and Merkel discs in skin	Mechanical pressure against body surface
Baroreceptors	Carotid sinus (artery)	Pressure changes in fluid (blood) that bathes them
Stretch	Muscle spindle in skeletal muscle	Stretching of muscle
Auditory	Hair cells in organ inside ear	Vibrations (sound waves)
Balance	Hair cells in organ inside ear	Fluid movement
THERMORECEPTORS	Certain free nerve endings	Change in temperature (heating, cooling)
NOCICEPTORS (PAIN RECEPTORS)*	Certain free nerve endings	Tissue damage (e.g., distortions, burns)
CHEMORECEPTORS		
Internal chemical sense	Carotid bodies in blood vessel wall	Substances (O_2, CO_2, etc.) dissolved in extracellular fluid
Taste	Taste receptors of tongue	Substances dissolved in saliva, etc.
Smell	Olfactory receptors of nose	Odors in air, water
OSMORECEPTORS	Hypothalamic osmoreceptors	Change in water volume (solute concentration) of fluid that bathes them
PHOTORECEPTORS		
Visual	Rods, cones of eye	Wavelengths of light

*Extremely intense stimulation of any sensory receptor also may be perceived as pain.

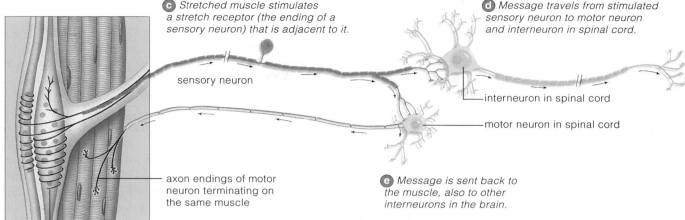

ⓒ Stretched muscle stimulates a stretch receptor (the ending of a sensory neuron) that is adjacent to it.

sensory neuron

ⓓ Message travels from stimulated sensory neuron to motor neuron and interneuron in spinal cord.

interneuron in spinal cord

motor neuron in spinal cord

axon endings of motor neuron terminating on the same muscle

ⓔ Message is sent back to the muscle, also to other interneurons in the brain.

ⓑ muscle spindle

Figure 14.2 Example of a sensory pathway—in this case, from receptors called muscle spindles to the spinal cord and brain.

"see stars" when your eye is poked, even in the dark. The mechanical pressure on photoreceptors in the eye generates signals that the associated optic nerve carries to the brain, which always interprets signals from an optic nerve as "light." As described in Section 14.2, the brain has what amounts to a detailed map of the sources of different sensory stimuli.

Second, a strong signal makes receptors fire action potentials more often and longer. The same receptor can detect the sounds of a whisper and a screech. The brain senses the difference through frequency variations in the signals that the receptor sends to it.

Third, a stronger stimulus can recruit more sensory receptors than a weaker stimulus can. Gently tap a spot of skin on your arm and you activate only a few receptors. Press hard on the same spot and you activate more. The increase translates into action potentials in many sensory neurons at once. Your brain interprets the combined activity as an increase in the intensity of the stimulus. Figure 14.1 charts an example of this effect.

In some cases the frequency of action potentials slows or stops even when the stimulus continues at constant strength. For instance, after you put on a T-shirt, you quickly become only dimly aware of its pressure against your skin. This diminishing response to an ongoing stimulus is called **sensory adaptation**.

Some mechanoreceptors adapt rapidly to a sustained stimulus and only signal when it starts and stops. Other receptors adapt slowly or not at all; they help the brain monitor particular stimuli all the time.

The gymnast in Figure 14.2a is holding his position in response to signals from his skin, skeletal muscles, joints, tendons, and ligaments. For example, how fast and how far a muscle stretches depends on activation of stretch receptors in muscle spindles (Section 13.4). By responding to changes in the length of muscles, his brain helps him maintain his balance and posture.

In the rest of this chapter we explore examples of the body's sensory receptors. Receptors that are found at more than one location in the body contribute to somatic ("of the body") sensations. Other receptors are restricted to sense organs, such as the eyes or ears, and contribute to what are called the "special senses."

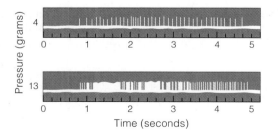

Figure 14.1 *Animated!* Action potentials recorded from a single pressure receptor of the human hand. The recordings correspond to variations in stimulus strength. A thin rod was pressed against the skin with the pressure indicated on the vertical axis of this diagram. Vertical bars above each thick horizontal line represent individual action potentials. The increases in frequency correspond to increases in the strength of the stimulus.

A sensory system has sensory receptors for specific stimuli, nerve pathways that conduct information from receptors to the brain, and brain regions that receive and process the information.

The brain senses a stimulus based on which nerves carry the incoming signals, the frequency of action potentials traveling along each axon, and the number of axons that have been recruited.

14.2 Somatic Sensations

LINKS TO SECTIONS 4.8, 10.3, AND 13.8

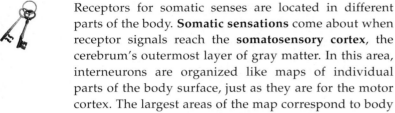

Somatic sensations start with receptors in body surface tissues, skeletal muscles, and the walls of internal organs.

Receptors for somatic senses are located in different parts of the body. **Somatic sensations** come about when receptor signals reach the **somatosensory cortex**, the cerebrum's outermost layer of gray matter. In this area, interneurons are organized like maps of individual parts of the body surface, just as they are for the motor cortex. The largest areas of the map correspond to body parts where there is the greatest density of sensory receptors. These body parts, including the fingers, thumbs, and lips, have the sharpest sensory acuity and require the most intricate control (Figure 14.3).

RECEPTORS NEAR THE BODY SURFACE SENSE TOUCH, PRESSURE, AND MORE

There are thousands of sensory receptors in your skin, providing information about touch, pressure, cold, warmth, and pain (Figure 14.4). Logically enough, places with the most sensory receptors, such as the fingertips and the tip of the tongue, are the most sensitive to stimulation. Less sensitive areas, such as the back of the hand, don't have nearly as many receptors.

Several types of **free nerve endings** in the epidermis and many connective tissues detect touch, pressure, heat, cold, or pain. These nerve endings are simple structures.

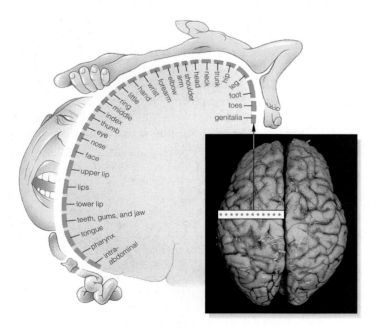

Figure 14.3 *Animated!* The somatosensory cortex "map" of body parts. This strip of cerebral cortex is a little wider than 2.5 centimeters (an inch), from the top of the head to just above the ear.

Basically, they are thinly myelinated or unmyelinated ("naked") dendrites of sensory neurons. One type coils around hair follicles and detects the movement of the hair inside. That might be how, for instance, you become aware that a spider is gingerly making its way across your arm. Free nerve endings sensitive to chemicals such as histamine may be responsible for the sensation of itching.

Encapsulated receptors are more complex. They are enclosed in a capsule of epithelial or connective tissue and are named for the biologist who discovered them. One type, Merkel's discs, adapt slowly and are the most important receptors for steady touch. In lips, fingertips, eyelids, nipples, and genitals there are many Meissner's corpuscles, which are sensitive to light touching. Deep in the dermis and in joint capsules are Ruffini endings, which respond to steady touching and pressure.

The Pacinian corpuscles widely scattered in the skin's dermis are sensitive to deep pressure and vibrations. They also are located near freely movable joints (like shoulder and hip joints) and in some internal organs. Onionlike layers of membrane alternating with fluid-filled spaces enclose this sensory receptor's ending. This arrangement enhances the receptor's ability to detect rapid pressure changes associated with vibrations.

Sensing limb motions and changes in body position relies on mechanoreceptors in skin, skeletal muscles, joints, tendons, and ligaments. Examples include the stretch receptors of muscle spindles described in Section 14.1.

PAIN IS THE PERCEPTION OF BODILY INJURY

Pain is perceived injury to some body region. The most important pain receptors are free nerve endings called *nociceptors* (from the Latin word *nocere*, "to do harm"). Several million of them are distributed throughout the skin and in internal tissues, except for the brain.

Somatic pain starts with nociceptors in skin, skeletal muscles, joints, and tendons. One group is the source of prickling pain, like the jab of a pin when you stick your finger. Another contributes to itching or the feeling of warmth caused by chemicals such as histamine. Sensations of *visceral pain*, which is associated with internal organs, are related to muscle spasms, muscle fatigue, too little blood flow to organs, and other abnormal conditions.

When cells are damaged, they release chemicals that activate neighboring pain receptors. The most potent are bradykinins. They open the floodgates for histamine, prostaglandins, and other substances associated with inflammation (Section 10.3).

When signals from pain receptors reach interneurons in the spinal cord, the interneurons release a chemical

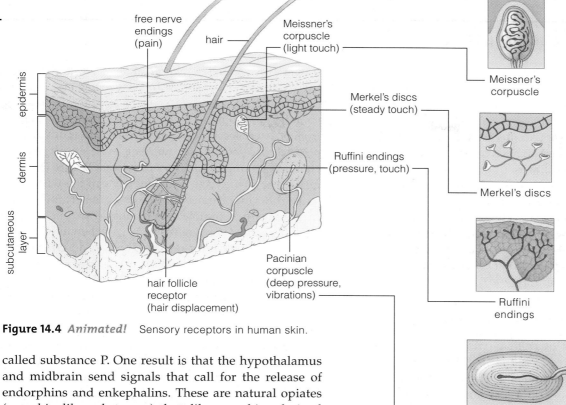

Figure 14.4 *Animated!* Sensory receptors in human skin.

called substance P. One result is that the hypothalamus and midbrain send signals that call for the release of endorphins and enkephalins. These are natural opiates (morphinelike substances) that, like morphine derived from opium poppies, reduce our ability to perceive pain. Morphine, hypnosis, and natural childbirth techniques may also stimulate the release of these natural opiates.

REFERRED PAIN IS A MATTER OF PERCEPTION

A person's perception of pain often depends on the brain's ability to identify the affected tissue. Get hit in the face with a snowball and you "feel" the contact on facial skin. However, sensations of pain from some internal organs may be wrongly projected to part of the skin surface. This response, called *referred pain*, is related to the way the nervous system is built. Sensory information from the skin and from certain internal organs may enter the spinal cord along the same nerve pathways, so the brain can't accurately identify their source. For example, as shown in Figure 14.5, a heart attack can be felt as pain in skin above the heart and along the left shoulder and arm.

Referred pain is not the same as the *phantom pain* reported by amputees. Often they sense the presence of a missing body part, as if it were still there. In some undetermined way, sensory nerves that were severed during the amputation continue to respond to the trauma. The brain projects the pain back to the missing part, past the healed region.

Various kinds of free nerve endings and encapsulated receptors detect touch, pressure, heat and cold, pain, limb motions, and changes in body position.

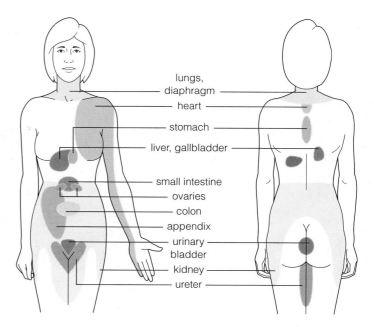

Figure 14.5 *Animated!* Referred pain. When receptors in some internal organs detect painful stimuli, the brain projects the sensation to certain skin areas instead of localizing the pain at the organs.

14.3 Taste and Smell: Chemical Senses

LINKS TO
SECTIONS
5.3, 13.7,
AND 13.8

Some of life's simple pleasures—a delicious meal, the perfume of a rose—are available to us through the chemical "magic" of two special senses, taste and smell.

Taste and smell are *chemical* senses. They begin at chemoreceptors, which are activated when they bind a chemical substance that is dissolved in fluid around them. Although these receptors wear out, new ones replace them. In both cases, sensory information travels from the receptors through the thalamus and on to the cerebral cortex, where perceptions of the stimulus take shape and are fine-tuned. The input also travels to the limbic system, which can integrate it with emotional states and stored memories.

GUSTATION IS THE SENSE OF TASTE

The technical term for taste is *gustation* (as in gusto!). Sensory organs called taste buds hold our **taste receptors** (Figure 14.6). You have about 10,000 taste buds scattered over your tongue, the roof of your mouth (the palate), and your throat.

A taste bud has a pore through which fluids in the mouth (including, of course, saliva) contact the surface of receptor cells. The stimulated receptor in turn stimulates a sensory neuron, which conveys the message to centers in the brain where the stimulus is interpreted. Every perceived taste is some combination of five primary tastes: sweet, sour, salty, bitter, and *umami* (the brothy or savory taste we associate with aged cheese and meats).

Strictly speaking, the flavors of most foods are some combination of the five basic tastes, plus sensory input from olfactory receptors in the nose. Simple as this sounds, research has shown that our taste sense encompasses a complex set of molecular mechanisms. *Science Comes to Life* on the facing page examines some of these findings.

The olfactory element of taste is extremely important. In addition to odor molecules in inhaled air, molecules of volatile chemicals are released as you chew food. These waft up into the nasal passages. There, as described next, the "smell" inputs contribute to the perception of a smorgasbord of complex flavors. This is why anything that dulls your sense of smell—such as a head cold—also seems to diminish food's flavor.

OLFACTION IS THE SENSE OF SMELL

Olfactory receptors (Figure 14.7) detect water-soluble or volatile (easily vaporized) substances. We now know that when odor molecules bind to receptors on olfactory neurons in cells of the nose's olfactory epithelium, the resulting action potential travels directly to olfactory bulbs in the frontal area of the brain. There, other neurons forward the message to a center in the cerebral cortex, which interprets it as "fresh bread," "pine tree," or some other substance.

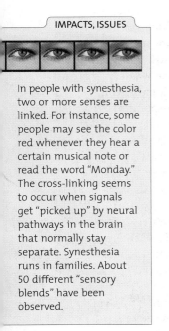

IMPACTS, ISSUES

In people with synesthesia, two or more senses are linked. For instance, some people may see the color red whenever they hear a certain musical note or read the word "Monday." The cross-linking seems to occur when signals get "picked up" by neural pathways in the brain that normally stay separate. Synesthesia runs in families. About 50 different "sensory blends" have been observed.

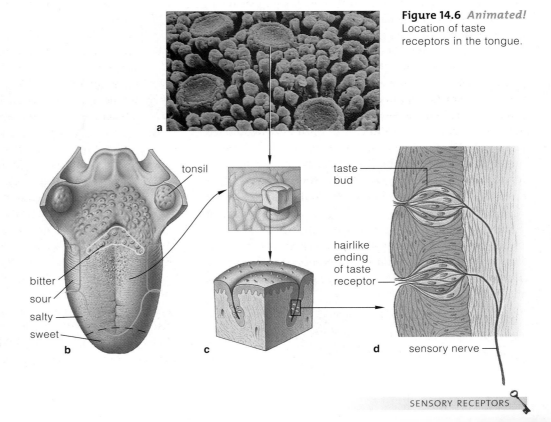

Figure 14.6 *Animated!* Location of taste receptors in the tongue.

tonsil

taste bud

hairlike ending of taste receptor

bitter
sour
salty
sweet

sensory nerve

a

b

c

d

SENSORY RECEPTORS

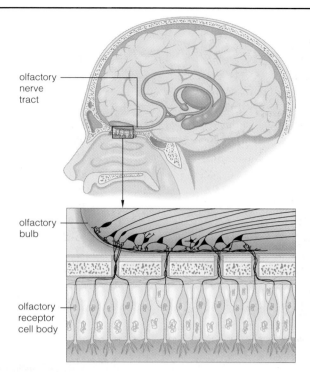

olfactory
nerve
tract

olfactory
bulb

olfactory
receptor
cell body

Figure 14.7 *Animated!* Sensory pathway leading from olfactory receptors in the nose to primary receiving centers in the brain.

From an evolutionary perspective, olfaction is an ancient sense—and for good reason. Food, potential mates, and predators give off substances that can diffuse through air (or water) and so give clues or warnings of their whereabouts. Even with our rather insensitive sense of smell, we humans have about 10 million olfactory receptors in patches of olfactory epithelium in the upper nasal passages. (A bloodhound has more than 200 million.)

Just inside your nose, next to the vomer bone (Section 5.3), is a *vomeronasal organ*, or "sexual nose." (Some other mammals also have one.) Its receptors detect pheromones, which are signaling chemicals with roles in social interactions of many animal species. Pheromones can affect the behavior—and maybe the physiology—of other individuals. For instance, one or more pheromones in the sweat of females may account for the common observation that women of reproductive age who are in regular, close contact with one another often come to have their menstrual periods on a similar schedule.

Taste depends on receptors in sensory organs called taste buds in the tongue. The receptors bind molecules dissolved in fluid. Sensory neurons then relay the message to the brain. The five primary tastes are sweet, sour, salty, bitter, and umami.

Olfaction (smell) relies on receptors in patches of epithelium in the upper nasal passages. Neural signals along olfactory neurons travel directly to the olfactory bulbs in the brain.

14.4 A Tasty Morsel of Sensory Science

Taste buds make eating not only a means of securing nutrients, but also one of life's pleasures. In ways that have been poorly understood until recently, the sensory receptors in taste buds distinguish the five main taste categories you've just read about.

Each category is associated with particular "tastant" molecules. When you eat food, however, which taste category (or combination of them) you ultimately perceive depends on the chemical nature of the signal and on how it is processed by the receptor. In each case, some event causes the receptor cell to release a neurotransmitter that triggers action potentials in a nearby sensory neuron.

For example, when you taste "salt," the receptor cell's response is due to the influx of Na^+ through sodium ion channels in its plasma membrane. When tastant molecules are acidic—that is, they release hydrogen ions that block membrane potassium ion channels—a receptor responds with a "sour" message. Cells that detect bitter substances may have receptors sensitive to as many as 100 different trigger tastants. Many toxic chemicals (including plant alkaloids such as nicotine and morphine) taste bitter, an adaptation that may help protect us from ingesting dangerous substances. Familiar bitter-tasting alkaloids are caffeine and quinine, the mouth-puckering tastant in tonic water. And while many "sweet" tastants are sugars, others are amino acids or alcohols. Both bitter and sweet tastes are detected by specific proteins inside the receptor. The taste category called *umami* also is triggered by amino acids, notably glutamate. Its name was bestowed by the Japanese researcher who identified it.

Each taste bud has receptors that can respond to tastants in at least two—and in some cases all five—of the taste classes. Various tastants commingle (together with odors) into our perceptions of countless flavors.

Not all taste receptors are equally sensitive. "Bitter" ones tend to be extremely sensitive and so can detect tiny amounts of bitter tastants—and thus potential poisons. Sour tastants are needed in higher concentrations before the stimulus registers. Even higher levels of sweet and salty substances must be present for the stimulus to register. So why can relatively small amounts of artificial sweeteners so readily sweeten foods? Their molecular characteristics make them 150 times (aspartame) to more than 600 times (saccharin) as potent as plain sucrose.

14.5 Hearing: Detecting Sound Waves

The sense of hearing depends on structures in the ear that trap and process sounds traveling through air.

Sounds are waves of compressed air. They are a form of mechanical energy. If you clap your hands, you force out air molecules, creating a low-pressure state in the area they vacated. The pressure variations can be depicted as a wave form, and the *amplitude* of its peaks corresponds to loudness. The *frequency* of a sound is the number of wave cycles per second. Each cycle extends from the start of one wave to the start of the next (Figure 14.8).

The sense of hearing starts with vibration-sensitive mechanoreceptors deep in the ear. When sound waves travel down the ear's auditory canal, they reach a membrane and make it vibrate. The vibrations cause a fluid inside the ear to move, the way water in a waterbed sloshes. In your ear, the moving fluid bends the tips of hairs on mechanoreceptors. With enough bending, the end result will be action potentials sent to the brain, where they are interpreted as sound.

THE EAR GATHERS AND SENDS "SOUND SIGNALS" TO THE BRAIN

Each of your ears consists of three regions (Figure 14.9*a*), each with its own role in hearing. The *outer ear* provides a pathway for sound waves to enter the ear, setting up vibrations. The vibrations are amplified in the *middle ear*. In the *inner ear*, vibrations of different sound frequencies are "sorted out" as they stimulate different patches of receptors. Inner ear structures include *semicircular canals*, which are involved in balance—the topic of Section 14.6. It also contains the coiled **cochlea** (KAHK-lee-uh), where key events in hearing take place. As you'll now read, a coordinated sequence of events in the ear's various regions provides the brain with the auditory input it can interpret to give us a hearing sense.

SENSORY HAIR CELLS ARE THE KEY TO HEARING

Hearing begins when the outer ear's fleshy flaps collect and channel sound waves through the auditory canal to the **tympanic membrane** (the eardrum). Sound waves

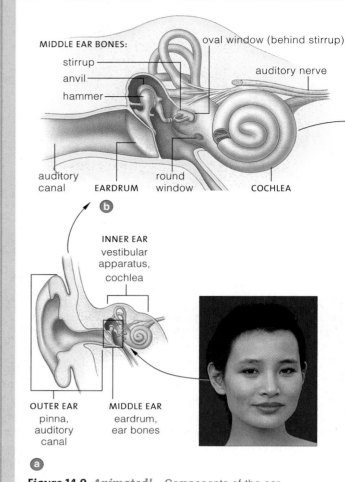

Figure 14.9 *Animated!* Components of the ear.

cause the membrane to vibrate, which in turn causes vibrations in a leverlike array of three tiny bones of the middle ear: the *malleus* ("hammer"), *incus* ("anvil"), and stirrup-shaped *stapes*. The vibrating bones transmit their motion to the *oval window*, an elastic membrane over the entrance to the cochlea. The oval window is much smaller than the tympanic membrane. So, as the middle-ear bones vibrate against its small surface with the full energy that struck the tympanic membrane, the force of the original vibrations is amplified.

Now the action shifts to the cochlea. If we could uncoil the cochlea, we would see that a fluid-filled chamber folds around an inner *cochlear duct* (Figure 14.9*c*). Each "arm" of the outer chamber functions as a separate compartment (the *scala vestibuli* and *scala tympani*, respectively). The amplified vibrations of the oval window create pressure waves in the fluid within the chambers. In turn, these waves are transmitted to the fluid in the cochlear duct. On the floor of the cochlear duct is a *basilar membrane*,

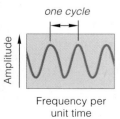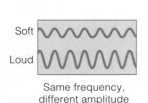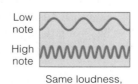

Figure 14.8 *Animated!* Wavelike properties of sound.

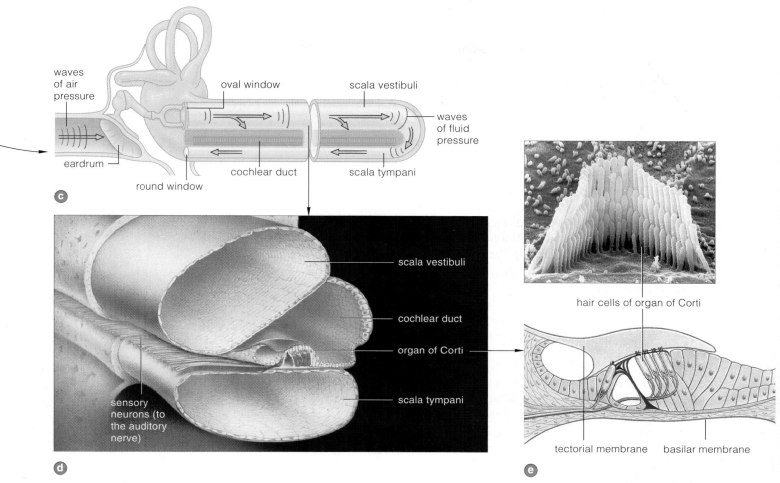

waves of air pressure

oval window

scala vestibuli

waves of fluid pressure

eardrum

cochlear duct

scala tympani

round window

c

scala vestibuli

cochlear duct

organ of Corti

scala tympani

sensory neurons (to the auditory nerve)

d

hair cells of organ of Corti

tectorial membrane

basilar membrane

e

and resting on the basilar membrane is a specialized **organ of Corti**, which includes sensory **hair cells**.

Slender projections at the cell tips rest against an overhanging **tectorial** ("rooflike") **membrane**, which is not a membrane at all but a jellylike structure. When pressure waves in the cochlear fluid vibrate the basilar membrane, its movements can press hair cell projections against the tectorial membrane so that the projections bend like brush bristles. Affected hair cells release a neurotransmitter, triggering action potentials in neurons of the auditory nerve, which carries them to the brain.

Different sound frequencies cause different parts of the basilar membrane to vibrate—and, accordingly, to bend different groups of hair cells. Apparently, the total number of hair cells stimulated in a given region determines the loudness of a sound. The perceived tone or "pitch" of a sound depends on the frequency of the vibrations that excite different groups of hair cells. The higher the frequency, the higher the pitch.

Eventually, pressure waves en route through the cochlea push against the *round window*, a membrane at the far end of the cochlea. As the round window bulges outward toward the air-filled middle ear, it serves as a "release valve" for the force of the waves. Air also moves through an opening in the middle ear into the *eustachian tube*. This tube runs from the middle ear to the throat (pharynx), permitting air pressure in the middle ear to be equalized with the pressure of outside air. When you change altitude (say, during a plane trip), this equalizing process makes your ears "pop."

Sounds such as amplified music and the thundering of jet engines are so intense that long-term exposure to them can permanently damage the inner ear (Section 14.7). Sounds produced by these modern technologies exceed the functional range of the evolutionary ancient hair cells in the ear.

Hearing relies on mechanoreceptors called hair cells, which are attached to membranes inside the cochlea of the inner ear. Pressure waves generated by sound cause membrane vibrations that bend hair cells. The bending produces action potentials in neurons of the auditory nerve.

14.6 Balance: Sensing the Body's Natural Position

Like most other animals, we humans apparently have a sense of the "natural" position for the body (and its parts), given the predictable way we return to it after being tilted or turned upside down. The baseline against which our brain assesses the body's displacement from its natural position is called the "equilibrium position."

Our sense of balance relies partly on messages from receptors in our eyes, skin, and joints. In addition, there are organs of equilibrium located in a part of the inner ear called the **vestibular apparatus**. This "apparatus" is a closed system of sacs and three fluid-filled **semicircular canals** (Figure 14.10). The canals are positioned at right angles to one another, corresponding to the three planes of space. Inside them, some sensory receptors monitor dynamic equilibrium—that is, rotating head movements. Elsewhere in the vestibular apparatus are the receptors that monitor the straight-line movements of acceleration and deceleration.

The receptors attuned to rotation are on a ridge of the swollen base of each semicircular canal (Figure 14.11). As in the cochlea, these receptors are sensory hair cells; their delicate hairs project up into a jellylike *cupula* ("little cap"). When your head rotates horizontally or vertically or tilts diagonally, fluid in a canal corresponding to that direction moves in the opposite direction. As the fluid presses against the cupula, the hairs bend. This bending

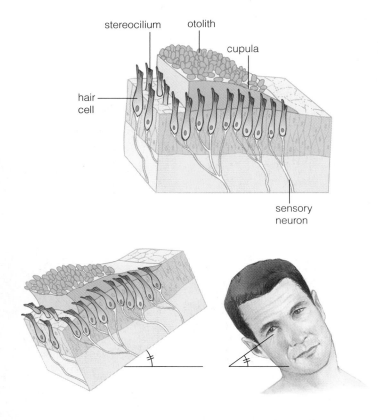

Figure 14.11 How otoliths move in response to gravity when the head tilts.

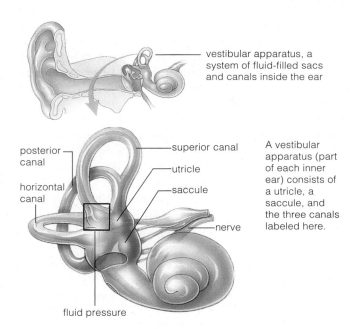

Figure 14.10 *Animated!* The vestibular apparatus, an organ of equilibrium.

is the first step leading to action potentials that travel to the brain—in this case, along the vestibular nerve.

The head's position in space tracks *static* equilibrium. The receptors attuned to it are located in two fluid-filled sacs in the vestibular apparatus, the utricle and saccule shown in Figure 14.10. Each sac contains an *otolith* organ, which has hair cells embedded in a jellylike "membrane." The material also contains hard bits of calcium carbonate called *otoliths* ("ear stones"). Movements of the membrane and otoliths signal changes in the head's orientation relative to gravity, as well as straight-line acceleration and deceleration. For example, if you tilt your head, the otoliths slide in that direction, the membrane mass shifts, and tips of the hair cells bend (Figure 14.11). The otoliths also press on hair cells if your head accelerates, as when you start running or are riding in an accelerating vehicle.

Action potentials from the vestibular apparatus travel to reflex centers in the brain stem. As the signals are integrated with information from your muscles and eyes, the brain orders compensating movements that

Figure 14.12 Champion skater Sarah Hughes demonstrating her brain's ability to monitor inputs from her eyes and muscles in ways that help her keep her balance while executing a difficult maneuver on the ice.

help you keep your balance when you stand, walk, dance, or move your body in other ways (Figure 14.12).

Motion sickness can result when extreme or continuous motion overstimulates hair cells in the balance organs. It can also be caused by conflicting signals from the ears and eyes about motion or the head's position. As people who are predisposed to motion sickness know all too well, action potentials triggered by the sensory input can reach a brain center that governs the vomiting reflex.

Balance involves a sense of the natural position for the body or its parts. This sense relies heavily on sensory signals from the vestibular apparatus, a closed system of fluid-filled canals and sacs in the inner ear.

The semicircular canals are situated at angles that correspond to the three planes of space. Sensory receptors inside them detect rotation, acceleration, and deceleration of the head.

Otolith organs contain sensory hair cells embedded in a jellylike membrane. Movements of the membrane and otoliths signal changes in the head's orientation relative to gravity, as well as straight-line acceleration and deceleration.

14.7 Disorders of the Ear

The hearing apparatus of our ears is remarkably sturdy, but its functioning also can be damaged by a variety of illnesses and injuries.

Children have short eustachian tubes, so they especially are susceptible to **otitis media**—a painful inflammation of the middle ear that usually is caused by the spread of a respiratory infection such as a cold. The usual treatment is a course of antibiotics. In some cases pus and fluid can build up and cause the eardrum to tear. The rupture usually will heal on its own.

Ear infections, taking lots of aspirin, and other triggers can cause the ringing or buzzing in the ears known as **tinnitus**. Many cases of chronic tinnitus have no detectable cause. While the condition is not a serious health threat, it can be extremely annoying.

Deafness is the partial or complete inability to hear. Some people suffer from congenital (inborn) deafness, and in other cases aging, disease, or environmentally caused damage is the culprit. About one-third of adults in the United States will suffer significant hearing loss by the time they are 65. Researchers believe that most cases of this progressive deafness are due to the long-term effects of living in a noisy world.

The loudness of a sound is measured in decibels. A quiet conversation occurs at about 50 decibels. Rustling papers make noise at a mere 20 decibels. The delicate sensory hair cells in the inner ear (Figure 14.13) begin to be damaged when a person is exposed to sounds louder than about 75–85 decibels over long periods. Some MP3 players can crank out sound at well over 100 decibels. At 130 decibels—typical of a rock concert or shotgun blast—permanent damage can occur much more quickly. Protective earwear is a must for anyone who regularly operates noisy equipment or who works around noisy machinery such as aircraft.

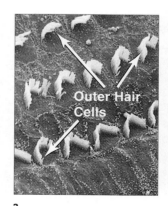
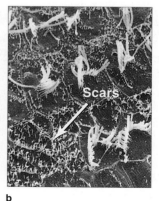

a   b

Figure 14.13 (**a**) Healthy sensory hair cells of the inner ear. (**b**) Hair cells damaged by exposure to loud noise.

14.8 Vision: An Overview

All organisms may be sensitive to light. Vision, however, requires (1) a system of photoreceptors and (2) brain centers that can receive and interpret the patterns of action potentials from different parts of the photoreceptor system.

The sense of **vision** is an awareness of the position, shape, brightness, distance, and movement of visual stimuli. Our **eyes** are sensory organs that contain tissue with a dense array of photoreceptors.

THE EYE IS BUILT FOR PHOTORECEPTION

The eye has three layers (Table 14.2), sometimes called "tunics." The outer layer consists of a sclera and a transparent **cornea**. The middle layer consists mainly of a choroid, ciliary body, and iris. The key feature of the inner layer is the retina (Figure 14.14).

The *sclera*—the dense, fibrous "white" of the eye— protects most of the eyeball, except for a "front" region formed by the cornea. Moving inward, the thin, dark-pigmented *choroid* underlies the sclera. It prevents light from scattering inside the eyeball and contains most of the eye's blood vessels.

Behind the transparent cornea is a round, pigmented **iris** (after *irid*, which means "colored circle"). The iris has more than 250 measurable features (such as pigments and fibrous tissues). This is why, as you read earlier, the iris can be used for identification. Look closely at someone's eye, and you will see a "hole" in the center of

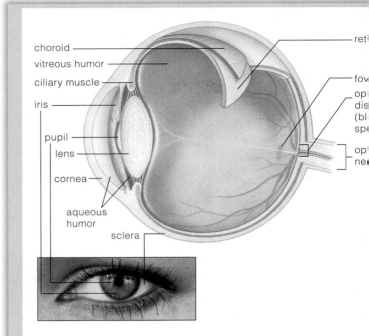

Figure 14.14 *Animated!* Structure of the eye.

the iris. This *pupil* is the entrance for light. When bright light hits the eye, circular muscles in the iris contract and shrink the pupil. In dim light, radial muscles contract and enlarge the pupil.

Behind the iris is a saucer-shaped **lens**, with onionlike layers of transparent proteins. Ligaments attach the lens to smooth muscle of the *ciliary body*; this muscle functions in focusing light, as we will see shortly. The lens focuses incoming light onto a dense layer of photoreceptor cells behind it, in the retina. A clear fluid, *aqueous humor* (body fluids were once called "humors"), bathes both sides of the lens. A jellylike substance (*vitreous humor*) fills the chamber behind the lens.

The **retina** is a thin layer of neural tissue at the back of the eyeball. It has a pigmented basement layer that covers the choroid. Resting on the basement layer are densely packed photoreceptors that are linked with a variety of neurons. Axons from some of these neurons converge to form the optic nerve at the back of the eyeball. The optic nerve is the trunk line to the thalamus— which, recall, sends signals on to the **visual cortex**. The place where the optic nerve exits the eye is a "blind spot" because there are no photoreceptors there.

The surface of the cornea is curved. This means that incoming light rays hit it at different angles and, as they pass through the cornea, their trajectories (paths) bend (Figure 14.15*a*). There, because of the way the rays were

Table 14.2	Parts of the Eye
Wall of eyeball	(three layers)
Sensory Tunic (inner layer)	*Retina.* Absorbs, transduces light energy *Fovea.* Increases visual acuity
Vascular Tunic (middle layer)	*Choroid.* Blood vessels nutritionally support wall cells; pigments prevent light scattering
	Ciliary body. Its muscles control lens shape; its fine fibers hold lens upright
	Iris. Adjusting iris controls incoming light
	Pupil. Serves as entrance for light
	Start of optic nerve. Carries signals to brain
Fibrous Tunic (outer layer)	*Sclera.* Protects eyeball *Cornea.* Focuses light
Interior of eyeball	
Lens	Focuses light on photoreceptors
Aqueous humor	Transmits light, maintains pressure
Vitreous body	Transmits light, supports lens and eyeball

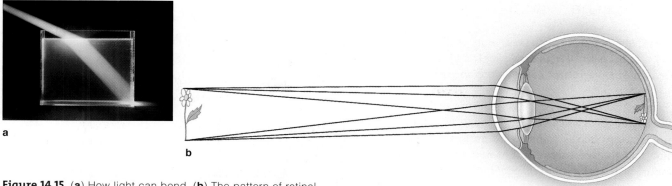

a

b

Figure 14.15 (**a**) How light can bend. (**b**) The pattern of retinal stimulation in the eye. Being curved, the cornea alters the trajectories of light rays as they enter the eye. The pattern is upside-down and reversed left to right, compared to the stimulus.

Figure 14.16 *Animated!* Focusing light on the retina by adjusting the lens (visual accommodation). A ciliary muscle encircling the lens attaches to it. (**a**) When it contracts, the lens bulges. The focal point moves closer and brings close objects into focus. (**b**) When the muscle relaxes, the lens flattens, so the focal point moves farther back. This can bring distant objects into focus.

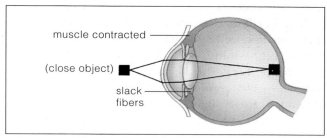

a Accommodation for close objects (lens bulges)

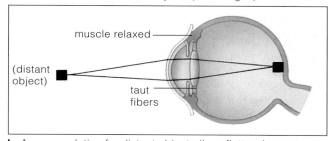

b Accommodation for distant objects (lens flattens)

bent at the curved cornea, the rays converge at the back of the eyeball. They stimulate the retina in a pattern that is upside-down and reversed left to right relative to the original source of the light rays. Figure 14.15*b* gives a simplified diagram of this outcome. The "upside-down and backwards" orientation is corrected in the brain.

EYE MUSCLE MOVEMENTS FINE-TUNE THE FOCUS

Light rays from sources at different distances from the eye strike the cornea at different angles. As a result, they will be focused at different distances behind it, and adjustments must be made so that the light will be focused precisely on the retina. Normally, the lens can be adjusted so that the focal point coincides exactly with the retina. A ciliary muscle adjusts the shape of the lens. As you can see in Figure 14.14 the muscle encircles the lens and attaches to it by ligaments. When the muscle contracts, the lens bulges, so the focal point moves closer. When the muscle relaxes, the lens flattens, so the focal point moves farther back (Figure 14.16). Adjustments like these are called *accommodation*. If they are not made, rays from distant objects will be in focus at a point just in front of the retina, and rays from very close objects will be focused behind it.

Sometimes the lens can't be adjusted enough to place the focal point on the retina. Sometimes also, the eyeball is not shaped quite right. The lens is too close to or too far

away from the retina, so accommodation alone cannot produce a precise match. Eyeglasses or contact lenses can correct these problems, which are called farsightedness and nearsightedness, respectively. Section 14.10 examines a variety of eye disorders.

Eyes are sensory organs specialized for photoreception.

In the outer eye layer, the sclera protects the eyeball and the cornea focuses light.

In the middle layer, the choroid prevents light scattering, the iris controls incoming light, and the ciliary body and lens aid in focusing light on photoreceptors.

Photoreception occurs in the retina of the inner layer.

Adjustments in the position or shape of the lens focus incoming visual stimuli onto the retina.

14.9 From Visual Signals to "Sight"

LINKS TO
SECTIONS
13.2, 13.3,
AND 13.7

Our vision sense is based on the sensory pathway from the retina to the brain. It is an excellent example of how different neurons can interrelate to one another in the nervous system.

"Seeing" something is a multistep process that begins when our eyes receive raw visual information. The information then is transmitted and processed in ways that lead to awareness of light and shadows, of colors, and of near and distant objects in the world around us.

RODS AND CONES ARE THE PHOTORECEPTORS

The flow of information begins as light reaches the retina, at the back of the eyeball. The retina has a basement layer, a pigmented epithelium on top of the choroid. Resting on this layer are 150 million photoreceptors called **rod cells** and **cone cells** (Figure 14.17 and Table 14.3). Rod cells detect very dim light. At night or in dark places, they detect changes in light intensity across the visual field—the start of coarse perception of motion. Cone cells detect bright light—the start of sharp vision and perception of color in the daytime or in brightly lit spaces. (You don't see color in moonlight because the light isn't bright enough to stimulate cones.)

VISUAL PIGMENTS IN RODS AND CONES INTERCEPT LIGHT ENERGY

The outer part of a rod cell contains stacks of several hundred membrane disks, each packed with more than a billion molecules of a visual pigment called **rhodopsin**. The membrane stacks and the large number of pigment molecules hugely increase the odds that rods will detect light energy, which comes packaged as photons. (Each photon is a given amount of light energy.) The action potentials that result when rod pigments absorb even a few photons can allow a person to see objects in dimly lit surroundings such as dark rooms or late at night.

Each rhodopsin molecule consists of a protein (opsin) to which a signal molecule, *cis*-retinal, is bound. The retinal is derived from vitamin A. That's one reason why too little vitamin A in the diet can impair a person's vision, especially at night.

When the photons of blue-green light stimulate rhodopsin, it changes shape. The change is the start of the process that converts light energy to action potentials. It triggers a cascade of reactions that alter the distribution of ions across the rod cell's plasma membrane. As a result, there is a slow down in the ongoing release of a neurotransmitter that inhibits neurons next to the rods. No longer inhibited, the neurons start sending signals about the visual stimulus on toward the brain.

Table 14.3	Rods and Cones Compared	
CELL TYPE	**SENSITIVE TO**	**RELATED PERCEPTION**
Rod	Dim light	Coarse perception of movement
Cone	Bright light	Daytime vision and perception of color

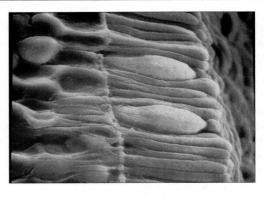

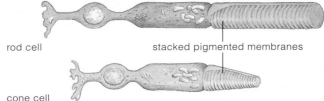

rod cell   stacked pigmented membranes

cone cell

Figure 14.17 Photoreceptors: rods and cones.

Daytime vision and the sense of color start when photons are absorbed by cone cells, each with a different kind of visual pigment—red, green, or blue. Here again, the absorption of photons curtails the release of a neurotransmitter that would otherwise prevent the neurons next to the photoreceptors from firing.

Near the center of the retina is a funnel-shaped depression called the **fovea** (Figure 14.18). Photoreceptors are denser there than anywhere else in the retina. Visual acuity, the ability to discriminate between two objects, also is greatest there. The fovea's cluster of cones enables you to distinguish between neighboring points in space—like the *e* and the period at the end of this sentence.

THE RETINA PROCESSES SIGNALS FROM RODS AND CONES

Neurons in the eye are organized in layers above the rods and cones. As you can see in Figure 14.19, signals flow from rods and cones to *bipolar* interneurons, then to interneurons called *ganglion cells*. The axons of ganglion cells form the two optic nerves to the brain.

SENSORY SYSTEMS

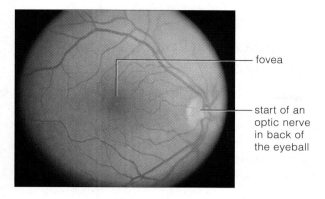

Figure 14.18 Location of the fovea and the start of the optic nerve.

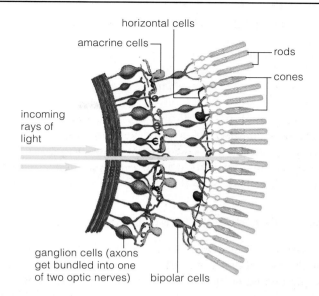

Figure 14.19 *Animated!* Organization of photoreceptors and sensory neurons in the retina.

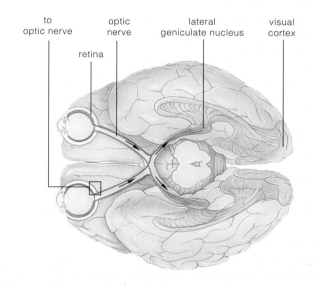

Figure 14.20 *Animated!* Sensory pathway from the retina to the brain.

Before visual signals leave the retina, they converge dramatically. Input from the 150 million photoreceptors funnels onto only 1 million ganglion cells. Signals also flow sideways among *horizontal* cells and *amacrine* cells. These neurons act jointly to dampen or strengthen the signals before they reach ganglion cells. In other words, a great deal of synaptic integration and processing goes on even before visual information is sent to the brain.

RECEPTIVE FIELDS IN THE RETINA Different neurons in the eye respond to light stimuli in different ways. The retina's surface is organized into "receptive fields," areas that influence the activity of individual sensory neurons. For example, for each ganglion cell, the field is a circle. Some cells respond best to a small spot of light, ringed by dark, in the field's center. Others respond to motion, to a spot of a particular color, or to a rapid change in light intensity—when you switch on the light in a dark room, for instance. In one experiment, certain neurons fired when a hard-edged bar was oriented in some ways but not others. These differences in receptive fields of different neurons help prevent the brain from being bombarded with a confusing array of visual signals.

SIGNALS MOVE ON TO THE VISUAL CORTEX The part of the outside world that a person actually sees is called the "visual field." The right side of each retina intercepts light from the left half of the visual field and the left side intercepts light from the right half. As you can see in Figure 14.20, signals from each eye "criss-cross." The optic nerve leading out of each eye delivers signals from the left visual field to the right cerebral hemisphere, and signals from the right go to the left hemisphere.

Axons of the optic nerves end in an island of gray matter in the cerebrum (the lateral geniculate nucleus). Its layers each have a map corresponding to receptive fields of the retina. Each map's interneurons deal with one aspect of a visual stimulus—its form, movement,

depth, color, texture, and so on. After initial processing all the visual signals travel rapidly, at the same time, to different parts of the visual cortex. There, a final round of integration produces the sensation of sight.

Rods and cones are the eye's photoreceptors. Rods detect dim light. Cones detect bright light and provide our sense of color.

The eye analyzes information on the distance, shape, brightness, position, and movement of a visual stimulus.

Visual signals move through layers of neurons in the retina before moving on to the brain.

14.10 Disorders of the Eye

For us humans, our eyes are the single most important source of information about the outside world. It's no wonder then that we pay a lot of attention to eye disorders.

Problems that disrupt normal eye functions range from injuries and diseases to inherited abnormalities and natural changes associated with aging. The outcomes range from some relatively harmless conditions, such as nearsightedness, to total blindness.

MISSING CONE CELLS CAUSE COLOR BLINDNESS

Occasionally, some or all of the cone cells that selectively respond to light of red, green, or blue are missing. The rare people who have only one of the three kinds of cones are totally color-blind. They see the world only in shades of gray.

Consider a common inherited abnormality, **red-green color blindness**. It shows up most often in males, for reasons you can read about in Chapter 21. The retina lacks some or all of the cone cells with pigments that normally respond to light of red or green wavelengths. Most of the time, color-blind people have trouble distinguishing red from green only in dim light. However, some cannot distinguish between the two even in bright light.

MALFORMED EYE PARTS CAUSE COMMON FOCUSING PROBLEMS

Some inherited vision problems are due to misshapen eye structures that affect the eye's ability to focus light. In **astigmatism**, for example, one or both corneas have an uneven curvature; they cannot bend incoming light rays to the same focal point.

In **myopia**, or nearsightedness, the eyeball is wider than it is high, or the ciliary muscle responsible for adjusting the lens contracts too strongly. Then, images of distant objects are focused in front of the retina instead of on it (Figure 14.21a). **Hyperopia**, farsightedness, is the opposite problem. The eyeball is "taller" than it is wide (or the lens is "lazy"), so close images are focused behind the retina (Figure 14.21b).

THE EYES ALSO ARE VULNERABLE TO INFECTIONS AND CANCER

The eyes are vulnerable to pathogens including viruses, bacteria, and fungi. Health authorities estimate that in the U.S., about 1 in every 50 visits to a doctor's office is for **conjunctivitis**, inflammation of the transparent membrane (the conjunctiva) that lines the inside of the eyelids and

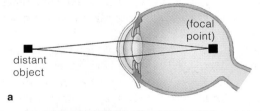

a

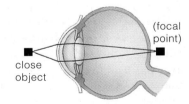

b

Figure 14.21 *Animated!* Examples of nearsighted and farsighted vision.

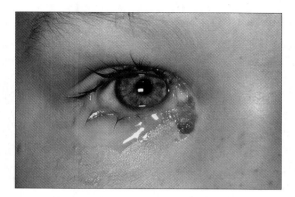

Figure 14.22 A child with conjunctivitis.

covers the sclera (the white of the eye). Symptoms include redness, discomfort, and a discharge. In children, conjunctivitis usually is caused by a bacteria infection; in adults it more often is triggered by allergy (Figure 14.22). Most cases of conjunctivitis are easily treated with antibiotics.

Trachoma is a highly contagious disease that has blinded millions, mostly in North Africa and the Middle East. The culprit is a bacterium that also is responsible for the sexually transmitted disease chlamydia (Chapter 16). Trachoma damages both the eyeball and the conjunctiva. Then, other bacteria can enter the damaged tissues and cause secondary infections. In time the cornea can become so scarred that blindness follows.

Various forms of herpes simplex, a virus that causes cold sores and genital herpes, also can infect the cornea. Because blindness can result from a **herpes infection** in the eyes, a pregnant woman who has a history of genital herpes likely will be delivered by Caesarian section to avoid any chance of exposing her newborn to the virus.

Malignant melanoma is the most common eye cancer. It typically develops in the choroid (the eye's middle layer) and may not trigger noticeable vision problems until it has spread to other parts of the body. About 1 in 20,000 babies is born with **retinoblastoma**, a cancer of the retina. Because it can readily spread along the optic nerve to the brain, the affected eye often is removed surgically. If both eyes are affected, radiation therapy may be used to try to save one of them.

AGING INCREASES THE RISK OF CATARACTS AND SOME OTHER EYE DISORDERS

Cataracts, clouding of the eye's lens, are associated with aging, although an injury or diabetes can also cause them to develop. The underlying change may be an alteration in the structure of transparent proteins that make up the lens. This change in turn may skew the trajectory of incoming light rays. If the lens becomes totally opaque, no light can enter the eye.

Even a normal lens loses some of its natural flexibility as we grow older. This normal stiffening is why people over 40 years old often must start wearing eyeglasses.

Elderly people can suffer **macular degeneration**, in which a portion of the retina breaks down and is replaced by scar tissue. As a result, a "blind spot" develops. Often both eyes are affected. Treatment is difficult unless the problem is detected early.

Glaucoma results when too much aqueous humor builds up inside the eyeball. Blood vessels that service the retina collapse under the increased fluid pressure. An affected person's vision deteriorates as neurons of the retina and optic nerve die. Although chronic glaucoma often is associated with advanced age, the problem really starts in a person's middle years. If detected early, the fluid pressure can be relieved by drugs or surgery before the damage becomes severe.

MEDICAL TECHNOLOGIES CAN REMEDY SOME VISION PROBLEMS AND TREAT EYE INJURIES

Today many different procedures are used to correct eye disorders. In *corneal transplant surgery*, the defective cornea is removed; then an artificial cornea (made of clear plastic) or a natural cornea from a donor is stitched in place. Within a year, the patient is fitted with eyeglasses or contact lenses. Similarly, cataracts sometimes can be surgically corrected by removing the lens and replacing it with an artificial one.

Severely nearsighted people may opt for procedures that eliminate the need for corrective lenses. So-called "lasik" (for laser-assisted in situ keratomilieusis) and "lasek" (for laser-assisted subepithelial keratectomy) use a laser to reshape the cornea. All or part of the surface of the cornea is peeled back and then replaced into position after the defect being treated is corrected. *Conductive keratoplasty* (CK) uses radio waves to reshape the cornea and bring near vision back into focus.

Retinal detachment is the eye injury we read about most often. It may follow a physical blow to the head or an illness that tears the retina. As the jellylike vitreous body oozes through the torn region, the retina is lifted from the underlying choroid. In time it may peel away entirely, leaving its blood supply behind. Early symptoms of the damage include blurred vision, flashes of light that occur in the absence of outside stimulation, and loss of peripheral vision. Without medical help, the person may become totally blind in the damaged eye.

A detached retina may be treatable with *laser coagulation*, a painless technique in which a laser beam seals off leaky blood vessels and "spot welds" the retina to the underlying choroid.

Summary

Section 14.1   A stimulus is a form of energy that the body detects by means of sensory receptors. A sensation is a conscious awareness that stimulation has occurred. Perception is understanding what the sensation means.

Sensory receptors are endings of sensory neurons or specialized cells next to them. They respond to stimuli, which are specific forms of energy, such as mechanical pressure and light.

  a. Mechanoreceptors detect mechanical energy that is associated with changes in pressure (e.g., sound waves), changes in position, or acceleration.

  b. Thermoreceptors detect the presence of or changes in radiant energy from heat sources.

  c. Nociceptors (pain receptors) detect tissue damage. Their signals are perceived as pain.

  d. Chemoreceptors detect chemical substances that are dissolved in the body fluids around them.

  e. Osmoreceptors detect changes in water volume (hence solute concentrations) in the surrounding fluid.

  f. Photoreceptors detect light.

A sensory system has sensory receptors for specific stimuli and nerve pathways from those receptors to receiving and processing centers in the brain. The brain assesses each stimulus based on which nerve pathway is delivering the signals, how often signals are traveling along each axon of the pathway, and the number of axons that were recruited into action. When sensory adaptation occurs, the response to a stimulus decreases.

The special senses include taste, smell, hearing, balance, and vision. The receptors associated with these senses typically are in sense organs or another specific body region.

 See how the intensity of a sensory stimulus affects the frequency of action potentials to the brain.

Section 14.2   Somatic sensations include touch, pressure, pain, temperature, and muscle sense. Receptors associated with these sensations occur in various parts of the body. Their signals are processed in the somatosensory cortex of the brain. The simplest receptors, which include various mechanoreceptors, thermoreceptors, and nociceptors, are free nerve endings in the skin or internal tissues. Some somatic sensations also arise when encapsulated receptors respond to stimuli.

Learn about many of the sensory receptors in skin.

Section 14.3   Taste and smell are chemical senses. Their sensory pathways travel from chemoreceptors to processing regions in the cerebral cortex and limbic system. Taste buds in the tongue and mouth contain the taste receptors. The sense of smell relies on olfactory receptors in patches of epithelium in the upper nasal passages.

Section 14.5   The sense of hearing requires components of the outer, middle, and inner ear that respectively collect, amplify, and respond to sound waves that vibrate the tympanic membrane (eardrum). The vibrations are transferred to fluid in the cochlea of the inner ear, where they in turn vibrate the tectorial membrane. Ultimately the fluid movements bend sensory hair cells in the organ of Corti. The bending triggers neural signals that are carried to the brain via the auditory nerve.

Explore the structure and function of the ear.

Section 14.6   Balance organs are located in the vestibular apparatus of the inner ear. Sensory receptors in these semicircular canals (including hair cells) detect gravity, velocity, acceleration, and other factors that affect body positions and movements.

Section 14.8   Eyes are the sensory organs associated with the sense of vision. Key eye structures include the cornea and lens, which focus light; the iris, which adjusts incoming light; and the retina, which contains photoreceptors (rods and cones). The optic nerve at the back of the eyeball transmits visual signals to the visual cortex in the brain.

 Investigate the structure and function of the eye.

Section 14.9   The rod cells and cone cells detect dim and bright light, respectively. Light detection in rods depends on changes in the shape of the visual pigment rhodopsin. The visual pigments in cones respond to colors. Visual signals are processed in the retina before being sent on to the brain. In the retina, abundant receptors in the fovea provide sharp visual acuity.

Learn about the organization of the retina and how visual stimuli are processed.

Review Questions

1. When a receptor cell detects a specific kind of stimulus, what happens to the stimulus energy?

2. Name six categories of sensory receptors and the type of stimulus energy that each type detects.

3. How do somatic sensations differ from special senses?

4. Explain where free nerve endings are located in the body and note some functions of the various kinds.

5. What is pain? Describe one type of pain receptor.

6. What are the stimuli for taste receptors?

7. How do "smell" signals arise and reach the brain?

8. Label the parts of the ear:

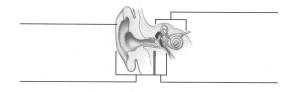

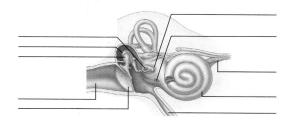

9. In the ear, sound waves cause the tympanic membrane to vibrate. What happens next in the middle ear? In the inner ear?

10. Label the parts of the eye:

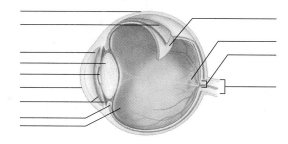

11. How does the eye focus the light rays of an image? What do nearsighted and farsighted mean?

Self-Quiz

Answers in Appendix V

1. A _____ is a specific form of energy that can elicit a response from a sensory receptor.

2. Awareness of a stimulus is called a _____.

3. _____ is understanding what particular sensations mean.

4. A sensory system is composed of _____.
   a. nerve pathways from specific receptors to the brain
   b. sensory receptors
   c. brain regions that deal with sensory information
   d. all of the above

5. _____ detect energy associated with changes in pressure, body position, or acceleration.
   a. Chemoreceptors   c. Photoreceptors
   b. Mechanoreceptors   d. Thermoreceptors

6. Detecting substances present in the body fluids that bathe them is the function of _____.
   a. thermoreceptors   c. mechanoreceptors
   b. photoreceptors   d. chemoreceptors

7. Which of the special senses is based on the following events? Membrane vibrations cause fluid movements, which lead to bending of mechanoreceptors and firing of action potentials.
   a. taste   c. hearing
   b. smell   d. vision

8. Rods differ from cones in the following ways:
   a. They detect dim light, not bright light.
   b. They have a different visual pigment.
   c. They are not located in the retina.
   d. all of the above
   e. a and b only

9. The outer layer of the eye includes the _____.
   a. lens and choroid   c. retina
   b. sclera and cornea   d. both a and c are correct

10. The inner layer of the eye includes the _____.
    a. lens and choroid   c. retina
    b. sclera and cornea   d. start of optic nerve

11. Your visual field is _____.
    a. a specific, small area of the retina
    b. what you actually "see"
    c. the area where color vision occurs
    d. where the optic nerve starts

12. Match each of the following terms with the appropriate description.
    ____ somatic senses   a. produced by strong
         (general senses)   stimulation
    ____ special senses   b. endings of sensory
    ____ variations in   neurons or specialized
         stimulus intensity   cells next to them
    ____ action potential   c. taste, smell, hearing,
    ____ sensory receptor   balance, and vision
                                 d. frequency and number of
                                    action potentials
                                 e. touch, pressure,
                                    temperature, pain, and
                                    muscle sense

Critical Thinking

1. Juanita started having bouts of dizziness. Her doctor asked her whether "dizziness" meant she felt lightheaded as if she were going to faint, or whether it meant she had sensations of *vertigo*—that is, a feeling that she herself or objects near her were spinning around. Why was this clarification important for the diagnosis?

2. Michael, a 3-year-old, experiences chronic middle-ear infection, which is common among youngsters, in part due to an increase in antibiotic-resistant bacteria. This year, despite antibiotic treatment, an infection became so advanced that he had trouble hearing. Then his left eardrum ruptured and a jellylike substance dribbled out. The pediatrician told Michael's parents not to worry, that if the eardrum had not ruptured on its own she would have had to drain it. Suggest a reason why the physician concluded that this procedure would have been needed.

3. Jill is diagnosed with sensorineural deafness, a disorder in which sound waves are transmitted normally to the inner ear but they are not translated into neural signals that travel to the brain. Sometimes the cause is a problem with the auditory nerve, but in Jill's case it has to do with a problem in the inner ear itself. Where in the inner ear is the disruption most likely located?

4. Larry goes to the doctor complaining that he can't see the right side of the visual field with either eye. Where in the visual signal-processing pathway is the problem?

Explore on Your Own

As Section 14.10 described, there are various forms of color blindness. Figure 14.23 shows simple tests, called Ishihara plates, which are standardized tests for different forms of color blindness. For instance, you may have one form of red-green color blindness if you see the numeral "7" instead of "29" in the circle in part *a*. You may have another form if you see a "3" instead of an "8" in the circle in part *b*.

If you do this exercise and have questions about your color vision, visit your doctor to determine whether additional testing is in order.

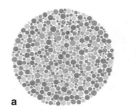
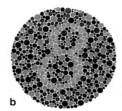

a   b

Figure 14.23 Color blindness tests.

15 THE ENDOCRINE SYSTEM

Hormones in the Balance

In 2001, researchers at Dartmouth College discovered what may be another villainous role for the poison arsenic. It appears to be an endocrine disrupter, a chemical that affects health by interfering with normal hormonal processes. Along with some other chemicals, arsenic upsets the action of hormones by blocking them or mimicking them. The problem with a mimic is that, unlike natural hormones, it can't be turned off. As a result, the body loses control of the affected function. The Dartmouth team discovered that arsenic disrupts the action of glucocorticoids, hormones that help regulate blood sugar and that are "on" switches for genes that may protect against cancer.

Arsenic is present in water supplies in many areas. Long-term exposure to it in drinking water is associated with bladder, lung, and skin cancers, birth defects, and other problems. In 2001, around the same time that the Dartmouth study was published, the Environmental Protection Agency cited the risks and lowered the allowable arsenic levels in water supplies. In 2003 some factions lobbied to get the levels increased again.

Other possible endocrine disrupters are also coming under scrutiny. One is atrazine, a widely used herbicide. Golf courses, cornfields, sorghum crops—all have been doused with it to kill weeds. Atrazine now is found in groundwater throughout the American Midwest. Some scientists, including Tyrone Hayes (*right*), suspect it is linked to reproductive problems in several species of frogs.

Other suspects are PCBs, chemicals that were long used as fluid insulation in electrical transformers. Now banned, PCBs linger in the environment. They have been implicated in reproductive disorders in humans.

Research on endocrine disrupters is controversial. Some researchers suspect that they are contributing to an earlier onset of puberty and to low sperm counts. Other scientists dismiss the hypotheses as junk science. Ongoing studies should clarify the picture.

This chapter focuses on hormones—their sources, targets, and interactions. What you learn here may help you evaluate research that may affect human life in a big way.

 How Would You Vote? Some pesticides may disrupt hormone function in humans and other animals. Should they remain in use while researchers study their safety? Cast your vote online at www.thomsonedu.com/biology/starr/humanbio.

 ## Key Concepts

HOW HORMONES WORK
Hormones control many body functions and influence behavior. Hormones bind to and activate receptors on target cells. Their signals are converted into forms that work inside target cells to bring about a response.

THE ENDOCRINE SYSTEM
Most hormones are released from endocrine glands and tissues. The hypothalamus and pituitary glands control much of this activity. In addition, some hormones are released in response to chemical changes in particular tissues.

Links to Earlier Concepts

This chapter builds on your understanding of the roles of different cell structures (3.3, 3.4). It expands on what you have learned about the roles of two key brain components, the hypothalamus and the pituitary gland (13.7), and provides more examples of how homeostatic feedback loops help regulate body functions (4.9).

You will also see more examples of how proteins in cell plasma membranes function in physiological processes (3.3)—in this case, by serving as receptors for hormone molecules.

15.1 The Endocrine System: Hormones

LINKS TO
SECTIONS
3.3 AND 14.3

The activities of billions of cells must be integrated in order for the body to function normally. This integration depends on signaling molecules. The nervous system's neurotransmitters are one kind of signaling molecule, and hormones are another.

HORMONES ARE SIGNALING MOLECULES THAT ARE CARRIED IN THE BLOODSTREAM

All the body's signaling molecules—neurotransmitters, pheromones, local signaling molecules, and hormones—act on target cells. A **target cell** is any cell that has receptors for the signaling molecule and that may alter its activities in response. A target may or may not be next to the cell that sends the signal.

Hormones, our main topic here, are secreted by the body's endocrine glands, endocrine cells, and some neurons. They travel the bloodstream to target cells some distance away. Many types of body cells also release "local signaling molecules" that alter conditions within nearby tissues. Prostaglandins are an example. Their targets include smooth muscle cells in the walls of bronchioles, which then constrict or dilate and so alter air flow in the lungs (Section 11.5). Certain exocrine glands secrete **pheromones**, which we touched on briefly in Chapter 14. Unlike other signaling molecules, a pheromone acts on targets *outside* the body. It diffuses through air (or water) to the cells of other animals of the same species. Pheromones help integrate behaviors, such as those related to reproduction. You may recall from Section 14.3 that the vomeronasal organ in the human nose can detect pheromones. Do pheromones act to trigger impressions, such as spontaneous good or bad "feelings" about someone you just met? We don't yet know the answer to that fascinating question.

HORMONE SOURCES: THE ENDOCRINE SYSTEM

The word hormone—from the Greek *hormon*, "to set in motion"—was coined in 1900 by scientists studying food digestion in dogs. They discovered that a certain substance (which they dubbed "secretin") released by gland cells in the canine GI tract could stimulate the pancreas. Later researchers identified other hormones and their sources. There are several major sources of hormones in the human body, as you can see in Figure 15.1.

These hormone-producing glands, organs, and cells became known as the **endocrine system**. The name is misleading, because it implies that there is a separate hormone-based control system for the body. (*Endon* means "within"; *krinein* means "separate.") However, from biochemical studies and electron microscopy, we now know that endocrine sources and the nervous system function in intricately connected ways, as you will see later in this chapter.

HORMONES OFTEN INTERACT

Today we also know that often, two or more hormones affect the same process. There are three common kinds of hormone "partnerships":

1. **Opposing interaction**. The effect of one hormone may oppose the effect of another. Insulin, for example, reduces the level of glucose in the blood, and glucagon increases it.

2. **Synergistic interaction**. The combined action of two or more "cooperating" hormones may be required to trigger a certain effect on target cells. For instance, a woman's mammary glands can't produce and secrete milk without the synergistic interaction of three other hormones: prolactin, oxytocin, and estrogen.

3. **Permissive interaction**. One hormone can exert its effect on a target cell only when a different hormone first "primes" the target cell. For example, even if one of a woman's eggs is fertilized, she can become pregnant only if the lining of her uterus has been exposed to estrogens, then to progesterone.

IMPACTS, ISSUES

Dioxin is a by-product of a variety of industrial processes. It also was a contaminant of Agent Orange, a defoliant used during the Vietnam conflict. Soldiers who handled it developed diabetes twice as often as other service personnel. Dioxin is pervasive in the environment and accumulates in fatty tissues. One way to limit your exposure to it is to limit your consumption of animal fat.

Hormones are signaling molecules secreted by endocrine glands, endocrine cells, and some neurons. The bloodstream distributes hormones to distant target cells.

Together, the glands and cells that secrete hormones make up the endocrine system.

Hormones may interact in opposition, in cooperation (synergistically), or permissively (a target cell must be primed by exposure to one hormone in order to respond to a second one).

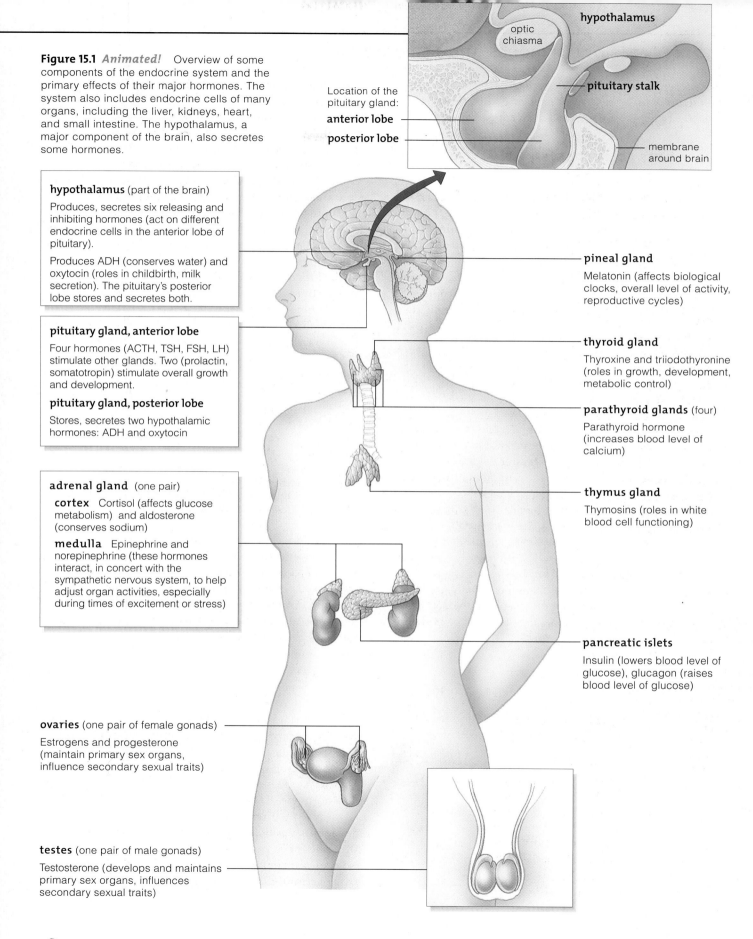

Figure 15.1 *Animated!* Overview of some components of the endocrine system and the primary effects of their major hormones. The system also includes endocrine cells of many organs, including the liver, kidneys, heart, and small intestine. The hypothalamus, a major component of the brain, also secretes some hormones.

Location of the pituitary gland:

anterior lobe

posterior lobe

hypothalamus

optic chiasma

pituitary stalk

membrane around brain

hypothalamus (part of the brain)

Produces, secretes six releasing and inhibiting hormones (act on different endocrine cells in the anterior lobe of pituitary).

Produces ADH (conserves water) and oxytocin (roles in childbirth, milk secretion). The pituitary's posterior lobe stores and secretes both.

pituitary gland, anterior lobe

Four hormones (ACTH, TSH, FSH, LH) stimulate other glands. Two (prolactin, somatotropin) stimulate overall growth and development.

pituitary gland, posterior lobe

Stores, secretes two hypothalamic hormones: ADH and oxytocin

adrenal gland (one pair)

cortex Cortisol (affects glucose metabolism) and aldosterone (conserves sodium)

medulla Epinephrine and norepinephrine (these hormones interact, in concert with the sympathetic nervous system, to help adjust organ activities, especially during times of excitement or stress)

ovaries (one pair of female gonads)

Estrogens and progesterone (maintain primary sex organs, influence secondary sexual traits)

testes (one pair of male gonads)

Testosterone (develops and maintains primary sex organs, influences secondary sexual traits)

pineal gland

Melatonin (affects biological clocks, overall level of activity, reproductive cycles)

thyroid gland

Thyroxine and triiodothyronine (roles in growth, development, metabolic control)

parathyroid glands (four)

Parathyroid hormone (increases blood level of calcium)

thymus gland

Thymosins (roles in white blood cell functioning)

pancreatic islets

Insulin (lowers blood level of glucose), glucagon (raises blood level of glucose)

15.2 Types of Hormones and Their Signals

LINKS TO
SECTIONS
2.10, 2.11, 3.2,
AND 3.3

Like other signaling molecules, hormones bind with protein receptors of target cells. What happens next depends on whether a hormone is a steroid or a peptide hormone.

HORMONES COME IN SEVERAL CHEMICAL FORMS

Hormones vary in their chemical structure, which affects how they function. **Steroid hormones** are lipids derived from cholesterol. **Amine hormones** are modified amino acids. **Peptide hormones** consist of a few amino acids. **Protein hormones** are longer amino acid chains. Table 15.1 lists some examples of each.

Regardless of their chemical makeup, hormones affect cell activities by binding to protein receptors of target cells. The signal is then transduced, or converted, into a form that can work in the cell. Then the cell's activity changes:

Some hormones cause a target cell to increase its uptake of a substance, such as glucose. Others stimulate or inhibit the target in ways that alter its rates of protein synthesis, modify existing proteins or other structures in the cytoplasm, or even change a cell's shape.

Two factors have a major influence on how a target cell responds to hormone signals. To begin with, different hormones activate different kinds of mechanisms in target cells. And second, not all types of cells can respond to a given signal. For instance, many types of cells have receptors for the hormone cortisol, so it has widespread effects in the body. If only a few cell types have receptors for a hormone, its effects in the body are limited to the receptive locations.

STEROID HORMONES INTERACT WITH CELL DNA

Cells in the adrenal glands and in the primary reproductive organs—ovaries and testes—all make steroid hormones. Estrogen made in the ovaries and testosterone made in the testes are familiar examples. Thyroid hormones and vitamin D differ chemically from steroid hormones but behave like them.

Figure 15.2*a* illustrates how a steroid hormone may act. Being lipid-soluble, it may diffuse directly across the lipid bilayer of a target cell's plasma membrane. Once inside the cytoplasm, the hormone molecule usually moves into the nucleus and binds to a receptor. In some cases it binds to a receptor in the cytoplasm, and then the hormone–receptor complex enters the nucleus. There the complex interacts with a particular gene—a segment of the cell's DNA. Genes carry the instructions for making proteins. By turning genes on or off, steroid hormones turn protein synthesis on or off. This change in a target cell's activity is the response to the hormone signal.

Some steroid hormones act in another way. They bind receptors on cell membranes and change the membrane properties in ways that affect the target cell's function.

NONSTEROID HORMONES ACT INDIRECTLY, BY WAY OF SECOND MESSENGERS

Nonsteroid hormones—the amine, peptide, and protein hormones—do not enter a target cell. Their chemical makeup makes them water-soluble, so they can't cross a target cell's lipid-rich plasma membrane. Instead, when this type of hormone binds to receptors in the plasma membrane, the binding sets in motion a series of reactions that activate enzymes. These reactions lead to the target cell's response.

For instance, consider a liver cell that has receptors for glucagon, a peptide hormone. As sketched in Figure 15.2*b*, this type of receptor spans the plasma membrane and extends into the cytoplasm. When a receptor binds glucagon, the cell produces a **second messenger**, a small molecule in the cytoplasm that relays signals from hormone–receptor complexes into the cell. A molecule called **cyclic AMP** (cyclic adenosine monophosphate) is this messenger. (The hormone itself is the "first messenger.")

An activated enzyme (adenylate cyclase) launches a cascade of reactions by converting ATP to cyclic AMP. Molecules of cyclic AMP are signals for the cell to activate molecules of another enzyme called a protein kinase. These act on other enzymes, and so forth, until a final

Table 15.1	Categories of Hormones and a Few Examples
Steroid hormones	Estrogens, progesterone, testosterone, aldosterone, cortisol
Amines	Melatonin, epinephrine, norepinephrine, thyroid hormone (thyroxine, triiodothyronine)
Peptides	Oxytocin, antidiuretic hormone, calcitonin, parathyroid hormone
Proteins	Growth hormone (somatotropin), insulin, prolactin, follicle-stimulating hormone, luteinizing hormone

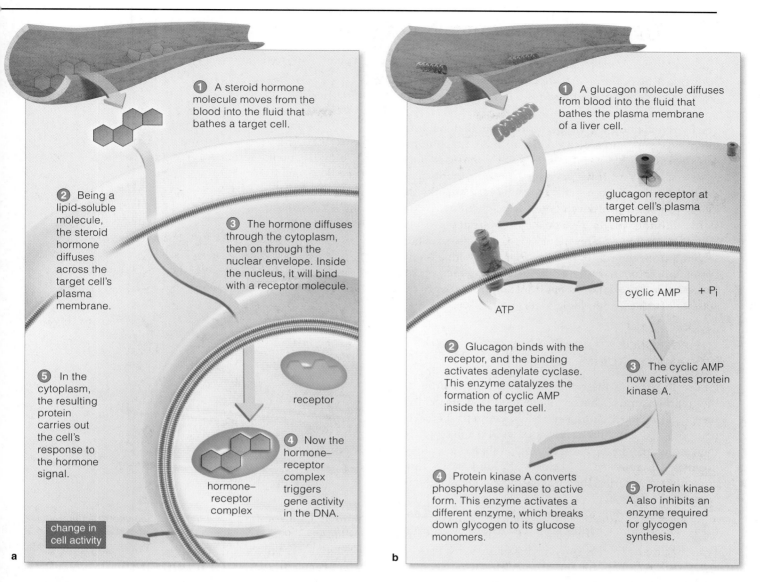

Figure 15.2 (**a**) Example of a mechanism by which a steroid hormone initiates changes in a target cell's activities. (**b**) Example of how a peptide hormone initiates changes in the activity of a target cell. Here, glucagon binds to a receptor and triggers reactions inside the cell. Cyclic AMP, a type of second messenger, relays the signal to the cell's interior.

reaction converts stored glycogen in the cell to glucose. Soon a huge number of molecules are taking part in the final response to the glucagon–receptor complex.

Epinephrine is another amine hormone. Like glucagon, it combines with specific receptors at the surface of the target cell. Binding triggers the release of cyclic AMP as a second messenger that assists in the target cell response.

A slightly different example is a muscle cell that has receptors for insulin, a protein hormone. Among other things, when insulin binds to the receptor, the complex stimulates transporter proteins to insert themselves into the plasma membrane so that the cell can take up glucose faster. The signal also activates enzymes that catalyze reactions allowing the cell to store glucose.

Hormones interact with receptors at the plasma membrane or in the cytoplasm of target cells. Ultimately, the hormone influences protein synthesis in a target cell.

Steroid hormones interact with a target cell's DNA after entering the nucleus or after binding a receptor in the cell's cytoplasm. Some steroid hormones act by altering properties of the plasma membrane itself.

With other types of hormones, the signal for change in a cell's activity comes when the hormone binds to membrane receptors and an enzyme system is activated. Often a second messenger relays the signal to the cell's interior, where the full response unfolds.

15.3 The Hypothalamus and Pituitary Gland: Major Controllers

LINKS TO
SECTIONS
5.1, 9.5,
AND 13.7

The hypothalamus and pituitary gland interact as a major brain center that controls activities of other organs, many of which also have endocrine functions.

The **hypothalamus** is a part of the forebrain that monitors internal organs and states related to their functioning, such as eating. It also influences some behaviors, such as sexual behavior. It has secretory neurons that extend down into the slender stalk to its base, then into the lobed, pea-sized **pituitary gland**.

In addition to its nervous system functions, the hypothalamus makes hormones. Two of these are later secreted from the pituitary's *posterior* lobe. Others have targets in the *anterior* lobe of the pituitary, which makes and secretes its own hormones. Most of these govern the activity of other endocrine glands (Table 15.2).

THE POSTERIOR PITUITARY LOBE PRODUCES ADH AND OXYTOCIN

Figure 15.3 shows the cell bodies of certain neurons in the hypothalamus. Their axons extend downward into the posterior lobe, ending next to a capillary bed. The neurons make antidiuretic hormone (ADH) and oxytocin, then store them in the axon endings. When one of these hormones is released, it diffuses through tissue fluid and enters capillaries, then travels the bloodstream to its targets.

ADH acts on cells of kidney nephrons and collecting ducts. Recall from Chapter 12 that ADH promotes water reabsorption when the body must conserve water.

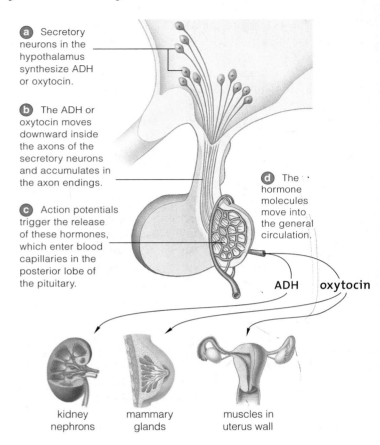

a Secretory neurons in the hypothalamus synthesize ADH or oxytocin.

b The ADH or oxytocin moves downward inside the axons of the secretory neurons and accumulates in the axon endings.

c Action potentials trigger the release of these hormones, which enter blood capillaries in the posterior lobe of the pituitary.

d The hormone molecules move into the general circulation.

ADH   oxytocin

kidney nephrons   mammary glands   muscles in uterus wall

Figure 15.3 *Animated!* Links between the hypothalamus and the posterior lobe of the pituitary. Also shown are main targets of the posterior lobe's hormones.

Table 15.2	Summary of Hormones Released from the Pituitary Gland			
Pituitary Lobe	**Secretions**	**Designation**	**Main Targets**	**Primary Actions**
POSTERIOR Nervous tissue (extension of hypothalamus)	Antidiuretic hormone	ADH	Kidneys	Induces water conservation required in control of extracellular fluid volume (and, indirectly, solute concentrations)
	Oxytocin	OT	Mammary glands	Induces milk movement into secretory ducts
			Uterus	Induces uterine contractions
ANTERIOR Mostly glandular tissue	Corticotropin	ACTH	Adrenal cortex	Stimulates release of adrenal steroid hormones
	Thyrotropin	TSH	Thyroid gland	Stimulates release of thyroid hormones
	Gonadotropins: Follicle-stimulating hormone	FSH	Ovaries, testes	In females, stimulates egg formation; in males, helps stimulate sperm formation
	Luteinizing hormone	LH	Ovaries, testes	In females, stimulates ovulation, corpus luteum formation; in males, promotes testosterone secretion, sperm release
	Prolactin	PRL	Mammary glands	Stimulates and sustains milk production
	Growth hormone (also called somatotropin)	GH (STH)	Most cells	Promotes growth in young; induces protein synthesis, cell division; roles in glucose, protein metabolism in adults

THE ENDOCRINE SYSTEM

Through the gamut of events that can cause a drop in blood pressure—from water lost in sweat to severe blood loss from an injury—the hypothalamus monitors the shifts and releases ADH into the bloodstream when blood pressure falls below a set point. ADH causes the arterioles in some tissues to constrict, and so systemic blood pressure rises. (For this reason, ADH is sometimes called vasopressin.)

Oxytocin has roles in reproduction in both males and females. For example, in pregnant women it triggers muscle contractions in the uterus during labor and causes milk to be released when a mother nurses her infant. New studies suggest that oxytocin is a "cuddle hormone" that helps to stimulate affectionate behavior. In sexually active people, both male and female, it apparently is a chemical trigger for feelings of satisfaction after sexual contact.

THE ANTERIOR PITUITARY LOBE PRODUCES SIX OTHER HORMONES

Inside the pituitary stalk, a capillary bed picks up hormones secreted by the hypothalamus and delivers them to another capillary bed in the anterior lobe. There the hormones leave the bloodstream and act on various target cells. As Figure 15.4 shows, those anterior pituitary cells produce and secrete six hormones:

Corticotropin	ACTH
Thyrotropin	TSH
Follicle-stimulating hormone	FSH
Luteinizing hormone	LH
Prolactin	PRL
Growth hormone (somatotropin)	GH (or STH)

All these hormones have widespread effects. ACTH and TSH orchestrate secretions from the adrenal glands and thyroid gland, respectively. FSH and LH both influence reproduction, as you'll read in Chapter 16. Prolactin is best known for its role in stimulating and sustaining the production of breast milk, after other hormones have primed the tissues. There also is evidence that it promotes the synthesis of the male sex hormone testosterone.

Growth hormone (GH) affects most body tissues. It stimulates protein synthesis and cell division and has a major influence on growth, especially of cartilage and bone. You may recall from Chapter 5 that GH sustains the epiphyseal plates at the ends of growing long bones. GH is equally important as a "metabolic hormone." It stimulates cells to take up amino acids and promotes the breakdown and release of fat stored in adipose tissues, making more fatty acids available to cells. GH also adjusts the rate at which cells take up glucose. In this way it helps to maintain proper blood levels of that cellular fuel.

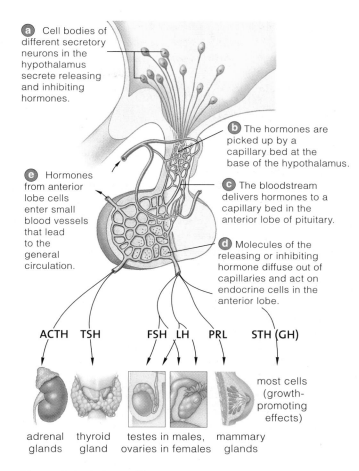

a Cell bodies of different secretory neurons in the hypothalamus secrete releasing and inhibiting hormones.

b The hormones are picked up by a capillary bed at the base of the hypothalamus.

e Hormones from anterior lobe cells enter small blood vessels that lead to the general circulation.

c The bloodstream delivers hormones to a capillary bed in the anterior lobe of pituitary.

d Molecules of the releasing or inhibiting hormone diffuse out of capillaries and act on endocrine cells in the anterior lobe.

ACTH TSH   FSH LH   PRL   STH (GH)

most cells (growth-promoting effects)

adrenal glands   thyroid gland   testes in males, ovaries in females   mammary glands

Figure 15.4 *Animated!* Links between the hypothalamus and the anterior lobe of the pituitary. Also shown are main targets of the anterior lobe's secretions.

Most hypothalamic hormones that act in the anterior pituitary are **releasers** that stimulate target cells to secrete other hormones. For example, GnRH (gonadotropin-releasing hormone) triggers the secretion of FSH and LH, both of which are classified as gonadotropins. Likewise, TRH (thyrotropin-releasing hormone) stimulates the secretion of TSH. Other hypothalamic hormones are **inhibitors**. They *block* secretions from their targets in the anterior pituitary. One of them, somatostatin, inhibits the secretion of growth hormone and thyrotropin.

The hypothalamus and pituitary gland interact to control the secretion of numerous hormones. The pituitary's posterior lobe stores and secretes ADH and oxytocin, both of which target specific types of cells.

The anterior lobe of the pituitary produces and secretes six hormones: ACTH, TSH, FSH, LH, PRL, and GH. These trigger the release of other hormones from other endocrine glands, with wide-ranging effects throughout the body.

15.4 Factors That Influence Hormone Effects

The effects of a hormone will depend on a variety of factors, including how well controls operate, interactions with other hormones, and the status of target cells.

PROBLEMS WITH CONTROL MECHANISMS CAN RESULT IN SKEWED HORMONE SIGNALS

The body does not churn out enormous numbers of hormone molecules. Two researchers, Roger Guilleman and Andrew Schally, realized this when they isolated TRH, the first-known releasing hormone. In four years of work, they dissected 500 tons of brains and 7 metric tons of hypothalamic tissue from sheep and ended up with only a pinhead-sized amount of TRH.

In general, endocrine glands release small quantities of hormones in short bursts. Controls over the frequency of hormone release prevent hormones from being either overproduced or underproduced. If something interferes with the controls, the body's form and functioning may be altered in abnormal ways.

For example, as we noted in Section 15.3, the pituitary gland releases growth hormone. Because this hormone has such widespread effects on bodily growth, if the pituitary secretes too much or too little of it the impact can be profound. For instance, **gigantism** results when growth hormone is overproduced during childhood. Affected adults are proportionally like an average-sized person but much larger (Figure 15.5*a*). **Pituitary dwarfism** results when the pituitary makes too little growth hormone. Affected adults are proportionally similar to an average person but much smaller.

What happens if too much growth hormone is secreted during adulthood, when long bones such as the femur no longer can lengthen? Bone, cartilage, and other connective tissues in the hands, feet, and jaws thicken abnormally. So do epithelia of the skin, nose, eyelids, lips, and tongue. The result is **acromegaly** (Figure 15.5*b*).

As another example, ADH secretion may fall or stop if the pituitary's posterior lobe is damaged, as by a blow to the head. This is one cause of **diabetes insipidus**. A person with this disease excretes a great deal of dilute urine—so much that serious dehydration can occur. Hormone replacement therapy is an effective treatment for this form of diabetes.

Figure 15.5 (**a**) A child affected by pituitary gigantism. This boy is twelve years old and six feet, five inches tall. His mother is standing beside him.

(**b**) Acromegaly, resulting from excessive production of GH during adulthood. Before this person reached maturity, she was symptom-free.

a

b

HORMONE INTERACTIONS, FEEDBACK, AND OTHER FACTORS ALSO INFLUENCE A HORMONE'S EFFECTS

At least four factors can influence the effects of a given hormone. To begin with, hormones often interact with one another, as noted in Section 15.1. Also, negative feedback mechanisms usually control the secretion of hormones. When the concentration of a hormone rises or falls in some body region, the change triggers events that either slow or boost further secretion. Target cells also may react differently to a hormone at different times, depending on the hormone's concentration and on how the cell's hormone receptors are functioning at that moment. Finally, environmental cues, such as light, can trigger or prevent the release of a hormone. Table 15.3 lists hormones from sources other than the pituitary gland. The rest of this chapter will provide examples of their effects and how they are controlled.

Normally, the release of a hormone is tightly regulated. These controls and a hormone's effects are influenced by hormone interactions, feedback mechanisms, variations in the state of target cells, and sometimes environmental cues.

Table 15.3   Hormone Sources Other Than the Hypothalamus and Pituitary

Source	Secretion(s)	Main Targets	Primary Actions
PANCREATIC ISLETS	Insulin	Muscle, adipose tissue	Lowers blood-sugar level
	Glucagon	Liver	Raises blood-sugar level
	Somatostatin	Insulin-secreting cells	Influences carbohydrate metabolism
ADRENAL CORTEX	Glucocorticoids (including cortisol)	Most cells	Promote protein breakdown and conversion to glucose
	Mineralocorticoids (including aldosterone)	Kidney	Promote sodium reabsorption; control salt–water balance
ADRENAL MEDULLA	Epinephrine (adrenalin)	Liver, muscle, adipose tissue	Raises blood level of sugar, fatty acids; increases heart rate, force of contraction
	Norepinephrine	Smooth muscle of blood vessels	Promotes constriction or dilation of blood vessel diameter
THYROID	Triiodothyronine, thyroxine	Most cells	Regulate metabolism; have roles in growth, development
	Calcitonin	Bone	Lowers calcium levels in blood
PARATHYROIDS	Parathyroid hormone	Bone, kidney	Elevates levels of calcium and phosphate ions in blood
THYMUS	Thymosins, etc.	Lymphocytes	Have roles in immune responses
GONADS:			
Testes (in males)	Androgens (including testosterone)	General	Required in sperm formation, development of genitals, maintenance of sexual traits; influence growth, development
Ovaries (in females)	Estrogens	General	Required in egg maturation and release; prepare uterine lining for pregnancy; required in development of genitals, maintenance of sexual traits; influence growth, development
	Progesterone	Uterus, breasts	Prepares, maintains uterine lining for pregnancy; stimulates breast development
PINEAL	Melatonin	Hypothalamus	Influences daily biorhythms
ENDOCRINE CELLS OF STOMACH, GUT	Gastrin, secretin, etc.	Stomach, pancreas, gallbladder	Stimulate activity of stomach, pancreas, liver, gallbladder
LIVER	IGFs (Insulin-like growth factors)	Most cells	Stimulate cell growth and development
KIDNEYS	Erythropoietin	Bone marrow	Stimulates red blood cell production
	Angiotensin*	Adrenal cortex, arterioles	Helps control blood pressure, aldosterone secretion
	Vitamin D3*	Bone, gut	Enhances calcium resorption and uptake
HEART	Atrial natriuretic hormone	Kidney, blood vessels	Increases sodium excretion; lowers blood pressure

*These hormones are not produced in the kidneys but are formed when enzymes produced in kidneys activate specific substances in the blood.

15.5 The Thymus, Thyroid, and Parathyroid Glands

LINKS TO
SECTIONS
5.1 AND 10.3

Thymus gland hormones stimulate T cells to mature, while hormones from the thyroid gland are vital to normal development and metabolism. Parathyroid hormone helps regulate calcium levels in the blood.

THYMUS GLAND HORMONES AID IMMUNITY

The thymus gland lies beneath the upper part of the breastbone or sternum (see Figure 15.1). The hormones it releases, called thymosins, help infection-fighting T cells mature. The thymus is quite large in children but it shrinks to a relatively small size as an adolescent matures into adulthood.

THYROID HORMONES AFFECT METABOLISM, GROWTH, AND DEVELOPMENT

The **thyroid gland** is located at the base of the neck in front of the trachea, or windpipe (Figure 15.6). Its main secretions, thyroxine (T_4) and triiodothyronine (T_3), are known jointly as *thyroid hormone* (TH). TH affects the body's overall metabolic rate, growth, and development. The thyroid also makes calcitonin. This hormone helps lower the level of calcium (and of phosphate) in blood. Proper feedback control is essential to the functioning of both these hormones.

For instance, thyroid hormones cannot be synthesized without iodide, a form of iodine. Iodine-deficient diets cause one or both lobes of the thyroid gland to enlarge (Figure 15.7). The enlargement, a **simple goiter**, occurs after low blood levels of thyroid hormones cause the anterior pituitary to secrete TSH (the thyroid-stimulating hormone thyrotropin). The thyroid attempts to make the hormones but cannot do so, which leads to continued secretion of TSH, and so on, in a sustained, but abnormal feedback loop. *Hypothyroidism* is the clinical name for low blood levels of thyroid hormones. Affected adults tend to be overweight, sluggish, intolerant of cold, confused, and depressed. Simple goiter is no longer common in places where people use iodized salt.

Graves disease and other so-called toxic goiters are the result of *hyperthyroidism*, or excess thyroid hormones in the blood. Symptoms include increased heart rate and blood pressure and unusually heavy sweating. Some cases are autoimmune disorders, in which antibodies wrongly stimulate thyroid cells. In other cases the cause can be traced to inflammation or a tumor in the thyroid gland. Some people are genetically predisposed to the disorder.

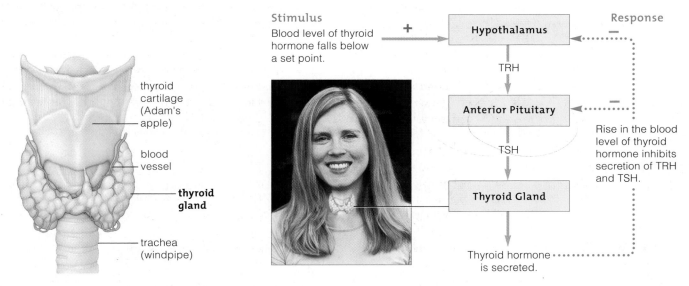

Figure 15.6 *Animated!*   The feedback loop that controls the secretion of thyroid hormone.

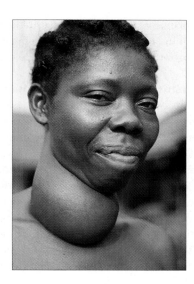

Figure 15.7 A case of goiter caused by a diet low in the micronutrient iodine.

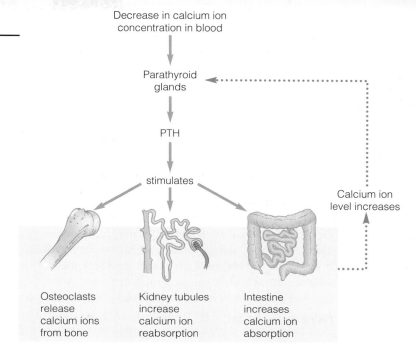

Figure 15.8 How PTH regulates calcium homeostasis.

PTH FROM THE PARATHYROIDS IS THE MAIN CALCIUM REGULATOR

We humans have four **parathyroid glands** located on the back of the thyroid gland, as shown in the diagram here. These little glands secrete parathyroid hormone (PTH), the main regulator of the calcium level in blood. Calcium is important for muscle contraction as well as

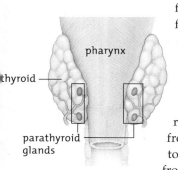

for the activation of enzymes, the formation of bone, blood clotting, and other tasks. The parathyroids secrete more PTH when the blood level of calcium falls below a set point, and they reduce their secretions when the calcium level rises. The hormone calcitonin from the thyroid gland contributes to processes that remove calcium from the blood.

You may recall that Section 5.1 discussed bone remodeling, the process in which bone is deposited or broken down, depending on the level of calcium in the blood. PTH is the hormone in charge of remodeling, and it acts on the skeleton and kidneys. When the blood level of calcium falls below a set point, PTH prompts the bone cells called osteoclasts to secrete enzymes that digest bone tissue (Figure 15.8). This process releases calcium ions (and phosphate) that can be used elsewhere in the body. In the kidneys, PTH also stimulates the

reabsorption of calcium from the filtrate flowing through nephrons. At the same time, PTH helps to activate vitamin D. The activated form, which is also a hormone, improves the absorption of calcium from food in the GI tract.

In children who have vitamin D deficiency, too little calcium and phosphorus are absorbed, so the rapidly growing bones do not develop properly. Children who have the resulting bone disorder, **rickets**, develop bowed legs and other skeletal abnormalities.

Calcium has so many essential roles in the body that disorders related to parathyroid functioning can be quite serious. For example, excess PTH (*hyperparathyroidism*) causes so much calcium to be withdrawn from a person's bones that the bone tissue is dangerously weakened. The excess calcium in the bloodstream may cause kidney stones, and muscles don't function normally. The central nervous system's operations may be so disrupted that the affected person dies.

Thymosins produced in the thymus help T cells mature.

Thyroid hormones affect metabolism, growth, and development. Negative feedback loops control the output of these and other endocrine glands.

Parathyroid glands release PTH, the main regulator of calcium levels in blood.

15.6 Adrenal Glands and Stress Responses

LINKS TO
SECTIONS
7.8, 10.4, 12.6,
AND 13.6

Different parts of the adrenal glands secrete hormones that help regulate blood levels of glucose, influence blood pressure, and regulate blood circulation, among other roles.

THE ADRENAL CORTEX PRODUCES GLUCOCORTICOIDS AND MINERALOCORTICOIDS

We have two adrenal glands, one on top of each kidney. The outer part of each gland is the **adrenal cortex** (Figure 15.9). There, cells secrete two major types of steroid hormones, the glucocorticoids and mineralocorticoids.

Glucocorticoids raise the blood level of glucose. For instance, the body's main glucocorticoid, *cortisol*, is secreted when the body is stressed and glucose is in such demand that its blood level drops to a low set point. That level is an alarm signal; it starts a stress response, which a negative feedback mechanism later cuts off. Among other effects, it promotes protein breakdown in muscle and stimulates the liver to take up amino acids, from which liver cells synthesize glucose in a process called **gluconeogenesis**. Cortisol also reduces how much glucose tissues such as skeletal muscle take up from the blood. This effect is sometimes called "glucose sparing." Glucose sparing is extremely important in homeostasis, for it helps ensure that the blood will carry enough glucose to meet the needs of the brain, which generally cannot use other molecules for fuel. Cortisol also promotes the breakdown of fats and the use of the resulting fatty acids for energy.

Figure 15.9 diagrams how negative feedback governs the release of cortisol. In this example, when the blood level of cortisol rises above a set point, the hypothalamus begins to secrete less of the releasing hormone CRH. The anterior pituitary responds by secreting less ACTH, and the adrenal cortex secretes less cortisol. In a healthy person, daily cortisol secretion is highest when the blood glucose level is lowest, usually in the early morning. Chronic severe *hypoglycemia*, an ongoing low glucose concentration in the blood, can develop when the adrenal cortex makes too little cortisol. Then, the mechanisms that spare glucose and generate new supplies in the liver do not operate properly.

Glucocorticoids also suppress inflammation. The adrenal cortex increases its secretion of these chemicals when a person experiences unusual physical stress such as a painful injury, severe illness, or an allergic reaction. The ample supply of cortisol and other signaling molecules helps speed recovery. That is why doctors prescribe cortisol-like drugs, such as cortisone, for patients with asthma and serious inflammatory disorders. Cortisone is the active ingredient in many over-the-counter products for treating skin irritations.

Long-term use of large doses of glucocorticoids has serious side effects, including suppressing the immune system. Long-term stress has the same effect, as you'll read shortly.

For the most part, **mineralocorticoids** adjust the concentrations of mineral salts, such as potassium and sodium, in the extracellular fluid. The most abundant mineralocorticoid is aldosterone. You may recall from Section 12.6 that aldosterone acts on the distal tubules of kidney nephrons, stimulating them to reabsorb sodium ions and excrete potassium ions. The reabsorption of sodium in turn promotes reabsorption of water from the tubules as urine is forming. A variety of circumstances, such as falling blood pressure or falling blood levels of sodium (falling blood volume as water moves out by osmosis), can trigger the release of aldosterone.

In a developing fetus and early in puberty, the adrenal cortex also secretes large amounts of sex hormones. The main ones are androgens (male sex hormones). Female sex hormones (estrogens and progesterone) are also produced. In adults, however, the reproductive organs generate most sex hormones.

HORMONES FROM THE ADRENAL MEDULLA HELP REGULATE BLOOD CIRCULATION

The **adrenal medulla** is the inner part of the adrenal gland shown in Figure 15.9. It contains neurons that release two substances, epinephrine and norepinephrine. Both act as neurotransmitters when they are secreted by neurons elsewhere in the body. When the adrenal medulla secretes them, however, their hormonelike effects help regulate blood circulation and carbohydrate use when the body is stressed or excited. For example, they increase the heart rate, dilate arterioles in some areas and constrict them in others, and dilate bronchioles. Thus the heart beats faster and harder, more blood is shunted to heart and muscle cells from other regions, and more oxygen flows to energy-demanding cells throughout the body. These are aspects of the fight–flight response noted in Chapter 13.

The operation of the adrenal medulla provides another example of negative feedback control. For example, when the hypothalamus sends the necessary signal (by way of sympathetic nerves) to the adrenal medulla, the neuron axons will start to release norepinephrine into the synapse between the axon endings and the target cells. Soon, norepinephrine molecules collect in the synapse, setting the stage for a localized negative feedback mechanism. As the accumulating norepinephrine binds to receptors on the axon endings, the release of norepinephrine shuts down in short order.

THE ENDOCRINE SYSTEM

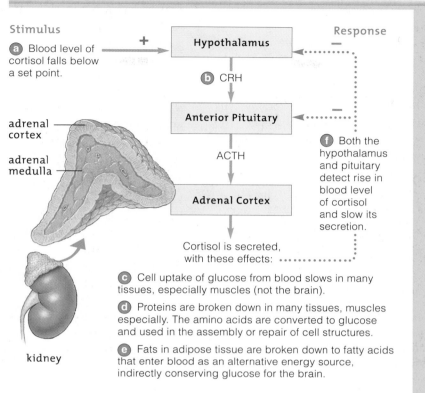

Stimulus

a Blood level of cortisol falls below a set point.

Response

+ → **Hypothalamus** ← **−**

b CRH

adrenal cortex

adrenal medulla

Anterior Pituitary ← **−**

ACTH

f Both the hypothalamus and pituitary detect rise in blood level of cortisol and slow its secretion.

Adrenal Cortex

Cortisol is secreted, with these effects:

c Cell uptake of glucose from blood slows in many tissues, especially muscles (not the brain).

d Proteins are broken down in many tissues, muscles especially. The amino acids are converted to glucose and used in the assembly or repair of cell structures.

kidney

e Fats in adipose tissue are broken down to fatty acids that enter blood as an alternative energy source, indirectly conserving glucose for the brain.

Figure 15.9 *Animated!* Structure of the adrenal gland. One gland rests atop each kidney. The diagram shows a negative feedback loop that governs the secretion of cortisol.

LONG-TERM STRESS CAN DAMAGE HEALTH

As you've just read, when the body is stressed, nervous system commands trigger the fight–flight response and the release of cortisol, epinephrine, and norepinephrine. In daily life, most people also encounter a wide variety of psychosocial stressors—an exam, financial difficulties, a new job or romance, and the like. As you can see from this short list, some stressors are positive, others are negative. Not everyone reacts the same way to life's challenges, but there is ample evidence that being routinely "stressed out" by negative stressors may contribute to hypertension and related cardiovascular disease. And because cortisol suppresses the immune system, people who experience a lot of "bad" stress also may be more susceptible to disease. Chronic negative stress also is linked to insomnia, anxiety, and depression.

Fortunately, research also shows that social connections seem to moderate the effects of stress, as does regular physical exercise. Friends, family, support groups, and counselors can not only make you feel better, they may make you healthier as well.

The adrenal cortex secretes glucocorticoids such as cortisol and mineralocorticoids such as aldosterone.

Cortisol raises blood glucose levels and suppresses inflammation. Aldosterone helps regulate blood pressure by adjusting the reabsorption of potassium and sodium in the kidneys.

The adrenal medulla makes two hormones, epinephrine and norepinephrine, that adjust blood circulation and the use of blood glucose in the fight–flight response to stress.

15.7 The Pancreas: Regulating Blood Sugar

LINK TO SECTION 7.5

Insulin and glucagon from the pancreas are examples of hormones that work antagonistically, the action of one opposing the action of the other. Controls over when these two hormones are secreted maintain the glucose level in blood.

The pancreas is a gland with both exocrine *and* endocrine functions. As described in Chapter 7, its exocrine cells release digestive enzymes into the small intestine. The endocrine cells of the pancreas are located in roughly 2 million scattered clusters. Each cluster, a **pancreatic islet**, contains three types of hormone-secreting cells:

1. *Alpha cells* secrete *glucagon*. Between meals, cells use the glucose delivered to them by the bloodstream. When the blood glucose level decreases below a set point, secreted glucagon acts on cells in the liver and muscles. It causes glycogen (a storage polysaccharide) and amino acids to be converted to glucose. In this way glucagon raises the glucose level in the blood.

2. *Beta cells* secrete the hormone *insulin*. After meals, when a lot of glucose is circulating in the blood, insulin stimulates muscle and adipose cells to take up glucose. It also promotes synthesis of fats, glycogen, and to a lesser extent, proteins, and inhibits the conversion of proteins to glucose. In this way insulin lowers the glucose level in the blood.

3. *Delta cells* secrete *somatostatin*. This hormone acts on beta cells and alpha cells to inhibit secretion of insulin and glucagon, respectively. Somatostatin is part of several hormone-based control systems. For example, it is released from the hypothalamus to block secretion of growth hormone; it is also secreted by cells of the GI tract, where it acts to inhibit the secretion of various substances involved in digestion.

Figure 15.10 shows how pancreatic hormones help keep blood glucose levels fairly constant, even with all the variations in when and how much we eat. When the body can't produce enough insulin or when target cells can't respond to it, the body does not store glucose in the normal way. Then, body mechanisms for metabolizing carbohydrates, proteins, and fats are disrupted.

> *Alpha cells of the pancreatic islets secrete glucagon when the blood level of glucose falls below a set point. Islet beta cells secrete insulin when blood levels of glucose rise above the set point.*

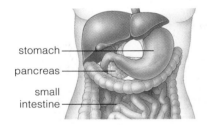

stomach
pancreas
small intestine

Figure 15.10 *Animated!* How cells that secrete insulin and glucagon respond to a change in the level of glucose in blood. These two hormones work antagonistically to maintain the glucose level in its normal range.

(**a**) *After* a meal, glucose enters blood faster than cells can take it up and its level in blood increases. In the pancreas, the increase (**b**) stops alpha cells from secreting glucagon and (**c**) stimulates beta cells to secrete insulin. In response to insulin, (**d**) adipose and muscle cells take up and store glucose, and cells in the liver synthesize more glycogen. As a result, insulin *lowers* the blood level of glucose (**e**).

(**f**) *Between* meals, the glucose level in blood falls. The decrease (**g**) stimulates alpha cells to secrete glucagon and (**h**) slows the insulin secretion by beta cells. (**i**) In the liver, glucagon causes cells to convert glycogen back to glucose, which enters the blood. As a result, glucagon *raises* the blood level of glucose (**j**).

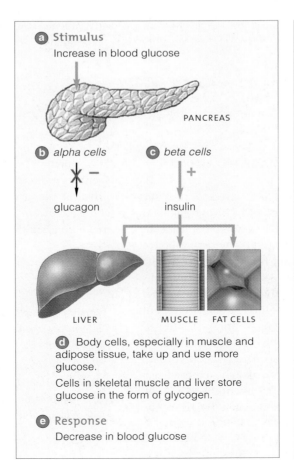

a Stimulus
Increase in blood glucose

PANCREAS

b *alpha cells*

c *beta cells*

glucagon

insulin

LIVER   MUSCLE   FAT CELLS

d Body cells, especially in muscle and adipose tissue, take up and use more glucose.

Cells in skeletal muscle and liver store glucose in the form of glycogen.

e Response
Decrease in blood glucose

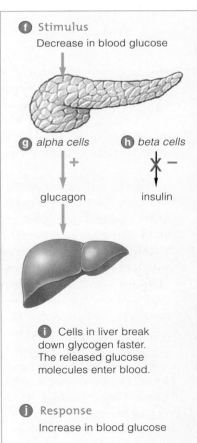

f Stimulus
Decrease in blood glucose

g *alpha cells*

h *beta cells*

glucagon

insulin

i Cells in liver break down glycogen faster. The released glucose molecules enter blood.

j Response
Increase in blood glucose

15.8 Disorders of Glucose Homeostasis

Chronically having too much or too little glucose in your blood is a serious, even life-threatening condition.

Too little insulin can lead to **diabetes mellitus**. Because target cells can't take up glucose from blood, glucose builds up in the blood (*mellitus* means "honey" in Greek). The kidneys move excess glucose into the urine, water is also lost, and the body's water–solute balance is upset. Affected people become dehydrated and extremely thirsty. They also lose weight as their glucose-starved cells break down protein and fats for energy. Fat breakdown releases ketones, so these acids build up in the blood and urine. This leads to excess water loss, which in turn can lead to dangerously low blood pressure and heart failure. Another outcome is **metabolic acidosis**, a lower than optimal pH in blood that can disrupt brain function.

In **type 1 diabetes**, an autoimmune response destroys beta cells in the pancreas. Only about 1 in 10 diabetics is type 1, the more immediately dangerous of the two types of diabetes. It may be caused by a viral infection in combination with genetic susceptibility. Symptoms tend to appear early in life so type 1 diabetes also is called "juvenile-onset diabetes." Affected people survive with insulin injections, but their life span may be shortened by associated cardiovascular problems.

TYPE 2 DIABETES IS A GLOBAL HEALTH CRISIS

In **type 2 diabetes**, insulin levels are close to or above normal, but for any of several reasons target cells can't respond properly to the hormone. The beta cells break down and produce less and less insulin. According to the World Health Organization, in the United States and other developed countries type 2 diabetes has reached crisis proportions, right along with its major risk factor—obesity.

Although we don't know exactly why, blood loaded with sugar damages capillaries. Over time, the blood supply to the kidneys, eyes, lower legs, and feet may be so poor that cells and tissues die. This fact explains some of the awful complications of diabetes (Table 15.4), including amputations due to gangrene in blood-starved tissues.

Diabetes also correlates strongly with cardiovascular disease. Even diabetics in their 20s and 30s are at high risk of suffering a stroke or heart attack.

METABOLIC SYNDROME IS A WARNING SIGN

As many as 20 million Americans unknowingly have "prediabetes"—slightly elevated blood sugar that increases the risk of developing type 2 diabetes. Useful diagnostic tools are urinalysis that looks for signs of elevated glucose, and a fasting glucose test that measures the baseline

Figure 15.11 A diabetic checks his blood glucose by placing a blood sample into a glucometer. Compared with Caucasians, Hispanics and African Americans are about 1.5 times more likely to be diabetic. Native Americans and Asians are at even greater risk.

amount of glucose in the blood several hours after a person has eaten.

An early indicator that someone may be at risk for diabetes is a constellation of features that are lumped together as **metabolic syndrome**. These features are:

- A waist measuring more than 35 inches for males and more than 40 inches for females. This characteristic is sometimes called being "apple shaped."

- Blood pressure of 130/85 mm Hg or higher

- Low levels (under 40 mg/dL for males, 50 mg/dL for females) of HDL, the "good" cholesterol

- Fasting glucose of 110 mg/dL or higher

- Fasting triglyceride level of 150 mg/dL or higher

Type 2 diabetes can be controlled by a combination of proper diet, regular exercise, and sometimes by drugs that improve insulin secretion or activity. Many people with diabetes become expert at monitoring their blood glucose and adjusting their meals to match (Figure 15.11).

Table 15.4	Some Complications of Diabetes
Eyes	Changes in lens shape and vision; damage to blood vessels in retina; blindness
Skin	Increased susceptibility to bacterial and fungal infections; patches of discoloration; thickening of skin on the back of hands
Digestive system	Gum disease; delayed stomach emptying that causes heartburn, nausea, vomiting
Kidneys	Increased risk of kidney disease and failure
Heart and blood vessels	Increased risk of heart attack, stroke, high blood pressure, and atherosclerosis
Hands and feet	Impaired ability to sense pain; formation of calluses, foot ulcers; possible amputation of toes, a foot, or leg because of tissue death caused by poor circulation

15.9 Some Final Examples of Integration and Control

LINKS TO
SECTIONS
7.8, 9.2, 10.2,
AND 14.3

Endocrine cells in parts of the brain, the heart, and even the GI tract produce hormones. They and some other signaling molecules have major effects on a range of body functions.

LIGHT/DARK CYCLES INFLUENCE THE PINEAL GLAND, WHICH PRODUCES MELATONIN

Like other animals, humans are physiologically sensitive to light. Many ancient vertebrates had a light-sensitive "third eye" on top of the head. In humans a version of this photosensitive organ still exists, as a lump of tissue in the brain called the **pineal gland**. The pineal gland secretes the hormone *melatonin* into cerebrospinal fluid and the bloodstream. Melatonin influences sleep/wake cycles, and possibly some aspects of human reproduction.

Melatonin is secreted in the dark, so the amount in the bloodstream varies from day to night. It also changes with the seasons, because winter days are shorter than summer days.

The human cycle of sleep and arousal is evidence of an internal **biological clock** that seems to tick in synchrony with day length. Melatonin seems to influence the clock, which can be disturbed by circumstances that alter a person's accustomed exposure to light and dark. Jet lag is an example; some air travelers use melatonin supplements to try to adjust their sleep/wake cycles more quickly.

Seasonal affective disorder, or **SAD**, hits some people in winter. Symptoms typically include depression and an overwhelming desire to sleep. The problem may result from a biological clock that is out of sync with changes in day length during winter, when days are shorter and nights longer. The symptoms get worse when a person with SAD takes melatonin. On the other hand, symptoms improve dramatically when the person is exposed to intense light, which shuts down the pineal gland.

Some researchers have proposed that a drop in melatonin may help trigger the onset of puberty, when the reproductive organs and structures start to mature. For instance, if disease destroys the pineal gland, an affected child can enter puberty prematurely. There is still much more to learn about this possible link.

HORMONES ALSO ARE PRODUCED IN THE HEART AND GI TRACT

Beyond the endocrine glands we have been considering, hormones are also made and secreted by specialized cells elsewhere. For example, the two heart atria secrete *atrial natriuretic peptide*, or ANP. This hormone has a variety of effects, including helping to regulate blood pressure. When your blood pressure rises, ANP acts to inhibit the reabsorption of sodium ions—and hence water—in the kidneys. As a result, more water is excreted, the blood volume decreases, and blood pressure falls.

The digestive tract produces the hormones gastrin and secretin, among others. You may recall that gastrin stimulates the release of stomach acid when proteins are being digested. Secretin stimulates the pancreas to secrete bicarbonate.

Many body cells can detect changes in their chemical environment and alter their activity to match. The "local signaling molecules" they release act on the secreting cell itself or in its immediate vicinity. Cells quickly take up most of the molecules, so that only a few enter the general circulation. Prostaglandins and growth factors, our next topics, are examples.

PROSTAGLANDINS HAVE MANY EFFECTS

Biochemists have identified more than sixteen different kinds of the fatty acids called **prostaglandins**. In fact, the plasma membranes of most cells contain the precursors of prostaglandins. They are released continually, but the rate at which they are synthesized often increases in response to chemical changes in a particular area.

What are some known effects of prostaglandins? With signals from hormones (epinephrine and norepinephrine) as the trigger, at least two prostaglandins cause smooth muscle in the walls of blood vessels to constrict or dilate, helping to adjust blood flow in the area. Similar prostaglandin effects occur in the smooth muscle of the airways. Prostaglandins may aggravate inflammation and allergic responses to dust and pollen.

Prostaglandins have a major impact on reproductive organs. For example, many women experience painful cramping and heavy bleeding when they menstruate, both effects due to prostaglandins acting on smooth muscle of the uterus. (Drugs such as ibuprofen and aspirin block the synthesis of prostaglandins, relieving the discomfort.) Prostaglandins also influence the menstrual cycle in other ways, and along with oxytocin they stimulate contractions of the uterus during labor. We will look much more closely at some of these events in Chapter 17.

GROWTH FACTORS INFLUENCE CELL DIVISION

A doctor treating someone with major spinal cord damage, like the athletes in Figure 15.12, could one day have a powerful chemical arsenal at hand. Researchers are unraveling the workings of hormonelike proteins called **growth factors**—and working to convert this knowledge into treatments for specific kinds of tissue damage.

Figure 15.12 Growth factors that spur the growth of neurons may one day be part of the standard treatment for people who have severe spinal cord injuries. Already, experiments have shown that NGF can help severed nerves regrow.

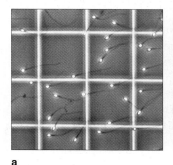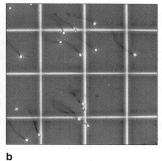

a   **b**

Figure 15.13 Normal and low sperm counts. The grid lines help clinicians count sperm. (**a**) Normally, there are about 113 million sperm per milliliter of semen per sample. (**b**) Low sperm count of 60 to 70 million sperm per milliliter. Human sperm counts have been declining.

Growth factors influence growth by regulating the rate at which certain cells divide. *Epidermal growth factor* (EGF) influences the growth of many cell types. So does *insulinlike growth factor* (IGF) made by the liver. *Nerve growth factor* (NGF) is another example. It promotes the survival and growth of neurons in developing embryos. NGF seems to define the direction in which the embryonic neurons grow: Target cells lay down a chemical path that leads the elongating axons to them.

The list of known growth factors is expanding rapidly. For instance, various ones enhance the rate at which wounds heal or stimulate the growth of blood vessels. This latter type might be harnessed to perform that function in cardiac muscle that has been damaged by a heart attack. Promising cancer research is exploring ways to block growth factors that spur the growth of blood vessels that supply malignant tumors.

PHEROMONES MAY BE IMPORTANT COMMUNICATION MOLECULES IN HUMANS

In discussing the sense of smell in Section 14.3, we touched on possible human pheromones. It's not surprising that humans may communicate via pheromones; some of our close primate relatives (such as rhesus monkeys), and bears, dogs, various insects, and many other animals make pheromones that act as territory markers, sex attractants, and other signals to members of their own species. Pheromones are released outside the individual and then travel (through the air, for instance) to reach another individual. The various hypotheses about human pheromones are still tentative, but research on this subject is continuing.

ARE ENDOCRINE DISRUPTERS AT WORK?

The chapter introduction discussed the controversy over endocrine disrupters—substances in the environment that some biologists suspect are causing problems with the reproduction or development of various species. Between 1938 and 1990, according to one study, the sperm counts of males in Western countries declined about 40 percent. Approximately fifty studies since then support these findings: Sperm counts *have* gone down (Figure 15.13). Are environmental estrogens the culprits? Possibly. Several pesticides are estrogen mimics; they bind to estrogen receptors on cells. Cells of both males and females have these receptors, and males who work with the pesticide—and estrogen mimic—Kepone have lower than normal sperm counts. Recently a well-controlled study of geographic differences in the quality of semen showed that men from Columbia, Missouri, had fewer healthy sperm than men from New York, Minneapolis, or Los Angeles. The researchers suspect that exposure to some agricultural chemicals may play a role. More studies are now under way.

Endocrine cells in the pineal gland, heart, and GI tract all produce hormones. Other cells in various tissues produce local signaling molecules, such as prostaglandins, which act on the secreting cell itself or in the immediate vicinity.

Growth factors help regulate the rate at which target cells divide.

Summary

Section 15.1 Hormones and other signaling molecules help ensure that the activities of individual body cells mesh in ways that benefit the whole body. Hormones are produced by cells and glands of the endocrine system. They move through the bloodstream to distant target cells.

Other signaling molecules include neurotransmitters, local signaling molecules such as prostaglandins, and pheromones. All are chemical secretions by one cell that adjust the behavior of other, target cells. Any cell with receptors for the signal is the target.

Hormones may interact in opposition, synergistically (in cooperation), or permissively (a target cell must first be primed by one hormone in order to respond to a second one).

Section 15.2 Steroid and nonsteroid hormones exert their effects on target cells by different mechanisms.

Receptors for steroid (and thyroid) hormones are inside target cells. The hormone-receptor complex binds to the DNA, and binding activates genes and the synthesis of proteins.

Amine, peptide, and protein hormones interact with receptors on the plasma membrane of target cells. Responses to them are often mediated by a second messenger, such as cyclic AMP, inside the cell.

Most of these nonsteroid hormones alter the activity of target cell proteins. The resulting target cell responses help maintain homeostasis in extracellular fluid or contribute to normal development or reproductive functioning.

Section 15.3 The hypothalamus and pituitary gland interact to integrate many body activities.

ADH and oxytocin, two hypothalamic hormones, are stored in and released from the posterior lobe of the pituitary. ADH influences extracellular fluid volume. Oxytocin has roles in reproduction.

Six additional hypothalamic hormones are releasers or inhibitors. They control secretions of various cells of the pituitary's anterior lobe.

Of the six hormones produced in the anterior lobe, two (prolactin and growth hormone) have general effects on cells in a variety of body tissues. Four (ACTH, TSH, FSH, and LH) act on specific endocrine glands.

Thomson NOW! *Study how the hypothalamus and pituitary interact.*

Section 15.4 Hormones are produced in small amounts, usually in short bursts. If too much or too little of a hormone is produced, the body's form and functioning may become abnormal.

Body responses to hormones may be influenced by hormone interactions, homeostatic feedback loops to the hypothalamus and pituitary, variations in hormone concentrations, and the number and kinds of receptors on a target cell.

Section 15.5 Thyroid hormone affects overall metabolism, growth, and development. The thyroid also makes calcitonin, which helps lower blood levels of calcium and phosphate. Parathyroid hormone is the main regulator of blood calcium levels.

Section 15.6 The adrenal cortex makes two kinds of steroid hormones, the glucocorticoids and mineralocorticoids. Glucocorticoids, mainly cortisol, raise the blood level of glucose and suppress inflammation. Mineralocorticoids adjust concentrations of minerals such as potassium and sodium in body fluids.

The adrenal medulla releases epinephrine and norepinephrine. Their hormonelike effects include the regulation of blood pressure and the metabolism of carbohydrates. (Certain neurons also release them as neurotransmitters.)

Thomson NOW! *See how negative feedback maintains cortisol levels.*

Section 15.7 Blood levels of glucose are regulated by insulin and glucagon, which are secreted in the pancreatic islets by beta and alpha cells, respectively. Insulin stimulates muscle and adipose cells to take up glucose, while glucagon stimulates glucose-releasing reactions in muscle and the liver. Negative feedback governs both processes. Somatostatin released by islet delta cells can inhibit the release of insulin, glucagon, and some other hormones.

Thomson NOW! *See how the actions of insulin and glucagon regulate blood sugar.*

Section 15.9 The pineal gland in the brain produces melatonin in response to light/dark cycles. Melatonin influences sleep/wake cycles as part of an internal biological clock related to day length.

The heart and GI tract secrete hormones that help adjust blood pressure and operate in digestion. Many cells produce prostaglandins in response to local chemical changes. Effects of prostaglandins range from adjusting blood flow in an area to promoting contraction of smooth muscle. Hormonelike growth factors regulate the rate at which cells divide.

Review Questions

1. Distinguish among hormones, neurotransmitters, local signaling molecules, and pheromones.

2. A hormone molecule binds to a receptor on a cell membrane. It doesn't enter the cell; rather, the binding activates a second messenger inside the cell that triggers an amplified response to the hormonal signal. Is the signaling molecule a steroid or a nonsteroid hormone?

3. Which hormones produced in the posterior and anterior lobes of the pituitary gland have the targets indicated? (*Fill in the blanks using the abbreviations noted in Section 15.3.*)

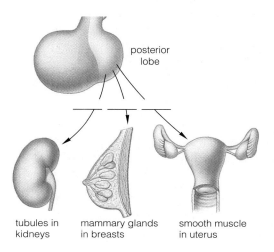

posterior
lobe

tubules in
kidneys

mammary glands
in breasts

smooth muscle
in uterus

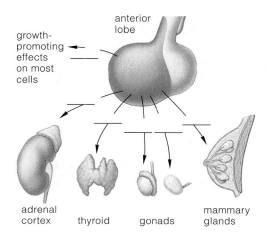

anterior
lobe

growth-
promoting
effects
on most
cells

adrenal
cortex

thyroid

gonads

mammary
glands

4. Name the main endocrine glands and state where each is located in the body.

5. Give two examples of feedback control of hormone activity.

Self-Quiz
Answers in Appendix V

1. _____ are molecules released from a signaling cell that have effects on target cells.
   a. Hormones
   b. Neurotransmitters
   c. Local signaling molecules
   d. Pheromones
   e. a and b
   f. All of the above

2. Hormones are produced by _____.
   a. endocrine glands and cells
   b. some neurons
   c. exocrine cells
   d. a and b
   e. a and c
   f. a, b, and c

3. ADH and oxytocin are hypothalamic hormones secreted from the pituitary's _____ lobe.
   a. anterior
   b. posterior
   c. primary
   d. secondary

4. _____ has effects on body tissues in general.
   a. ACTH
   b. TSH
   c. LH
   d. Growth hormone

5. Which of the following stimulate the secretion of hormones?
   a. neural signals
   b. local chemical changes
   c. hormonal signals
   d. environment cues
   e. All of the above can stimulate hormone secretion.

6. _____ lowers blood sugar levels; _____ raises the level of blood sugar.
   a. Glucagon; insulin
   b. Insulin; glucagon
   c. Gastrin; insulin
   d. Gastrin; glucagon

7. The pituitary detects a rising hormone concentration in blood and inhibits the gland that is secreting the hormone. This is a _____ feedback loop.
   a. positive
   b. negative

8. Second messengers assist _____.
   a. steroid hormones
   b. nonsteroid hormones
   c. only thyroid hormones
   d. both a and b

9. Match the hormone source with the closest description.
   ____ adrenal cortex
   ____ adrenal medulla
   ____ thyroid gland
   ____ parathyroids
   ____ pancreatic islets
   ____ pineal gland
   ____ thymus
   a. affected by day length
   b. cortisol source
   c. roles in immunity
   d. adjust(s) blood calcium level
   e. epinephrine source
   f. insulin, glucagon
   g. hormones require iodine

10. Match the endocrine control concepts.
   ____ oxytocin
   ____ ACTH
   ____ ADH
   ____ growth hormone
   ____ estrogen
   a. released by the anterior pituitary and affects the adrenal gland
   b. influences extracellular fluid volume
   c. has general effects on growth
   d. triggers uterine contractions
   e. a steroid hormone

The Endocrine System   287

Critical Thinking

1. Addison's disease develops when the adrenal cortex doesn't secrete enough mineralocorticoids and glucocorticoids. President John F. Kennedy was diagnosed with the disease when he was a young man. Before he started treatment with hormone replacement therapy, he was hypoglycemic and lost weight. Which missing hormone was responsible for his weight loss? How might Addison's disease have affected his blood pressure?

2. A physician sees a patient whose symptoms include sluggishness, depression, and intolerance to cold. After eliminating other possible causes, the doctor diagnoses an endocrine disorder. What disorder fits the symptoms? Why does the doctor suspect that the underlying cause is a malfunctioning anterior pituitary gland?

3. Marianne is affected by type 1 insulin-dependent diabetes. One day, after injecting herself with too much insulin, she starts to shake and feels confused. Following her doctor's suggestion, she drinks a glass of orange juice—a ready source of glucose—and soon her symptoms subside. What caused her symptoms? How would a glucose-rich snack help?

4. Some of the people in a remote village in Pakistan have an inherited form of dwarfism (Figure 15.14). The men are about 130 centimeters (a little over 4 feet) tall and the women about 115 centimeters (3 feet, 6 inches) tall. Northwestern University researchers discovered that the affected villagers have low levels of somatotropin, but a normal gene for this growth hormone. However, the gene coding for a receptor for one of the hypothalamic-releasing hormones is mutated. That receptor occurs on cells of the anterior pituitary. Explain how a faulty receptor may cause the abnormality.

Figure 15.14
Scientist Hiralal Maheshwari, with two men who have a heritable form of pituitary dwarfism.

Explore on Your Own

This Student Stress Scale lists a variety of life events that cause stress for young adults. The score for each event represents its relative impact on stress-related physiological responses. In general, people who score 300 points or more have the highest stress-related health risk. A score of 150–300 points indicates a moderate (50-50) stress-related health risk. A score below 150 indicates the lowest stress-related health risk, about a 1 in 3 chance of a significant, negative change in health status.

Although this test is only a general measure of stress, it can help you decide if you can benefit from adding to or improving your stress management activities, such as getting exercise, including some "down time" in your daily schedule, or seeking counseling.

Event	Points	
Death of a close family member	100	___
Death of a close friend	73	___
Parents' divorce	65	___
Jail term	63	___
Major personal injury or illness	63	___
Marriage	58	___
Being fired from a job	50	___
Failing an important course	47	___
Change in health of family member	45	___
Pregnancy (or causing one)	45	___
Sex problems	44	___
Serious argument with close friend	40	___
Change in financial status	39	___
Change of major	39	___
Trouble with parents	39	___
New romantic interest	38	___
Increased workload at school	37	___
Outstanding personal achievement	36	___
First quarter/semester in college	35	___
Change in living situation	31	___
Serious argument with instructor	30	___
Lower grades than expected	29	___
Change in sleeping habits	29	___
Change in social activities	29	___
Change in eating habits	28	___
Chronic car trouble	26	___
Change in number of family get-togethers	26	___
Too many missed classes	25	___
Change of college	24	___
Dropping more than one class	23	___
Minor traffic violations	20	___

Total _____

Adapted from the Holmes and Rahe Life Event Scale.

Sperm with a Nose for Home?

Human sperm are more than just champion swimmers. It seems that they can sense a variety of chemicals and navigate toward the source. Some researchers say this "nose for home" could be how sperm find their way to a woman's egg.

Back in the 1990s scientists discovered that human sperm have olfactory receptors virtually identical to those in the nose. Then, in 2003, a team of German investigators identified an olfactory receptor they dubbed hOR17-4, and showed that it responds to several chemicals used commercially to add a pleasing floral scent to various products. One of the compounds, called bourgeonal, causes sperm to make a beeline for the odor source.

Since it's unlikely that human eggs manufacture bourgeonal, the search is on for a chemically similar sperm attractant made by human eggs, or by cells in the female reproductive tract.

How does this kind of research apply to the real world? One outcome might be a test that screens a man's sperm for those that are most strongly attracted to the "egg scent." Those sperm could then be used for artificial insemination when a couple has trouble conceiving naturally. On the flip side, a substance that *blocked* the ability of sperm to "sniff out" their targets might be the basis for a new contraceptive method.

In this chapter we turn our focus to the male and female reproductive systems—the only body system that does not contribute to homeostasis. Instead, its role is to continue our species. For both men and women, the **reproductive system** consists of a pair of primary reproductive organs, or **gonads**, plus accessory glands and ducts. Male gonads are **testes** (singular: testis), and female gonads are **ovaries**. The testes produce sperm and the ovaries produce egg cells. Both release sex hormones that influence reproduction. We'll conclude the chapter with a look at how sexually transmitted diseases can affect reproductive organs.

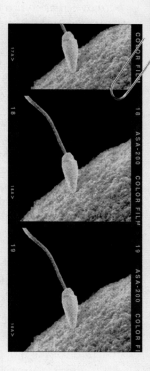

☑ *How Would You Vote?* *In recent years the rate of teenage pregnancies in the United States has fallen slightly. One contributing factor has been greater access to contraception. Some people feel strongly that teens should not use contraception without parental consent. What's your opinion? Cast your vote online at www.thomsonedu .com/biology/starr/humanbio.*

Key Concepts

THE MALE REPRODUCTIVE SYSTEM
A male's reproductive system consists of testes and accessory ducts and glands. Hormones control its functions, including making sperm.

THE FEMALE REPRODUCTIVE SYSTEM
A pair of ovaries are a female's primary reproductive organs. Hormones control their functions, including the development of oocytes (eggs).

SEXUAL INTERCOURSE AND FERTILITY
Sexual intercourse between a male and female is the usual first step toward pregnancy. Various methods exist for limiting or enhancing fertility.

SEXUALLY TRANSMITTED DISEASES
Sexual contact can transmit bacteria, viruses, and other disease-causing pathogens.

Links to Earlier Concepts

This chapter builds on what you have learned about hormones, including the steroid sex hormones estrogen and testosterone (15.1, 15.2). You will see more examples of how negative feedback loops regulate basic body functions (4.9), in this case the production of sperm in males and the menstrual cycle in females.

You will also expand your knowledge of the specialized cell structures called flagella, which propel sperm (3.8), and you will once again encounter chromosomes, the structures that carry genes (3.5).

16.1 The Male Reproductive System

LINKS TO
SECTIONS
2.7, 3.5,
AND 15.9

On any given day, millions of sperm are developing in an adult male's reproductive tract. The testes also secrete hormones that govern reproductive functions and traits associated with maleness.

SPERM (AND EGGS) DEVELOP FROM GERM CELLS

Cells in a male's gonads that give rise to sperm are sometimes called *germ cells*, from a Latin word that means "to sprout." As described in a later section, germ cells in a female's ovaries give rise to eggs. All germ cells are *diploid*—like nearly all other body cells, they have a normal number of chromosomes, which is 46. By contrast, sperm and eggs, which unite during reproduction, can have only 23 chromosomes. This is termed a *haploid* number of chromosomes because it is one-half the normal number. Sperm and eggs are also called *gametes* [GAM-eets], from a Greek word that means "to marry." When two haploid gametes unite at fertilization, the diploid chromosome number is restored. With these principles in mind, let's begin our tour of the male reproductive system.

SPERM FORM IN TESTES

Figure 16.1 shows an adult male's reproductive system and Table 16.1 lists the functions of its organs. In an embryo that is genetically programmed to become male, two testes form on the abdominal cavity wall. Before birth, the testes descend into the scrotum, a pouch of skin below the pelvic region. When a baby boy is born, his testes are fully formed miniatures of the adult organs.

Figure 16.2 shows the position of the scrotum in an adult male. If sperm cells are to develop properly, the temperature inside the scrotum must stay a few degrees cooler than body core temperature. To this end, a control mechanism stimulates or inhibits the contraction of smooth muscles in the scrotum's wall. It helps assure that the scrotum's internal temperature does not stray far from 95°F. When the air just outside the body gets too cold, contractions draw the scrotum closer to the body mass, which is warmer. When the air is warmer outside, the muscles relax and lower the scrotum.

Inside each testis are a large number of small, highly coiled tubes, the **seminiferous tubules**. Sperm begin to form in these tubules, as you'll read in Section 16.2.

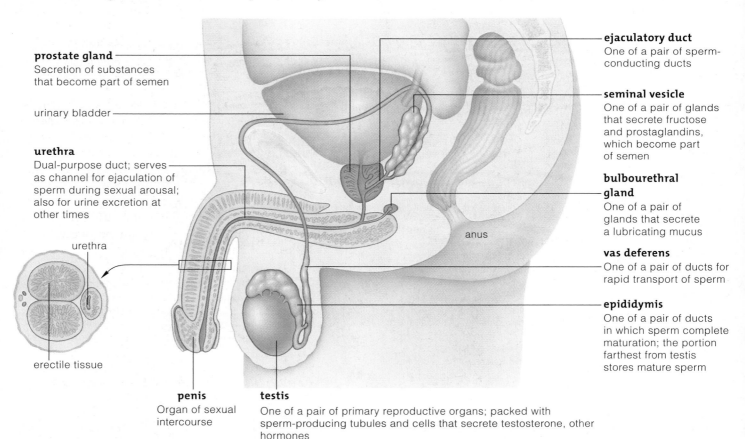

prostate gland
Secretion of substances that become part of semen

urinary bladder

urethra
Dual-purpose duct; serves as channel for ejaculation of sperm during sexual arousal; also for urine excretion at other times

urethra

erectile tissue

penis
Organ of sexual intercourse

testis
One of a pair of primary reproductive organs; packed with sperm-producing tubules and cells that secrete testosterone, other hormones

ejaculatory duct
One of a pair of sperm-conducting ducts

seminal vesicle
One of a pair of glands that secrete fructose and prostaglandins, which become part of semen

bulbourethral gland
One of a pair of glands that secrete a lubricating mucus

vas deferens
One of a pair of ducts for rapid transport of sperm

epididymis
One of a pair of ducts in which sperm complete maturation; the portion farthest from testis stores mature sperm

anus

Figure 16.1 *Animated!* Parts of the male reproductive system and their functions.

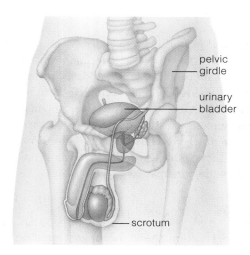

pelvic girdle

urinary bladder

scrotum

Figure 16.2 Position of the male reproductive system relative to the pelvic girdle and urinary bladder.

Table 16.1	Organs and Accessory Components of the Human Male Reproductive System	
Reproductive Organs		
	Testis (2)	Sperm, sex hormone production
	Epididymis (2)	Sperm maturation site and subsequent storage
	Vas deferens (2)	Rapid transport of sperm
	Ejaculatory duct (2)	Conduction of sperm to penis
	Penis	Organ of sexual intercourse
Accessory Glands		
	Seminal vesicle (2)	Secretion of large part of semen
	Prostate gland	Secretion of part of semen
	Bulbourethral gland (2)	Production of mucus that functions in lubrication

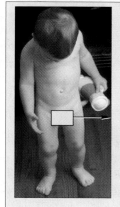

SPERM MATURE AND ARE STORED IN THE COILED EPIDIDYMIS

Human sperm are not quite mature when they leave the testes. First they enter a pair of long, coiled ducts, the epididymides (singular: epididymis). Gland cells in the walls of these ducts secrete substances that trigger the finishing touches on sperm. Until sperm leave the body, they are stored in the last stretch of each epididymis.

When a male is sexually aroused, contracting muscle in the walls of his reproductive organs propels mature sperm into and through a pair of thick-walled tubes, the **vas deferentia** (singular: vas deferens). From there, contractions move sperm through a pair of ejaculatory ducts and on through the urethra to the outside. The urethra passes through the **penis**, the male sex organ, and also carries urine.

SUBSTANCES FROM SEMINAL VESICLES AND THE PROSTATE GLAND HELP FORM SEMEN

Glandular secretions become mixed with sperm as they travel through the urethra. The result is **semen**, a thick fluid that is eventually expelled from the penis during sexual activity. As semen is beginning to form, a pair of **seminal vesicles** secrete fructose. The sperm use this sugar for energy. Seminal vesicles also secrete certain kinds of prostaglandins. You may recall from Section 15.9 that these signaling molecules can induce muscle contractions. During sex, the prostaglandins cause contractions in muscles of a female's reproductive tract, and so aid the movement of sperm through it toward the egg.

Substances secreted by the **prostate gland** probably help buffer the acidic environment that sperm encounter in the female reproductive tract. The vaginal pH is about 3.5 to 4.0, but sperm motility improves at pH 6. Two **bulbourethral glands** secrete mucus-rich fluid into the urethra when a male is sexually aroused. This fluid neutralizes acids in any traces of urine in the urethra, and this more alkaline environment creates more hospitable surroundings for the 150 to 350 million sperm that pass through the channel in a typical ejaculation.

The testes and prostate gland both are sites where cancer can develop. At least 5,000 cases of testicular cancer are diagnosed each year in the United States, mostly among young men. This cancer kills about half of its victims. Prostate cancer, which is more common among men over 50, kills 40,000 older men annually—almost the same mortality rate recorded for breast cancer in women. As with other cancers, early detection is the key to survival. Causes and treatments of cancers are the subject of Chapter 23.

Males have a pair of testes—primary reproductive organs that produce sperm and sex hormones—as well as accessory glands and ducts.

Sperm develop mainly in the seminiferous tubules of the testes. When sperm are nearly mature, they leave each testis and enter the long, coiled epididymis, where they remain until ejaculated.

Secretions from the seminal vesicles and the prostate gland mix with sperm to form semen.

16.2 How Sperm Form

LINKS TO SECTIONS 3.4, 3.8, AND 15.3

Sperm are specialized to unite with eggs in reproduction. Here, we trace the steps by which sperm develop.

SPERM FORM IN SEMINIFEROUS TUBULES

A testis is smaller than a golf ball, yet packed inside it are 125 meters—over 400 feet—of seminiferous tubules. As many as 30 wedge-shaped lobes divide the interior, and each holds two or three coiled tubules (Figure 16.3*a*).

Inside the walls of seminiferous tubules are cells called *spermatogonia* (Figure 16.3*b*). They are the starting point for several rounds of cell division, including a type called *mitosis* and a type called *meiosis*. You'll read more about mitosis and meiosis in Chapter 19; here the main thing to keep in mind is that meiosis is necessary to form sperm and eggs.

Spermatogonia develop into *primary spermatocytes*, which become *secondary spermatocytes* after a first round of meiosis (meiosis I). A second round of cell division (meiosis II) produces *spermatids*. The spermatids gradually develop into *spermatozoa*, or simply **sperm**, the male gametes. The "tail" of each sperm, a flagellum, arises at the end of the process, which takes nine to ten weeks. All the while, the developing cells are nourished by and receive chemical signals from neighboring **Sertoli cells** that line the seminiferous tubule.

The testes produce sperm from puberty onward. Millions are in different stages of development on any given day. A mature sperm has a tail, a midpiece, and a head (Figure 16.3*c*). Inside the head, a nucleus contains DNA organized into chromosomes. An enzyme-containing cap, the **acrosome**, covers most of the head. Its enzymes help the sperm penetrate protective material around an egg at fertilization. In the midpiece, mitochondria supply energy for the tail's movements.

HORMONES CONTROL SPERM FORMATION

Male reproductive function depends on testosterone, LH, and FSH. **Leydig cells** (also called interstitial cells), located in tissue between the seminiferous tubules in testes (Figure 16.4*a*), secrete **testosterone**. This hormone governs the growth, form, and functions of the male reproductive tract. It stimulates sexual behavior, and at puberty it promotes the development of male **secondary sexual traits**, including facial hair and deepening of an adolescent male's voice.

LH (luteinizing hormone) and **FSH** (follicle-stimulating hormone) are released from the anterior lobe of the pituitary gland (Figure 16.4*b*). These two hormones were named for their effects in females, but are chemically the same in males.

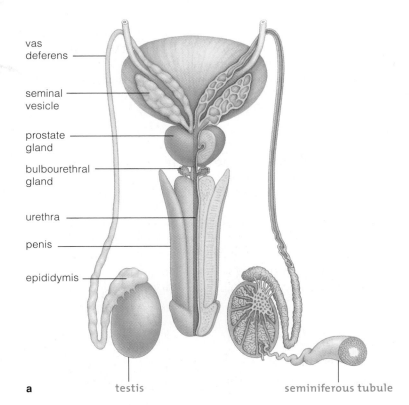

a   testis   seminiferous tubule

vas deferens
seminal vesicle
prostate gland
bulbourethral gland
urethra
penis
epididymis

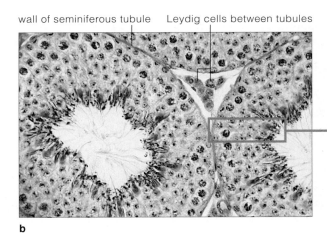

wall of seminiferous tubule   Leydig cells between tubules

b

Figure 16.3 *Animated!* (**a**) The male reproductive tract viewed from behind. (**b**) Leydig cells in tissue spaces between seminiferous tubules. In this light micrograph you can see parts of three of the tubules. (**c**) How sperm form, starting with a diploid germ cell. Cell divisions by mitosis, then meiosis, produce haploid cells that develop into sperm. (**d**) The structure of a mature sperm, the male gamete.

Since the hypothalamus controls secretions of LH, FSH, and testosterone, it controls the formation of sperm. When the testosterone level in a male's blood falls below a set point, the hypothalamus secretes GnRH. This releasing hormone prompts the pituitary's anterior lobe to release LH and FSH, which have targets in the testes. LH stimulates Leydig cells to secrete testosterone, which stimulates diploid germ cells to become sperm. Sertoli cells have FSH receptors. FSH is crucial to starting sperm formation (called *spermatogenesis*) at puberty, but researchers do not know whether it is essential for the normal functioning of mature testes.

A high level of testosterone in a male's blood inhibits the release of GnRH. Also, when the sperm count is high, Sertoli cells release inhibin, a hormone that acts on the hypothalamus and pituitary to inhibit the release of GnRH and FSH. Accordingly, feedback loops to the hypothalamus begin to operate, causing testosterone secretion and sperm formation to decline.

The formation of sperm depends on the hormones testosterone, LH, and FSH. Testosterone also governs the development of secondary sexual traits. Feedback loops from the testes to the hypothalamus and pituitary gland control the secretion of these hormones.

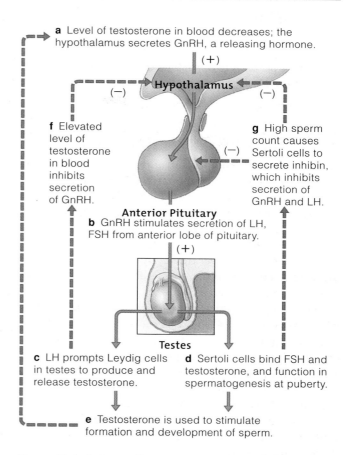

a Level of testosterone in blood decreases; the hypothalamus secretes GnRH, a releasing hormone.

Hypothalamus

f Elevated level of testosterone in blood inhibits secretion of GnRH.

g High sperm count causes Sertoli cells to secrete inhibin, which inhibits secretion of GnRH and LH.

Anterior Pituitary

b GnRH stimulates secretion of LH, FSH from anterior lobe of pituitary.

Testes

c LH prompts Leydig cells in testes to produce and release testosterone.

d Sertoli cells bind FSH and testosterone, and function in spermatogenesis at puberty.

e Testosterone is used to stimulate formation and development of sperm.

Figure 16.4 *Animated!* Negative feedback loops to the hypothalamus and pituitary gland from the testes.

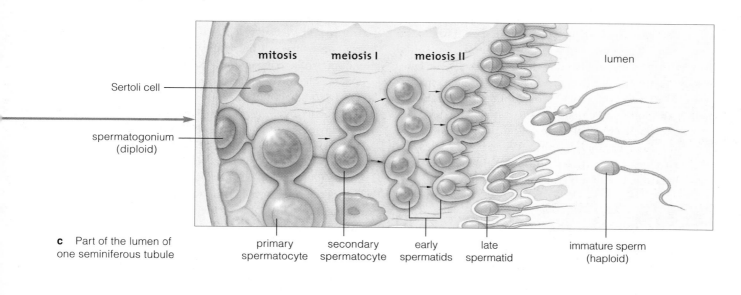

mitosis   meiosis I   meiosis II   lumen

Sertoli cell

spermatogonium (diploid)

c Part of the lumen of one seminiferous tubule

primary spermatocyte

secondary spermatocyte

early spermatids

late spermatid

immature sperm (haploid)

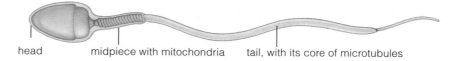

d Sketch of a mature human sperm. The head consists of DNA surrounded by the acrosome.

head   midpiece with mitochondria   tail, with its core of microtubules

16.3 The Female Reproductive System

We now consider the female reproductive system. Its biological function is to nurture developing offspring from conception until birth.

OVARIES ARE A FEMALE'S PRIMARY REPRODUCTIVE ORGANS

Figure 16.5 shows the parts of the female reproductive system and Table 16.2 summarizes their functions. A female's primary reproductive organs are her two **ovaries**. The ovaries release sex hormones, and during a woman's reproductive years they also produce eggs. The ovarian hormones influence the development of female secondary sexual traits. These traits include the "filling out" of breasts, hips, and buttocks as fat deposits accumulate in those areas.

A female's immature eggs are called **oocytes**. When an oocyte is released from an ovary, it moves into the neighboring **oviduct** (sometimes called a *fallopian tube*). The oviducts are where a sperm may fertilize an egg. Fertilized or not, an egg travels down the oviduct into the hollow, pear-shaped **uterus**. In this organ, a baby can grow and develop. The wall of the uterus consists of a thick layer of smooth muscle (the myometrium) and an interior lining, the **endometrium**. The endometrium includes epithelium, connective tissue, glands, and blood vessels. The lower part of the uterus is the *cervix*. The *vagina* leads from the cervix to the body surface. It is a muscular tube that receives the penis and sperm and functions as part of the birth canal.

A female's external genitals are collectively called the *vulva*. Outermost are a pair of fat-padded skin folds, the *labia majora*. They enclose a smaller pair of skin folds, the *labia minora*, that are laced with blood vessels. The labia minora partly enclose the *clitoris*, a small organ sensitive to sexual stimulation. From a developmental standpoint, the female's clitoris is analogous to a male's penis.

A female's urethra opens about midway between her clitoris and her vaginal opening. Whereas in males the urethra carries both urine and sperm, in females it is separate and is not involved in reproduction.

Table 16.2	Female Reproductive Organs
Ovaries	Produce oocytes and sex hormones
Oviducts	Conduct oocytes from ovary to uterus
Uterus	Chamber where new individual develops
Cervix	Secretes mucus that enhances sperm movement into uterus and (after fertilization) reduces the embryo's risk of bacterial infection
Vagina	Organ of sexual intercourse; birth canal

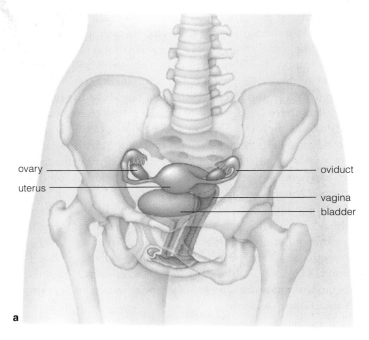

a

Figure 16.5 *Animated!* (**a**) Position of the female reproductive system relative to the pelvic girdle and urinary bladder. (**b**) Parts of the system and their functions.

DURING THE MENSTRUAL CYCLE, AN OOCYTE IS RELEASED FROM AN OVARY

Like all female primates, a woman has a **menstrual cycle**. It takes about twenty-eight days to complete one cycle, although this can vary from month to month and from woman to woman. During the cycle, an oocyte matures (from a *primary* oocyte to a *secondary* oocyte) and is released from an ovary. All the while, hormones are priming the endometrium to receive and nourish an embryo in case the oocyte is fertilized. If the oocyte is *not* fertilized, a blood-rich fluid starts flowing out through the vaginal canal. This recurring flow is **menstruation**, and it marks the first day of a new cycle. The disintegrating endometrium is being sloughed off, only to be rebuilt once again.

The events just sketched out advance through three phases (Table 16.3). The cycle starts with a *menstrual phase*. This is the time of menstruation, when the endometrium disintegrates. Next comes the *proliferative phase*, when the endometrium begins to thicken again. The end of this phase coincides with ovulation—the release of an oocyte from an ovary. During the cycle's final phase, called the *progestational* ("before pregnancy") *phase*, an endocrine structure called the corpus luteum ("yellow body") forms. It secretes a flood of the sex hormones **progesterone** and **estrogen**, which prime the endometrium for pregnancy.

All three phases are governed by feedback loops to the hypothalamus and pituitary gland from the ovaries.

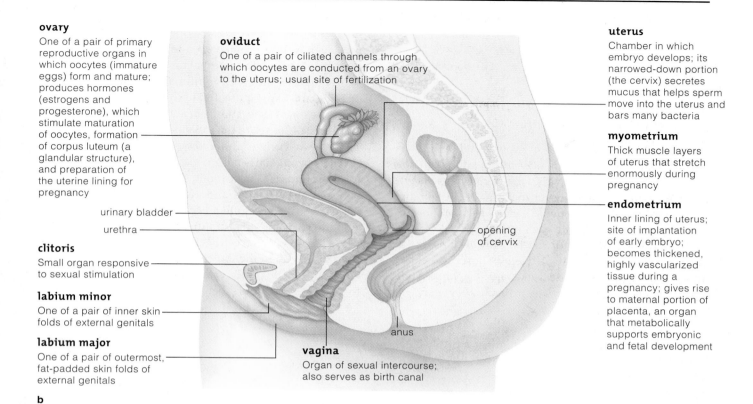

ovary
One of a pair of primary reproductive organs in which oocytes (immature eggs) form and mature; produces hormones (estrogens and progesterone), which stimulate maturation of oocytes, formation of corpus luteum (a glandular structure), and preparation of the uterine lining for pregnancy

oviduct
One of a pair of ciliated channels through which oocytes are conducted from an ovary to the uterus; usual site of fertilization

uterus
Chamber in which embryo develops; its narrowed-down portion (the cervix) secretes mucus that helps sperm move into the uterus and bars many bacteria

myometrium
Thick muscle layers of uterus that stretch enormously during pregnancy

endometrium
Inner lining of uterus; site of implantation of early embryo; becomes thickened, highly vascularized tissue during a pregnancy; gives rise to maternal portion of placenta, an organ that metabolically supports embryonic and fetal development

urinary bladder

urethra

clitoris
Small organ responsive to sexual stimulation

labium minor
One of a pair of inner skin folds of external genitals

labium major
One of a pair of outermost, fat-padded skin folds of external genitals

opening of cervix

anus

vagina
Organ of sexual intercourse; also serves as birth canal

b

Table 16.3	Phases of the Menstrual Cycle	
Phase	**Events**	**Days of the Cycle***
Menstrual phase	Menstruation; endometrium breaks down	1–5
	Follicle matures in ovary; endometrium rebuilds	6–13
Proliferative phase	Endometrium begins to thicken, ovulation occurs	14
Progestational phase	Lining of endometrium develops to receive a possible embryo	15–28

*Assumes a 28-day cycle.

FSH and LH promote cyclic changes in the ovaries, which correspond closely with the menstrual cycle and are described in the following section.

A female's first menstruation, or *menarche*, usually occurs between the ages of ten and sixteen. Menstrual cycles continue until *menopause*, which usually occurs in a woman's late 40s or early 50s. By then, her body's secretion of reproductive hormones has diminished, as has her sensitivity to pituitary reproductive hormones. The decreasing estrogen levels may trigger a range of temporary symptoms, including moodiness and "hot flashes." These sudden bouts of sweating and feeling uncomfortably warm result when blood vessels in the skin dilate. Section 17.13, which covers aging in various body systems, describes other physiological changes associated with menopause. When a woman's menstrual cycles stop altogether, the fertile phase of her life is over.

In *endometriosis*, endometrial tissue spreads and grows outside the uterus. Scar tissue may form on one or both ovaries or oviducts, leading to infertility. In the United States, as many as 10 million women are affected each year. Endometriosis may develop when menstrual flow backs up through the oviducts and spills into the pelvic cavity. Or perhaps some cells became situated in the wrong place when the woman was a developing embryo, then were stimulated to grow during puberty, when her sex hormones became active. Regardless, the symptoms include pain during menstruation, sex, or urination. Treatment ranges from doing nothing in mild cases to surgery to remove the abnormal tissue or sometimes even the whole uterus.

Ovaries, a female's primary reproductive organs, produce oocytes (immature eggs) and sex hormones. Endometrium lines the uterus, where embryos develop.

Sex hormones—estrogens and progesterone—are secreted as part of a menstrual cycle during a female's reproductive years.

16.4 The Ovarian Cycle: Oocytes Develop

LINKS TO
SECTIONS
13.8 AND 15.3

As the menstrual cycle proceeds, a cycle in the ovaries produces an oocyte—the first step toward pregnancy.

IN THE OVARIAN CYCLE, HORMONES GUIDE THE STEPS LEADING TO OVULATION

A newborn girl's ovaries contain about 2 million primary oocytes. All but about 300 are later resorbed, though new research suggests that the ovaries may make fresh oocytes until menopause. In each oocyte, meiosis I begins but then is halted by genetic instructions. Meiosis resumes, usually in one oocyte at a time, with each menstrual cycle.

In the **ovarian cycle**, a primary oocyte develops further and is ovulated (Figure 16.6). Step *a* shows a primary oocyte near an ovary's surface. A layer of *granulosa cells* surrounds and nourishes it. The primary oocyte and the cell layer around it make up a **follicle**. At the start of a menstrual cycle, the hypothalamus is secreting enough GnRH to make the anterior pituitary step up *its* secretion of FSH and LH (Figure 16.7). The blood level of those hormones increases, and *that* causes the follicle to grow. (FSH, recall, is short for follicle-stimulating hormone.) The ovarian cycle is under way.

The oocyte starts to grow, and more layers of cells form around it. Glycoprotein deposits widen the space between these layers and the oocyte. With time the deposits coat the oocyte with a **zona pellucida**.

Both FSH and LH stimulate cells outside the zona pellucida to secrete estrogens. An estrogen-containing fluid builds up in the follicle (now called a secondary or Graafian follicle), and estrogen levels in the blood start to rise. Several hours before being released from the

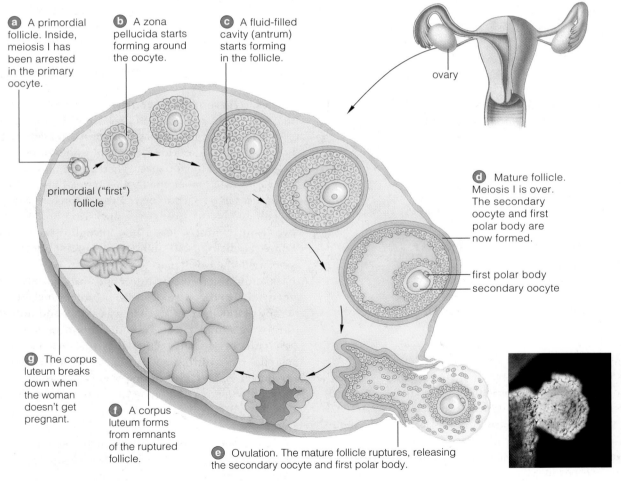

ⓐ A primordial follicle. Inside, meiosis I has been arrested in the primary oocyte.

ⓑ A zona pellucida starts forming around the oocyte.

ⓒ A fluid-filled cavity (antrum) starts forming in the follicle.

ovary

primordial ("first") follicle

ⓓ Mature follicle. Meiosis I is over. The secondary oocyte and first polar body are now formed.

first polar body
secondary oocyte

ⓖ The corpus luteum breaks down when the woman doesn't get pregnant.

ⓕ A corpus luteum forms from remnants of the ruptured follicle.

ⓔ Ovulation. The mature follicle ruptures, releasing the secondary oocyte and first polar body.

Figure 16.6 *Animated!* Cyclic changes in the ovary, which is shown in cross section. A follicle stays in the same place in an ovary all through the menstrual cycle. It does not "move around" as in this diagram, which shows the *sequence* of events. In the cycle's first phase, a follicle grows and matures. At ovulation, the second phase, the mature follicle ruptures and releases a secondary oocyte. In the third phase, a corpus luteum forms from the follicle's remnants. It self-destructs if the woman does not become pregnant. The micrograph shows a secondary oocyte being released from an ovary. It will enter an oviduct, the passageway to the uterus.

THE FEMALE REPRODUCTIVE SYSTEM

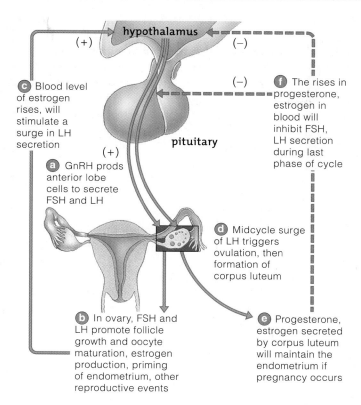

hypothalamus

(+)   (−)

(−)

c Blood level of estrogen rises, will stimulate a surge in LH secretion

f The rises in progesterone, estrogen in blood will inhibit FSH, LH secretion during last phase of cycle

(+)

pituitary

a GnRH prods anterior lobe cells to secrete FSH and LH

d Midcycle surge of LH triggers ovulation, then formation of corpus luteum

b In ovary, FSH and LH promote follicle growth and oocyte maturation, estrogen production, priming of endometrium, other reproductive events

e Progesterone, estrogen secreted by corpus luteum will maintain the endometrium if pregnancy occurs

Figure 16.7 *Animated!* Feedback control of hormonal secretion during an ovarian (and menstrual) cycle. A positive feedback loop from an ovary to the hypothalamus causes a surge in LH secretion. This surge triggers ovulation. Afterward, negative feedback loops to the hypothalamus and pituitary inhibit FSH secretion. They prevent another follicle from maturing until the cycle is completed.

ovary, the oocyte completes the meiotic cell division (meiosis I) that was arrested years before. Now, there are two cells. One, a large, **secondary oocyte**, gets most of the cytoplasm. The other cell is the *first polar body*. (It may divide again.) The secondary oocyte also gets a haploid number of chromosomes—the required number for a gamete. It now begins a second round of meiosis (meiosis II), which again is arrested in preparation for fertilization by a sperm.

About halfway through the ovarian cycle, a woman's pituitary gland detects the rising estrogen level. It releases LH, which causes vascular changes that make the follicle swell. The surge also causes enzymes to break down the bulging follicle wall, which soon ruptures. Fluid escapes, along with the secondary oocyte and polar body (Figure 16.6e). The midcycle surge of LH has triggered **ovulation**— the release of a secondary oocyte from the ovary.

Once released into the abdominal cavity, the secondary oocyte enters an oviduct. Long, ciliated projections from the oviduct (called *fimbriae*) extend like an umbrella over part of the ovary. Movements of the projections and cilia sweep the oocyte into the channel. If fertilization takes

place, it usually occurs while the oocyte is in the oviduct. At fertilization, the oocyte will finish meiosis II and become a mature **ovum**, the *egg*.

THE OVARIAN CYCLE DOVETAILS WITH THE MENSTRUAL CYCLE

As Section 16.3 noted, estrogens released early in the menstrual cycle stimulate growth of the endometrium and its glands, paving the way for a pregnancy. Just before the midcycle LH surge, cells of the follicle wall start secreting estrogens and progesterone. At ovulation, the estrogens act on tissue around the cervical canal, which leads to the vagina. The cervix starts to secrete large amounts of a thin, clear mucus—an ideal medium for sperm to swim through. Blood vessels grow rapidly in the thickened endometrium.

After ovulation, another structure dominates events. Granulosa cells left behind in the follicle differentiate into the **corpus luteum**. The midcycle surge of LH triggers formation of this structure, hence the name *luteinizing* hormone.

Recall that the corpus luteum secretes progesterone as well as some estrogen. The progesterone prepares the woman's reproductive tract for the arrival of an embryo. For example, it causes mucus in the cervix to become thick and sticky, which may prevent bacteria from entering the uterus. Progesterone also maintains the endometrium during a pregnancy.

A corpus luteum lasts for about twelve days. During that time, the hypothalamus signals for a decrease in FSH secretion, which prevents other follicles from developing. If no embryo implants in the endometrium, the corpus luteum secretes prostaglandins that disrupt its own functioning.

After the corpus luteum breaks down, progesterone and estrogen levels fall rapidly, so the endometrium also starts to break down. Deprived of oxygen and nutrients, its blood vessels constrict and its tissues die. Blood escapes from the ruptured walls of weakened capillaries. The blood and sloughed endometrial tissues make up the menstrual flow. As the cycle begins anew a few days later, the rising levels of estrogen stimulate regrowth of the endometrium.

In the ovarian cycle, a midcycle surge of LH triggers ovulation, the release of the secondary oocyte and the polar body from the ovary.

The cyclic release of hormones helps pave the way for fertilization of an egg and prepares the endometrium and other parts of a female's reproductive tract for pregnancy.

16.5 Visual Summary of the Menstrual and Ovarian Cycles

The menstrual cycle has been compared to a hormonal symphony, with many parts being brought together into a harmonious whole. Before you continue your reading, take a moment to review Figure 16.8. It correlates the cyclic changes in the ovary and uterus with the changes in hormone levels that bring about the events of each menstrual cycle.

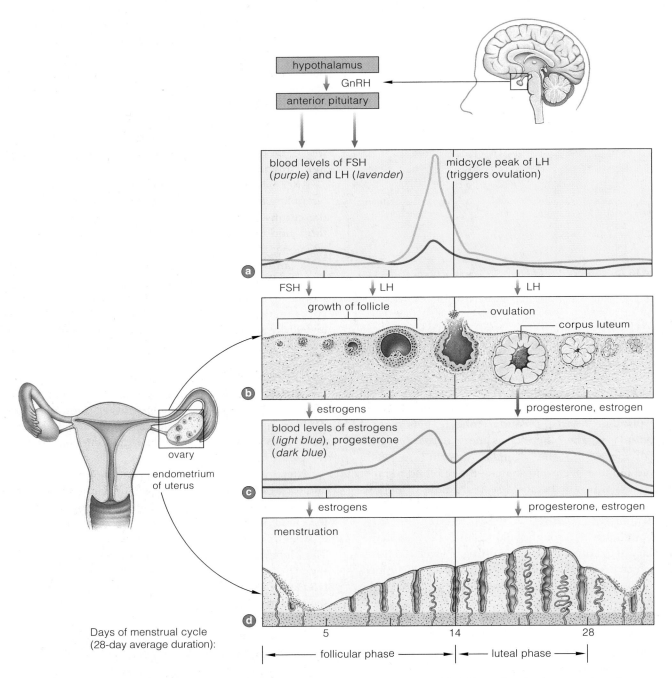

Figure 16.8 *Animated!* Hormones and their effects during one menstrual cycle. (**a**) GnRH, a releasing hormone from the hypothalamus, stimulates the anterior pituitary to secrete FSH and LH. (**b**) FSH and LH stimulate a follicle to grow, an oocyte to mature, and the ovaries to secrete progesterone and estrogens that cause rebuilding of the endometrium. (**c**) A midcycle LH surge triggers ovulation and the formation of a corpus luteum. Progesterone and some estrogens released by the corpus luteum maintain the endometrium, but if no pregnancy occurs, they stop being released and the corpus luteum breaks down.

THE FEMALE REPRODUCTIVE SYSTEM

16.6 Sexual Intercourse

The penis and vagina are mechanically compatible for sexual intercourse, which may lead to pregnancy.

SEXUAL INTERCOURSE INVOLVES PHYSIOLOGICAL CHANGES IN BOTH PARTNERS

Coitus and copulation are both technical terms for sexual intercourse. The male sex act involves an *erection*, in which the limp penis stiffens and lengthens. It also involves *ejaculation*, the forceful expulsion of semen into the urethra and out from the penis. As shown in Figure 16.1, the penis has lengthwise cylinders of spongy tissue. The outer cylinder has a mushroom-shaped tip (the glans penis). Inside it is a dense array of sensory receptors that are activated by friction. In a male who is not sexually aroused, the large blood vessels leading into the cylinders are constricted. In aroused males, these blood vessels vasodilate, so blood flows into the cylinders faster than it flows out. Blood collects in the spongy tissue, and the organ stiffens and lengthens—a mechanism that helps the penis penetrate into the female's vagina.

In a female, arousal includes vasodilation of blood vessels in her genital area. This causes vulvar tissues to engorge with blood and swell. Mucus-rich secretions flow from the cervix, lubricating the vagina.

During coitus, pelvic thrusts stimulate the penis as well as the female's clitoris and vaginal wall. The mechanical stimulation triggers rhythmic, involuntary contractions in smooth muscle in the male reproductive tract, especially the vas deferens and the prostate. The contractions rapidly force sperm out of each epididymis. They also force the contents of seminal vesicles and the prostate gland into the urethra. The resulting mixture, semen, is ejaculated into the vagina.

During ejaculation, a sphincter closes off the neck of the male's bladder and prevents urine from being excreted. Ejaculation is a reflex response; once it begins, it cannot be stopped.

Emotional intensity, heavy breathing, and heart pounding, as well as generalized contractions of skeletal muscles, accompany the rhythmic throbbing of the pelvic muscles. For both partners, **orgasm**—the culmination of the sex act—typically is accompanied by strong sensations of release, warmth, and relaxation.

Some people mistakenly believe that unless a woman experiences orgasm, she cannot become pregnant. This is not true, however. A female can become pregnant from intercourse *regardless* of whether she experiences orgasm, and even if she is not sexually aroused. All that is required is that a sperm meet up with a secondary oocyte that is traveling down one of her oviducts.

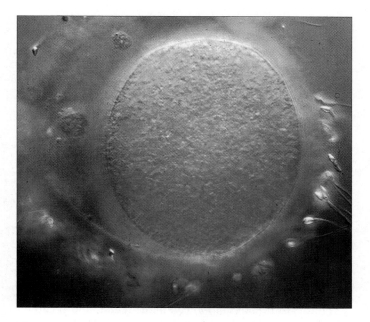

Figure 16.9 A secondary oocyte surrounded by sperm. If fertilization ensues, it will set the stage for the development of a new individual, continuing the human life cycle.

INTERCOURSE CAN PRODUCE A FERTILIZED EGG

If sperm enter the vagina a few days before or after ovulation or anytime between, an ovulated egg may be fertilized. Within thirty minutes after ejaculation, muscle contractions in the uterus move the sperm deeper into the female reproductive tract. Only a few hundred sperm will actually reach the upper portion of the oviduct, which is where fertilization usually takes place. The remarkable micrograph in Figure 16.9 shows living sperm around a secondary oocyte.

As you will read in Chapter 17, the meeting of sperm and secondary oocyte is the first of several intricately orchestrated events that lead to actual **fertilization**—the beginning of a new individual.

Sexual intercourse (coitus) typically involves a sequence of physiological changes in both partners.

During arousal, blood vessels dilate so that more blood flows to the penis (males) and vulva (females). Orgasm involves muscular contractions (including those leading to ejaculation of semen into the vagina) and sensations of release, warmth, and relaxation.

A female may become pregnant through intercourse even if she is not sexually aroused or does not experience orgasm.

Fertilization can occur when a sperm encounters a secondary oocyte, usually in the oviduct.

SEXUAL INTERCOURSE AND FERTILITY

Reproductive Systems **299**

16.7 Controlling Fertility

Many sexually active people choose to exercise control over whether their activity will produce a child. Here we consider the biological bases of different forms of birth control.

NATURAL BIRTH CONTROL IS CHANCY

The most effective method of birth control is complete *abstinence*—no sexual intercourse whatsoever. A modified form of abstinence is the *rhythm method*, also called the "fertility awareness" or *sympto-thermal method*. The idea is to refrain from intercourse during the woman's fertile period, starting a few days before ovulation and ending a few days after. Her fertile period is identified and tracked by keeping records of the length of her menstrual cycles and sometimes by examining her cervical secretions and taking her temperature each morning when she wakes up. (Core body temperature rises by one-half to one degree just after ovulation.) The method is not very reliable (Figure 16.10). Ovulation can be irregular, and it can be easy to miscalculate. Also, sperm already in the vaginal tract may survive until ovulation.

Withdrawal, removing the penis from the vagina before ejaculation, also is not very effective because fluid released from the penis before ejaculation may contain sperm. *Douching*, or rinsing out the vagina with a chemical right after intercourse, is next to useless. It takes less than 90 seconds for sperm to move past the cervix into the uterus.

SURGICAL SOLUTIONS ARE RELIABLE

Controlling fertility by surgical intervention is less chancy. In *vasectomy*, a physician makes a tiny incision in a man's scrotum, then severs and ties off each vas deferens (Figure 16.11*a*). The procedure takes about twenty minutes and requires only a local anesthetic. Afterward, sperm can't leave the testes and so can't be present in the man's semen. Having a vasectomy does not disrupt male sex hormones. A vasectomy alternative is the Vasclip, a hinged plastic device about the size of a rice grain, which simply closes off the vas deferens.

In *tubal ligation*, a woman's oviducts are cauterized or cut and tied off (Figure 19.11*b*). The procedure most often is performed in a hospital.

PHYSICAL AND CHEMICAL BARRIERS VARY IN EFFECTIVENESS

Spermicidal foam and spermicidal jelly kill sperm. They are packaged in an applicator and placed in the vagina just before intercourse. Neither is reliable unless used with another device, such as a diaphragm or condom.

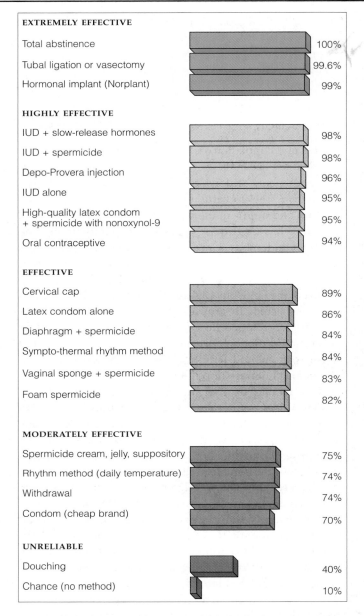

EXTREMELY EFFECTIVE

Total abstinence	100%
Tubal ligation or vasectomy	99.6%
Hormonal implant (Norplant)	99%

HIGHLY EFFECTIVE

IUD + slow-release hormones	98%
IUD + spermicide	98%
Depo-Provera injection	96%
IUD alone	95%
High-quality latex condom + spermicide with nonoxynol-9	95%
Oral contraceptive	94%

EFFECTIVE

Cervical cap	89%
Latex condom alone	86%
Diaphragm + spermicide	84%
Sympto-thermal rhythm method	84%
Vaginal sponge + spermicide	83%
Foam spermicide	82%

MODERATELY EFFECTIVE

Spermicide cream, jelly, suppository	75%
Rhythm method (daily temperature)	74%
Withdrawal	74%
Condom (cheap brand)	70%

UNRELIABLE

| Douching | 40% |
| Chance (no method) | 10% |

Figure 16.10 Comparison of the effectiveness of some contraceptive methods in the United States. Percentages shown are based on the number of unplanned pregnancies per 100 couples who used the method as the only form of birth control for one year. For example, "94% effectiveness" for oral contraceptives (the birth control pill) means that, on average, 6 of every 100 women using them will become pregnant.

A *diaphragm* is a flexible, dome-shaped device that is positioned over the cervix before intercourse. It must be fitted by a doctor, used with foam or jelly, and inserted correctly with each use. The *cervical cap* is smaller and can be left in place for up to three days with just a single dose of spermicide. The *contraceptive sponge* is a disposable disk that contains a spermicide and covers the cervix. After being wetted it is inserted up to 24 hours before intercourse. No prescription or special fitting is required.

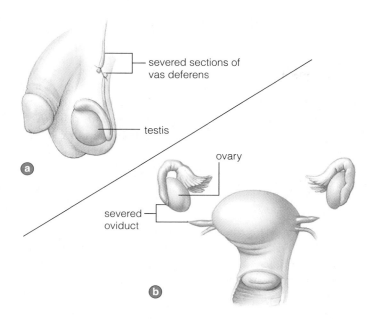

Figure 16.11 Surgical methods of birth control. (**a**) Vasectomy and (**b**) tubal ligation.

The *intrauterine device*, or IUD, is a plastic or metal device that is placed into the uterus, where it hampers implantation of a fertilized egg. Available by prescription, IUDs have been associated with a variety of complications and any woman considering getting one should discuss the matter fully with her physician.

Condoms are thin, tight-fitting sheaths of latex or animal skin worn over the penis during intercourse. An intact condom is about 85 to 93 percent reliable, and latex condoms help prevent the spread of sexually transmitted diseases. A pouchlike latex "female condom" that is inserted into the vagina has also been developed.

A widely used method of fertility control is the *birth control pill*—any of a number of formulations of synthetic estrogens and progesterones. These hormones block the normal release of anterior pituitary hormones (LH and FSH) that are required for eggs to mature and be ovulated. Oral contraceptives are prescription drugs and must be matched with each patient's needs.

Used as directed, the pill is one of the most reliable methods of controlling fertility. Often, the hormone blend corrects erratic menstrual cycles and reduces cramping. Some users experience (usually temporary) side effects, including nausea and weight gain. Continued use may lead to blood clots in at-risk women. Complications are more likely in women who smoke, and most physicians won't prescribe an oral contraceptive for a smoker.

NuvaRing is a flexible plastic ring that slides into the vagina. It slowly releases the same hormones used in birth control pills and must be replaced once a month.

Products such as injections that contain progestin (Depo-Provera, Lunelle) or hormone-containing implants (Norplant) inhibit ovulation or prevent implantation of the embryo. Both can cause heavier menstrual periods, and Norplant rods can be difficult to remove.

Medically, pregnancy only begins after an embryo implants. *Morning-after pills* such as mifepristone (RU-486) and Preven interfere with the hormones that control events between ovulation and implantation. Contrary to their common name, these chemicals actually work up to seventy-two hours after unprotected intercourse.

Researchers are working to develop new and better methods of fertility control. Examples include implants that biodegrade and so don't require surgical removal. Other efforts are aimed at developing a contraceptive for men that reduces the sperm count.

ABORTION IS HIGHLY CONTROVERSIAL

An induced or surgical *abortion* removes or dislodges an implanted embryo or fetus from the womb. In that sense, the procedure has little to do with fertility, because the pregnancy is already under way. More than 1,500,000 abortions are performed in the United States each year, even while the difficult legal and social conflict over legalized abortion rages on.

During the first trimester (twelve weeks), abortions performed in a clinical setting usually are fast, painless, and free of complications. Even so, polls show that for both medical and moral reasons, the majority of people in the U.S. view sexually responsible behavior as being preferable to an abortion. Aborting a late-term fetus is extremely controversial unless the mother's life is threatened.

This textbook cannot offer any "right" answers to a question about the morality of abortion or any other reproductive decision. It can only offer a serious explanation of how a new individual develops to help you objectively assess the biological basis of human life.

The most effective methods for preventing conception are abstinence, chemical barriers to conception, and surgery or implants that block the vas deferens or oviducts. A frank discussion with a physician is the best starting point for fertility control.

16.8 Options for Coping with Infertility

LINK TO SECTION 15.3

In the United States, about one in every six couples is infertile—unable to conceive a child after a year of trying. Causes run the gamut from hormonal imbalances that prevent ovulation, oviducts blocked by effects of disease, a low sperm count, or sperm that are defective in a way that impairs fertilization.

FERTILITY DRUGS STIMULATE OVULATION

In about one-third of cases, infertility can be traced to poor quality oocytes or to irregular or absent ovulation. These situations are most common in women over the age of 37. A couple's first resort may be fertility drugs, in the hope that one or more ovarian follicles will produce a healthy oocyte. One commonly used drug, clomiphene, stimulates the pituitary gland to release FSH. As noted in Section 15.3, this hormone triggers ovulation. A drug called *human menopausal gonadotropin* (hMG) is basically a highly purified form of FSH. Injected directly into the bloodstream, it stimulates ovulation in 70 to 90 percent of women who receive it.

Although fertility drugs have been used with great success since the 1970s, they can cause undesirable side effects, including the fertilization of several eggs at once. The result is a high-risk pregnancy that can result in babies with neurological and other problems.

ASSISTED REPRODUCTIVE TECHNOLOGIES INCLUDE ARTIFICIAL INSEMINATION AND IVF

Artificial insemination was one of the first methods of *assisted reproductive technology*, or ART. In this approach, semen is placed into a woman's vagina or uterus, usually by syringe, around the time she is ovulating. This procedure may be chosen when a woman's partner has a low sperm count, because his sperm can be concentrated prior to the procedure. In *artificial insemination by donor* (AID), a sperm bank provides sperm from an anonymous donor. AID produces about 20,000 babies in the United States every year.

In vitro fertilization (IVF) is literally "fertilization in glass." If a couple's sperm and oocytes are normal, they can be used. Otherwise, variations of the technology are available that use sperm, oocytes, or both, from donors (Figure 16.12). Sperm and oocytes are placed in a glass laboratory dish in a solution that simulates the fluid in oviducts. If fertilization takes place, about 12 hours later *zygotes* (fertilized eggs in the first stage of development) are transferred to a chemical solution that will support further development. Two to four days later, one or more embryos are transferred to the woman's uterus. An embryo implants in about 20 percent of cases. In vitro fertilization often produces more embryos than

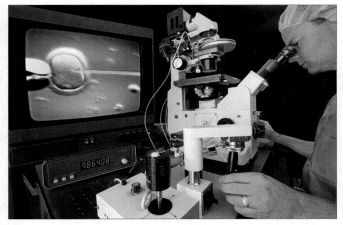

Figure 16.12 Doctor inserting a human sperm into an egg during in vitro fertilization. He is viewing the cell through a microscope. The procedure is magnified on a monitor. The egg, held in place by the tip of a pipette, is being pierced by a microneedle (the thin "line" on the right).

NEW WAYS TO MAKE BABIES

Artificial Insemination and Embryo Transfer	In Vitro Fertilization

Artificial Insemination and Embryo Transfer

1. Father is infertile. Mother is inseminated by donor and carries child.

2. Mother is infertile but able to carry child. Egg donor is inseminated with father's sperm. Then embryo is transferred and mother carries child.

3. Mother is infertile and unable to carry child. Egg donor is inseminated with father's sperm and carries child.

4. Both parents are infertile, but mother is able to carry child. Egg donor is inseminated by sperm donor. Then embryo is transferred and mother carries child.

In Vitro Fertilization

1. Mother is fertile but unable to conceive. Egg from mother and sperm from father are combined in laboratory. Embryo is placed in mother's uterus.

2. Mother is infertile but able to carry child. Egg from donor is combined with sperm from father and implanted in mother.

3. Mother is fertile but father is infertile. Egg from mother is combined with sperm from donor.

4. Both parents are infertile, but mother can carry child. Egg and sperm from donors are combined in laboratory, then embryo is transferred to mother.

5. Mother is infertile and unable to carry child. Egg of donor is combined with sperm from father. Embryo is transferred to donor who carries child.

6. Both parents are fertile, but mother is unable to carry child. Egg from mother and sperm from father are combined. Embryo is transferred to surrogate.

7. Father is infertile. Mother is fertile but unable to carry child. Egg from mother is combined with sperm from donor. Embryo is transferred to surrogate mother.

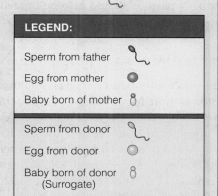

LEGEND:

Sperm from father

Egg from mother

Baby born of mother

Sperm from donor

Egg from donor

Baby born of donor (Surrogate)

In traditional in vitro fertilization, several early cell clusters may be inserted into the uterus to improve the odds that at least one will survive. More than one often does. In one study, 40 percent of IVF patients gave birth to twins. The transfer of a slightly more advanced embryo (called a blastocyst), a more recent technique, allows the cluster to develop longer before transfer into the uterus. Survival chances are better, so fewer have to be implanted. This reduces the risk of multiple births.

Figure 16.13 Some options for assisted reproductive technologies.

can be used in a given procedure. The fate of unused embryos (which are stored frozen) has prompted ethical debates, such as whether such embryos should be used as a source of embryonic stem cells (Chapter 4).

A procedure called ICSI is a variation on IVF. ICSI stands for *i*ntra*c*ytoplasmic *s*perm *i*njection. A single sperm is injected into an egg using a tiny glass needle. Although IVF and ICSI are both in common use, evidence is mounting that babies conceived through any form of in vitro fertilization have a much higher risk of low birth weight and related developmental problems later on.

In *IVF with embryo transfer* (Figure 16.13) a fertile female volunteer is inseminated with sperm from a man whose female partner is infertile. If a pregnancy results, the developing embryo is transferred to the infertile woman's uterus or to a "surrogate mother." This approach is technically difficult and has major legal complications. It isn't a common solution to infertility.

In a technique called GIFT (*g*amete *i*ntrafallopian *t*ransfer) sperm and oocytes are collected and placed into an oviduct (fallopian tube). About 20 percent of the time, the oocyte is fertilized and a normal pregnancy follows. An alternative is ZIFT (*z*ygote *i*ntrafallopian *t*ransfer). First, oocytes and sperm are placed in a laboratory dish. If fertilization occurs, the zygote is placed in a woman's oviducts. GIFT and ZIFT have about the same success rate as in vitro fertilization.

Commonly used fertility drugs include hormones that stimulate ovulation.

A variety of assisted reproductive technologies now exist. In vitro fertilization brings together sperm and oocytes in a laboratory dish, where conception may occur. Other techniques for overcoming infertility include intrafallopian transfers and artificial insemination.

16.9 A Trio of Common Sexually Transmitted Diseases

We turn now to diseases that are transmitted during sexual activity. Three of the most common ones are chlamydia, gonorrhea, and syphilis, all caused by bacteria.

CHLAMYDIAL INFECTIONS AND PID ARE MOST COMMON IN YOUNG PEOPLE

One of the most common **sexually transmitted diseases (STDs)** is caused by the bacterium *Chlamydia trachomatis* (Figure 16.14*a*). This infection is often called **chlamydia** for short. Each year an estimated 3 million Americans are infected, about two-thirds of them under age 25. Around the world, *C. trachomatis* infects roughly 90 million people annually. At least 30 percent of newborns who are treated for eye infections and pneumonia were infected with *C. trachomatis* during birth.

The bacterium infects cells of the genital and urinary tract. Infected men may have a discharge from the penis and a burning sensation when they urinate. Women may have a vaginal discharge as well as burning and itching. Often, however, *C. trachomatis* is a "stealth" STD with no outward signs of infection. About 80 percent of infected women and 40 percent of infected men don't have noticeable symptoms—yet they can still pass the bacterium to others.

Once a bout of chlamydia is under way, the bacteria will migrate to the person's lymph nodes, which become enlarged and tender. Impaired lymph drainage can cause swelling in the surrounding tissues.

Chlamydia can be treated with antibiotics. However, because so many people are unaware they're infected, this STD does a lot of damage. Between 20 and 40 percent of women with genital chlamydial infections develop **pelvic inflammatory disease (PID)**. PID strikes about 1 million women each year, most often sexually active women in their teens and twenties.

Although PID can arise when microorganisms that normally inhabit the vagina ascend into the pelvic region (typically as a result of excessive douching), it is also a serious complication of both chlamydial infection and gonorrhea. Usually, a woman's uterus, oviducts, and ovaries are affected. Pain may be so severe that infected women often think they are having an attack of acute appendicitis. If the oviducts become scarred, additional complications, such as chronic pelvic pain and even sterility, can result. PID is the leading cause of infertility among young women. An affected woman may also have chronic menstrual problems.

As soon as PID is diagnosed, a woman usually will be prescribed a course of antibiotics. Advanced cases can require hospitalization and hysterectomy (removal of the uterus). A woman's partner should also be treated, even if the partner has no symptoms.

GONORRHEA MAY INITIALLY HAVE NO SYMPTOMS

Like chlamydial infection, **gonorrhea** can be cured if it is diagnosed promptly. Gonorrhea is caused by *Neisseria gonorrhoeae* (Figure 16.14*b*). This bacterium (also called gonococcus) can infect epithelial cells of the genital tract, the rectum, eye membranes, and the throat. Each year in the United States there are about 650,000 new cases reported; there may be up to 10 million unreported cases. Part of the problem is that the initial stages of the disease can be so uneventful that, as with chlamydial infection, a carrier may be unaware of being infected.

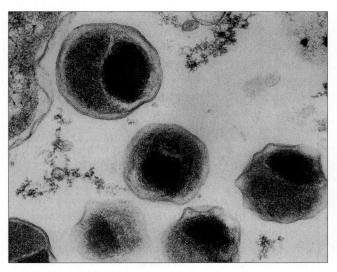

a

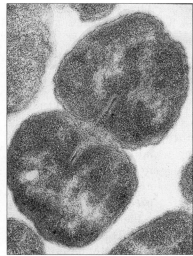

b

Figure 16.14 (**a**) Color-enhanced micrograph of *Chlamydia trachomatis* bacteria. (**b**) *Neisseria gonorrhoeae*, or gonococcus, a bacterium that typically is seen as paired cells, as shown here.

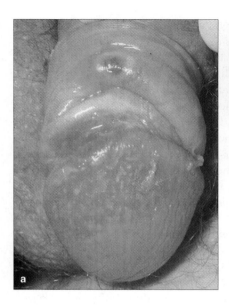

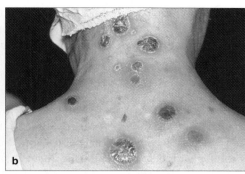

Early on, males have symptoms that usually are easy to detect. Within a week, yellow pus begins to ooze from the penis. Urinating is more frequent and may be painful. A man can become sterile if untreated gonorrhea leads to inflammation of his testicles or scarring of the vas deferens.

The early stages of gonorrhea can be dangerously asymptomatic in females. For example, a woman may not experience burning while urinating, and she may not have a vaginal discharge that seems abnormal. In the absence of worrisome symptoms, a woman's gonorrhea infection may well go untreated and all the while, the bacteria may be spreading into her oviducts. Eventually, she may experience violent cramps, fever, and vomiting. She may even become sterile due to scarring and blocking of her oviducts from pelvic inflammatory disease.

Antibiotics can kill the gonococcus and thus prevent complications of gonorrhea. Penicillin was once the most commonly used drug treatment. Unfortunately, antibiotic-resistant strains of gonococcus have developed. As a result, many doctors now order testing to determine the strain responsible for a particular patient's illness and then treat the infection with an appropriate antibiotic.

Many people believe that once cured of gonorrhea, they can't be reinfected. That is not true, partly because there are at least sixteen different strains of *N. gonorrhoeae*.

SYPHILIS AFFECTS A WIDE RANGE OF ORGANS

Syphilis is caused by the bacterium *Treponema pallidum.* There are an estimated 12 million new cases every year in the United States.

The bacterium, a *treponeme*, is transmitted by sexual contact. Once it reproduces, an ulcer called a chancre ("shanker," Figure 16.15*a*) develops. Usually the chancre is flat rather than bumpy, is not painful, and teems with treponemes. It becomes visible 1 to 8 weeks after infection and is a symptom of the *primary stage* of syphilis. Syphilis can be diagnosed in a cell sample taken from a chancre. By then, however, bacteria have already moved into the person's bloodstream.

The *secondary stage* of syphilis begins a couple of months after the chancre appears. Lesions can develop in mucous membranes, the eyes, bones, and the central nervous system. A blotchy rash breaks out over much of the body (Figure 16.15*b*). After the rash goes away, the infection enters a latent stage that can last for years. In the meantime, the disease does not produce major outward symptoms and can be detected only by laboratory tests.

Usually, the *tertiary stage* of syphilis begins from 5 to 20 years after infection. Lesions may develop in the skin and internal organs, including the liver, bones, and aorta. Scars form; the walls of the aorta can weaken. Treponemes also damage the brain and spinal cord in ways that lead to various forms of insanity and paralysis. Infected women who become pregnant typically have miscarriages, stillbirths, or sickly and syphilitic infants.

Penicillin may cure syphilis during the early stages, although antibiotic-resistant strains have now developed.

Chlamydial infection is the most common STD caused by a bacterium. It is curable with antibiotics, as gonorrhea and syphilis often are. However, there are now some antibiotic-resistant strains of the gonorrhea and syphilis bacteria.

Pelvic inflammatory disease is a dangerous complication of chlamydial infection and gonorrhea.

16.10 The Human Immunodeficiency Virus and AIDS

LINKS TO
SECTIONS
10.2, 10.5, 10.6,
AND 10.7

HIV infection rates continue to skyrocket. Worldwide, roughly 11 of every 1,000 adults between the ages of 15 and 49 are infected. Virtually all will develop AIDS.

AIDS is a group of diseases caused by infection with **HIV**, the **human immunodeficiency virus**. HIV destroys T cells, crippling the immune system. It leaves the body vulnerable to infections and rare forms of cancer (Figure 16.16). Physicians diagnose AIDS if a patient has a severely depressed immune system, tests positive for HIV, and has one or more "indicator diseases," including types of pneumonia, cancer, recurrent yeast infections, and drug-resistant tuberculosis. Worldwide, HIV has infected an estimated 34 million to 46 million people (Table 16.4).

HIV IS TRANSMITTED IN BODY FLUIDS

HIV is transmitted when body fluids, especially blood and semen, of an infected person enter another person's tissues. The virus can enter through any kind of cut or abrasion, anywhere on or in the body. HIV-infected blood also can be present on toothbrushes and razors; on needles used to inject drugs intravenously, pierce ears, do acupuncture, or create tattoos; and on contaminated medical equipment.

The most common mode of transmission is sex with an infected partner. HIV in semen and vaginal secretions enters a partner's body through epithelium lining the penis, vagina, rectum, or (rarely) mouth. Anything that damages the epithelial linings, such as other sexually transmitted diseases, anal intercourse, or rough sex, increases the odds that the virus will be transmitted.

HIV is not effectively transmitted by food, air, water, casual contact, or insect bites. However, infected mothers can transmit HIV to their babies during pregnancy, birth, and breast-feeding. HIV also travels in tiny amounts of infected blood in syringes that are shared and reused by IV drug abusers and patients in cash-strapped hospitals of developing countries.

Almost half of HIV-infected adults worldwide are women. Some of those infections are due to intravenous drug abuse, but most are the result of sexual contact with infected men. In the United States about 15 percent of new infections in men come from heterosexual contact. Young people are also being hit hard; in recent years, more young adults in the United States have died from AIDS than from any other single cause.

HIV INFECTION BEGINS A TITANIC STRUGGLE

HIV is a retrovirus with a lipid envelope, a bit of plasma membrane acquired as it budded from an infected cell. Various proteins spike from the envelope, span it, or line its inner surface. Inside the envelope, viral coat proteins enclose two RNA strands and several copies of *reverse transcriptase*, a retroviral enzyme. Once inside a host cell, this enzyme uses the RNA as a template to make DNA, which gets inserted into a host chromosome.

HIV can only infect cells that have a certain type of surface receptor. Macrophages, dendritic cells, and helper T cells (Section 10.6) have this receptor. Once the viral enzyme is in a cell, it uses the viral RNA as a template to make DNA, genetic instructions in the form of genes that then are inserted into one of the host cell's chromosomes. In some cells, the inserted genes remain silent but are activated in a later round of infection. Eventually, though, instructions for making new viral particles are read out. A process called *transcription* rewrites the genetic message in DNA as RNA, and these RNA instructions then are "translated" into protein (Chapter 22). These steps are summarized in Figure 16.17.

After HIV successfully infects a person, virus particles begin to circulate in the bloodstream. At this stage, many people have a bout of flulike symptoms. B cells make antibodies to HIV that can be detected by diagnostic tests for HIV infection. Armies of helper T cells and killer T cells also form. During some phases of infection, however, the virus infects an estimated 2 *billion* helper T cells and produces *100 million to 1 billion new HIV particles* each day. They bud from the plasma membrane of the helper T cell or are released when the membrane ruptures.

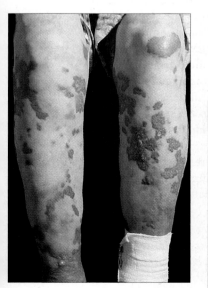

Figure 16.16 The lesions that are a sign of Kaposi's sarcoma.

Region	AIDS Cases	New HIV Cases
Sub-Saharan Africa	25,400,000	3,100,000
South/Southeast Asia	7,100,000	890,000
Latin America	1,700,000	240,000
Central Asia/East Europe	1,400,000	210,000
East Asia	1,100,000	290,000
North America	1,000,000	44,000
Western/Central Europe	610,000	21,000
Middle East/North Africa	540,000	92,000
Caribbean Islands	440,000	53,000
Australia/New Zealand	35,000	5,000

Table 16.4   Global Cases of HIV and AIDS*

*Global estimates as of December 2004, www.unaids.org

SEXUALLY TRANSMITTED DISEASES

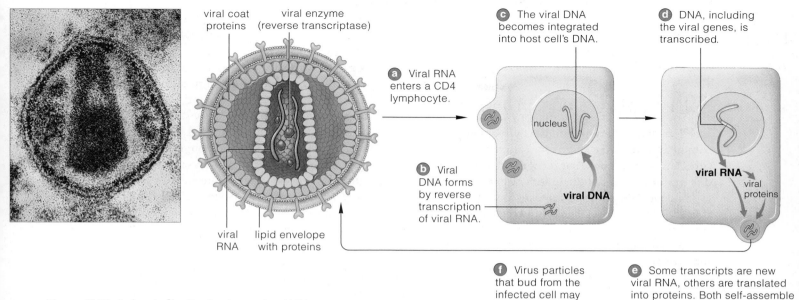

viral coat proteins

viral enzyme (reverse transcriptase)

c The viral DNA becomes integrated into host cell's DNA.

d DNA, including the viral genes, is transcribed.

a Viral RNA enters a CD4 lymphocyte.

nucleus

b Viral DNA forms by reverse transcription of viral RNA.

viral DNA

viral RNA

viral proteins

viral RNA

lipid envelope with proteins

f Virus particles that bud from the infected cell may attack a new one.

e Some transcripts are new viral RNA, others are translated into proteins. Both self-assemble into new virus particles.

Figure 16.17 *Animated!* Replication cycle of HIV.

Over time, billions of HIV particles and masses of infected T cells accumulate in lymph nodes. The number of circulating virus particles also increases and the body produces fewer and fewer helper T cells to replace those it has lost. As the number of healthy helper T cells drops, the person may lose weight and experience symptoms such as fatigue, nausea, heavy night sweats, enlarged lymph nodes, and a series of minor infections. With time, one or more of the typical AIDS indicator diseases appear. These are the diseases that eventually kill the individual.

About 5 percent of HIV-infected people don't develop symptoms of AIDS. Some may have been infected with a less virulent strain of HIV. Others may have a genetic mutation that results in the absence of the necessary receptor on some T cells and macrophages. As a result, the person is more resistant to HIV infection. People who have the mutation are *not* immune to HIV and AIDS. However, the mutation does slow the rate at which HIV infects cells, and thus the onset of AIDS. This delay allows time for a counterattack by anti-HIV treatments.

WHAT ABOUT DRUGS AND VACCINES?

Currently available drugs do not cure HIV-infected people, because we cannot go after HIV genes that are already inserted into someone's DNA. Also, since HIV mutates so rapidly, it can rapidly develop resistance to drugs. Even so, researchers have developed a fairly effective arsenal of anti-HIV drugs. Protease inhibitors block the action of HIV protease, an enzyme required for the assembly of new virus particles. Other drugs inhibit an enzyme that HIV needs to replicate itself.

At present the preferred treatment is a drug "cocktail" that often consists of a protease inhibitor and two anti-HIV drugs. This regimen can sometimes suppress HIV rather effectively, at least for a time. The drug cocktails are costly, however, and they may have serious side effects. The search also is on for compounds that might disrupt the ability of HIV to enter cells. Such "entry inhibitors" are now being tested in humans.

As you read in the chapter introduction, making an effective AIDS vaccine is a tall order. A vaccine works by stimulating the immune system to respond to proteins (antigens) produced by the invading virus. But as already noted, HIV mutates rapidly as it replicates in the immune system. In a single person it can have many different genetic forms, each form presenting the immune system with a different antigen. No single vaccine can keep up with this challenge.

Despite the obstacles, researchers are not giving up. Some efforts revolve around producing a synthetic virus with just enough HIV components to activate the immune system. At this writing, there are a wide variety of experimental vaccines in the pipeline.

AIDS is caused by the human immunodeficiency virus (HIV). HIV is a retrovirus, with RNA instead of DNA. It is transmitted only when blood, semen, or certain other body fluids of an infected person enter another person's tissues.

When HIV infects a cell, its RNA is integrated into the host cell's DNA. Eventually the host cell begins producing new HIV particles.

16.11 A Rogue's Gallery of Other STDs

A variety of viruses, parasites, and fungi cause disorders that can be transmitted by sexual contact. Some of these STDs are merely inconvenient. Others are serious threats to health.

GENITAL HERPES IS A LIFELONG INFECTION

Infections with herpes simplex viruses, or HSV, are extremely contagious. HSV is transmitted by contact with active viruses or sores that contain them (Figure 16.18). Mucous membranes of the mouth or genitals and broken or damaged skin are especially susceptible.

In 2005 the National Institutes of Health estimated that in the United States, one in five people over the age of twelve—roughly 45 million people—have one of the two strains of HSV that cause **genital herpes**. Type 1 strains infect mainly the lips, tongue, mouth, and eyes. Type 2 strains cause most genital infections. Symptoms most often develop within two weeks after infection, although sometimes they are mild or absent. Usually, small, painful blisters erupt on the penis, vulva, cervix, urethra, or anal tissues. The sores can also occur on the buttocks, thighs, or back. The initial flare-up may cause flulike symptoms for several days. Within three weeks the sores crust over and heal.

Every so often the virus may be reactivated. Then it produces new, painful sores at or near the original site of infection. Recurrences can be triggered by stress, sexual intercourse, menstruation, a rise in body temperature, or other infections.

There is no cure for herpes. Between flare-ups, HSV simply is latent in nervous tissue. However, several antiviral drugs inhibit the virus's ability to reproduce. They also reduce the shedding of virus particles from sores, and sores are often less painful and heal faster.

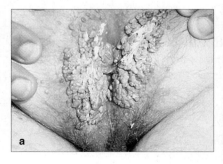

virus particles

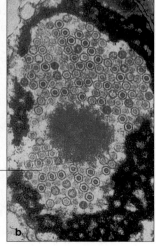

Figure 16.18 (**a**) Genital warts caused by the human papillomavirus. (**b**) Particles of herpes virus in an infected cell.

HUMAN PAPILLOMAVIRUS CAN CAUSE CANCER

Genital warts are painless growths caused by infection of epithelium by the **human papillomavirus** (**HPV**). The warts can develop months or years after a person is exposed to the virus. Usually they occur in clusters on the penis, the cervix, or around the anus (Figure 16.18*b*). Certain forms of HPV are thought to cause more than 80 percent of cases of invasive cervical cancer, a rare but serious form of cervical cancer. Any woman who has a history of genital warts should tell her physician, who may recommend an annual *Pap smear*, which is a test for abnormal growth of cervix cells.

HEPATITIS CAN BE SEXUALLY TRANSMITTED

Two types of hepatitis can be transmitted through sex. Like HIV, the **hepatitis B** virus (HBV) is transmitted in blood or body fluids such as saliva, vaginal secretions, and semen. However, HBV is far more contagious than HIV. The number of sexually transmitted hepatitis B cases is growing; in the United States, about 750,000 people are living with the disease, and about 80,000 new cases are reported each year. The virus attacks the liver. A key symptom is jaundice, yellowing of the skin and whites of the eyes as the liver loses its ability to process bilirubin pigments produced by the breakdown of hemoglobin from red blood cells. In about 10 percent of cases the HBV infection becomes chronic. Carriers are people who don't have symptoms but who can easily spread infection to their intimate contacts. Chronic hepatitis can lead to liver cirrhosis or cancer. The only treatment is rest. However, people at known risk for getting the disease (such as health care workers and anyone who requires repeated blood transfusions) can be vaccinated against the virus.

In 2005 more than 170 million people worldwide were living with the **hepatitis C** virus (HVC), which causes severe liver cirrhosis and sometimes cancer. It is carried in the blood and can reside in the body for years before symptoms develop. Long associated with IV drug abuse, HVC can be transmitted sexually if contaminated blood enters a sex partner's body through cut or torn skin.

SOME STDS ARE CAUSED BY PARASITES

Several animal parasites can be transmitted by close body contact. One is **pubic lice**, also called crab lice or simply "crabs" (Figure 16.19*a*). These tiny relatives of spiders usually turn up in the pubic hair, although they can make their way to any hairy spot on the body. They cling to hairs and attach their small, whitish eggs ("nits") to the base of the hair shaft. Itching and irritation can be

SEXUALLY TRANSMITTED DISEASES

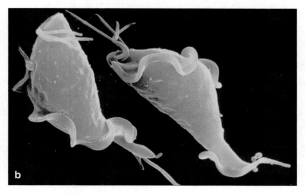

Figure 16.19 (**a**) A crab louse, magnified 120 times. Crab lice are large enough to be visible on the skin, generally as moving brownish dots. (**b**) The protozoan parasite *Trichomonas vaginalis*, which causes trichomoniasis.

intense when the parasites bite into the skin and suck blood. Antiparasitic drugs get rid of pubic lice.

Many microorganisms may live inside the vagina, although its rather acidic pH usually keeps pathogens in check. When certain vaginal infections do occur, they can be transmitted to a sex partner during intercourse. Any factor that alters the vagina's usual chemistry (such as taking an antibiotic) can trigger overgrowth of *Candida albicans*, a type of yeast (a fungus) that often lives in the vagina. A vaginal yeast infection, or **candidiasis**, causes a "cottage cheesy" discharge and itching and irritation of the vulva. A male may notice itching, redness, and flaky skin on his penis. Yeast infections are easily treated by over-the-counter and prescription medications, but both partners may need to be treated to prevent reinfection.

Trichomonas vaginalis, a protozoan parasite (Figure 16.19*b*), can cause the severe vaginal inflammation called **trichomoniasis**. The symptoms include a foul-smelling vaginal discharge and burning and itching of the vulva. An infected male may find urination painful and have a discharge from the penis, both due to an inflamed urethra. Usually both partners are treated with an antibiotic.

> *Common sexually transmitted diseases include genital herpes, genital warts, type B hepatitis, and infections by certain fungi and parasites.*

16.12 Eight Steps to Safer Sex

The only people who are not at risk of STDs are those who are celibate (never have sex) or who are in a long-term, mutually monogamous relationship in which both partners are disease-free. The following guidelines can help you minimize your risk of acquiring or spreading an STD.

1. Use a latex condom during either genital or oral sex to greatly reduce your risk of being exposed to HIV, gonorrhea, herpes, and other diseases. With the condom, use a spermicide that contains nonoxynol-9, which may help kill virus particles. Condoms are available for men and women.

2. Limit yourself to one partner who also has sex only with you.

3. Get to know a prospective partner before you have sex. A friendly but frank discussion of your sexual histories, including any previous exposure to an STD, is very helpful.

4. If you decide to become sexually intimate, be alert to the presence of sores, a discharge, or any other sign of possible trouble in your partner's genital area.

5. Avoid abusing alcohol and drugs. Studies show that alcohol and drug abuse both are correlated with unsafe sex practices.

6. Learn about and be alert for symptoms of STDs. If you have reason to think you have been exposed, abstain from sex until a medical checkup rules out any problems. Self-treatment won't help. See a doctor or visit a clinic.

7. Take all prescribed medication and don't share it with a partner. Unless both of you take a full course of medication, your chances of reinfection will be great. Your partner may need to be treated even if he or she does not have symptoms.

8. If you do become exposed to an STD, avoid sex until medical tests confirm that you are not infected.

Figure 16.20 NBA legend Magic Johnson, a torchbearer of the 2002 Winter Olympics. He contracted HIV through heterosexual sex and credits his survival to AIDS drugs and informed medical care. He continues his campaign to educate others about AIDS.

Summary

Section 16.1 Testes are a male's primary reproductive organs. The male reproductive system also includes accessory ducts and glands.

Sperm develop mostly in the seminiferous tubules and mature in the epididymis. The seminal vesicles, bulbourethral glands, and prostate gland produce fluids that mix with sperm, forming semen.

A vas deferens leading from each testis transports sperm outward when a male ejaculates.

Thomson NOW! *Learn about the male reproductive system.*

Section 16.2 The hormones testosterone, LH (luteinizing hormone), and FSH (follicle-stimulating hormone) control the formation of sperm. They are part of feedback loops among the hypothalamus, anterior pituitary, and testes. Sertoli cells, which line the seminiferous tubules, nourish sperm. Leydig cells in tissue between the tubules secrete testosterone.

A mature sperm cell has a head, midpiece, and tail. Covering much of the head is the acrosome, which contains enzymes that help a sperm penetrate an egg.

In both males and females, gonadotropin-releasing hormone (GnRH) from the hypothalamus stimulates the anterior pituitary to release LH and FSH.

Section 16.3 The paired ovaries, which produce eggs, are a female's primary reproductive organs. Accessory glands and ducts, such as the oviducts, are also part of the female reproductive system. Oviducts open into the uterus, which is lined by the endometrium.

Unless a fertilized egg begins to grow in the uterus, the endometrium proliferates, then is shed in the three-phase menstrual cycle, which averages about 28 days.

Thomson NOW! *Learn about the female reproductive system.*

Sections 16.4, 16.5 The menstrual cycle overlaps with an ovarian cycle. At the end of each menstrual period, a follicle (containing an oocyte) matures in an ovary. Under the influence of hormones, the endometrium starts to rebuild.

A midcycle peak of LH triggers ovulation, the release of a secondary oocyte from the ovary.

A corpus luteum forms from the remainder of the follicle. It secretes progesterone that prepares the endometrium to receive a fertilized egg and helps maintain the endometrium during pregnancy. When no egg is fertilized, the corpus luteum degenerates, and the endometrial lining is shed through menstruation.

The hormones estrogen, progesterone, FSH, and LH control the maturation and release of eggs, as well as changes in the endometrium. They are part of feedback loops involving the hypothalamus, anterior pituitary, and ovaries.

 Observe the cyclic changes in an ovary and the effects of hormones on the menstrual cycle.

Section 16.6 Coitus (sexual intercourse) is the usual way in which egg (a secondary oocyte) and sperm meet for fertilization. It typically involves a sequence of physiological changes in both partners. Orgasm is the culmination of the sex act.

Sections 16.7, 16.8 An increasing variety of physical, chemical, surgical, or behavioral interventions are available for controlling unwanted pregnancies and for helping infertile couples. Inevitably, efforts to control fertility raise important ethical questions.

Sections 16.9–16.12 Sexually transmitted diseases (STDs) are passed by sexual activity. AIDS is a group of diseases caused by infection with the human immunodeficiency virus (HIV). HIV destroys T cells, dendritic cells, and macrophages, crippling the immune system. It is transmitted when blood, semen, or another contaminated body fluid of an infected person enters the body. Sexual contact and IV drug abuse are the most common modes of HIV transmission.

In addition to AIDS, viral STDs include genital herpes, genital warts (HPV), and viral hepatitis. Bacteria cause chlamydia, gonorrhea, and syphilis. Untreated STDs can seriously harm health. Only people who abstain from sexual contact or who are in an infection-free monogamous relationship can be sure of not being exposed to an STD.

Review Questions

1. Distinguish between:
   a. seminiferous tubule and vas deferens
   b. sperm and semen
   c. Leydig cells and Sertoli cells
   d. primary oocyte and secondary oocyte
   e. follicle and corpus luteum
   f. the three phases of the menstrual cycle

2. Which hormones influence the development of sperm?

3. Which hormones influence the menstrual and ovarian cycles?

4. List four events that are triggered by the surge of LH at the midpoint of the menstrual cycle.

5. What changes occur in the endometrium during the ovarian cycle?

6. Label the parts of the male reproductive system and state their functions.

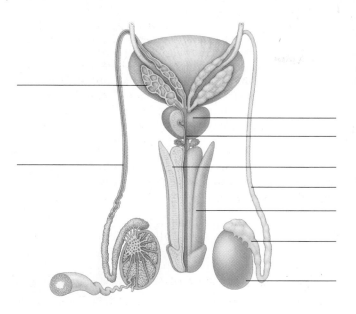

7. Label the parts of the female reproductive system and list their functions.

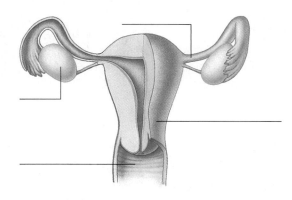

8. Figure 16.21 shows the billowing opening to the oviduct into which an ovulated oocyte is swept. Which oocyte stage is ovulated? What happens to it if (a) it encounters a sperm cell there or (b) it does not meet up with sperm?

Figure 16.21 The entrance to an oviduct, the tubelike channel to the uterus.

Self-Quiz

Answers in Appendix V

1. Besides producing gametes (sperm and eggs), the primary male and female reproductive organs also produce sex hormones. The _____ and the pituitary gland control secretion of both.

2. _____ production is continuous from puberty onward in males; _____ production is cyclic and intermittent in females.
   a. Egg; sperm   c. Testosterone; sperm
   b. Sperm; egg   d. Estrogen; egg

3. The secretion of _____ controls the formation of sperm.
   a. testosterone   c. FSH
   b. LH   d. all of the above are correct

4. During the menstrual cycle, a midcycle surge of _____ triggers ovulation.
   a. estrogen   c. LH
   b. progesterone   d. FSH

5. Which is the correct order for one turn of the menstrual cycle?
   a. corpus luteum forms, ovulation, follicle forms
   b. follicle grows, ovulation, corpus luteum forms

6. In order for sexual intercourse to produce a pregnancy, both partners must experience _____.
   a. orgasm   c. affection
   b. ejaculation   d. none of the above

Critical Thinking

1. Counselors sometimes advise a couple who wish to conceive a child to use an alkaline (basic) douche immediately before intercourse. Speculate about what the doctors' reasoning might be.

2. In the "fertility awareness" method of birth control, a woman gauges her fertile period each month by monitoring changes in the consistency of her vaginal mucus. What kind of specific information does such a method provide? How does it relate to the likelihood of getting pregnant?

3. Some women experience premenstrual syndrome (PMS), which can include a distressing combination of mood swings, fluid retention (edema), anxiety, backache and joint pain, food cravings, and other symptoms. PMS usually develops after ovulation and lasts until just before or just after menstruation begins. A woman's doctor can recommend strategies for managing PMS, which often include diet changes, regular exercise, and use of diuretics or other drugs. Many women find that taking vitamin B6 and vitamin E helps reduce pain and other symptoms. Although the precise cause of PMS is unknown, it seems clearly related to the cyclic production of ovarian hormones. After reviewing Figure 16.6, suggest which hormonal changes may trigger PMS in affected females.

4. Some infertile couples are willing to go to considerable lengths to have a baby (Figure 16.13). From your reading of Section 16.8, which of the variations of reproductive technologies produces a child that is least related (genetically) to the infertile couple? Would you view having a child by that method as preferable to adopting a baby? Why?

5. The absence of menstrual periods, or amenorrhea, is normal in pregnant and postmenopausal women and in girls who have not yet reached puberty. However, in females of reproductive age amenorrhea can result from tumors of the pituitary or adrenals. Based on discussions in this chapter and Chapter 15, speculate about why such tumors might disrupt monthly menstruation.

Explore on Your Own

Public health agencies maintain statistics on the incidence of STDs. They use the numbers to measure the success of public education efforts, to identify increases in reported cases of various STDs, and to monitor the appearance of drug-resistant strains of disease-causing organisms. Table 16.5 below shows the estimated number of new cases of seven STDs in the United States and around the world. Infection by human papillomavirus (HPV) is the most widespread and fastest growing STD in the United States.

To explore how these health concerns are affecting your community or state, go online and find out if your local or state public health department maintains statistics on STDs (most do). Then see which are the most prevalent STDs in your area and whether the numbers have been rising or declining. If someone thinks they may have been exposed, what resources are available for confidential testing?

Table 16.5 Estimated New STD Cases per Year*		
STD	U.S. Cases	Global Cases
HPV infection	5,500,000	20,000,000
Trichomoniasis	5,000,000	174,000,000
Chlamydia	3,000,000	92,000,000
Genital herpes	1,000,000	20,000,000
Gonorrhea	650,000	62,000,000
Syphilis	70,000	12,000,000
AIDS	40,000	4,900,000

*Global data on HPV and genital herpes were last compiled in 1997.

Fertility Factors and Mind-Boggling Births

In December of 1998, Nkem Chukwu of Texas gave birth to octuplets—six girls and two boys. Born prematurely, the babies' combined weight was just over ten pounds. Odera, the smallest, weighed less than a pound (520 grams) and died of heart and lung failure six days later. The other newborns had to remain in the hospital for three months, but now are healthy youngsters.

Chukwu had received a fertility drug, which caused many eggs to mature and be ovulated at the same time. She had the option to reduce the number of embryos but chose to carry all of them to term.

As Chapter 16 noted, multiple births are becoming common, increasing almost 60 percent since the mid-1980s. The incidence of triplets and other higher-order multiple births has quadrupled.

The sharp increase in higher-order multiple births worries some doctors. Carrying more than one embryo increases the risk of miscarriage, premature delivery, and delivery complications that require surgery, such as cesarean section. Compared to single births, newborn weights are lower and mortality rates are higher. The babies are more likely to have development delays and other problems. Also, the parents face more physical, emotional, and financial burdens.

With this chapter, we consider how a human being develops. We start with principles that govern how all the specialized cells and tissues of an adult come into being—a biological journey we all have made.

 How Would You Vote? *Should we restrict the use of fertility drugs to conditions that could limit the number of embryos that form? Cast your vote online at www.thomsonedu.com/biology/starr/humanbio.*

Key Concepts

EARLY DEVELOPMENT
A new individual develops in gene-guided steps that begin when gametes—sperm and eggs—form in parents. Each step builds on body structures formed in the preceding one.

PRENATAL DEVELOPMENT
Early development forms a multicellular embryo and its organs. In the fetal phase, organs and other structures grow and mature.

BIRTH AND LATER DEVELOPMENT
Body structures and functioning change throughout life as a person moves from infancy into childhood, adolescence, adulthood, and the later years.

Links to Earlier Concepts

This chapter builds on the principles of reproduction introduced in Chapter 16 and draws on your understanding of hormones that influence the menstrual cycle (16.4).

Here you will also learn the basics of how organ systems such as the digestive system (Chapter 7), nervous system (Chapter 13), and male and female reproductive systems (Chapter 16) start to develop in an embryo. You will use your knowledge of the cardiovascular system as you study some special features of this system in a developing fetus. You will see how a cascade of hormones of the hypothalamus and pituitary set the stage for birth (15.3), and you will learn more about the effects of aging on various organ systems.

17.1 The Six Stages of Early Development: An Overview

LINKS TO SECTIONS 4.8, 10.5, 16.2, AND 16.4

Biologists divide the early development of the human body into six stages, beginning when gametes form.

IN THE FIRST THREE STAGES, GAMETES FORM, AN EGG IS FERTILIZED, AND CLEAVAGE OCCURS

Development begins when sperm or eggs—the **gametes**—form and mature in the male and female who will become a new individual's parents. The next stage is **fertilization**. It begins when a sperm enters a secondary oocyte. After a sequence of steps, fertilization produces a **zygote** (ZYE-goat, "yoked together"), the first cell of the new individual.

Next comes **cleavage**, when cell divisions convert the zygote to a ball of cells (Figure 17.1). This is the point in your existence when you first became a multicellular creature. The first cleavage divides the zygote into two cells. After the third round of cleavage, there are sixteen embryonic cells arranged in a compact ball called a *morula* (MOE-roo-lah) from a Latin word for mulberry.

One of the more interesting results of cleavage is that each new cell—called a *blastomere*—ends up with a particular portion of the egg's cytoplasm. Which bit of cytoplasm a blastomere receives helps determine the developmental fate of cells that arise from it. For instance, one blastomere may receive cytoplasm that contains molecules of a protein that can activate, say, the gene coding for a certain hormone. Later on, *only* the descendants of that blastomere will make the hormone.

IN STAGE FOUR, THREE PRIMARY TISSUES FORM

After cleavage comes *gastrulation* (gas-trew-LAY-shun), a process that rearranges the morula's cells. It lays out the basic organization for the body as cells are arranged into three primary tissues, called **germ layers**. The outer layer is called **ectoderm**, the middle layer **mesoderm**, and the innermost layer **endoderm**. Subgroups of cells in each layer will give rise to the various tissues and organs in the body (Table 17.1).

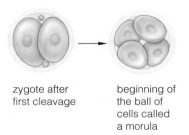

zygote after first cleavage

beginning of the ball of cells called a morula

Figure 17.1 How cleavage in a zygote creates a ball of cells. In the diagram of the first cleavage, the small spheres are polar bodies (Section 16.4).

Table 17.1	Tissues and Organs Derived from the Three Germ Layers in an Embryo
Germ Layer	**Body Parts in an Adult**
Ectoderm	Nervous system and sense organs Pituitary gland Outer layer of skin (epidermis) and its associated structures, such as hair
Mesoderm	Cartilage, bone, muscle, and various connective tissues Cardiovascular system (including blood) Lymphatic system Urinary system Reproductive system Outer layers of the digestive tube and of structures that develop from it, including parts of the respiratory system
Endoderm	Lining of the digestive tube and of structures that develop from it, such as the lining of the respiratory airways

IN STAGES FIVE AND SIX, ORGANS BEGIN TO FORM, THEN GROW AND BECOME SPECIALIZED

Organogenesis is the name for the overall process by which organs form. During this phase, different sets of cells get their basic biological identity—that is, they come to have a specific structure and function. Their identity assigned, cells can give rise to different tissues (nervous tissue, muscle tissue, and so on), which in turn become arranged in organs. In the final stage of development, *growth and tissue specialization*, our organs grow larger and take on the properties required for them to function in specialized ways—such as pumping blood or filtering wastes. This stage continues into adulthood as, for example, the reproductive organs mature.

Three crucial processes accomplish the changes that mold our specialized tissues and organs. The first of these processes is **cell determination**. It establishes which of several possible developmental paths an embryonic cell can follow—for example, whether its fate is to become the forerunner of some kind of nervous tissue, or of epithelium. It's a little like freshman college students being divided into liberal arts majors, business majors, science majors, and so on. In an early embryo, a given cell's fate (and, eventually, the fate of its descendants) depends on where in the embryo the cell originates—the portion of the egg's cytoplasm that a blastomere receives. As an embryo's development progresses, each cell's fate also is influenced by physical interactions and chemical signaling that goes on between groups of cells.

Next, a gene-guided process of **cell differentiation** takes place. To continue our analogy, think of a group of

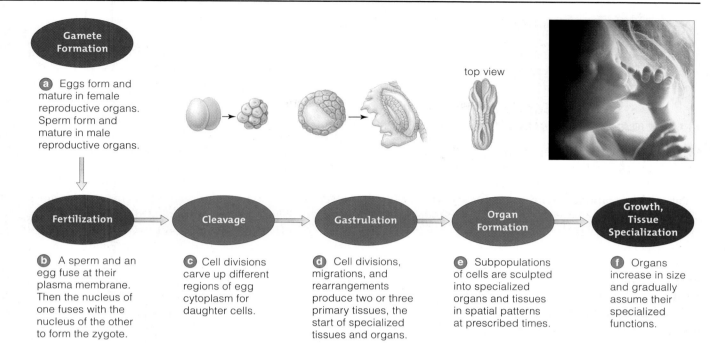

Gamete Formation

a Eggs form and mature in female reproductive organs. Sperm form and mature in male reproductive organs.

top view

Fertilization

b A sperm and an egg fuse at their plasma membrane. Then the nucleus of one fuses with the nucleus of the other to form the zygote.

Cleavage

c Cell divisions carve up different regions of egg cytoplasm for daughter cells.

Gastrulation

d Cell divisions, migrations, and rearrangements produce two or three primary tissues, the start of specialized tissues and organs.

Organ Formation

e Subpopulations of cells are sculpted into specialized organs and tissues in spatial patterns at prescribed times.

Growth, Tissue Specialization

f Organs increase in size and gradually assume their specialized functions.

Figure 17.2 *Animated!* The development of an embryo from fertilization to about 6 weeks. (**a–f**) For clarity, the membranes surrounding the embryo are not shown. Several stages are shown in cross section.

college science majors, some of whom go on to specialize in biology while others specialize in physics, still others in chemistry, and so forth. As cells differentiate, they come to have specific structures and the ability to make products that are associated with particular functions. For example, you may remember from Chapter 10 how various subsets of T cells, with different functions, differentiate in the thymus.

Morphogenesis ("the beginning of form") produces the shape and structure of each body region. It involves cell division in limited areas and growth and movements of cells and tissues from one place to another. For instance, most of the bones of your face are descended from cells that migrated from the back of your head when you were an early embryo.

As you will read shortly, during morphogenesis sheets of tissue fold and certain cells die on cue. Figure 17.2 summarizes the six stages of development. It is important to remember that by the end of each stage, the embryo has become more complex than it was before. Normal development requires that each stage be completed before the next one begins.

Development begins when gametes form in each parent. The next stages are fertilization, then cleavage of the zygote, then gastrulation, organogenesis, and finally the growth and specialization of tissues.

Each stage of embryonic development builds on structures that were formed during the stage preceding it. For proper development, each stage must be successfully completed before the next begins.

Conjoined twins form when an embryo partially splits after day 12. The twins remain joined, usually at the chest or abdomen. In 2002, a team at UCLA's Mattel Hospital successfully separated these Guatemalan sisters who had been joined at the head.

LINKS TO
SECTIONS
16.2, 16.4,
AND 16.6

If sperm enter a female's vagina during the fertile period of her menstrual cycle, an oocyte can be fertilized and an embryo can begin to develop.

FERTILIZATION UNITES SPERM AND OOCYTE

As sperm swim through the cervix and uterus and into the oviducts, they are not quite ready to fertilize an oocyte. First, *capacitation* occurs. In this process, chemical changes weaken the membrane over the sperm's acrosome. Only a sperm that is capacitated ("made able") can fertilize an oocyte (Figure 17.3). Of the millions of sperm in the vagina after an ejaculation, just several hundred reach the upper part of an oviduct, which is where fertilization usually occurs. Uterine muscle contractions help move sperm toward the oviducts.

When a capacitated sperm contacts an oocyte, enzymes are released from the now-fragile region of cell membrane covering the acrosome. Many sperm can reach and bind to the oocyte, and acrosome enzymes clear a path through the zona pellucida. Usually, however, only one sperm fuses with the oocyte. Rapid chemical changes in the oocyte cell membrane block more sperm from entering.

Fusion with a sperm stimulates the completion of the cell division process (meiosis II) that began when the oocyte was being formed in an ovary (Section 16.4). The result is a mature egg, or **ovum** (plural: ova), plus another polar body. (Remember that one or, often, two polar bodies are produced when meiosis I gives rise to the secondary oocyte; thus there usually are three tiny polar bodies "packaged" with the ovum.) The nuclei of the sperm and ovum swell up, then fuse. Recall that a sperm or oocyte has only twenty-three chromosomes, *half* the number present in other body cells. Fertilization combines them into a full diploid set of forty-six chromosomes. Thus a zygote has all the DNA required to guide proper development of the embryo.

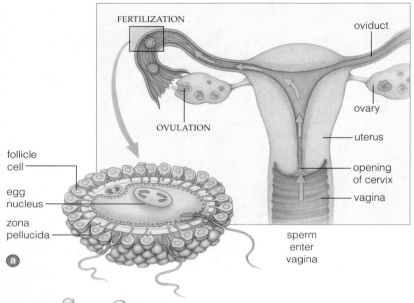

follicle cell

egg nucleus

zona pellucida

a

b

nuclei fuse

fusion of sperm nucleus with egg nucleus

c

d

Figure 17.3 *Animated!*
Fertilization. (**a**) Many sperm surround a secondary oocyte. Acrosomal enzymes clear a path through the zona pellucida. (**b**) When a sperm penetrates the secondary oocyte, cortical granules in the oocyte cytoplasm release substances that prevent other sperm from penetrating the zona pellucida. Penetration also stimulates the second meiotic division of the oocyte's nucleus. (**c**) The sperm tail degenerates; its nucleus enlarges and fuses with the oocyte nucleus. (**d**) At fusion, fertilization is completed. The zygote has formed.

CLEAVAGE PRODUCES A MULTICELLULAR EMBRYO

For several days the zygote moves down the oviduct, sustained by nutrients from the ovum or from maternal secretions. On the way, three cleavages convert the single-celled zygote into a morula (Figure 17.4), the ball of cells described in Section 17.1. The morula's cells occupy the same volume as the zygote did, although they are smaller and their shape and activities differ.

When the morula reaches the uterus, a fluid-filled cavity begins to open up in it. This change transforms the morula into a **blastocyst** (*blast-* = bud). It has two tissues: a surface epithelium called the *trophoblast* (*tropho-* = to nourish) and a small clump of

EARLY DEVELOPMENT

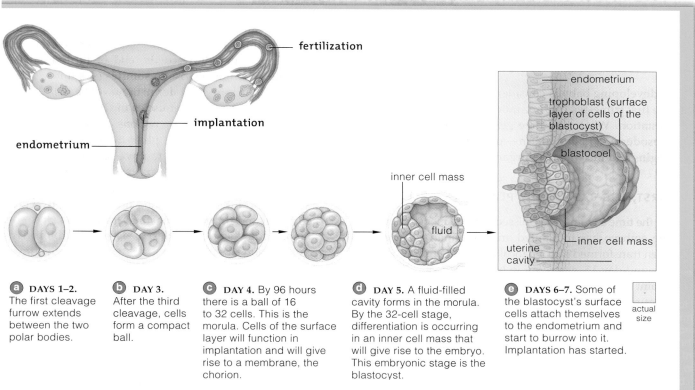

(a) DAYS 1–2. The first cleavage furrow extends between the two polar bodies.

(b) DAY 3. After the third cleavage, cells form a compact ball.

(c) DAY 4. By 96 hours there is a ball of 16 to 32 cells. This is the morula. Cells of the surface layer will function in implantation and will give rise to a membrane, the chorion.

(d) DAY 5. A fluid-filled cavity forms in the morula. By the 32-cell stage, differentiation is occurring in an inner cell mass that will give rise to the embryo. This embryonic stage is the blastocyst.

(e) DAYS 6–7. Some of the blastocyst's surface cells attach themselves to the endometrium and start to burrow into it. Implantation has started.

actual size

Figure 17.4 *Animated!* Steps from fertilization through implantation.

cells called the **inner cell mass** (Figure 17.4*e*). The **embryo** develops from the inner cell mass. Sometimes a split separates the two cells produced by the first cleavage, the inner cell mass, or an even later stage. Then, separate embryos develop as *identical twins*, who have the same genetic makeup. *Fraternal twins* result when two eggs are fertilized at roughly the same time by different sperm. Fraternal twins need not be the same sex and they don't necessarily look any more alike than other siblings do.

IMPLANTATION GIVES A FOOTHOLD IN THE UTERUS

About a week after fertilization, **implantation** begins as the blastocyst breaks out of the zona pellucida. Cells of the epithelium then invade the endometrium and cross into the underlying connective tissue. This gives the blastocyst a foothold in the uterus. As time passes it will sink deep into the connective tissue of the uterus, and the endometrium will close over it.

Occasionally a fertilized egg implants in the wrong place—in the oviduct or even in the external surface of the ovary or in the abdominal wall. This *ectopic* (*tubal*) *pregnancy* cannot go to full term and must be terminated by surgery. Sometimes it leads to permanent infertility.

Implantation is complete two weeks after the secondary oocyte was ovulated. Menstruation, which would begin at this time if the woman were not pregnant, doesn't occur because the implanted blastocyst secretes HCG (human chorionic gonadotropin). HCG stimulates the corpus luteum to continue secreting both estrogen and progesterone, which prevent the uterus lining from being shed. By the third week of pregnancy, HCG can be detected in the mother's blood or urine. At-home pregnancy tests use chemicals that change color when urine contains HCG.

Fertilization of an egg by a sperm produces a zygote, a single cell with a full set of parental chromosomes. Further development produces a multicellular blastocyst that implants in the endometrium of the uterus.

17.5 The First Eight Weeks—Human Features Emerge

By the end of the fourth week of the embryonic period, the embryo has grown to 500 times its original size. Over the next few weeks recognizable human features will appear.

In an embryo's first few weeks of life, it grows rapidly and its cells begin to specialize. Morphogenesis begins to sculpt limbs, fingers, and toes. The circulatory system becomes more intricate, and the umbilical cord forms. Growth of the all-important head now surpasses that of any other body region (Figure 17.10*a*). The embryonic period ends as the eighth week draws to a close. The embryo is no longer merely "a vertebrate." As you can see from Figure 17.10*c*, its features now clearly define it as a human.

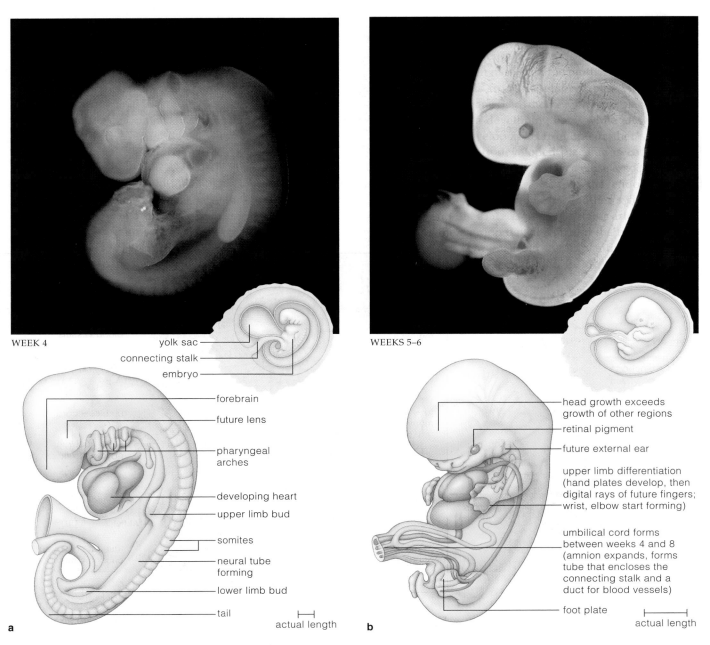

WEEK 4

yolk sac
connecting stalk
embryo

forebrain
future lens
pharyngeal arches
developing heart
upper limb bud
somites
neural tube forming
lower limb bud
tail

actual length

a

WEEKS 5–6

head growth exceeds growth of other regions
retinal pigment
future external ear

upper limb differentiation (hand plates develop, then digital rays of future fingers; wrist, elbow start forming)

umbilical cord forms between weeks 4 and 8 (amnion expands, forms tube that encloses the connecting stalk and a duct for blood vessels)

foot plate

actual length

b

Figure 17.10 *Animated!* (**a**) Human embryo at four weeks. As is true of all vertebrates, it has a tail and pharyngeal arches. (**b**) The embryo at five to six weeks after fertilization. (**c**, *facing page*) An embryo poised at the boundary between the embryonic and fetal periods. It now has features that are distinctly human. It is floating in fluid within the amniotic sac. The chorion, which normally covers the amniotic sac, has been opened and pulled aside.

As the second half of the first trimester gets under way, gonads begin to develop. In an embryo that has inherited X and Y sex chromosomes, a sex-determining region of the Y chromosome now triggers development of testes (Figure 17.11). Sex hormones made by the testes then influence the development of the entire reproductive system. An embryo with XX sex chromosomes will be female, and female reproductive structures begin to form in her body. Notice that no hormones are required to stimulate development of female gonads—all that is necessary is the *absence* of testosterone.

After eight weeks the embryo is just over 1 inch long, its organ systems are formed, and it is designated a **fetus**. As the first trimester ends, a heart monitor can detect the fetal heartbeat. The genitals are well formed, and a doctor often can determine a baby's sex using ultrasound.

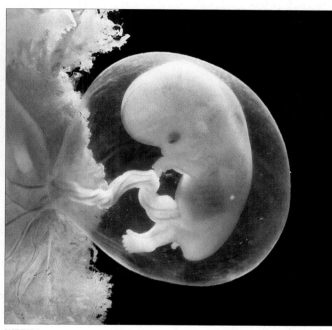

WEEK 8

final week of embryonic period; embryo looks distinctly human compared to other vertebrate embryos

upper and lower limbs well formed; fingers and then toes have separated

early tissues of all internal, external structures now developed

tail has become stubby

c   actual length

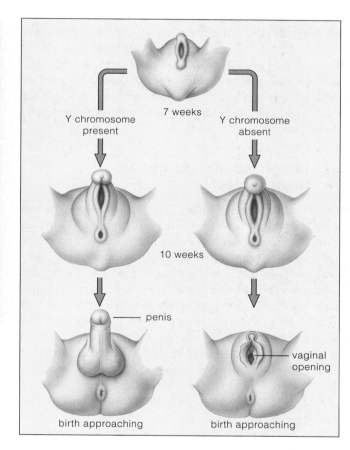

Figure 17.11 Developing genitals of male and female embryos.

MISCARRIAGE

Miscarriage, the spontaneous expulsion of an embryo or fetus, occurs in more than 20 percent of all conceptions, usually during the first trimester. Many factors can trigger a miscarriage (also called spontaneous abortion), but in as many as half the cases the embryo (or the fetus) has one or more genetic disorders that prevent it from developing normally.

During the first eight weeks of life an embryo gradually develops distinctly human body features. At the end of this period the developing individual is termed a fetus.

17.6 Development of the Fetus

LINKS TO SECTIONS 9.3 AND 11.5

In the second and third trimesters, organs and organ systems gradually mature in preparation for birth.

IN THE SECOND TRIMESTER MOVEMENTS BEGIN

When the fetus is three months old, it is about 4.5 inches long. Soft, fuzzy hair (the lanugo) covers its body. Its reddish skin is wrinkled and protected from abrasion by a thick, cheesy coating called the *vernix caseosa.*

The second trimester of development extends from the start of the fourth month to the end of the sixth. Figure 17.12 shows what the fetus looks like at 16 weeks. Its tiny facial muscles now produce frowns, squints, and sucking movements—evidence of a sucking reflex. Before the second trimester ends, the mother can easily feel her fetus's arms and legs move. During the sixth month, its eyelids and eyelashes form.

ORGAN SYSTEMS MATURE DURING THE THIRD TRIMESTER

The third trimester extends from the seventh month until birth. At seven months the fetus is about 11 inches long, and soon its eyes will open. Although the fetus is growing much larger and rapidly becoming "babylike," not until the middle of the third trimester will it be able to survive on its own. Although development might seem relatively complete by the seventh month, at that age few fetuses can maintain a normal body temperature or breathe normally. However, with intensive medical care, fetuses as young as 23 to 25 weeks have survived early delivery. A baby born before seven months' gestation is at high risk of *respiratory distress syndrome* (described in Chapter 11) because its lungs lack surfactant and so can't expand adequately. The longer the baby can stay in its mother's uterus, the better. By the ninth month, its survival chances are about 95 percent.

THE BLOOD AND CIRCULATORY SYSTEM OF A FETUS HAVE SPECIAL FEATURES

The steady maturation of its organs and organ systems readies the fetus for independent life. For the circulatory system, however, the path toward independence requires a detour. Several temporary bypass vessels form and will function until birth. As Figure 17.13 shows, two umbilical arteries inside the umbilical cord transport deoxygenated blood and metabolic wastes from the fetus to the placenta. There, the fetal blood gives up wastes, takes on nutrients, and exchanges gases with the mother's blood. Fetal hemoglobin is slightly different from adult hemoglobin. It binds oxygen more readily, helping ensure that adequate

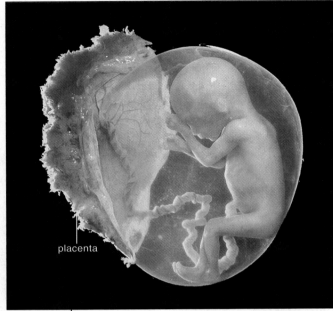

placenta

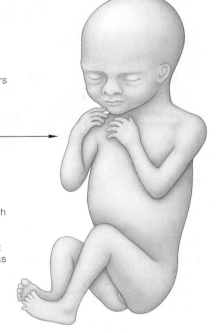

WEEK 16 ⎯⎯

Length:	16 centimeters (6.4 inches)
Weight:	200 grams (7 ounces)

WEEK 29

Length:	27.5 centimeters (11 inches)
Weight:	1,300 grams (46 ounces)

WEEK 38 (full term)

Length:	50 centimeters (20 inches)
Weight:	3,400 grams (7.5 pounds)

During fetal period, length measurement extends from crown to heel (for embryos, it is the longest measurable dimension, as from crown to rump).

Figure 17.12 (*top*) The fetus at 16 weeks. During the fetal period, movements begin as soon as nerves establish functional connections with developing muscles. Legs kick, arms wave, fingers grasp, the mouth puckers. These reflex actions will be vital skills in the world outside the uterus. The drawing shows a baby at full term—ready to be born.

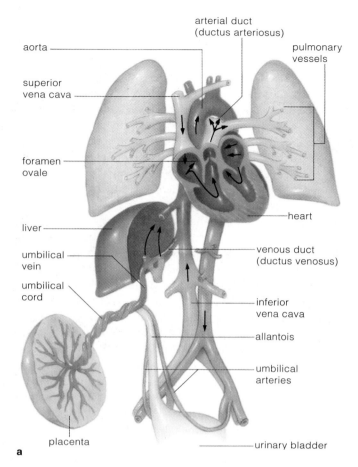

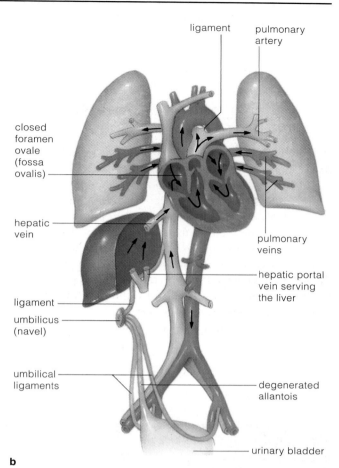

Figure 17.13 Blood circulation in a fetus (*arrows*). (**a**) Umbilical arteries carry deoxygenated blood from fetal tissues to the placenta. There blood picks up oxygen and nutrients from the mother's bloodstream and returns to the fetus via the umbilical vein. Blood mainly bypasses the lungs, moving through the foramen ovale and the arterial duct. It bypasses the liver by moving through the venous duct.

(**b**) At birth the foramen ovale closes, and the pulmonary and systemic circuits of blood flow become completely separate. The arterial duct, venous duct, umbilical vein, and portions of the umbilical arteries become ligaments, and the allantois degenerates.

oxygen will reach developing fetal tissues. The oxygenated blood, enriched with nutrients, returns from the placenta to the fetus in the umbilical vein.

Other temporary vessels divert blood past the lungs and liver. These organs don't develop as rapidly as some others, because (by way of the placenta) the mother's body can perform their functions. The lungs of a fetus are collapsed and won't function for gas exchange until the newborn takes its first breaths after birth. Until then, its lung tissues receive only enough blood to sustain their development. A little of the blood entering the heart's right atrium flows into the right ventricle and moves on to the lungs. Most of it, however, travels through a gap in the interior heart wall (called the *foramen ovale*, or "oval opening") or into an arterial duct (*ductus arteriosus*) that bypasses the nonfunctioning lungs entirely.

Likewise, most blood bypasses the fetal liver because the mother's liver performs most liver functions (such as

nutrient processing) until birth. Nutrient-laden blood from the placenta travels through a venous duct (the *ductus venosus*) past the liver and on to the heart, which pumps it to body tissues. At birth, blood pressure in the heart's left atrium increases. This causes a valvelike flap of tissue to close off the foramen ovale, which then gradually seals and separates the pulmonary and systemic circuits of blood flow (Figure 17.13*b*). The temporary vessels that have formed in a fetus gradually close during the first few weeks after birth.

The organs and organ systems of a fetus mature during the second and third trimesters. Because the fetus exchanges gases and receives nutrients via its mother's bloodstream, its circulatory system develops temporary vessels that bypass the lungs and liver until birth.

17.7 Birth and Beyond

LINKS TO
SECTIONS
15.3 AND 16.2

Birth, or parturition, takes place about 39 weeks after fertilization—about 280 days from the start of the woman's last menstrual period.

HORMONES TRIGGER BIRTH

Usually within two weeks of a pregnant woman's "due date," the birth process, "labor," begins when smooth muscle in her uterus starts to contract. These contractions are the indirect result of a cascade of hormones from the fetus's hypothalamus, pituitary, and adrenal glands, which is triggered by an as-yet-unknown signal that says, in effect, it's time to be born. The hormonal flood causes the placenta to produce more estrogen. Rising estrogen in turn calls for a rush of oxytocin and of prostaglandins (also produced by the placenta), which stimulate the uterine contractions. For about the next 2 to 18 hours, the contractions will become stronger, more painful, and more frequent.

LABOR HAS THREE STAGES

Labor is divided into three stages that we can think of loosely as "before, during, and after." In the first stage, uterine contractions push the fetus against its mother's cervix. Initial contractions occur about every 15 to 30 minutes and are relatively mild. As the cervix gradually dilates to a diameter of about 10 centimeters (4 inches, or "5 fingers"), contractions become more frequent and intense. Usually, the amniotic sac ruptures during this stage, which can last 12 hours or more.

The second stage of labor, actual birth of the fetus, typically occurs less than an hour after the cervix is fully dilated. This stage is usually brief—under 2 hours. Strong contractions of the uterus and abdominal muscles occur every 2 or 3 minutes, and the mother feels an urge to push. Her efforts and the intense contractions move the soon-to-be newborn through the cervix and out through the vaginal canal, usually head first (Figure 17.14). Complications can develop if the baby begins to emerge in a "bottom-first" (*breech*) position; the attending physician may use hands or forceps to aid the delivery.

After the baby is expelled, the third stage of labor gets under way. Uterine contractions force fluid, blood, and the placenta (now called the afterbirth) from the mother's body. The umbilical cord—the lifeline to the mother—is now severed. A lasting reminder of this separation is the scar we call the navel—the site where the umbilical cord was attached.

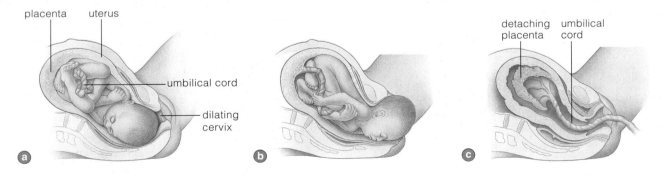

Figure 17.14 *Animated!* Expulsion of the fetus during birth. The afterbirth—the placenta, fluid, and blood—is expelled shortly afterward.

BIRTH AND LATER DEVELOPMENT

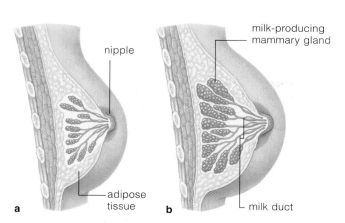

Figure 17.15 **Animated!** (**a**) Breast anatomy. (**b**) Breast of a lactating female.

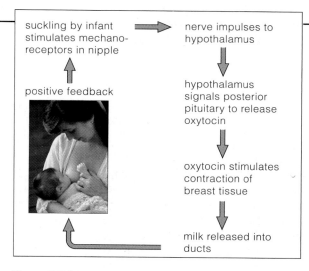

Figure 17.16 How a positive feedback mechanism keeps milk flowing to a suckling infant.

Without the placenta to remove wastes, carbon dioxide builds up in the baby's blood. Together with other factors, including handling by medical personnel, this stimulates control centers in the brain, which respond by triggering inhalation—the newborn's crucial first breath.

As the infant's lungs begin to function, the bypass vessels of the fetal circulation begin to close, soon to shut completely. The fetal heart opening, the foramen ovale, normally closes slowly during the first year of life.

Most full-term pregnancies end in the birth of a healthy infant. Yet babies born prematurely—especially before about eight months of intrauterine life—can suffer complications because their organs have not developed to the point where they can function independently. Then, attempts to sustain the baby's life under conditions that will permit the necessary additional development may require a variety of advanced medical technologies. Even then, the majority of extremely premature infants do not survive.

HORMONES ALSO CONTROL MILK PRODUCTION IN A MOTHER'S MAMMARY GLANDS

Milk production provides an excellent example of how hormones may interact in the body. In this case, a total of four hormones are involved. During pregnancy, estrogen and progesterone stimulate the growth of mammary glands and ducts in the mother's breasts (Figure 17.15). For the first few days after birth, those glands produce colostrum, a pale fluid that is rich in proteins, antibodies, minerals, and vitamin A. Then prolactin secreted by the pituitary stimulates milk production, or **lactation**.

The "let-down" or flow of milk from a nursing mother's mammary glands is a reflex and an example of positive feedback (Figure 17.16). When a newborn nurses, mechanoreceptors in the nipple send nerve impulses to the hypothalamus, which in turn stimulates the mother's pituitary to release oxytocin, which causes the mother's breast tissues to contract. This forces milk into the ducts. This response continues as long as the baby suckles. Oxytocin also triggers contractions of uterine muscle that will help to "shrink" the uterus back to its normal size.

The mother's cervix dilates during the first stage of labor. The baby is born during the second stage. In the third stage, uterine contractions expel the placenta.

Lactation, or milk production, begins a few days after birth. It is stimulated by the hormone prolactin, which is released from the mother's pituitary and acts on her breast (mammary gland) tissues.

Suckling triggers a reflex in which oxytocin released from the pituitary acts to force milk into mammary ducts. The response continues as long as the infant suckles.

IMPACTS, ISSUES

In 2004 a Korean scientist announced that he had cloned a human embryo—that is, created a line of cells genetically identical to an embryonic cell. The goal was to obtain human stem cells that could be used to grow replacement tissues. It turned out that the researcher had faked his results, and several nations have outlawed research that creates, then destroys embryos for the purpose of obtaining stem cells. Yet we know that many laboratories are working full steam to succeed at this "therapeutic cloning." You can be sure that you will be hearing a great deal more about such controversial research efforts.

17.8 Potential Disorders of Early Development

From fertilization until birth, a woman's future child is at the mercy of her diet, health habits, and lifestyle. This section looks at common concerns with regard to nutrition, the risk of infection, and the use of legal and illegal drugs.

GOOD MATERNAL NUTRITION IS VITAL

A pregnant woman must nourish her unborn child as well as herself. In general, the same balanced diet that is good for her should also provide her developing baby with all the carbohydrates, lipids, and proteins it needs. Vitamins and minerals are a different story, however. Physicians recommend that a pregnant woman take supplemental vitamins and minerals, not only for her own benefit but also to meet the needs of her fetus. This is particularly true for the nutrient folic acid (folate), which is required for the neural tube to develop properly. If too little folic acid is available, a birth defect called **spina bifida** ("split spine") may develop, in which the neural tube doesn't close and separate from ectoderm. The infant may be born with part of its spinal cord exposed inside a cyst. Infection is a serious danger, and the resulting neurological problems can include poor bowel and bladder control. To prevent neural tube defects, folic acid now is added to wheat flour and other widely used foods.

A pregnant woman must eat enough to gain between 20 and 35 pounds, on average. If she gains much less than that, she may be putting her fetus at risk. Infants who are severely underweight have more complications after delivery. As birth approaches, the growing fetus demands more and more nutrients from the mother's body. For example, the brain grows the most in the weeks just before and after birth. Poor nutrition during that time, especially protein deficiency, can have repercussions on intelligence and other brain functions later in life.

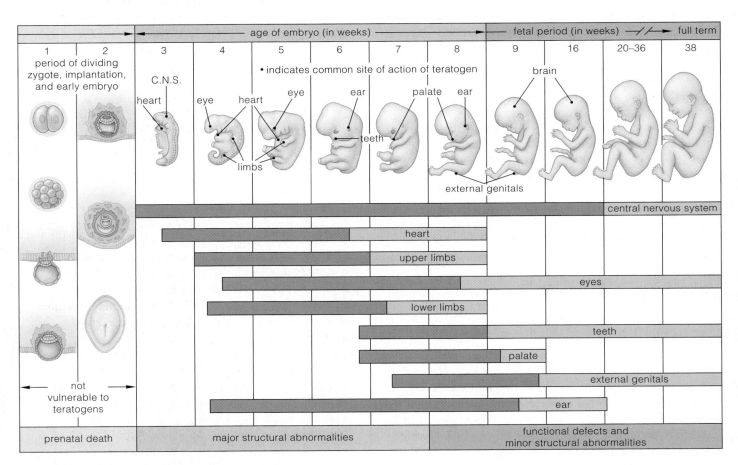

Figure 17.17 *Animated!* Sensitivity to teratogens. Light blue also indicates periods in which organs are most sensitive to damage from alcohol, viral infection, and so on. Numbers signify the week of development.

INFECTIONS PRESENT SERIOUS RISKS

A pregnant woman's IgG antibodies cross the placenta. They can help protect her developing infant from all but the most severe bacterial infections. Other **teratogens**—agents that can cause birth defects—are more serious threats. Some viral diseases can be dangerous during the first six weeks of pregnancy, when the organs of a fetus are forming (Figure 17.17). For example, if a pregnant woman contracts **rubella** (German measles) during this time, there is a 50 percent chance that some organs of the embryo won't form properly. If she contracts the virus when the embryo's ears are forming, her newborn may be deaf. With time, the risk of damage diminishes, and vaccination before pregnancy can eliminate it entirely.

PRESCRIPTION DRUGS CAN HARM

During its first trimester in the womb, an embryo is extremely sensitive to drugs the mother takes. In the 1960s many women using the tranquilizer thalidomide gave birth to infants with missing or severely deformed arms and legs. Although it wasn't known at the time, thalidomide alters the steps required for normal limbs to develop. When the connection became clear, thalidomide was withdrawn from the market (although it now has other medical uses). However, other commonly used tranquilizers—as well as some sedatives and barbiturates—might cause similar, although less severe, damage. Even certain anti-acne drugs, such as retinoic acid, increase the risk of facial and cranial deformities. The antibiotic streptomycin causes hearing problems and may adversely affect the nervous system; a pregnant woman who uses the antibiotic tetracycline may have a child whose teeth are yellowed.

ALCOHOL AND OTHER DRUGS CAN ALSO HARM

Like many other drugs, alcohol crosses the placenta and affects the fetus. *Fetal alcohol syndrome* (FAS) is a constellation of defects that can result from alcohol use by a pregnant woman. Tragically, FAS is one of the most common causes of mental retardation in the United States. Babies born with it typically have a smaller than normal brain and head, facial deformities, poor motor coordination, and, sometimes, heart defects (Figure 17.18). The symptoms can't be reversed; FAS children never catch up, physically or mentally. Between 60 and 70 percent of alcoholic women give birth to infants with

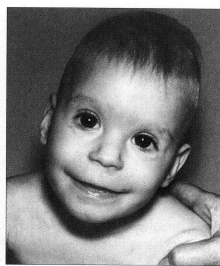

Figure 17.18 An infant with fetal alcohol syndrome (FAS). Obvious symptoms are low and prominent ears, poorly developed cheekbones, and a long, smooth upper lip. The child may have growth problems and abnormalities of the nervous system.

FAS. There may be no "safe" drinking level during pregnancy. Many doctors urge near or total abstinence from alcohol during pregnancy.

A pregnant woman who uses cocaine, especially crack, prevents her child's nervous system from developing normally. As a result, the child may be chronically irritable as well as abnormally small.

Research evidence suggests that tobacco smoke reduces the level of vitamin C in a pregnant woman's blood, and in that of her fetus as well. Cigarette smoke also harms the growth and development of a fetus in other ways. A pregnant woman who smokes daily will give birth to an underweight newborn even if the mother's weight, nutritional status, and all other relevant variables are the same as those of pregnant nonsmokers. A pregnant smoker also has a greater risk of miscarriage, stillbirth, and premature delivery. A long-term study at Toronto's Hospital for Sick Children showed that toxins in tobacco build up even in the fetuses of nonsmokers who are exposed to secondhand smoke at home or work.

Just how cigarette smoke damages a fetus is not known. However, its demonstrated effects are additional evidence that the placenta cannot protect a developing fetus from every danger.

17.9 Prenatal Diagnosis: Detecting Birth Defects

A growing number of options now enable us to detect more than 100 genetic disorders before a child is born.

Amniocentesis samples fluid from within the amnion, the sac that contains the fetus (Figure 17.19). During the fourteenth to sixteenth weeks of pregnancy, the thin needle of a syringe is inserted through the mother's abdominal wall, into the amnion. The physician must take care that the needle doesn't puncture the fetus and that no infection occurs. Amniotic fluid contains sloughed fetal cells; as the syringe withdraws fluid, some of those cells are included. They are then cultured and tested for genetic abnormalities.

Chorionic villus sampling (CVS) uses tissue from the chorionic villi of the placenta. CVS is tricky. Using ultrasound, the physician guides a tube through the vagina, past the cervix, and along the uterine wall, then removes a small sample of chorionic villus cells by suction. The method can be used by the eighth week of pregnancy; results are available within days. Both CVS and amniocentesis involve a small risk of triggering miscarriage. With CVS there also is a slight chance the future child will have missing or underdeveloped fingers or toes.

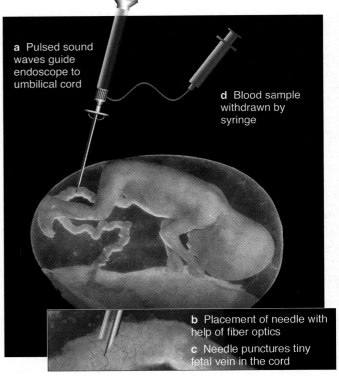

a Pulsed sound waves guide endoscope to umbilical cord

d Blood sample withdrawn by syringe

b Placement of needle with help of fiber optics

c Needle punctures tiny fetal vein in the cord

Figure 17.20 Fetoscopy for prenatal diagnosis.

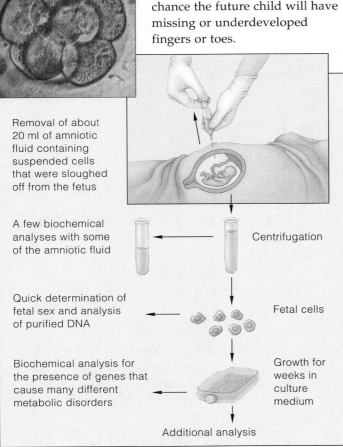

Removal of about 20 ml of amniotic fluid containing suspended cells that were sloughed off from the fetus

A few biochemical analyses with some of the amniotic fluid

Centrifugation

Quick determination of fetal sex and analysis of purified DNA

Fetal cells

Biochemical analysis for the presence of genes that cause many different metabolic disorders

Growth for weeks in culture medium

Additional analysis

Figure 17.19 *Animated!* Procedure for amniocentesis. *(inset, above)* An eight-cell-stage human embryo.

Physicians also have available several methods of embryo screening. In *preimplantation diagnosis*, an embryo conceived by in vitro fertilization (Section 16.8) is analyzed for genetic defects using recombinant DNA technology. The testing occurs at the eight-cell stage (Figure 17.19, *inset*). According to one view, the tiny, free-floating ball is a *pre*-pregnancy stage. Like the unfertilized eggs discarded monthly during menstruation, the ball is not attached to the uterus. All cells in the ball have the same genes and are not yet committed to giving rise to specialized cells of a heart, lungs, or other organs. Doctors take one of the undifferentiated cells and analyze its genes for suspected disorders. If the cell has no detectable genetic defects, the ball is inserted into the uterus. Embryo screening is designed to help parents who are at high risk of having children with a genetic birth defect. Even so, it raises questions of morality in the minds of some people.

Fetoscopy allows direct visualization of the developing fetus. A fiber-optic device, an endoscope, uses pulsed sound waves to scan the uterus and visually locate parts of the fetus, umbilical cord, or placenta (Figure 17.20). Fetoscopy has been used to diagnose blood cell disorders, such as sickle-cell anemia and hemophilia. Like amniocentesis and CVS, fetoscopy has risks; it increases the risk of a miscarriage by 2 to 10 percent.

17.10 From Birth to Adulthood

After a child enters the world, a gene-dictated course of further growth and development leads to adulthood.

THERE ARE MANY TRANSITIONS FROM BIRTH TO ADULTHOOD

Table 17.2 summarizes the prenatal (before birth) and postnatal (after birth) stages of life. A newborn is called a *neonate*. During infancy, which lasts until about 15 months of age, the child's nervous and sensory systems mature rapidly, and a series of growth spurts makes its body longer. Figure 17.21 shows how body proportions change during childhood and adolescence. In adolescence, **puberty** marks the arrival of sexual maturity as a person's reproductive organs begin to function. Sex hormones trigger the appearance of secondary sex characteristics such as pubic and underarm hair, and behavior changes. A mix of hormones triggers another growth spurt at this time. Boys usually grow most rapidly between the ages of 12 and 15, whereas girls tend to grow most rapidly between the ages of 10 and 13. After several years, the

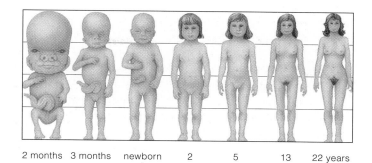

2 months 3 months newborn 2 5 13 22 years

Figure 17.21 *Animated!* Changes in body proportions during prenatal and postnatal growth.

influence of sex hormones causes the cartilaginous plates near the ends of long bones to harden into bone. Humans stop growing by their early twenties.

ADULTHOOD IS ALSO A TIME OF BODILY CHANGE

Although in the United States the average life expectancy is 72 years for males and 79 years for females, we reach the peak of our physical potential in adolescence and early adulthood. A healthy diet, regular exercise, and other beneficial lifestyle habits can go far in keeping a person vigorous for decades of adult life. Even so, after about age 40, body parts begin to undergo structural changes. There is also a gradual loss of efficiency in bodily functions, as well as increased sensitivity to environmentally induced stress. This steady deterioration is built into the life cycle of all organisms in which cells become highly specialized. The process, technically called *senescence*, is what we all know as aging.

Aging leads to many structural changes in the body. Beginning around age 40, there is a gradual decline in bone and muscle mass. Our skin develops more wrinkles, and more fat is deposited. Less obvious are a variety of gradual physiological changes. This chapter's concluding sections explore the phenomenon of aging, beginning with some ideas about its causes.

Table 17.2	Stages of Human Development: A Summary	
PRENATAL PERIOD		
1. Zygote	Single cell resulting from union of sperm and egg at fertilization	
2. Morula	Solid ball of cells produced by cleavages	
3. Blastocyst	Ball of cells with surface layer and inner cell mass	
4. Embryo	All developmental stages from 2 weeks after fertilization until end of eighth week	
5. Fetus	All developmental stages from the ninth week until birth (about 39 weeks after fertilization)	
POSTNATAL PERIOD		
6. Newborn (neonate)	Individual during the first 2 weeks after birth	
7. Infant	Individual from 2 weeks to about 15 months after birth	
8. Child	Individual from infancy to about 12 or 13 years	
9. Pubescent	Individual at puberty, when secondary sexual traits develop; girls between 10 and 16 years, boys between 13 and 16 years	
10. Adolescent	Individual from puberty until about 3 or 4 years later; physical, mental, emotional maturation	
11. Adult	Early adulthood (between 18 and 25 years); bone formation and growth completed. Changes proceed very slowly afterward.	
12. Old age	Aging culminates in general body deterioration	

Following birth, development proceeds through childhood and adolescence, which includes the arrival of sexual maturity at puberty. Puberty is the gateway to the adult phase of life. After about age 30, developmental changes associated with aging become increasingly apparent.

17.11 Time's Toll: Everybody Ages

LINKS TO
SECTIONS
2.4, 2.5, 4.2, 5.3,
5.6, 6.5, 16.1,
AND 16.3

Time takes a toll on body tissues and organs. To some extent, our genes determine how long each of us will live.

Aging is a gradual loss of vitality as cells, tissues, and organs function less and less efficiently. At about age 40, the skin begins to noticeably wrinkle and sag, body fat tends to accumulate, and muscles and joints are more easily injured and take longer to heal. Stamina declines, and we become increasingly susceptible to disorders such as heart disease, arthritis, and cancer.

Structural changes in certain proteins may contribute to many changes we associate with aging (Figure 17.22). Remember from Chapter 4 that many connective tissues consist largely of collagen. A collagen molecule is stabilized by molecular bonds that form cross-link segments of the chain. As a person grows older, new cross-links develop, and the protein becomes more and more rigid. Changes in collagen's structure in turn can alter the structure and functioning of organs and blood vessels that contain it. Age-related cross-linking is also thought to affect many enzymes and possibly DNA.

Figure 17.22 As we age, structural and functional changes affect virtually all body tissues and organs. Graying hair, "age spots," and skin wrinkles are just three outward signs of these changes.

GENES MAY DETERMINE THE MAXIMUM HUMAN LIFE SPAN

Does an internal, biological clock control aging? That's one prominent hypothesis. After all, each species has a maximum life span. For example, we know the maximum is about 20 years for dogs and 12 weeks for butterflies. So far as we can document, no human has lived beyond 122 years. The consistency of life span within species is a sign that genes help govern aging.

One idea is that each type of cell, tissue, and organ is like a clock that ticks at its own genetically set pace. When researchers investigated this possibility, they grew normal human embryonic cells, all of which divided about 50 times, then died.

In the body, human cells divide eighty or ninety times, at most. As discussed in Chapter 19, cells copy their chromosomes before they divide. Capping the ends of chromosomes are repeated stretches of DNA called *telomeres*. A bit of each telomere is lost during each cycle of cell division. When only a nub remains, cells stop dividing and die.

Cancer cells, and the cells in gonads that give rise to both sperm and oocytes, are exceptions to this rule. Both these types of cells make telomerase, an enzyme

that causes telomeres to lengthen. Apparently, that is why such cells can divide over and over, without dying.

CUMULATIVE DAMAGE TO DNA MAY ALSO PLAY A ROLE IN AGING

A "cumulative assaults" hypothesis proposes that aging results from mounting damage to DNA combined with a decline in DNA's mechanisms of self-repair. Chapter 2 described how free radicals can damage DNA and other biological molecules. If changes in DNA aren't fixed, they may endanger the synthesis of enzymes and other proteins that are required for normal cell operations.

Some interesting studies of aging have implicated problems in the processes by which DNA replicates and repairs itself. For instance, researchers have correlated Werner's syndrome, a disorder that causes premature aging in young adults, with a harmful mutation in the gene that carries instructions for an enzyme that is thought to be essential for DNA self-repair. With a "bad" form of this enzyme, accumulating DNA damage may progressively undermine cell functions.

Ultimately, it's quite possible that aging involves processes in which genes, free radical damage, a decline in DNA repair mechanisms, and even other factors all come into play.

> *Aging may result from a combination of factors, including an internal biological clock that ticks out the life spans of cells, and the accumulation of errors in and damage to DNA.*

IMPACTS, ISSUES

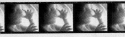

In the United States and elsewhere, some fertility clinics have begun helping women in their fifties and sixties become pregnant. The most common method is in vitro fertilization using donated eggs. A number of these women have given birth, in some cases to twins or triplets. Many medical professionals discourage the practice, citing its medical, social, and psychological impacts on both mother and child.

BIRTH AND LATER DEVELOPMENT

17.12 Aging Skin, Muscle, Bones, and Reproductive Systems

Some obvious signs of aging show up in our skin, muscles, skeleton, and reproductive systems.

CHANGES IN CONNECTIVE TISSUE AFFECT SKIN, MUSCLES, AND BONES

Skin changes often are early obvious signs of aging. The normal replacement of sloughed epidermis through cell division begins to slow. Cells called fibroblasts are a major component of connective tissue, and the number of them in the dermis starts to decrease. Also, the elastin fibers that give skin its flexibility are slowly replaced with more rigid collagen. As a result of these changes, the skin becomes thinner and less elastic, so it sags and wrinkles develop. Wrinkling increases as less fat is stored in the hypodermis, the layer beneath the dermis. The skin also becomes drier as sweat and oil glands begin to break down and are not replaced. The loss of sweat glands and subcutaneous fat is one reason why older people tend to have difficulty regulating their body temperature. As hair follicles die or become less active, there is a general loss of body hair. And as pigment-producing cells die and are not replaced, the remaining body hair begins to appear gray or white.

Fibers in skeletal muscle atrophy, in part because of a corresponding loss of motor neurons that synapse with muscle fibers. In general, aging muscles lose mass and strength, and lost muscle tends to be replaced by fat and, with time, by collagen. Importantly, however, the extent to which this muscle replacement takes place depends on a person's diet and exercise habits. Typically, an 80-year-old has about half the muscle strength he or she had at 30. Staying physically active can help slow all these changes (Figure 17.23).

Our bones become weaker, more porous, and brittle as we age. Over the years bones lose some collagen and elastin, but mainly bones weaken from the loss of calcium and other minerals after about age 40. Older people may be prone to develop osteoporosis. Women naturally have less bone calcium than men do, and they begin to lose it earlier. Without medical intervention, some women lose as much as half of their bone mass by age 70; therapeutic drugs are now available to help retard calcium loss.

With the passing years, intervertebral disks gradually deteriorate, reducing the distance between vertebrae. This is why people tend to get shorter, generally by about a centimeter every ten years from middle age onward.

Ninety percent of people over 40 have some degree of joint breakdown. The cartilage in joints deteriorates from the sheer wear and tear of daily movements, the surfaces of the joined bones begin to wear away, and the joints become more difficult to move. At least 15 percent of adults develop osteoarthritis, which you may recall is a

Figure 17.23 Moderate physical activity that is maintained as a person ages slows age-related deterioration of the muscular and skeletal systems, among other benefits.

chronic inflammation of cartilage, in one or more joints. Although many factors contribute to osteoarthritis, it is most common in older people. This observation suggests that age-related changes in bone are often involved.

REPRODUCTIVE SYSTEMS AND SEXUALITY CHANGE

Levels of most hormones stay steady throughout life. However, the sex hormones are exceptions. Falling levels of estrogens and progesterone trigger menopause in women; in older men, falling levels of testosterone reduce fertility. That said, whereas menopause brings a woman's reproductive period to an end, men can and have fathered children into their 80s. Males and females both retain their capacity for sexual response well into old age.

Menopause usually begins in a woman's late 40s or early 50s. Over a period of several years, her menstrual periods become irregular, then stop altogether as her ovaries become less sensitive to the hormones FSH and LH (Chapter 15) and gradually stop secreting estrogen in response. For many women menopause is relatively free of unpleasant symptoms. However, declining estrogen levels may trigger "hot flashes" (intense sweating and uncomfortable warmth), thinning of the vaginal walls, and some loss of natural lubrication. Postmenopausal women also have increased risk of osteoporosis and heart disease. Hormone replacement therapy (HRT) can counter some side effects of estrogen loss, but over time it also brings an increased risk of certain cancers. For this reason many women opt not to have HRT.

After about age 50, men gradually begin to take longer to achieve an erection due to vascular changes that cause the penis to fill with blood more slowly. In the United States, more than half of men over 50 also have urinary tract problems caused by age-related enlargement of the prostate gland.

Changes in connective tissue contribute to age-related declines in the functioning of muscles, bones, and joints. Declining sex hormones lead to age-related changes in the male and female reproductive systems.

17.13 Age-Related Changes in Some Other Body Systems

LINKS TO
SECTIONS
7.12, 9.2, 10.3,
10.4, 10.9, 11.1,
12.2, 13.3, 13.4,
AND 14.10

Irreversible age-related changes take place in virtually every organ, from the brain on down.

THE NERVOUS SYSTEM AND SENSES DECLINE

You are born with most of the neurons you will ever have. Chances are that as you age, any that are lost will not be replaced. Even in a healthy person, brain neurons die throughout life, and as they do the brain shrinks slightly, losing about 10 percent of its mass after 80 years. On the other hand, the brain has more neurons than it "needs" for various functions. In addition, when certain types of neurons are lost or damaged, other neurons may produce new dendrites and synaptic connections and so take up the slack.

Over time, however, the death of some neurons and structural changes in others apparently do interfere with nervous system functions. For instance, in nearly anyone who lives to old age, tangled clumps of cytoplasmic fibrils develop in the cytoplasm of many neuron cell bodies. These *neurofibrillary tangles* may disrupt normal cell metabolism, although their exact effect is not understood. Clotlike plaques containing protein fragments called *beta amyloid* also develop between neurons.

Symptoms of the dementia called **Alzheimer's disease** (AD) include progressive memory loss and disruptive personality changes. In affected people, the brain tissue contains masses of neurofibrillary tangles and is riddled with beta amyloid plaques (Figure 17.24). It is not clear whether the amyloid plaques are a cause of Alzheimer's or simply one effect of another, unknown disease process.

For instance, the brains of Alzheimer's patients also have lower than normal amounts of the neurotransmitter acetylcholine, and some evidence suggests that this shortage may be related to beta amyloid buildup. Also under investigation is the hypothesis that AD results from chronic inflammation of brain tissue, just as inflammation leads to arthritis and promotes coronary artery disease.

Treatments for AD patients are limited. Drugs can temporarily help alleviate some symptoms or slow the progression of the disease. Researchers have also tested vaccines designed to stimulate the immune system to generate plaque-fighting antibodies. To date, however, the most promising candidates have had unacceptable side effects.

Some cases of AD are inherited. The increased risk is significant for people who inherit one version of a gene that codes for *apolipoprotein E*, a lipid-binding protein. Around 16 percent of the U.S. population has one or two copies of this gene, called apoE-4. Those with two copies have a 90 percent chance of developing AD. Of the AD-related genes discovered thus far, most are associated with early-onset Alzheimer's, which develops before the age of 65. However, many thousands of the 4 million Americans who have the disease first showed symptoms in their late 70s or 80s. Does genetics play a role in those cases, also? Possibly. More and more genes are being found to have forms that affect how much amyloid builds up in the brain. However, many investigators believe that AD probably has many contributing factors, including as-yet-undetermined environmental ones.

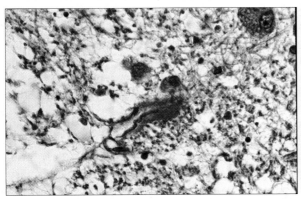

a

b

c

Figure 17.24 (**a**) A neurofibrillary tangle in brain tissue from a patient with Alzheimer's disease. (**b**) Three beta amyloid plaques. (**c**) Older people who do not have Alzheimer's disease also develop neurofibrillary tangles and beta amyloid plaques, but not nearly as many.

Even otherwise healthy people begin to have some difficulty with short-term memory after about age 60 (the so-called "senior moments") and may find it takes longer to process new information. Perhaps because aging CNS neurons tend to lose some of their insulating myelin sheath, older neurons do not conduct action potentials as efficiently. In addition, neurotransmitters such as acetylcholine may be released more slowly. As a result of such changes, movements and reflexes become slower, and some coordination is lost.

As we age, our sensory organs become less efficient at detecting or responding to stimuli. For example, the taste buds become less sensitive over time. As noted in Chapter 14, people also tend to become farsighted as they grow older because the lens of the eye loses its elasticity and is altered in other ways that prevent it from properly flexing to bend incoming light during focusing.

THE CARDIOVASCULAR AND RESPIRATORY SYSTEMS DETERIORATE

Our heart and lungs also function less efficiently with increasing age. In the lungs, walls of alveoli break down, so there is less total respiratory surface available for gas exchange. If a person does not develop an enlarged heart due to cardiovascular disease, the heart muscle becomes slightly smaller, and its strength and ability to pump blood diminish. As a result, less blood and oxygen are delivered to muscles and other tissues. In fact, decreased blood supply may be a factor in age-related changes throughout the body. Blood transport is also affected by structural changes in aging blood vessels. Elastin fibers in blood vessel walls are replaced with connective tissue containing collagen or become hardened with calcium deposits, and so vessels become stiffer. Cholesterol plaques and fatty deposits often cause further narrowing of arteries and veins (Section 9.14). This is why people often find that their resting blood pressure rises as they get older. However, as with the muscular and skeletal systems, lifestyle choices such as not smoking, eating a healthy diet, and getting regular exercise can help a person maintain vigorous respiratory and cardiovascular systems well past middle age.

THE IMMUNE, DIGESTIVE, AND URINARY SYSTEMS BECOME LESS EFFICIENT

Other organs and organ systems also change as the years go by. In the immune system, the number of T cells falls and B cells become less active. Older people are more likely to develop autoimmune diseases, such as rheumatoid arthritis. Why? One hypothesis holds that, as

Table 17.3 Some Physiological Changes in Aging

Age	Maximum Heart Rate	Lung Capacity	Muscle Strength	Kidney Function
25	100%	100%	100%	100%
45	94%	82%	90%	88%
65	87%	62%	75%	78%
85	81%	50%	55%	69%

Note: Age 25 is the benchmark for maximal efficiency of physiological functions.

DNA repair mechanisms become less effective, mutations in genes that code for self-markers are not fixed. If the markers change, this could provoke immune responses against the body's own cells.

In the aging digestive tract, glands in the mucous membranes that line the stomach and small and large intestines gradually break down, and the pancreas secretes fewer digestive enzymes. Although it is vital for older people to maintain adequate nutrition, we require fewer food calories as we age. By age 50, a person's basal metabolic rate (BMR) is only 80 to 85 percent of what it was in childhood and will keep declining about 3 percent every decade. This is why people tend to gain weight in middle age, unless they compensate for a falling BMR by consuming fewer calories, increasing their physical activity, or both.

Over time the muscular walls of the large intestine, bladder, and urethra become weaker and less flexible. As the urinary sphincter is affected, many older people experience urine leakage, or **urinary incontinence**. Women who have borne children may have more trouble with urinary incontinence because their pelvic floor muscles are weak. On the other hand, our kidneys may continue to function well, despite the fact that nephrons gradually break down and lose some of their ability to maintain the balance of water and ions in body fluids (Table 17.3). In general, however, even aging kidneys have more than enough nephrons to function well.

In many body systems, such as the nervous, sensory, and immune systems, aging correlates with the death of cells that are not replaced and reduced activity of other cells.

Ultimately, aging involves a steady decline in the finely tuned ebb and flow of substances and chemical reactions that maintain homeostasis.

Summary

Section 17.1 Human development unfolds in six stages:

a. The formation of gametes—eggs and sperm—which mature inside the reproductive organs of parents.

b. Fertilization, in which the DNA (on chromosomes) of a sperm and an egg are brought together in a single cell (the zygote).

c. Cleavage, when the fertilized egg undergoes cell divisions that form the early multicellular embryo. The destiny of various cell lines is established in part by the portion of cytoplasm inherited at this time.

d. Gastrulation, when the organizational framework of the whole body is laid out. Endoderm, ectoderm, and mesoderm form; all the tissues of the adult body will develop from these three germ layers.

e. Organogenesis, when organs start developing.

f. Growth and tissue specialization, when organs enlarge and acquire their specialized chemical and physical properties. Tissues and organs continue to mature as the fetus develops and even after birth.

In cell differentiation cells come to have specific structures and functions; morphogenesis produces the shape and structure of particular body regions. Both these processes are guided by genes.

 See what happens during fertilization, and track the stages in the formation of a human hand.

Section 17.2 When an oocyte fuses with a sperm, its arrested cell division resumes. The result is a mature egg, or ovum. Fertilization now produces a diploid zygote, a single cell that has a full set of the forty-six human chromosomes. During the first week or so after fertilization, cell divisions and other changes transform the zygote into a multicellular blastocyst, which attaches to the mother's uterus during implantation. The blastocyst includes the inner cell mass, a small clump of cells from which the embryo develops.

Section 17.3 Gastrulation and morphogenesis shape the basic body plan. A key step is the formation of the neural tube, the forerunner of the brain and spinal cord, from ectoderm. Mesoderm gives rise to somites that are the source of the skeleton and most muscles. During morphogenesis sheets of cells fold and cells migrate to new locations in the developing embryo.

 Observe the early stages of human development.

Section 17.4 During implantation the inner cell mass is transformed into an embryonic disk. Some of its cells give rise to four extraembryonic membranes that serve key functions (Table 17.4).

a. Yolk sac: contributes to the embryo's digestive tube and helps form blood cells and germ cells.

b. Allantois: its blood vessels become arteries in the umbilical cord and vessels of the placenta; they function in oxygen transport and waste excretion.

c. Amnion: a fluid-filled sac that surrounds and protects the embryo from mechanical shocks and keeps it from drying out.

d. Chorion: a protective membrane around the embryo and the other membranes; a major part of the placenta.

The embryo and its mother exchange nutrients, gases, and wastes by way of the placenta, a spongy organ of endometrium and extraembryonic membranes.

Section 17.5 The first eight weeks of development are the embryonic period; thereafter the developing individual is considered a fetus. By the ninth week of development, the fetus clearly looks human.

Section 17.6 During the last three months of gestation (the third trimester), the fetus grows rapidly and many organs mature. However, because the fetus exchanges gases and receives nourishment via its mother's bloodstream, its own circulatory system routes blood flowing to the lungs and liver through temporary blood vessels.

Section 17.7 Birth takes place approximately 39 weeks after fertilization. Labor advances through three stages; a baby is born at the end of stage two, and the afterbirth (placenta) is expelled in stage three.

Estrogen and progesterone stimulate growth of the mammary glands. At parturition, contractions of the uterus dilate the cervix and expel the fetus and afterbirth. After delivery, nursing causes the secretion of hormones that stimulate lactation—the production and release of milk.

Table 17.4	Summary of Extraembryonic Membranes
Membrane	**Function**
Yolk sac	Source of digestive tube; helps form blood cells and forerunners of gametes
Allantois	Source of umbilical blood vessels and vessels of the placenta
Amnion	Sac of fluid that protects the embryo and keeps it moist
Chorion	Forms part of the placenta; protects the embryo and the other extraembryonic membranes

Section 17.10 Human development can be divided into a prenatal period before birth, followed by the neonate (newborn) stage, childhood, adolescence, and adulthood. The process of aging is called senescence.

Sections 17.11–17.13 Over time the human body shows changes in structure and a decline in its functional efficiency. The precise cause of aging is unknown.

Review Questions

1. Define and describe the main features of the following developmental stages: fertilization, cleavage, gastrulation, and organogenesis.

2. Label the following stages of early development:

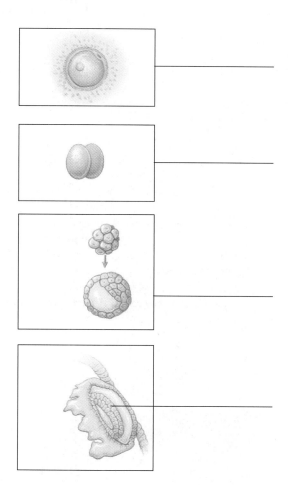

3. Define cell differentiation and morphogenesis, two processes that are critical for development. Which two mechanisms are the basic foundation for cell differentiation and morphogenesis?

4. Summarize the development of an embryo and a fetus. When are body parts such as the heart, nervous system, and skeleton largely formed?

Self-Quiz

Answers in Appendix V

1. Development cannot proceed properly unless each of the following processes is successfully completed before the next begins, starting with _____ .
   - a. gamete formation
   - b. fertilization
   - c. cleavage
   - d. gastrulation
   - e. organ formation
   - f. growth, tissue specialization

2. During cleavage, the _____ is converted to a ball of cells, which in turn is transformed into the _____ .
   - a. zygote; blastocyst
   - b. trophoblast; embryonic disk
   - c. ovum; embryonic disk
   - d. blastocyst; embryonic disk

3. In the week following implantation, cells of the _____ will give rise to the embryo.
   - a. blastocyst
   - b. trophoblast
   - c. embryonic disk
   - d. zygote

4. The developmental process called _____ produces the shape and structure of particular body regions.

5. _____ is the gene-guided process by which cells in different locations in the embryo become specialized.
   - a. Implantation
   - b. Neurulation
   - c. Cell differentiation
   - d. Morphogenesis

6. In a human zygote, the cell divisions of cleavage produce an embryonic stage known generally as a _____ .
   - a. zona pellucida
   - b. gastrula
   - c. blastocyst
   - d. larva

7. Match each developmental stage with its description.
   - ___ cleavage
   - ___ gamete formation
   - ___ organ formation
   - ___ cell differentiation
   - ___ gastrulation
   - ___ fertilization
   - a. egg and sperm mature in parents
   - b. sperm, egg nuclei fuse
   - c. germ layers form
   - d. zygote becomes a ball of cells called a morula
   - e. cells come to have specific structures and functions
   - f. starts when germ layers split into subgroups of cells

8. Of the four extraembryonic membranes, only the _____ is not needed in order for an embryo to develop properly.
   - a. yolk sac
   - b. allantois
   - c. amnion
   - d. chorion
   - e. This is a trick question, because all are needed.

9. Of the following, _____ cannot cross the placenta.
   - a. alcohol
   - b. the mother's antibodies
   - c. antibiotics
   - d. toxic substances in tobacco smoke
   - e. all can cross the placenta

Critical Thinking

1. How accurate is the statement "A pregnant woman must do everything for two"? Give some specifics to support your answer.

2. A renowned developmental biologist, Lewis Wolpert, once observed that birth, death, and marriage are not the most important events in human life—rather, Wolpert said, gastrulation is. In what sense was he correct?

3. One of your best friends tells you that she and her husband think she might be pregnant. She feels she can wait until she's several months along before finding an obstetrician. *You* think she could use some medical advice sooner, and you suggest she discuss her plans with a physician as soon as possible. What kinds of health issues might you be concerned about?

4. In an ectopic pregnancy, an embryo implants outside the mother's uterus, often in an oviduct (Figure 17.25). The complications of ectopic pregnancy are life-threatening for the mother, and in fact each year in the U.S. a few pregnant women die when their situation is not diagnosed in time. Tragically, the only option is to surgically remove the embryo, which was doomed from the beginning. Based on what you know about where an embryo normally develops, explain why an ectopic embryo could not have long survived.

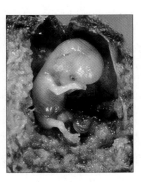

Figure 17.25 A tubal pregnancy.

Explore on Your Own

Housecats can carry the parasite that causes **toxoplasmosis**. In an otherwise healthy person the disease may only produce flulike symptoms, but it is dangerous for a pregnant woman and her fetus. A mother-to-be may suffer a miscarriage, and if the parasite infects a fetus it causes birth defects. An infected cat may not appear to be ill, but its feces will contain infectious cysts. This is why some physicians advise pregnant women to avoid contact with cats and not to clean sandboxes, take care of housecat "accidents," or empty a litterbox.

All that said, toxoplasmosis is not especially common—so is it something a cat-loving expectant mother should take seriously? To explore this health concern, research the kinds of birth defects caused by toxoplasmosis and find out what stance (if any) public health authorities in your community take on this issue. Is the disease more common in some regions or settings than in others? Can cat owners have their pets tested for the disease?

Virus, Virus Everywhere

In 336 B.C., 20-year-old Alexander the Great began carving out an empire that stretched across the Middle East and into India. He died twelve years later after he entered Babylon, the site of modern-day Baghdad.

By one account, Alexander became ill shortly after some ravens fell dead at his feet. When death came he was delirious with fever and paralyzed. To some researchers these and other symptoms suggest that Alexander was struck down by the West Nile virus. It causes encephalitis, a disease in which the brain becomes severely inflamed.

In 1999, researchers probing a disease outbreak in cows, horses, and people in and around New York City found West Nile virus in tissue samples. It was the first time anyone knew that the virus had entered the Western Hemisphere. Seven of the sixty-two people who got sick died. By 2003 nearly 9,000 human cases had been reported in North and Central America, with nearly 200 fatalities.

The West Nile virus usually is transmitted by mosquitoes, which pick it up while they are sucking the blood of a host—a bird, a farm animal, or a human. In North America, the virus has been found in more than forty different kinds of mosquitoes. As far as we know, the only way to get the virus is to be bitten by a mosquito that carries it.

Birds also get the H5N1 virus, which causes avian (bird) flu. Migrating geese have carried it from Asia into Europe and North America. People in close contact with an infected bird can catch the virus, which causes a potentially deadly respiratory illness. The genetic makeup of viruses can change rapidly. So, although millions of chickens and other birds have been killed in an effort to keep the virus from spreading, the worry is that a version of H5N1 will arise that can spread directly from human to human, leading to a massive wave of illness around the world. At present there is no vaccine for H5N1.

Infectious diseases have always been with us. With modern modes of travel and other societal changes, however, pathogens that once were restricted to limited areas now can travel to distant places and have a global impact on human health.

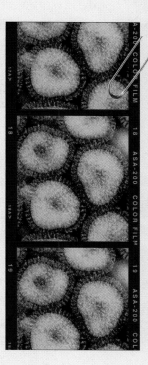

 How Would You Vote? Killing mosquitoes is the best defense against West Nile virus. Many local agencies now spray pesticides wherever mosquitoes are likely to breed. Some people object to spraying, fearing harmful effects on health or wildlife. Would you support a spraying program in your area? Cast your vote online at www.thomsonedu.com/biology/starr/humanbio.

 ## Key Concepts

THE NATURE OF INFECTIOUS DISEASE
A disease disrupts homeostasis so that one or more body functions do not occur normally. An infectious disease is one that can spread from person to person.

INFECTIOUS ORGANISMS
A wide variety of viruses, bacteria, protozoa, fungi, worms, and other pathogens can infect humans and cause mild to serious disease.

THE DISEASE PROCESS
Pathogens that cause infectious diseases all share some basic features, including the ability to evade the body's defenses. Such diseases are spread by direct or indirect contact, by inhalation, or by contact with a disease vector.

Links to Earlier Concepts

This chapter draws on your understanding of how innate and acquired immunity help protect the body from pathogens (10.1, 10.3). You will also see examples of how some pathogens use receptors on a cell's plasma membrane to gain entry to a cell (3.3) and how others use proteins or enzymes to attach to and invade cells or tissues (2.8).

18.1 Some General Principles of Infectious Disease

LINKS TO SECTIONS 4.1, 6.4, 10.1, AND 10.3

The body provides a hospitable environment for many normally harmless microorganisms. Pathogens must have features that allow them not only to overcome defenses, but to multiply and then move on to infect another host.

THE BODY IS HOME TO A GREAT MANY "FRIENDLY" MICROORGANISMS

You may recall from Chapter 10 that up to a thousand species of bacteria normally live on body surfaces. From birth onward, these and other "friendly" microorganisms colonize epithelial tissues of the skin, mouth, nasal cavity, the outer surface of the eye (the conjunctiva), the GI tract, the urethra, and in the case of females, the vagina (Figure 18.1). They all have some way of staying attached to us. For example, bacteria have projections coated with "sticky" proteins (aptly called *adhesins*) that "glue" them to epithelial cells. Even if you take a long, soapy shower, you can't remove many of the bacteria that normally live on your skin. By contrast, many pathogens and other microbial visitors don't have the necessary chemical or physical features to attach long-term to human cells, especially when the available skin surface is already packed with billions of resident microorganisms. Soap and water can easily carry pathogens away, which is why washing your hands helps protect against colds and flu.

DIFFERENT TYPES OF PATHOGENS CAUSE DISEASE IN DIFFERENT WAYS

"Disease" and "infection" are familiar words, even though you might not be able to explain exactly what they mean in biological terms. An **infection** occurs when a pathogen enters cells or tissues and multiplies. **Disease** develops when the body's defenses cannot be mobilized quickly enough to prevent a pathogen's activities from interfering with normal body functions. With infectious (contagious) diseases, the pathogen can move to another person, often in mucus, blood, or some other body fluid.

Harmful bacteria, viruses, and pathogens such as parasitic worms and fungi all cause disease in different ways (Table 18.1). Bacteria produce **toxins**, chemicals that poison or otherwise harm human cells. Many of the most powerful and dangerous bacterial toxins act directly on body cells. For example, the bacterial species *Clostridium botulinum* produces one of the most deadly biological toxins known—a neurotoxin that blocks transmission of nerve impulses by preventing neuron axons from releasing the neurotransmitter ACh (Section 6.4). Improperly canned, low-acid foods are a common source of the toxin, and eating only a tiny amount produces the potentially lethal disease called **botulism**.

Other bacterial toxins activate chemicals of immune responses, including cytokines and complement proteins (Section 10.1). They can trigger fever, diarrhea, and **septic shock**, which is a sudden and dangerous decline in blood pressure.

Viruses can cause disease by invading and destroying body cells. As an infected cell dies, new viral particles are released, spreading the infection. Some kinds of viruses also can become *latent* in cells—that is, they stay in an infected cell without multiplying, sometimes for a very long time, until stress or some other factor reactivates them. Other viruses alter cells in ways that lead to cancer.

Some pathogenic fungi release enzymes that break down tissues, as you will read shortly. Worms, protozoa, and other parasites also can enter the body and either damage cells or tissues directly, trigger harmful immune responses, or both. You will learn about some of these pathogens in Section 18.4.

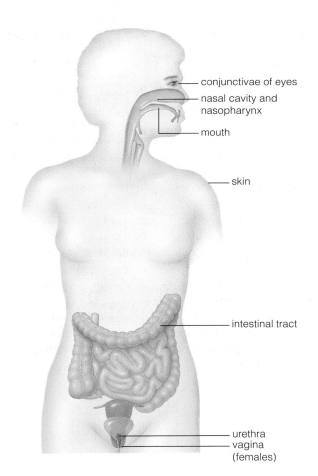

conjunctivae of eyes

nasal cavity and nasopharynx

mouth

skin

intestinal tract

urethra
vagina
(females)

Figure 18.1 Sites where normally harmless microorganisms colonize the body.

Table 18.1 Some Ways Pathogens Cause Disease

Type of Pathogen	Disease Mechanism
Bacteria	Produce toxins that poison cells and/or trigger damaging immune responses
Viruses	Kill body cells or cause cells to become cancerous
Fungi	Release enzymes that break down tissues
Parasites	Invade cells/tissues, trigger harmful immune responses

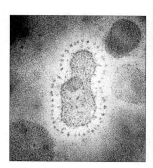 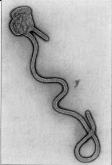

a SARS virus **b** Ebola virus

Figure 18.2 Two examples of emerging pathogens.

Paradoxically, our immune system's responses to viral infection also cause symptoms we associate with disease, such as fever and fatigue. As you read in Chapter 10, a controlled inflammatory response helps rid the body of pathogens, but if the response goes awry it can lead to serious damage, especially if a major organ or organ system is involved. For instance, if the testicles of a male who contracts the sexually transmitted disease gonorrhea become inflamed, the inflammation can progress to an immune response that leaves the man sterile.

TO CAUSE AN INFECTION, PATHOGENS MUST MEET SEVERAL REQUIREMENTS

A pathogen's **host** is an organism that the pathogen can infect. In addition to having a suitable host, a pathogen usually also must have the following:

1. Access to a *reservoir*, a place where the pathogen can survive and remain infectious. Reservoirs include other infected organisms, soil, bodies of water, and **carriers**—organisms (including other people) in which the pathogen is living without causing disease symptoms.

2. A means of leaving the reservoir and entering a host—for example, contaminating substances that the host uses as food.

3. A way of attaching to a host's body.

4. A mechanism for entering a host's tissues.

5. The ability to avoid the host's defenses.

6. The ability to reproduce inside the host.

7. A way to return to the reservoir or move to a new host, as when virus particles are expelled by a sneeze.

Scientists use attributes of pathogens to help make sense of the bewildering array of infectious diseases. One approach is to group diseases by their reservoirs, such as the bodies of certain animals, water, or soil. For example, humans are the only reservoirs for pathogens that cause the common cold, measles, and gonorrhea.

For an infectious disease categorized as a **zoonosis** (zoe-uh-NOH-sis), animals other than humans are the main reservoirs, but the pathogens can infect humans. Rabies, West Nile virus, and avian flu are examples. HIV may have begun as a zoonosis in other primates. As we have seen with HIV, one danger with a zoonosis is that genetic changes in the pathogen may permit it to begin using the human body as a reservoir, allowing it to be passed from person to person.

EMERGING DISEASES PRESENT NEW CHALLENGES

Today health officials worry especially about so-called **emerging diseases**. Emerging diseases are caused by pathogens that until recently did not infect humans or were present only in limited areas. Many are caused by viruses. This group includes the encephalitis caused by West Nile virus and the severe respiratory disease caused by the SARS virus (Figure 18.2*a*). Other examples are hemorrhagic fevers that cause massive bleeding. In this latter group are dengue fever and the illness caused by the Ebola virus (Figure 18.2*b*). Lyme disease is a major emerging bacterial disease in the United States that we consider later in the chapter.

Why is all this happening? Broadly speaking, a few factors stand out. For one, there are simply many more humans on the planet, interacting with their surroundings and with each other. Each person is a potential target for pathogens. Also, more people are traveling, and carrying diseases along with them. Another important factor is the misuse and overuse of antibiotics, a topic we will take up in Section 18.3.

Many microorganisms live on body surfaces and normally cause no harm.

In an infection, a pathogen enters cells or tissues. Disease develops when bacterial toxins, physical damage to cells and tissues, or other factors related to infection interfere with normal body functions.

18.2 Viruses and Infectious Proteins

LINKS TO
SECTIONS
2.12 AND 10.7

Viruses aren't high on anyone's "most popular" list. The Nobel Prize–winning biologist Sir Peter Medawar once called them "bad news wrapped in protein."

A **virus** is a piece of genetic material inside a protein coat. It is not a cell, but can infect the cells of other organisms. To reproduce itself a virus must take over the host cell's metabolic machinery.

We classify viruses by several criteria. One is which type of nucleic acid—DNA or RNA—makes up the genetic material. Another is the general type of host organism the virus infects. Some viruses infect animals, others plants, and still others, called bacteriophages, infect bacteria.

In general, a virus particle consists of a nucleic acid core inside a protein coat called a capsid. Sometimes the capsid also is enclosed, in a lipid envelope.

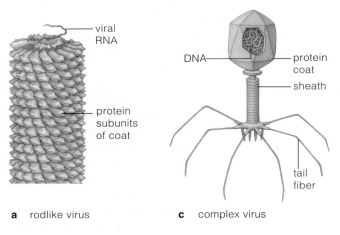

a rodlike virus

c complex virus

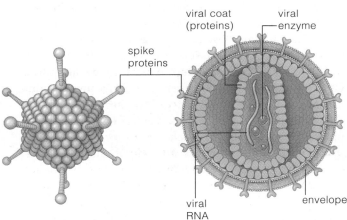

b polyhedral virus

d enveloped polyhedral virus

Figure 18.3 Virus structures. (**a**) A helical virus has a rod-shaped protein coat around its nucleic acid. (**b**) A polyhedral virus has a many-sided coat. (**c**) A complex virus, like this bacteriophage, has other structures attached to the coat. (**d**) An enveloped virus is surrounded by a membrane. HIV is shown here.

The coat around the particle consists of one or more protein subunits, often organized into the shapes shown in Figure 18.3. The coat protects the viral genetic material during the journey from one host cell to another. It also contains proteins that can bind with receptors on host cells. Some viruses also are surrounded by a membrane and are called *enveloped viruses.*

VIRUSES MULTIPLY INSIDE A HOST CELL

Different viruses multiply in different ways. In all cases, however, the process begins when a virus particle attaches to the host cell and either the whole virus or its genetic material enters the cell's cytoplasm. Next, the viral DNA or RNA is replicated (copied) and provides instructions for making enzymes and other proteins, using the host cell's metabolic machinery. These materials are used to assemble new virus particles, which then are released from the infected cell. Figure 18.4 shows these steps for an enveloped DNA virus infecting an animal cell.

A cell is a potential host if a virus can chemically recognize and lock on to receptors at the cell's surface. Differences in the receptors on different cell types are why a given virus often can attack only one type of cell. For instance, a flu virus can attack cells of respiratory epithelium but not liver cells, and a virus that causes hepatitis attacks liver cells but not cells of the airways.

When the multiplication cycle of a virus ends, the host cell usually dies and new virus particles are released. The virus may not kill the host cell outright, however. Instead, sometimes the virus becomes latent, as noted in Section 18.1. A common example is type 1 herpes simplex, which causes cold sores. It remains latent inside a ganglion (a cluster of neuron cell bodies) in facial tissue. Stressors such as a sunburn, falling ill, or emotional upsets can reactivate the virus. Then, virus particles move down the neurons to their tips near the skin. From there the virus particles infect epithelial cells, causing painful eruptions on the skin. Repeat outbreaks of genital herpes, caused by type 2 herpes simplex, happen the same way.

Another herpes virus, the Epstein-Barr virus (EBV), is commonly transmitted by kissing. An EBV infection can lead to **infectious mononucleosis**. Symptoms are a sore throat, overwhelming fatigue, and a mild fever. It can take a month or more to recover.

A **retrovirus** is an RNA virus that infects animal cells. Retroviruses establish yet another relationship with the host cell. This group's name comes from its "reverse" mode of pirating the host's genetic material. After the viral RNA chromosome enters the host cell cytoplasm, a viral enzyme called reverse transcriptase uses the RNA as a template for synthesizing a DNA molecule. The

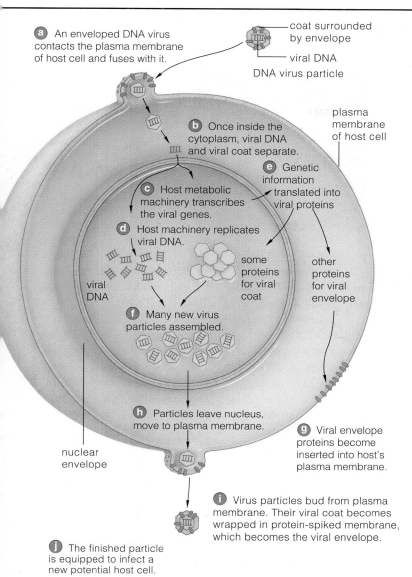

(a) An enveloped DNA virus contacts the plasma membrane of host cell and fuses with it.

coat surrounded by envelope

viral DNA

DNA virus particle

plasma membrane of host cell

(b) Once inside the cytoplasm, viral DNA and viral coat separate.

(c) Host metabolic machinery transcribes the viral genes.

(d) Host machinery replicates viral DNA.

(e) Genetic information translated into viral proteins

viral DNA

some proteins for viral coat

other proteins for viral envelope

(f) Many new virus particles assembled.

(h) Particles leave nucleus, move to plasma membrane.

nuclear envelope

(g) Viral envelope proteins become inserted into host's plasma membrane.

(i) Virus particles bud from plasma membrane. Their viral coat becomes wrapped in protein-spiked membrane, which becomes the viral envelope.

(j) The finished particle is equipped to infect a new potential host cell.

Figure 18.4 Multiplication cycle of an enveloped DNA virus infecting an animal cell.

new DNA molecule, called a *provirus*, then integrates into the host's DNA. This is what happens when a person becomes infected with HIV.

PRIONS ARE INFECTIOUS PROTEINS

A few rare, fatal degenerative diseases of the central nervous system are linked to small infectious proteins called **prions** (PREE-ons).

Prions are versions of otherwise normal proteins on brain neurons and some other types of cells. You may recall from Chapter 2 that proteins become folded into three-dimensional shapes. For some reason, prions are *mis*folded. Once in the body, they can cause normal versions of the protein to misfold and become prions

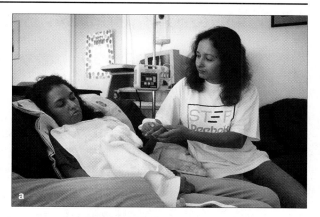

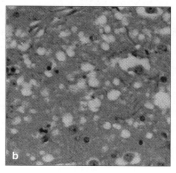

Figure 18.5
(a) Charlene Singh, the first known case of variant Creutzfeldt–Jakob disease, which is caused by prions. (b) Brain tissue damaged by BSE. The light-colored "holes" are areas where tissue was destroyed.

also. In the brain, massive clumps of them form and over time holes develop in the brain tissue, giving it a spongy appearance. As the disease progresses, muscle coordination and brain function are lost.

Prion diseases have been discovered in various species of animals. One example is BSE (for *bovine spongiform encephalitis*), which has come to be called "mad cow disease." Brain and spinal cord tissue from affected cattle can contain the prions. Humans who eat BSE-contaminated meat (such as brains, ground beef, sausage, and oxtails) are at risk for **variant Creutzfeldt–Jakob disease** (vCJD), which is caused by a prion that closely resembles the one that causes BSE. An outbreak of BSE in Britain in the late 1990s was linked to about 150 cases of vCJD in people who apparently consumed meat from the infected animals. One of them was an American woman who grew up in Britain (Figure 18.5).

Prions are also associated with a long-known form of CJD, which occurs worldwide. Most people with CJD are middle-aged or older, and about 15 percent of cases are thought to have a genetic origin.

A virus consists of nucleic acid enclosed in a protein coat and sometimes an outer envelope. Viruses multiply by pirating the metabolic machinery of a host cell.

The infectious proteins called prions cause various degenerative diseases of the nervous system.

18.3 Bacteria—The Unseen Multitudes

LINKS TO
SECTIONS
3.1, 7.3, 7.7,
AND 10.1

Bacteria, which are prokaryotes, were the first organisms on Earth. An estimated 500 to 1,000 species live harmlessly in each of us. Others are pathogens that cause disease.

Because bacteria are prokaryotes, they have no nucleus or other membrane-bound organelles. Most have a *cell wall* outside their plasma membrane (Figure 18.6). The wall is strong and fairly rigid, and helps maintain the shape of the bacterium. Although bacteria come in a range of shapes, three basic ones are common. A ball shape is a coccus (plural: cocci; from a word that means "berry"). A rod shape is a bacillus (plural: bacilli, which means "small staffs"). A "corkscrew"-shaped bacterial cell with one or more twists to it is a spirillum ("spiral"; plural: spirilla), sometimes called a *spirochete.*

| coccus | bacillus | spirillum |

Some kinds of bacteria have threadlike structures on the cell wall and plasma membrane. One type is a stiff protein filament called a *bacterial flagellum.* It rotates like a propeller to move the cell. Some kinds of bacteria have filaments called *pili* (singular: pilus) that help the cell stick to surfaces. The gonorrhea bacterium uses pili to attach to mucous membranes of the reproductive tract; the *Pseudomonas* bacterium in Figure 18.7 is using its pili to stick to the surface of a kitchen knife.

Bacteria reproduce by fission. The cell's DNA is copied, then the cell divides into two genetically identical daughter cells. Bacterial cells have just a single circular

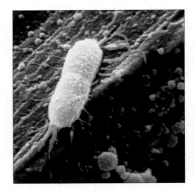

Figure 18.7
A *Pseudomonas* bacterium attached to the blade of a kitchen knife by way of its pili.

DNA molecule (a chromosome) to copy and parcel out to daughter cells. Under ideal conditions, some species can divide in about 20 minutes.

When some kinds of bacteria divide, the daughter cells can inherit one or more small circles of extra DNA. These DNA circles, which include a few genes, are called *plasmids.* One type, a "fertility" plasmid, carries genes that enable the bacterium to transfer plasmid DNA to another bacterial cell—genetic "instructions" that can include drug resistance, among other traits. Bacteria with this ability to transfer genes include some pathogens, such as *Salmonella* (a source of food-borne illness), and species of *Streptococcus* that cause various respiratory infections and **strep throat**.

BACTERIA PLAY BOTH POSITIVE AND NEGATIVE ROLES IN SOCIETY

We humans have many relationships with bacteria. We employ the metabolic machinery of some species to make cheeses, therapeutic drugs, and other useful items. As described in Chapter 22, bacteria (and plasmids) have been our partners in genetic engineering. Harmless *E. coli* bacteria in our colon make vitamin K, while other, pathogenic strains cause intestinal disease. In general, we tend to associate bacteria with disease.

After antibiotics were discovered in the 1940s, they were quickly harnessed to fight disease. An **antibiotic** is a substance that can destroy or inhibit the growth of bacteria and some other microorganisms. Bacteria and fungi produce most antibiotics. Some, such as penicillins, tetracyclines, and streptomycin, kill microorganisms by interfering with different life processes. For example, the penicillins break bonds that hold molecules together in the cell walls of susceptible bacteria.

Antibiotics don't work against viruses, which are not cells and so do not have a metabolism to disrupt. Body defenses such as the antiviral proteins called **interferons** (Section 10.1) may block replication of the virus inside

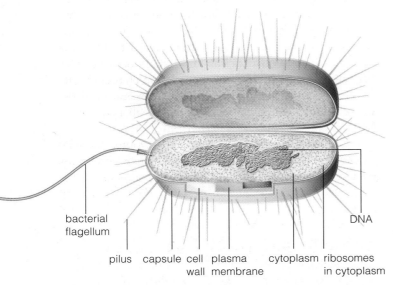

bacterial flagellum

pilus capsule cell wall plasma membrane cytoplasm ribosomes in cytoplasm

DNA

Figure 18.6 *Animated!* The structure of one kind of bacterium.

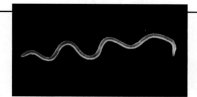

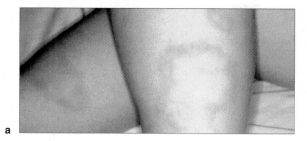

actual size: ●

a

b

Figure 18.8 Examples of bacteria linked with emerging diseases. (**a**) *Borrelia burgdorferi*, which causes Lyme disease. The lower photograph shows the bull's-eye rash that is a symptom of Lyme disease, now the most common tick-borne disease in the United States. (**b**) *Mycobacterium tuberculosis*, which causes TB.

cells. Antiviral drugs prevent virus particles from exiting host cells or interfere with the viral "life cycle" in some other way.

Today there are scores of prescribed antibiotics. All are potent drugs. Different ones can have side effects such as triggering an allergic response or reducing the effectiveness of birth control pills. Even more serious, however, is the emergence of antibiotic-resistant microbes.

A BIOLOGICAL BACKLASH TO ANTIBIOTICS IS UNDER WAY

Over the years, some doctors prescribed antibiotics for patients who had viral—not bacterial—illnesses. In some countries, antibiotics are not prescription drugs, so people buy and take the drugs whenever they don't feel well. Some patients stop taking an antibiotic when they start to feel better, without finishing the full recommended course of treatment. Antibiotics also have been added to soaps, kitchen wipes, and many other consumer products. All these practices have contributed to the proliferation of bacteria that are genetically resistant to antibiotics that might otherwise kill them. A key reason is that ill-advised and improper use of antibiotics wipes out susceptible bacteria, leaving behind resistant "super bugs." As that happens over and over, soon the only disease-causing bacteria left are those equipped to fend off one or more antibiotics. At present, the list of drug-resistant bacteria includes strains that cause some cases of tuberculosis, urinary tract infections, strep throat, STDs such as gonorrhea and syphilis, dysentery, childhood middle-ear infections, and surgical-wound infections.

Staphylococcus aureus, or staph A, is a bacterium that can cause pneumonia and wound infections that rapidly destroy tissue. It is one of several microbes that may soon be resistant to *all* available antibiotics. Researchers are racing to develop new antibiotics that combat disease-causing organisms in new, effective ways.

BACTERIA CAUSE SOME IMPORTANT EMERGING AND REEMERGING DISEASES

A major emerging disease in the United States is **Lyme disease**, which apparently arose in the mid-1900s. It is caused by the spirochete *Borrelia burgdorferi* (Figure 18.8*a*), which is transmitted by ticks when they suck blood. Early symptoms resemble the flu, but if the disease progresses it can cause crippling arthritis, as well as heart and neurological problems. Fortunately, Lyme disease can be cured with antibiotics.

The situation is less bright with **tuberculosis** (TB), a "reemerging" disease that attacks the respiratory system and produces pneumonialike symptoms, among other ills. It is caused by a bacillus, *Mycobacterium tuberculosis* (Figure 18.8*b*). The bacteria are transmitted in droplets produced by coughing or sneezing. Normally the immune system kills the bacilli. If small lesions (called tubercles) do form in the lungs, their healing will leave a scar that can be seen on a chest X ray.

By the 1970s the advent of antibiotics helped make TB relatively rare in developed countries. Today, however, TB is reemerging as a major global health threat, in part due to increased travel and immigration, new strains that are resistant to antibiotics, and other factors. People who live in crowded, unsanitary conditions (such as refugee camps and urban slums) are at much higher risk. Many recent cases have developed in people infected with HIV, whose immune systems are weakened.

According to the National Institute of Allergy and Infectious Diseases, in parts of Eastern Europe *all* new TB patients have a drug-resistant strain. Screening programs try to ferret out early-stage cases for treatment. In the meantime, 3 to 5 million new cases are being diagnosed each year.

Bacteria are microscopic prokaryotic cells. They and some other pathogens often can be killed by antibiotics, although resistant strains are becoming more common. Antibiotics are not effective against viruses.

18.4 Infectious Fungi, Protozoa, and Worms

LINKS TO
SECTIONS
7.9, 10.4,
AND 16.11

Fungi and protozoa ("first animals") that infect humans are single eukaryotic cells. Various worms are parasites—they live on or in a host organism for at least part of its life cycle.

PARASITIC FUNGI AND PROTOZOA ARE SMALL BUT POTENTIALLY DANGEROUS

Common fungal pathogens that affect humans include those that cause yeast infections, the confusingly named "ringworm," and athlete's foot (Figure 18.9a). The fungi behind athlete's foot and ringworm infections release enzymes that break down the keratin in skin. They also can trigger painful inflammation. A yeast infection arises when a change in the chemical conditions in the vagina or elsewhere causes overgrowth of *C. albicans* cells.

Entamoeba histolytica, often simply called an "amoeba," is a protozoan that forms a cyst at one stage of its life cycle. The cyst is a tough body covering that helps the organism wait out "bad times," such as a lack of food. Contaminated food and water are common reservoirs for cysts. Inside human intestines, the amoeba completes its life cycle and in the process causes **amoebic dysentery**, a type of severe diarrhea (Figure 18.9b). In places where raw sewage carries cysts of *E. histolytica* into public water supplies, amoebic dysentery is a leading cause of death among small children.

Giardia intestinalis (Figure 18.9c) also forms cysts that enter water or food supplies in contaminated feces. It causes **giardiasis**, bringing awful "rotten egg" belches, explosive diarrhea, and other symptoms. Antibiotics can cure both *Giardia* and amoebic dysentery.

Trypanosoma brucei causes **African sleeping sickness** (Figure 18.9d). This severe form of encephalitis is passed from person to person by bites of the tsetse fly. Untreated, the disease is fatal. At any given time, at least a million people in Africa are infected.

Watery diarrhea is one symptom of **cryptosporidiosis**, caused by a protozoan called *Cryptosporidium parvum*. In the United States, cryptosporidiosis is an emerging infectious disease. *C. parvum* is a tough character. Its oocytes (immature eggs) can even survive a two-hour soak in full-strength bleach! Like cysts of *Giardia* and amoebas, the oocytes are spread in water or food contaminated with the feces of humans or other animal hosts.

WORMS ALSO CAN BE A SERIOUS THREAT

Poor sanitation isn't a factor only in diseases caused by protozoa; it also is how many worm infections spread. Another, less common route is eating contaminated meat or fish. For people in developed countries, such as the United States, pinworm infections are the most familiar. A pinworm is a small, white roundworm; it looks like a quarter-inch fleck of white thread. The infection route is oral–fecal; that is, first the person consumes worm eggs, then the eggs hatch and worms develop, then female pinworms lay *their* eggs just outside the anus, then those eggs find their way to a person's mouth, and so on.

Some other infectious worms, including tapeworms, hookworms, whipworms, and large *Ascaris* roundworms, can seriously damage body tissues and organs. Most common in the tropics, serious worm infections can be treated with therapeutic drugs. Even so, many millions of people in various parts of the world share their bodies with worms, often without knowing it.

Some species of protozoa are pathogens that cause serious diseases in humans. Often, they are spread by way of water or food contaminated with animal feces.

Infectious worms can do serious damage to many tissues and organs.

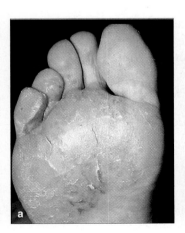
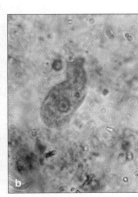

Figure 18.9 (**a**) Athlete's foot. (**b**) *Entamoeba histolytica*, which causes amoebic dysentery. This specimen has been stained, then photographed under a light microscope. (**c**) *Giardia intestinalis* causes intestinal disturbances. (**d**) *Trypanosoma brucei*, a protozoan that causes African sleeping sickness. It is shown next to a red blood cell.

18.5 Malaria: Efforts to Conquer a Killer

According to the World Health Organization, every year **malaria** kills nearly 3 million people, most of them children in Africa. And each year brings another 110 million new cases. The direct cause of malaria is a protozoan called *Plasmodium*. One of its life stages lives in the salivary glands of the female *Anopheles* mosquito. When the insect sucks blood from a person, *Plasmodium* travels from her salivary glands into the person's bloodstream. When it reaches the liver, severe illness and often a lifetime of frequent misery begin (Figure 18.10).

Shaking, chills, a high fever, and drenching sweats are classic symptoms of malaria. Symptoms abate for weeks or months, but relapses occur when dormant parasites become active. In time, a person with malaria may develop anemia (from the loss of red blood cells) and a greatly enlarged liver. As described in Section 20.5, some people, including those who are, or are descended from, West African blacks, may carry the gene for **sickle-cell anemia**—and this genetic heritage can help protect them from malaria. In people who inherit only one copy of the gene, red blood cells respond to infection in a way that cuts short the parasite life cycle.

Tropical Africa has always been malaria's stronghold. Today, many strains of *Plasmodium* have become drug-resistant, and the poorest people and countries in malaria-prone regions cannot easily afford the drugs that are available. These facts, and the awful toll malaria takes on the people of Africa, have spurred intensive efforts to develop a malaria vaccine. A major challenge is the complex life cycle of the pathogen, because it has turned out to be difficult to create a vaccine that will be effective against all its life stages.

A ray of hope has come from our increasing understanding of cell structure, and especially the different sorts of proteins that are present on the surfaces of cells. At this writing researchers are trying to develop a vaccine that recognizes a surface protein on the merozoite stage of *Plasmodium* (Figure 18.10d). This is the stage that invades red blood cells and causes the first real damage of malaria. If a vaccine can trigger a safe but effective immune response against this stage, it may be possible to end an initial infection before the pathogen becomes established in the liver. Clinical trials for this vaccine may have already begun by the time you are reading this book.

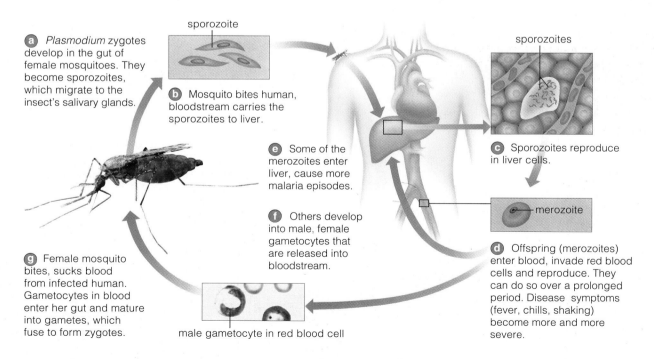

a *Plasmodium* zygotes develop in the gut of female mosquitoes. They become sporozoites, which migrate to the insect's salivary glands.

sporozoite

b Mosquito bites human, bloodstream carries the sporozoites to liver.

sporozoites

c Sporozoites reproduce in liver cells.

merozoite

e Some of the merozoites enter liver, cause more malaria episodes.

f Others develop into male, female gametocytes that are released into bloodstream.

d Offspring (merozoites) enter blood, invade red blood cells and reproduce. They can do so over a prolonged period. Disease symptoms (fever, chills, shaking) become more and more severe.

g Female mosquito bites, sucks blood from infected human. Gametocytes in blood enter her gut and mature into gametes, which fuse to form zygotes.

male gametocyte in red blood cell

Figure 18.10 *Animated!* Life cycle of one of the *Plasmodium* species that causes malaria.

18.6 Patterns of Infectious Diseases

LINKS TO
SECTIONS
10.1, 10.9,
AND 16.12

You can't avoid being exposed to infectious diseases, but you can limit your risk and be a better-informed health care consumer by understanding some basic characteristics of infectious microbes, including how they spread.

INFECTIOUS PATHOGENS SPREAD IN FOUR WAYS

By definition, an infectious disease can be transmitted from person to person. There are four common modes of transmission:

1. *Direct contact* with a pathogen, as by touching open sores or body fluids from an infected person. (This is where "contagious" comes from; the Latin *contagio* means "touch" or "contact.") Infected people can transfer pathogens from their hands, mouth, or genitals.

2. *Indirect contact*, as by touching doorknobs, tissues (or handkerchiefs), diapers, or other objects previously in contact with an infected person. As already noted, food and water can be contaminated by pathogens.

3. *Inhaling pathogens*, such as cold and influenza viruses, that have been spewed into the air by coughs and sneezes (Figure 18.11). This is the most common mode of transmission.

4. *Contact with a vector*, such as mosquitoes, flies, fleas, and ticks. A **disease vector** carries a pathogen from an infected person or contaminated material to new hosts. In some cases, part of the pathogen's life cycle must

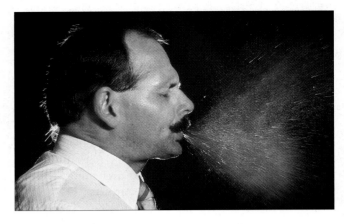

Figure 18.11 A full-blown sneeze. Inhaled pathogens spewed out during an unprotected sneeze can transmit colds, influenza, and other infectious diseases.

take place inside the vector, which is an intermediate host. Mosquitoes are the intermediate hosts for the West Nile virus and the *Plasmodium* parasites that cause malaria (Section 18.5).

Every year 5 to 10 percent of hospitalized people come down with a **nosocomial infection**—one that is acquired in a hospital, usually by direct contact. For example, despite the best precautions, bacteria may enter a person's urinary tract during a catheterization procedure. Why are nosocomial infections so common? Anyone who is sick enough to be hospitalized may have a compromised (and therefore less effective) immune system, and invasive medical procedures give bacteria easy access to tissues. Also, the intensive use of antibiotics in hospitals increases the chances that antibiotic-resistant pathogens will be present there. Hospitals usually are careful to monitor patients likely to be vulnerable to nosocomial infection.

DISEASES OCCUR IN FOUR PATTERNS

Infectious diseases sometimes are described in terms of the patterns in which they occur. In an **epidemic**, a disease rate increases to a level above what we would predict, based on experience. When cholera broke out all through Peru in 1991, that was an epidemic. The bubonic plague epidemic in fourteeth-century Europe killed 25 million people. When epidemics break out in several countries around the world in a given time span, they collectively are called a **pandemic**. AIDS is pandemic; it has spread worldwide since the first cases were identified in 1981.

A **sporadic disease**, such as whooping cough, breaks out irregularly and affects relatively few people. An **endemic disease**, such as the common cold, occurs more or less continuously. Many of the diseases noted in Table 18.2 are endemic in various parts of the world.

Table 18.2	Infectious Diseases: Global Health Threats*		
Disease	**Type of Pathogen**	**Estimated Deaths per Year**	
Diarrheas (includes amoebic dysentery, cryptosporidiosis)	Protozoa, virus, and bacteria	31 million	
Various respiratory infections (pneumonia, viral influenza, diphtheria, strep infections)	Virus, bacteria	7+ million	
Malaria	Protozoan	2.7 million	
Tuberculosis	Bacterium	2.4 million	
Hepatitis (includes A, B, C, D, E)	Virus	1–2 million	
Measles	Virus	220,000	
Schistosomiasis	Worm	200,000	
Whooping cough	Bacterium	100,000	
Hookworm	Worm	50,000+	

*Does not include AIDS-related deaths.

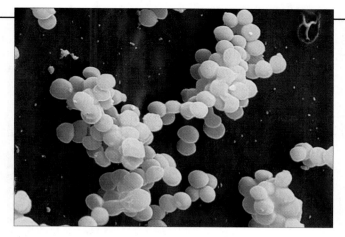

Figure 18.12 A virulent microbe: The bacterium *Staphylococcus aureus*, shown in a false-color micrograph.

VIRULENCE IS A MEASURE OF THE DAMAGE A PATHOGEN DOES

Pathogens are ranked according to their **virulence**—how likely it is that the pathogen will cause serious disease. Virulence depends on how fast the pathogen can invade tissues, how severe is the damage it causes, and which tissues it targets. For example, a virus that can cause pneumonia is more virulent than a virus that causes the sniffles. Rabies viruses are highly virulent because they target the brain. The SARS virus appears to be extremely virulent, because it makes people very sick very quickly.

Antibiotic resistance in certain bacteria, such as strains of *Staphylococcus aureus* (Figure 18.12), has made those microbes highly virulent. Infectious disease specialists have instituted a worldwide surveillance system to identify new resistant strains before they can become established.

THERE ARE MANY PUBLIC AND PERSONAL STRATEGIES FOR PREVENTING DISEASE

The best way to combat any disease is to prevent it in the first place. With infectious diseases, prevention depends on knowing how a disease is transmitted and what the pathogen reservoir is.

Figure 18.13 lists general strategies for preventing the transmission of pathogens that are present on the skin, in the respiratory tract, in the GI tract, and in blood. These strategies recognize that the human body, soil, water, and other animals all are reservoirs for a range of pathogens. Notice that regular hand washing tops the list for limiting your exposure to all but blood-borne pathogens. Public health measures include vaccination programs, standards for processing or treating supplies of food, drinking water, and blood products, and public dissemination of information on proper food-handling methods. Section 16.12 describes strategies for protecting yourself against sexually transmitted disease.

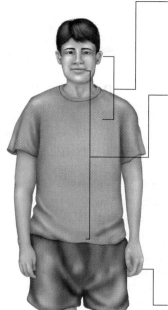

Respiratory tract
Preventative measures:
- Hand washing
- Cover mouth when coughing or sneezing
- Proper disposal of used tissues
- Vaccination programs

GI tract
Preventative measures:
- Hand washing
- Proper food storage, handling, and cooking
- Good public sanitation (sewage, drinking water)

Blood
Preventative measures:
- Avoid/prevent needle sharing/ IV drug abuse
- Maintain pure public blood supplies
- Vaccination programs against blood-borne pathogens (e.g., hepatitis B)

Skin
Preventative measures:
- Hand washing
- Limit contact with items used by an infected person

Figure 18.13 Disease prevention strategies are based on knowing how pathogens spread and what their reservoirs are.

Infectious diseases are transmitted by direct or indirect contact with pathogens, by being inhaled, or by vectors. A disease may turn up sporadically, it may become endemic to a particular region, or it may become epidemic or pandemic.

Some pathogens are extremely virulent—they can cause severe illness.

Preventing an infectious disease requires strategies for avoiding pathogen reservoirs and for limiting the chances that a given pathogen will be transmitted.

Summary

Section 18.1 An infection occurs when a pathogen enters the body and multiplies. Disease develops when the pathogen's activities interfere with normal body functioning. Pathogens cause disease in different ways: bacteria release toxins, viruses kill cells or trigger cancer, fungi produce enzymes that break down tissues, and parasites damage cells or tissues or trigger damaging immune responses such as inflammation.

Emerging diseases are ones that have never before affected large numbers of people around the world. They include the diseases caused by the West Nile virus, Ebola virus, and SARS virus. Some emerging diseases are zoonoses—they mainly infect other animals but also can infect humans. Reemerging diseases, such as tuberculosis, are diseases that have been well controlled in the past but are again being diagnosed in large numbers of people.

Section 18.2 A virus is a noncellular infectious particle. Viruses consist of nucleic acid (DNA or RNA) enclosed in a protein coat; some also have an outer envelope. A retrovirus, such as HIV, is an RNA virus that infects animal cells.

Viruses multiply by taking over the metabolic machinery of a host cell. They can't be killed by antibiotics, but may be susceptible to body defenses (interferons) and drugs that interfere with their ability to attach to host cells or reproduce inside them. Prion diseases are caused by infectious proteins smaller than viruses.

 Compare different forms of viruses and see how some of them can multiply.

Section 18.3 Bacteria are microscopic prokaryotic cells. Some species are used as living factories to produce therapeutic drugs and other products, but many other species cause disease. Overuse and misuse of antibiotics have contributed to the evolution of antibiotic-resistant bacteria.

Section 18.4 Pathogenic fungi include the species that cause athlete's foot, ringworm, and yeast infections. Some protozoa (single-celled eukaryotes) are harmful parasites. Often they are spread by way of water or food contaminated with feces from infected people or other animals. Some infections by worms also seriously harm tissues and organs.

 Observe the life cycle of the malaria-causing protozoan Plasmodium.

Section 18.6 An infectious disease may be transmitted by direct contact with a pathogen; by indirect contact (e.g., handling a contaminated object); by inhaling the pathogen; or through a disease vector that physically carries pathogens or contaminated material to new hosts. A nosocomial infection is one that is acquired in a hospital, usually by direct contact.

A disease epidemic makes more people ill than experience would have predicted. A pandemic occurs when epidemics break out more or less simultaneously in various places around the world. Virulence is a gauge of a pathogen's ability to cause serious disease.

Measures for preventing infectious diseases draw on our understanding of the reservoirs for pathogens and of the ways pathogens can be transmitted.

Review Questions

1. List at least four of the seven requirements a pathogen must meet in order to cause infectious disease.

2. What is a virus? What is a retrovirus? What is the difference between a virus and a prion?

3. What does it mean to say that a virus is latent?

4. Define the difference between a virus and a bacterium, and explain how bacteria reproduce.

5. What is an antibiotic? List the factors that have contributed to the emergence of antibiotic-resistant microbes.

6. What are the four main ways pathogens spread?

7. Explain what we mean by virulence, give an example of a highly virulent pathogen, and explain why it is classified this way.

Self-Quiz   *Answers in Appendix V*

1. A _____ is described as a noncellular infectious agent.
   - a. virus
   - b. bacterium
   - c. fungus
   - d. protozoan

2. _____ is a eukaryotic cell that causes disease when it is ingested in contaminated food or water.
   - a. An adenovirus
   - b. *Chlamydia trachomatis*
   - c. *Entamoeba histolytica*
   - d. A prion

3. Most pathogenic bacteria _____.
   - a. cause disease by secreting toxins that damage body cells
   - b. can enter the body in contaminated water or other substances
   - c. may be able to multiply so rapidly they overwhelm the immune system
   - d. a and b only
   - e. a, b, and c are all correct

4. Antibiotic resistance is a result of _____.
   - a. use of antibiotics against viruses
   - b. patients' failure to take a full course of the drug
   - c. self-prescribing of the drugs
   - d. b and c only
   - e. a, b, and c

5. An infectious disease may not be transmitted by
   a. a gene mutation.
   b. simply shaking hands with an infected person.
   c. being bitten by a flea.
   d. surgical instruments in a hospital.

6. Match the following terms and concepts:

   ____ endemic   a. causes serious disease
   ____ virulent   b. disease that is nearly always
         pathogen   present
   ____ prion   c. may become latent
   ____ epidemic   d. infectious protein
   ____ carrier   e. disease that occurs at a higher
   ____ virus   than expected rate
                       f. no apparent disease symptoms

Critical Thinking

1. A janitor in the cafe where you work has been diagnosed as HIV-positive, and a server has come down with type B hepatitis. Some other employees start a petition demanding that both people be required to wear a mask over the mouth and nose, not handle soiled dishes or food, and not use the employee restroom. Both infected employees strenuously object to the plan. You are asked to lead a discussion aimed at resolving the issue, and you decide to prepare a handout giving the scientific basis for making a decision in each case. What does the handout say?

2. A tourist returning from a tropical vacation comes down with monkeypox (Figure 18.14*a*), which is caused by a DNA virus. He rushes to the emergency room and pleads for an antibiotic, but the physician says she can't prescribe one. Why not?

3. The micrograph in Figure 18.14*b* shows bacteria on the tip of a pin. What general category of bacterium is shown? Thinking back to Chapter 10, what might occur in your body if you prick yourself with the pin and these bacteria are pathogenic?

Figure 18.15 Medieval attempt to deal with a bubonic plague epidemic—the Black Death—that may have killed half the people in Europe.

4. The mild pneumonia sometimes called "walking pneumonia" is caused by one species of an unusual group of bacteria called mycoplasmas. *Mycoplasma pneumoniae*, usually transmitted by respiratory droplets, causes pneumonia in about 10 percent of the people it infects. Antibiotics kill the pathogen. How would you classify (1) its mode of transmission and (2) its virulence?

5. In the Middle Ages bubonic plague struck Europe with a vengeance and killed an estimated one-third to one-half of the population. Not knowing that the disease is caused by a bacterium (*Yersinia pestis*) spread by fleas that live on rats, terrified people tried all sorts of methods to ward off the disease, including praying and dancing until they dropped (Figure 18.15). What is the disease vector in this instance? Which organism(s) is/are the reservoir?

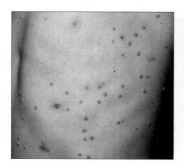

Figure 18.14 (**a**) Skin sores on a person infected with the virus that causes monkeypox. (**b**) Bacteria on the tip of a pin.

Explore on Your Own

Not long ago, researchers fighting rhinoviruses—the viruses that cause the common cold—reported they were nearing completion on the development of two new antiviral medicines. One prevents the cold virus from entering its target host cells (that is, it's an entry inhibitor). The other contains a protease inhibitor, which halts the actions of an enzyme many cold viruses need to replicate themselves. Both have been developed by "piggybacking" on research on HIV and AIDS.

A wealth of information on infectious diseases and their treatments is available on the World Wide Web. Starting, perhaps, with the website of the Centers for Disease Control and Prevention, go online and see what you can learn about these new cold remedies. What specific use is each designed for? What form does each take (e.g., nasal spray, pill, injection, etc.)? In the course of your search, can you uncover reports of any other new antiviral drugs?

Customized Contents for 7th edition of Human Biology

Author Dr. Alan I. Hecht

CHAPTER 2-TRANSMUTATION OF ELEMENTS

Radioactive isotopes are categorized by the type of particles they emit. Those that emit an **alpha (α) particle** are **alpha emitters.** Those that emit a **beta (β) particle** are **beta emitters.**

An alpha particle is defined as a **Helium nucleus.** That is, two protons and two neutrons. The symbol used to represent this is:

$$^4_2\text{He}$$

where the number four represents the mass number of helium and the number two represents the element's atomic number.

Because alpha particles have a large mass and a charge, they travel slowly and are easily absorbed by items such as tissues, paper and even human skin. This makes them rather harmless. However, if they are ingested or inhaled, they can be dangerous as they will be in direct contact with cells and may cause damage.

When an alpha emitter gives off one of these particles, it becomes another element or an isotope of that element. This change is referred to as **transmutation.** In order to determine which element or isotope an emitter will become, simple subtraction is performed. For example, to show the transmutation of Americium 241 to Neptunium 237, the following equation is used:

$$^{241}_{95}\text{Am} \longrightarrow\ ^{237}_{93}\text{Np} +\ ^4_2\text{He}$$

As you can see, the atomic mass of Americium was reduced by 4, which is the atomic mass of the alpha particle. The atomic number of Americium was reduced by 2, which is the atomic number of the alpha particle.

A beta particle is a high energy, high speed electron. The symbol used to represent this particle is:

$$_{-1}^{0}e$$

There is no atomic mass and the atomic number is negative one. However, it is not an electron that is found in the shells surrounding the nucleus of the atom. Instead, this electron comes from the breakdown of a neutron in the nucleus which is, in effect, a combination of a proton and an electron (thus it has no electrical charge). By releasing this electron from the nucleus, the proton that was originally associated with it is left behind to increase the atomic number by one. This, of course, changes the element.

Beta particles are more difficult to absorb than are alpha particles due to their higher energy level. Objects with the thickness of, for example, aluminum foil are needed to stop these particles. Beta particles are also more likely to cause damage to the human body. Prolonged exposure to beta particles may lead to cancer.

An example of beta emission is seen in the following equation:

$$_{6}^{14}C \longrightarrow {}_{7}^{14}N + {}_{-1}^{0}e$$

Here, radioactive Carbon-14, an isotope of Carbon-12 normally found in non-radioactive carbon-containing compounds, emits a beta particle and transmutates to Nitrogen. Carbon-14 is used to determine the age of fossils.

ENZYME ACTIVITY

Figure 3.24 shows how enzymes work on specific substrates to form products. The next question one might ask is, "How does the enzyme actually perform its action?" The answer lies in understanding that all functions in life require energy. In the case of reactions, **activation energy** is what is needed to complete the reaction. In the figure below, the upper curve represents the amount of activation energy needed to convert the reactants at the left into the products at the right. As you can see, this is the uncatalyzed reaction.

When an enzyme is added to this reaction, the activation energy required becomes less and is represented by the lower curve. This completes the reaction in a shorter amount of time.

A good way to think about this is to use an easy to understand example. Let's say you wanted to travel from the town "Reactants" to the town "Products." In order to do this you had to climb over a mountain (represented by the upper curve). If the mountain is unchanged in height, it would take you a certain amount of time and energy to make the journey.

Now a big saw blade comes along and cuts off the top of the mountain, making it lower (represented by the lower curve). It's easy to figure that you would spend less time and energy making the same trip from "Reactants" to "Products." This is how lowering

the activation energy speeds up a reaction.

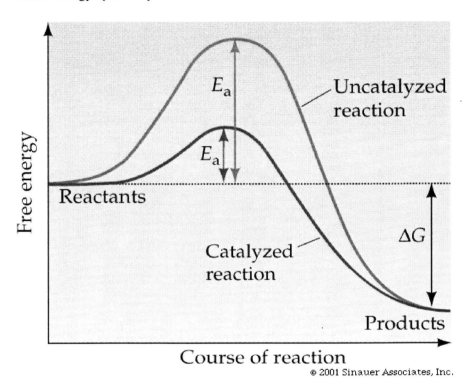

© 2001 Sinauer Associates, Inc.

CHAPTER 5-BONE CONTENT AND METABOLISM

It is commonly known that bones contain a large amount of the mineral calcium. The mineral salt found in the greatest abundance in bones is a calcium phosphate compound known as **hydroxyapatite**. This makes up bone mineral and the matrix of teeth. Its formula is $Ca_5(PO_4)_3(OH)$ but it is usually written as $Ca_{10}(PO_4)_6(OH)_2$ because the crystal is made up of two molecules.

In addition to calcium, bones also contain magnesium, sodium and fluoride, all of which help to play structural and metabolic roles in bone development and growth. Beyond these elements, bones also contain trace elements (elements that are needed in small quantities for growth and development) such as strontium, manganese, zinc and copper.

OSSIFICATION

As is noted in the body of this text, the **epiphyseal plate** (also known as the **growth plate**) is the cartilaginous site of long bones that is used to lengthen the bone during the growth period. This type of ossification, or hardening or calcification of soft tissue into bone, is referred to as **endochondral ossification**. This means that the development of bone is taking place within a precursor of cartilage (the growth plate).

This type of ossification accounts for the lengthening of the bone, but does not explain how the bone diameter increases. For this function, the bone relies on the **periosteum** (also mentioned in the body of the text). In addition, a similar layer of connective tissue, the **endosteum**, that lines the medullary cavity of the bone, is involved. Osteoblasts in the inner layers of these two membranes secrete bone matrix into which calcium is deposited. This increases the bone's diameter while it lengthens at the growth plates.

Where flat bones are concerned, a different type of ossification takes place. **Intramembranous ossification** occurs without the involvement or presence of a cartilage precursor. Instead, a membrane of embryonic connective tissue is replaced by bone. This type of ossification is seen in the skull bones, the jaw and the sternum.

SESAMOID BONES

Sesamoid bones are bones that are embedded within a tendon. The number of Sesamoid bones will vary from person to person depending on several factors. When counting the bones in the body we say that there are 206. Interestingly, this does not include the knee caps (patellae). Although just about everyone has two patellae, they are considered sesamoid bones and are not part of the count.

Sesamoid bones act to protect the tendon in which they are embedded. In addition they increase its mechanical effect. Because they are found associated with joints, they also help to protect the joint.

As mentioned above, the number of sesamoid bones will vary from individual to individual. This is due to several factors including genetics and the amount of stress that a particular joint is exposed to. For example, if a person were a professional handball player, he or she would develop more sesamoid bones in their playing hand than another individual, say, an accountant, might have in his or her hand.

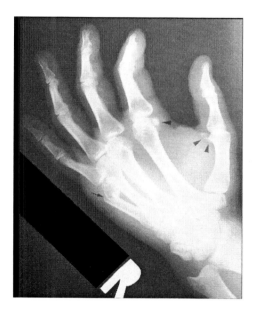

The three triangular arrowheads at the right side of this x-ray show typical sesamoid

bones in the hand.

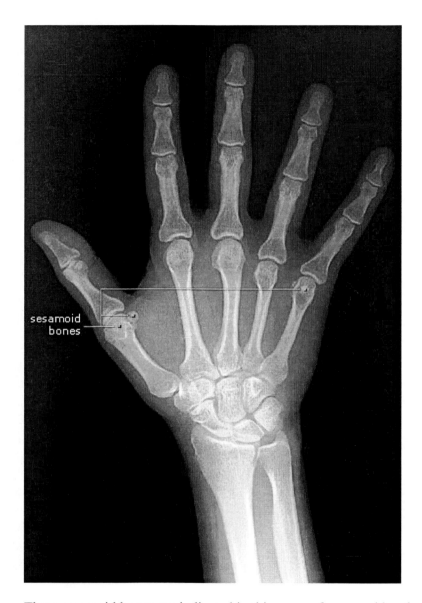

Three sesamoid bones are indicated in this x-ray of a normal hand.

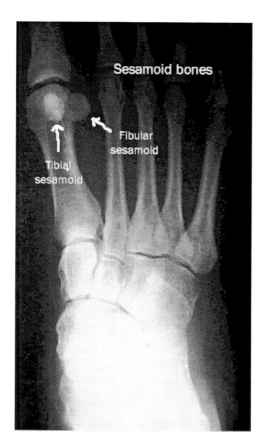

This x-ray shows two typical sesamoid bones in a normal foot.

CHAPTER 6-CHARACTERISTICS OF MUSCLES

Muscles possess several characteristics that give them the ability to do what they do. Without these qualities, muscles would not be able to function in the many ways that we observe when work is done by muscle contraction.

One characteristic is **contractility**. This is a muscle's ability to contract, or shorten into a more compact form. When this is accomplished, work is performed.

Another quality of muscles is **irritability** or **excitability**. These terms represent a muscle's ability to respond to a stimulus. That is, when the electrical signal (**action potential**) travels from a motor neuron to the muscle, the muscle is able to contract.

Conductivity is another quality that muscles possess. This means that muscle fibers may conduct electrical impulses (action potentials) along the plasma membrane (sarcolemma). This also helps to lead to muscle contraction.

Muscles also possess **elasticity**. This means that a muscle may stretch or contract and still return to its original size and shape.

The last characteristic of muscle is **extensibility**. This means that a muscle may stretch without causing any damage to its fibers.

NAMING MUSCLES

Many terms are used when referring to muscles. These terms are based on various characteristics of the muscles including direction of fibers, size, shape and other qualities. The following is a list of names specifically based on these aspects.

DIRECTION OF FIBERS:

Rectus: Parallel to the midline
Transverse: Perpendicular to the midline
Oblique: Diagonally to the midline

SIZE OF THE MUSCLE:

Maximus: Largest
Minimus: Smallest
Longus: Longest
Brevis: Shortest

NUMBER OF ORIGINS (HEADS):

Biceps: Two origins
Triceps: Three origins
Quadriceps: Four origins

SHAPE:

Deltoid: Triangular
Trapezius: Trapezoid
Serratus: Saw-toothed
Rhomboideus: Rhomboid (diamond) shaped

ACTION:

Flexor: Decrease the angle at a joint
Extensor: Increase the angle at a joint
Abductor: Move a bone away from the midline
Adductor: Move a bone toward the midline
Levator: Move upward
Depressor: Move downward
Supinator: Turn the palm upward or anteriorly
Pronator: Turn the palm downward or posteriorly
Sphincter: Decreases the size of an opening
Tensor: Makes a body part more rigid
Rotator: Moves a bone around its longitudinal axis

LOCATION:

Used to describe a structure near which the muscle resides. For example, the *Rectus femoris* is a muscle with fibers parallel to the midline that lies near the femur.

ORIGIN AND INSERTION:

Where the muscles begin and end. For example, the Sternomastoid muscle begins at the sternum and ends at the mastoid process of the temporal bone.

CHAPTER 8-MORE DETAILS ON WHITE BLOOD CELLS

As noted in this chapter, there are five types of leukocytes (white blood cells) divided into two categories. The **granulocytes** include **neutrophils**, **eosinophils**, and **basophils**. The **agranulocytes** include **lymphocytes** and **monocytes**.

Neutrophils, the most abundant leukocytes, are the first to arrive at the site of an infection. They are **phagocytic**, that is, they are able to engulf and digest foreign invaders such as bacteria or viruses.

Eosinophils are leukocytes that are designed to protect the body against parasitic worm infections. The granules in the eosinophils secrete various chemicals that are toxic to the parasites. Unfortunately, asthma and allergic reactions are often associated with the presence of large numbers of eosinophils in the lungs and respiratory tract. In these cases, the toxic chemicals that are supposed to be used against invading parasitic worms are released into the tissues of the lungs and respiratory system. This causes damage and the resulting symptoms.

Basophils are the least abundant of all leukocytes. They are involved in the **inflammatory response**. Basophils secrete **histamine** that is used for dilating blood vessels (**vasodilation**) so that more blood can reach an area that has been damaged. This speeds up the healing process. They also secrete **heparin**, an **anticoagulant** (chemical that interferes with blood clotting) used to keep the blood flowing to a damaged area so healing can continue. A third chemical secreted by basophils is **bradykinin**. This is used to stimulate a pain response so that the individual is aware of the fact that there is damage to tissue and intervention must occur.

Lymphocytes come in several forms. **B lymphocytes** are also known as **memory cells**. These cells must convert to **plasma cells** so that they can produce **antibodies**, chemicals used to protect the body against invaders and dangerous foreign proteins. Once programmed, these cells will be bale to make antibodies in the future any time that they are presented with the same intruders. This is known as the **anamnestic response**.

T lymphocytes are found as **killer T** or **helper T** cells. Killer T cells destroy cells that are infected with an invader or that are damaged or cancerous. Helper T cells activate another white blood cell known as a **natural killer cell** and also help to activate B and killer T cells. (See chapter 10-The Immune System for more details).

Monocytes are the largest of the leukocytes. When not needed, they merely circulate as monocytes and do not perform any specific functions. However, should an infection arise in tissue, the convert to **tissue macrophages** and are able to leave the bloodstream through capillary walls and enter the tissue to engulf and destroy the invaders. This process of "walking out" of the circulatory system is known as **diapedesis** (see figure 10.8) . Should bacteria enter the bloodstream, monocytes can convert to **circulating macrophages** and remove the invaders from the blood.

CHAPTER 9-HEART MURMURS

Heart murmurs are categorized in two ways. One type is due to **insufficiency** of one or more of the heart valves. This means that the valve or valves fail to close properly during the cardiac cycle. This allows blood to leak back into the chamber from which it came causing less blood to be pumped into the circulation. This backflow of blood is called **regurgitation** and the murmur is often referred to as a **regurgitory murmur**.

Regurgitory murmurs may be caused by congenitally malformed valve flaps that don't close properly or by **bacterial plaque** that forms on the valve flaps due to the presence of bacteria in the circulation that settle onto the valve flaps and interfere with closure. The back-pressure from contraction causes the weakened (insufficient) valves to allow small amounts of blood to pass through what would otherwise be a closed valve.

The other type of murmur is due to **stenosis** of a valve. That is, the diameter of the valve opening is reduced either due to congenital malformation or as a result of the buildup of bacterial or cholesterol plaque. This reduces the amount of blood that can flow through the valve at any given time and leads to murmurs which are classified as **whistling** or **blowing** murmurs. This is because the friction created by the rapid flow of blood through a narrowed opening creates a sound that resembles a person whistling or blowing.

Surgical correction of both types of murmurs is possible. If a person suffers from regurgitory murmurs, the entire valve may be replaced surgically. One such valve commonly in use today is the **St. Jude's Valve** which is best described as a ball in a basket. This type of valve is very efficient and has a long life span. Stenotic murmurs may be corrected by surgery designed to remove the plaque or to widen the narrow opening.

CHAPTER 10-CATEGORIES OF IMMUNITY

We can divide immunity into four separate categories, each with its own specific characteristics.

The first is **naturally acquired active immunity**. In this type of immunity there are two key words: Naturally and active. When immunity is naturally acquired, this means that the individual did not go out of their way to pick up the virus or bacteria that caused a particular illness. For example, catching a cold from another person. The term active indicates that the individual developed his or her own antibodies to the organism.

The next type of immunity is **naturally acquired passive immunity**. We've already defined the word naturally, but in this situation passive immunity indicates that any antibodies directed against a specific illness were made by somebody else. If this is the case, how did they get into the individual's body in a natural process? There is only one way that this is possible, and that is from the person's mother. During pregnancy antibodies may pass from the mother into the developing fetus. In addition, if the mother nurses the baby, milk will carry even antibodies that may enter the child.

A third type of immunity is **artificially acquired active immunity**. Once again, the term active has been explained, but in this scenario the immunity is developed due to artificial exposure to the antigen. Vaccination is the best example of this process. The use of hypodermic needles or oral introduction of a vaccine are considered artificial means of introducing the antigen to the body. However, once this is done, the individual will go on to developing his or her own antibodies.

The last category of immunity is **artificially acquired passive immunity**. Here, as in the previous type, a hypodermic needle is usually employed. What is introduced into the person is not a vaccine, but an already produced antibody or antitoxin. The antibody may have been made by another human or an animal such as a cow, sheep or horse. In addition, genetic engineering has made it possible for genetically modified bacteria to produce these antibodies. A good example of this type of immunity is the use of tetanus antitoxin that was created by genetically engineered bacteria or by vaccinated farm animals. This would be administered to a person who stepped on a rusty nail in the soil or who was bitten by a human or an animal when he or she has not had a tetanus booster for some time.

CHAPTER 11-SMOKER'S COUGH

As we all know, many smokers suffer from chronic coughs associated with their habit. The reason for this is a combination of factors including irritation from the content of the smoke, frequent respiratory infections, a buildup of inhaled particulates and other causes.

One of the interesting occurrences associated with smoking is the increase in coughing that takes place in many smokers when they decide to quit. One would imagine that a smoker would cough more while they are indulging in the habit rather than when they decide to stop. The reason for this paradox is related to the ciliated cells of the respiratory tract (see figure 11.2).

These cells are designed to trap inhaled particles and microorganisms and, when sufficient quantities of particles are collected, send signals to the medulla oblongata to stimulate a cough reflex. The problem lies in the damage caused by smoking. These cells are damaged or destroyed by smoking and can no longer stimulate a sufficient number of coughs to mechanically rid the respiratory tract of the particulates. There is a buildup of these substances over time.

When a person stops smoking, most of these cells can regenerate thanks to mitotic division of the cells that remained. When these new cells "wake up" and discover the collection of particles that has accumulated over time, they immediately go into action sending signals to the medulla oblongata to initiate substantial coughing. Within a few weeks, or so (depending on how many years of buildup has taken place), the respiratory tract is considerably cleaner and the coughing stops.

DAMAGE TO THE RESPIRATORY SYSTEM

The thoracic cavity in which the lungs reside is a vacuum. There should never be any air in the space around the lungs. Unfortunately, there are certain situations that will allow air to enter the thoracic cavity making breathing very difficult.

If an individual sustains an injury, such as a knife wound, that breaches the skin and underlying intercostal (rib) muscles, air in the atmosphere may enter the thoracic cavity on that side of the body, thus putting pressure on the lung. This will cause the lung to collapse.

Another situation where air may enter the thoracic cavity is in the case of a broken rib. With sufficient trauma a rib may break, even without causing a wound that is open to the outside, and push inward enough to puncture the lung. This will allow inhaled air to enter the thoracic cavity from within the lung each time an individual takes a breath. Both of the above situations have created a condition known as **traumatic (secondary) pneumothorax** (air in the thorax).

Secondary pneumothorax may also occur as the result of the presence of a serious lung infection or a tumor, both of which cause a weakening in the tissue.

On occasion, during development of the lung, a small cyst or **bleb** may be created. If this ruptures on its own, air may enter the thoracic cavity, once again from within the lung. This is called **spontaneous (primary) pneumothorax** and occurs in the absence of trauma. There are approximately 9000 cases in the United States each year mostly among tall, thin males between the ages of 20 and 40.

Small ruptures will clear up on their own within one to two weeks. Larger blebs will require a needle to aspirate the air from the cavity or even the insertion of a chest tube attached to a mechanical pump.

If blood enters the thoracic cavity, for any reason at all, the condition is known as **hemothorax**. Sometimes, whatever causes the pneumothorax to occur also damages tissue and causes bleeding so that both blood and air have entered the thoracic cavity. This condition is known as **hemopneumothorax**.

CHAPTER 13-SUMMARY OF CRANIAL NERVE FUNCTIONS

No.	Cranial Nerve Name	Function	Sensory/Motor
I	Olfactory	Smell	Sensory
II	Optic	Vision	Sensory
III	Oculomotor	Most eye movement, pupil constriction, proprioception*	Mostly motor
IV	Trochlear	Innervates one eye muscle, proprioception	Mostly motor
V	Trigeminal	Sensation on the face and cornea, stimulation of chewing muscles	Mixed
VI	Abducens	Innervates one eye muscle, proprioception	Mostly motor
VII	Facial	Movement of facial muscles, taste on anterior 2/3 of tongue, salivation, tears	Mixed
VIII	Vestibulocochlear	Hearing, balance	Sensory
IX	Glossopharyngeal	Gag reflex, taste on posterior 1/3 of tongue, regulation of blood pressure	Mixed
X	Vagus	Regulates heart rate, stimulates sweat glands, innervates muscles of speech, stimulates peristalsis*	Motor
XI	Accessory	Movement of shoulders and neck, proprioception	Mostly motor
XII	Hypoglossal	Movement of tongue, proprioception	Mostly motor

*Proprioception: The sense of relative position of a body part or parts.

*Peristalsis: The involuntary movement of food and feces through the digestive tract.

CHAPTER 15-SOME ADDITIONAL NOTES ON HORMONES

Growth Hormone (Somatotropin): Overproduction of growth hormone may lead to **diabetes mellitus**. This is due to the fact that growth hormone increases the rate of **glycogenolysis**, the conversion of stored glycogen back to glucose. As such, this will effectively raise the serum glucose levels, causing the beta cells of the pancreas to secrete insulin. When these cells are constantly called upon to do their job, they eventually "burn out," leading to diabetes mellitus.

It has been stated that underproduction of growth hormone leads to pituitary dwarfism. This condition of short stature is directly related to the presence of too little hormone. The individuals are short, but in proportion. Another form of dwarfism is **achondroplastic dwarfism**. In this condition, secretion of growth hormone is normal, but individuals possess a gene that causes abnormally short limbs. Their head and trunk are of normal size for their age. This puts them out of proportion. The gene is inherited in only 20% of the cases. In the remaining 80% of cases the mutation is new.